S0-BJL-778

The
APPRAISAL
of
FARM REAL ESTATE

The

APPRAISAL

of

FARM REAL ESTATE

---

by

ROBERT C. SUTER, Ph.D.

Department of Agricultural Economics
Purdue University

THE INTERSTATE
Printers & Publishers, Inc.

Danville, Illinois

Library of Congress catalog card number: 73-87894

First Printing, January, 1974
Second Printing, November, 1975

Preface and Acknowledgements

The appraisal of property is a unique profession and particularly so in the farm arena where a knowledge of agricultural things and considerable economic judgment are both involved.

It was in the 1930's that farm appraisers first began to gather together to pool their problems and swap ideas. Soon thereafter the American Rural Appraisal System was developed. Appraisal was defined (unfortunately) as an opinion. The typical operator was born (a rather unique character). Specific appraisal procedures were proposed (thou shall walk thy farms). The earnings approach to value was developed, and a normal value concept, using standardized prices, was advanced. All of this was a tremendous step forward. The farm manager-appraiser, in the agricultural Midwest at least, thus learned to appraise farms assuming a crop-share lease and a landlord's return.

However, once the system was accepted, certain so-called appraisal procedures had a tendency to become hitching posts rather than guideposts. This same appraiser was soon heard to say, "We've done it this way for years." He inferred, "This technique (mine) should be used by all appraisers." And, he sometimes said to the jury, "This value now, is based on my experience." This strong adherence to past appraisal practice, along with the somewhat self-centered belief in experience per se, has led to considerable divergency of opinion as well as a proliferation of appraisal societies.

In the meantime the problems involved in the appraisal of farm real estate have increased geometrically. Farms which sold in the 1930's for $55 to $60 per acre have sold in the early 1970's for $750 to $1,000 per acre, and sometimes more. Farm building costs and insurance coverages have both increased, the first often much faster than the latter. Residential, commercial, and industrial development has raised farm property taxes. In the loan arena the definitions of value have been changed and the loan ratios have been increased. But nothing has jarred the farm appraiser more than the highway engineer who has driven more and more stakes across our farms, often-times without even the property owner being informed of his or her rights. Many of societies' institutions and many of our farm property owners thus continue to raise the question, "What is this farm worth?"

The more adventurous farm appraisers have taken on many of these activities. They've developed, down through the years, a pretty good potpourri of procedure. However, not always have they taken time out to put their problems in perspective, to re-think the theories of value, or to get their technique down on paper. Thus the reason for this book.

The Appraisal of Farm Real Estate has been written to put many of our past as well as our current appraisal practices in perspective. The objective has not been to present something new; it has instead been to put the different concepts of value and much of our work—both past and present—down on paper so one can look at it in an organized fashion. This book has been written for those persons who are intrigued with the profession and for those who desire a firm foundation on which they can develop professionally. Hopefully, the book will not become a pattern but instead a point of departure from which one can study both current appraisal problems as well as those which may appear in the future.

One cannot, of course, learn how to appraise farms merely by reading a book. Nor can one learn how to teach an appraisal course this way either. This leads me to comment on two policies which are fairly unique at Purdue University and which have influenced the direction of this book. The first revolves around the emphasis some of the staff place on practical matters; the second involves the opportunity that the staff has to wander out into the real world.

The first eight weeks of the Purdue Farm Appraisal course are spent on principles; the second eight weeks are spent in bringing into the classroom those persons who do actual appraisal work. The first fellow in is usually a farm building valuator—an inspector, a claims man, or an adjustor for an insurance company. Then comes the Tippecanoe County Assessor. Then follows a couple of farm loan men, one from a government agency and one from a private lending institution. Then several fee appraisers appear, at least several who specialize in eminent domain or condemnation work. These fellows all present their problems, their appraisal practices, their approaches to value, and always a demonstration appraisal.

Unfortunately most farm appraisers do only one kind of appraisal. They specialize to the extent that they often fail to recognize or even appreciate problems other than their own. As a result, some of the words or terms used in this book may bother some appraisers. No attempt has been made to please everybody. I have seen and enjoyed a broad spectrum of valuation problems. I have listened to those of the insurance underwriter, those of the county assessor, those that belong to the farm loan man, and those unique to fee appraisers.

I have also had the opportunity to take time off to go and appraise farms myself, to find out some of the facts of life, including the questions being asked down on the farm, on the court house steps, and on the witness stand. Such experience is invaluable—one might say "priceless" where practical matters are to be taught in the classroom. Every teacher ought to have this kind of experience. Not always, of course, is it enjoyable. Some of it is like writing this book.

In the beginning the idea of writing another book was quite exciting. The assignment was taken on as a challenge. The *modus operandi* or plan of attack was easily worked out. Yet, sooner or later the nitty gritty gradually appeared, the glamour began to fade, and eventually the problems had to be wrestled with.

Following publication of *The Courage to Change*, several persons asked me, "How long did it take?" This time I kept track. And, for those readers who have some statistical bent, the following figures may be of interest. This book was outlined in August of 1968 and in final manuscript form in July of 1973. The rough draft required 85 days, the first revision 40 days, the second and third 22 days each, and the fourth, fifth, and sixth 12 days each. The miscellany required another 40 for a total of 245 days over the five-year period.

The problem, of course, is that it takes much longer to find the time to write a book than it does to write it. Dr. Charles E. French, Head of the Department of Agricultural Economics at Purdue University, was the person who continuously encouraged me to find that time. I am indebted to both him and to Professor Earl W. Kehrberg, one of my colleagues who read the entire manuscript and made comments throughout, to Lars Brink, Bill Newell, Monty Harris, Steve Weller, Lyle Spence, and several other students who also read various parts of the manuscript in various stages of development.

I asked several professional appraisers to read and to comment on the more traditional parts of the book—Clifford L. Orbaker of Bucks County, Pennsylvania, Virgil Heid of Indianapolis, William D. Davis, Jr., of Kansas City, and Dave Dunshee of Fresno, California, reviewed Chapters VI, VII, and VIII. I asked several other persons to review various chapters and parts. Professor Dwight P. Flanders of the University of Illinois reviewed Chapter II; Professor Arthur M. Weimer, Indiana University, Chapter III; Professor Lynn S. Robertson, Michigan State University, and Professor Eldon Hood, Purdue University, the section on Soils; W. Robert Peterson, Indiana Director of the Farmers Home Administration, Chapters IX and XII; Harold W. Walters, President of the National Association of Mutual Insurance Companies, Chapter X; Gerald Lucht, Tippecanoe County Deputy Assessor, and Professors James Papke in Industrial Management and J. B. Kohlmeyer in Agricultural Economics, Purdue University, Chapter XI; Professor Julian H. Atkinson, Purdue University, J. Ed Rutter, Prudential Insurance, James H. Reynolds, Equitable Life Assurance Society, Dean Hawkins, formerly with the Federal Land Bank and now with the State Bank of Salem, Indiana, and Marshall Burkes, formerly with the Farmers Home Administration, Chapter XII; Virgil Heid, Philip Banawitz, Kenneth Chitwood, Clifford Fry, and several other fee appraisers and expert witnesses, Chapter XIII.

This does not infer that all of the individuals are in full agreement with what I have said. But they did take time out to further challenge me, to raise additional questions, to point out some of the manuscript's earlier weaknesses, and to get me to correct some of the more obvious errors. In addition, I want to thank Martha W. Suter, who did all the illustrations, and Margaret Walker, who exhibited large amounts of patience in following the scribbles and arrows. No one, other than she, can possibly imagine the problems involved in typing a manuscript of mine. All I can say at this point, to anyone who has stumbled this far is, "It's all yours."

ROBERT C. SUTER

July 5, 1973

Table of Contents

CHAPTER   PAGE

I. Professional Farm Appraisal 1

Agriculture Today
Origins of Farm Value
A Farm Appraisal Defined
The Purpose of and Reasons for Appraisals
Four of the Problems
The Qualifications of a Farm Appraiser
The Objective of This Book

II. The Concept of Value 45

Value Versus Price
The Farm Real Estate Market
Present Market Value Defined
    (The Basis for All Appraisals)
Fifty-one Other Values

III. American Real Property Law 81

Real Estate Versus Property Versus Personalty
The Rights of the Property Owner
The Rights of the Sovereign
Legal Concepts and Definitions
The Transfer of Real Property by Conveyance
The Recording of the Evidence of Title
Legal Description

IV. Modus Operandi 117

The Appraiser's Job
The Typical Operator Concept
Getting Acquainted with a New Area
Client Relationships
Field Procedure
The Appraisal Report

CHAPTER   PAGE

V. The Appraiser's Handbook.......................................157

        Physical Features
        Agricultural Trends
        Economic Statistics
        Community Characteristics
        Miscellanea Compacta

VI. The Earnings or Income Capitalization Approach to Value..............243

        The Formula: Its Application
        Estimating Farm Receipts, Expenses, and Income
        Defining the Capitalization Rate
        Two Different Techniques
        A Major Footnote: How—When Not in Perpetuity?
        Areas of Importance and Use

VII. The Sales Comparison or Market Data Approach to Value..............291

        The Comparable Sale
        Sources of Sales Data
        The Presence or Absence of Unusual Conditions
        Verification, Inspection, and Classification
        Adjustments for Dissimilarities
        The Contract Sale
        Areas of Importance and Use

VIII. The Inventory or Cost Approach to Value..........................327

        The Summation Process
        Cost Is Not Necessarily Value
        Building and Improvement Costs
        Depreciation and Value That Remains
        Areas of Importance and Use
        The Final Step: Review and Summary

IX. The Valuation of Farm Buildings.................................351

        The Purposes of and Reasons for Farm Building Valuation
        Physical Inspection and Analysis
        Reproduction Versus Replacement Cost
        Kinds of Depreciation and Causes
        Five Different Values
        What if the Improvements Are Major Assets?
        Let's Illustrate: Thirteen Farm Buildings

X. **Appraisals for Property Insurance**.............................397

   The Purpose and Nature of Insurance
   The Indemnity Principle or Philosophy
   Actual Cash Value and Insured Value
   The Problem of Equitability and Insurance Rates
   Co-insurance and Valued Policies

XI. **Ad Valorem Tax Appraisals**.....................................419

   The Assessor's Job
   The Mass Appraisal Technique
   Preferential Treatment
   True Cash Value and Assessed Value
   Full Versus Fractional Assessment
   The Problem of Equitability and Equalization
   Gift and Estate Tax Appraisals

XII. **Appraisals for Farm Loans**.....................................461

   The Participants: Past and Present
   The Farm Mortgage Lender's Problem
   The Farm Loan Appraiser's Job
   The Bench-Mark Approach to Appraisal
   Normal Agricultural Values
   Loan Ratios and Liquidation Prices
   Private Loans Versus Government Grants

XIII. **Condemnation Appraisals**......................................507

   The Law of Eminent Domain
   The Property Owner's Problem
   The Definition of "Just Compensation"
   Fair Market Value
   The Problem of Damage
   The Question of Benefits
   Supplemental Appraisal Technique
   Courtroom Testimony
   Advisory Assistance and Relocation Payments

  Appendix 567

   Methods of Land Measurement
   An Appraisal Report
   The Organization of an Appraiser's Handbook
   Present Value Tables

  Index 607

CHAPTER 1

Professional Farm Appraisal

Farm real estate values have increased for almost 40 years—sometimes gradually, sometimes sporadically, sometimes with economic justification, and sometimes without.[1] Percentagewise, the increase has been fantastic; not just 300 or 400 percent, but 10-fold, 12-fold, and in some areas even more.

Farm property, of course, is held or owned for capital appreciation as well as to obtain farm earnings and to provide a place to live. Farm land is said to be a "good" investment sometimes regardless of or in spite of its current earnings. Yet meanwhile the improvements age, some become obsolete, and new ones are sometimes built. In any event, the buildings are insured; the property is taxed; the farm is used as collateral. An increased number of farms today are being condemned; what's worse, these farms are sometimes merely severed (partially condemned). More important, farm properties are bought and sold; they are transferred to the next generation, often without consideration (no money changes hands).

The continued increase in farm real estate values, along with these increased activities pertaining to farm property, has fostered a growing awareness on the part of many persons in the agricultural community of the need for the skills and expertise of the professional farm appraiser. The No. 1 question is "What is this farm worth?"

---

1. Farm property values also decline occasionally; however, at this point in time fewer and fewer persons are aware of the possibility, and even the better authors don't particularly want to remind them of the fact.

The farm appraiser's job is to investigate the major factors affecting value and to ascertain the present market value of the subject farm, as of a given date. The appraiser begins his appraisal with a physical inspection of the property, in this case a ranch east of Boulder, Wyoming.

Courtesy, U.S.D.A.

Let's illustrate: Henry Simpson purchased his first farm, a 100-acre tract, in the 1930's for $5,500. During the next three decades he added to his acreage and always at conservative prices. Henry was a successful farmer. He lived a full life; he did well financially. When he died he owned three farms, totaling over 1,300 acres. He left a widow, two sons, a married daughter, and no last will and testament.

Mother Simpson was the administrator of his estate and she relied heavily on son John along with a local attorney. Needless to say, the distribution of Henry's property, along with the federal estate and state inheritance taxes necessitated an inventory and a valuation. What were the three farms, the personal property, and his other assets worth?

John, one of Henry's sons, had gone to the nearby agricultural college; he had married, and was now farming the home farm. In fact, Henry had largely turned the farming operations over to him. During the last 10 years John had changed the rotations, applied more fertilizer, and increased crop yields. He had built a modern hog set-up using his own capital. His dad gave him a paper at the time, signifying, that in case of any unforeseen eventuality, John was to be reimbursed for his share of the remaining or unexhausted portion of these improvements. The paper covered the farrowing house and the finishing barn; however, it didn't include the concrete feed floor, or the two new Harvestores.

John had always figured that he would continue to farm the farm. His dad and mother wanted him to, and so did the rest of the family. There were two other children in the family—a younger boy, Bob, and a daughter, Sally. The three kids had always worked and played together; in fact, never had there been a serious disagreement. When children grow up, however, they often grow apart.

Bob also went to college. In fact, he stayed on and earned a Ph.D. He then obtained an excellent job in industry, and several years later became the youngest vice-president in the company. Bob stayed single. He now travels considerably (mostly on an expense account), and his income has always been more than sufficient. Bob has always figured that John would stay home and farm. He has had John's interest at heart, yet when the chips are down, he has also had a tendency to remain noncommittal.

Sally has been the happy-go-lucky one. She married while in college, was later divorced and remarried. Her income has never seemed to equal her level of living, but that's never bothered Sally. However, when Henry died, Sally's present husband, Sam, had just started a new business, and he was in need of capital. Sam wondered what the farm would sell for; he wondered how much money Sally would get.

With Mrs. Simpson's permission, the family attorney asked three persons to appraise the farm—a neighboring farmer, a man in the insurance business, and the local sale barn operator. All three of them were friends of the family. They came out to the farm, drove around it, and visited with Mrs. Simpson. They then placed a value of $550,000, or $425 per acre, on the farm for tax purposes.

The knowledge these three men had about the appraisal of farm real estate was not large. Their intentions were honorable. Yet in this case, the reason for making the appraisal influenced both their thinking and their final value figure. As a result their labors were lost.

That spring Sally and Sam were home. A new interstate highway was being built across one corner of the farm. Sam learned, much to his surprise, that the state was to pay $26,250 or $1,250 per acre for the 21 acres. What he did not know was that this award included both a temporary right-of-way and severance damage.

Sam spent the next several days quietly asking a few questions around town. He visited two banks, the county agricultural agent, the Soil Conservation Service, a local elevator, and several other places. He spent a half-day at the sale barn. He always ended up with the question, "If I were to buy some good farm land in this area what would I have to pay?" Unknowingly, his question sought the asking price of good farm land rather than its present market value.

The good farms in the area were held in strong hands; and Sam obtained many opinions. The values ranged from $550 to $900 per acre. Even the sale barn operator told him, confidentially of course, that that farm of Henry's would sell for at least $750 per acre. This figure was quite different from the one he and his two friends had arrived at for tax purposes.

After a family powwow Mother Simpson and John decided they needed a professional appraiser. This is what they got: a 24-page report, including a legal description of the property, a soils map, an estimate of the farm's productive capacity, a list of recent nearby farm sales, an inventory of each type of land and all buildings and improvements, along with their values, plus the farm's present market value.

The appraiser they hired used three different approaches to establish value. He did a careful budget of the dollar receipts and expenses which could be expected over the next 10 to 15 years under a typical operator. He then capitalized this income into the farm's value. He took a number of recent farm sales, compared them to the Simpson property, made various adjustments for several dissimilarities and tabulated them. He inventoried each type of land and each building, wrote up the exceptions, i.e., the ownership or rights that John had in several improvements, put a dollar value on each, and added them together.

In the final analysis, John and his wife acquired two tracts of land for $675 per acre. Bob purchased one tract for $750 per acre, kept it as an investment, and now rents it to John. When Sam and Sally studied their copy of the appraisal Sam admitted that he now knew more about a farm than ever before. He even thought it might be wise to have a professional appraiser look at his business.[2]

The appraisal profession is a challenging one in that no two farms are alike. A cropping pattern in the Cortland River Valley in upstate New York.

Courtesy, U.S.D.A.

Contrary to popular opinion, farms do not always sell at their present market value. A farm owner who decides to sell his farm today is often influenced by what he paid for that farm years ago. If he is not knowledgeable about the extent to which land values have increased, he may price his farm based on what it is worth to him, rather than what it is worth to all buyers and sellers in the marketplace.

Let's illustrate again. Harvey Wilson owned 140 acres. But he had been in ill health, had quit farming, and finally decided to sell out. A friend of his had sold real estate for a number of years on a part-time basis and Harvey listed the farm with him. Harvey and the realtor thought $84,000, or $600 per acre, would be a fair price.

The realtor had several friends, some of whom were prospects for Harvey's farm. One of them was John Stacy, a businessman who was looking for a good investment. Mr. Stacy had no agricultural background and no idea as to the value of the farm. Hence, he called a professional farm appraiser and asked him to appraise the 140 acres.

Mr. Stacy got a complete report. It included the income one might expect from the farm, a brief on a proposed highway interchange that might be located near the farm, and an analysis of some nearby farm sales, one of which had recently sold for residential development. The expected income was not very favorable. The proposed interchange was rather remote in time. However, the most likely future use of the tract was not for agricultural purposes. According to the appraiser, the tract's present market value was $140,000, or $1000 per acre.

Mr. Stacy then offered Mr. Wilson $80,000 and, somewhat to his surprise, his offer was accepted. A month later Mr. Stacy was offered $125,000 for his new investment. His realtor friend, however, advised him to hold, and as it turned out, it was well he did. Three years later 22.5 acres were taken by the State for a highway interchange. Mr. Stacy received $29,250. He then sold 1.0 acre to an oil company ($55,000) and 16.0 acres to a motel chain ($160,000). So he got his money back and then some. And the last we knew he still had 100+ acres left to sell.[3]

---

2. A similar version of Henry Simpson was published by the American Society of Farm Managers and Rural Appraisers in a brochure entitled "Who Knows What Land Is Worth?" around 1963.

3. An earlier version of Harvey Wilson was published by the Doane Agricultural Service in "Journeys from Farmland," Christmas 1959, and by *Successful Farming* in an article entitled "How to Find Out What Your Farm Is Worth" in April 1967.

The changes that are occurring in the agricultural community and in the total economy today are both many and complex. Henry Simpson purchased the first farm, 100 acres, for $55 per acre in the 1930's. He paid $2,000 cash and assumed a $3,500 mortgage. This now seems incredible. When he died his heirs relied on a neighbor and a few friends to appraise his estate. One's neighbors and friends always have various opinions as to value. So do realtors, brokers, salesmen, farm mortgage lenders, subdividers, contractors, and others in the realty businesses and building trades. Sometimes they also have vested interests. If Harvey Wilson, rather than take the advice of a friend, had spent a small amount of money for an appraisal of his 140 acres he could have been some $60,000 to $160,000 richer today.

Various persons buy and own farms for many different reasons. In fact, there are many origins of value. A pasture scene on a residential farm in eastern Pennsylvania.

Courtesy, U.S.D.A.

AGRICULTURE TODAY

No two farms are ever alike in terms of (1) the basic resources—land, labor, or capital—that are available, (2) the way these resources or factors of production are combined, or (3) in terms of the amounts of various crops and livestock produced. No two farm families ever think or act alike in terms of their goals or objectives, income requirements, or how they may attain various satisfactions.

The key word in today's agriculture is "change." The new technologies—improved varieties such as hybrid corn, added amounts of fertilizer, new insecticides and herbicides, larger corn planters, grain drills and harvesting equipment, sealed storage structures, mechanized feed and liquid manure handling facilities, and others—are the results of much agricultural research.

Favorable farm incomes following World War II and a real cost-price squeeze during the 1950's and 1960's stimulated the adoption of many of these new technologies by farmers. Their chief advantage was that they reduced costs of production and increased farm incomes.[4]

These new technologies have increased the farmer's ability to farm more acres and feed more livestock. They have increased his productivity and along with it the productivity of all other farm resources. In the process, however, a squeeze play for land has often developed. The farmer's ability to farm more acres has increased faster than his ability to acquire title to them. Farm land values have thus risen relative to both other resource costs and farm incomes.

Kinds of Farm Organization: Agriculture is a very competitive industry. The basic unit is the family operated farm. This family unit has shown a remarkable ability to survive periods of low prices, periods of high prices, a vast influx of technology, and in addition, government regulation. Two trends—(1) fewer and (2) larger farms—have dominated the statistics. Yet, contrary to these trends, which have occurred in other industries as well, the nation's farms continue to be relatively small businesses and largely family operated.

1. The Family Operated Farms. The family operated units may be classified as commercial, subsistence, part-time, or residential.

---

4. In a capitalistic society it is the innovator who receives the highest rewards. The neighbors often tend to merely follow if not lag behind. Those who wait lose out on much of the economic advantage that accompanies a new technology. Eventually, of course, the neighbors and others also add to the supply of agricultural products and hence the competition.

(Table 1). The commercial farms are located in the better land areas where the major emphasis is on the production of agricultural products for sale. Hence, these farms produce much of the nation's food and fiber. During the last two decades the operators on these units have found their competitive positions to be greatly enhanced through (a) the continued adoption of new technology (already mentioned), (b) the addition of increasingly larger amounts of capital, (c) specialization in those enterprises most advantageous to them, and (d) sizeable increases in size or volume.

These commercial farms or ranches have added tremendous amounts of capital to the farm family's labor. Relative to other industry today, the capital investment per man is extremely high in farming. This characteristic has led to the most productive agriculture in the world. The

The typical farm or ranch is difficult, if not impossible, to describe. This dairy farm in southern Ohio has been converted to beef.

Courtesy, J. C. Allen

commercial farms today are continuing to expand their volume of business. Some are now incorporating. This does not mean that corporate farms will take over; it merely means that the family operated commercial units are continuing to grow, along with the rest of the economy.

Table 1. Number of Farms and Value of Farm Products Sold.
By Kind of Farm Organization, United States, 1969.

Kind of Farm Organization	Total Value of Sales	Number of Farms		Value of Farm Products Sold	
		(1,000)	(Percent)	(Millions)	(Percent)
Commercial					
Elite	$100,000 and over	52.0	1.9	$15,327	33.6
Blue Ribbon	40,000 – 99,999	169.7	6.2	10,074	22.1
Upper Middle	20,000 – 39,999	331.0	12.1	9,267	20.3
Lower Middle	10,000 – 19,999	395.5	14.5	5,693	12.5
Low Income	5,000 – 9,999	390.4	14.3	2,814	6.2
(Sub-total)		(1,338.6)	(49.0)	(43,175)	(94.7)
Subsistence	2,500 – 4,999	395.1	14.5	1,346	3.0
	50 – 2,499[1]	996.5	36.5	1,088	2.3
Total, All Farms[1]		2,730.2	100.0	$45,609	100.0

Source: United States **Census of Agriculture**, 1969.
1. Includes 2.0 thousand abnormal farms.

At the same time one of the more surprising facets of American agriculture is the continued existence of many small-scale low-income farms—farms too small to provide either productive employment or an adequate level of living. These are often referred to as subsistence farms. They are found in the more mountainous areas and in the South. A few of them are scattered throughout the good land areas. Farming to the farm families who live on these farms is a way of life. Fishing and other pastimes take precedence over the business of farming. A little tobacco, a few goats, a couple of calves, and some sheep may provide some income; however, leisure is an equal if not more important source of satisfaction. One does not have to spend much time on a subsistence farm before realizing how unimportant it is to own a late model of anything.

There are many farms where the owner or operator has decided to combine a job in town with a farming operation. The owner essentially has two sources of income. His farm is a part-time farm. It is a means of increasing the family's income by working extra hours. Sometimes a sizeable acreage is farmed; however, usually only a trickle of farm produce ever goes to market. The part-time farm is both a method of getting started in farming and a method of retiring from farming. Success depends almost entirely on keeping the land, the improvements, and the capital invested in machinery and equipment in balance.

Where the farmer or farm-owner works in town and merely lives in the country—usually on 3 to 10 or more acres—this is a residential farm. Thanks to shorter working hours, the automobile, and improved highways, residential farming is now possible. The main source of income is the job in town. Usually little or no real farming is done, the exceptions sometimes being a garden and a quarter horse or two. Various satisfactions are obtained by getting away from the noise, the congestion, and the crowded conditions in the suburbs or city. There often appears to be more opportunity to develop creative activities. In many

The nation's farms are a diverse group. A brand new hog house, recently built on one of the more rolling farms in northern Indiana.

Courtesy, J. C. Allen

areas these so-called farmers have requested both bigger and better schools and other community facilities. Much to the concern of the natives, these requests have added to the community's costs far faster than the residential farmers' farms have added to the community's wealth or tax base.

2. Large-Scale Farms. Every so often a sizeable farming operation develops—3, 4, 5, sometimes 10 times the size of the typical family operated farm. These units are largely the result of extreme enterprise specialization. In some areas there is more control over certain resources such as climate. Marketing and other contractual agreements may lead to advantages in the sale of certain farm products. When successful, these large-scale farming operations are highly successful; yet when things go wrong, they have the dubious distinction of being highly unsuccessful. In other words, survival is not easy.

Agricultural production is subject to certain natural and biological processes. There is more chance for slippage between the acquisition of various resources, final farm production, and the income from such than with any other industry. Furthermore, the combined effect of the demand for agricultural products, which is relatively inelastic, and the supply of resources, which tends to move in or out of agriculture very slowly, leads to sizeable year-to-year fluctuations in both farm prices and farm incomes.

In order to be successful the large-scale farming operation must rely heavily on financial control and management. Unfortunately (or fortunately) the incentives found on the family owned and operated units are just not there. Thus, the family operated farm with its lower-valued resources and its farm-raised feeds fed to livestock, without going through the marketing channels, is a tough competitor. When the chips are down, the family operated farm often accepts either a low return to its labor, or a low return on its capital, and sometimes both.

Size of Farm and Types of Farming: Farm size varies tremendously in the United States. The *Census of Agriculture* periodically reports the number of acres per farm. These figures are not highly relevant, yet they approximate the amounts of land required to keep a farm operator, his family, and an occasional hired man fully employed under the different patterns of land utilization that exist all over the United States. In New York and New England it takes an average of only 98 to 279 acres; yet in the Mountain States an average of 566 to 6,486 acres are required (Table 2). More important than the number of acres farmed or the number of livestock that can be kept, of course, is the amount of farm products produced and the farm incomes that can be obtained. These data are not easily obtained, nor are they easy to interpret.

The nation's farms are a diverse group, so much so that the data are difficult to analyze; in fact, the typical farm is difficult to describe. A 397-acre dairy farm in upstate New York, producing milk for New York City, or a 114-acre truck-crop farm in New Jersey, producing vegetables for Philadelphia, has very little in common with the 7,500-acre cattle ranch in Cherry County, Nebraska, producing calves to be shipped to, and fattened on, still another 400-acre corn-hog farm in the Corn Belt. And, none of these places bear any resemblance to the 2,500-acre farm raising corn, cotton, and soybeans in the Mississippi Delta, the 65-acre gum operation or turpentine farm in Southern Georgia, the 2,800-acre wheat ranch in Montana, the citrus grove in

No two farms are alike in terms of either the basic resources or the crops and livestock raised. Seven hundred fifty steers have just been fed on a range in southern South Dakota.

Courtesy, U.S.D.A.

Table 2. Total Farm Acres per Farm.
All Farms, by States, 1964 and 1969.

Area, State	1964	1969	Area, State	1964	1969
The Pacific			**The Lake States**		
Washington	418	516	Minnesota	235	260
Oregon	516	620	Wisconsin	172	183
California	458	459	Michigan	145	153
The Mountain			**The Northeast**		
Montana	2,436	2,521	Maine	201	221
Idaho	516	566	Vermont	273	279
Wyoming	4,102	4,014	New Hampshire	194	211
Nevada	4,862	5,070	New York	185	196
Utah	816	867	Connecticut	119	120
Colorado	1,284	1,313	Massachusetts	112	123
Arizona	6,262	6,486	Rhode Island	94	98
New Mexico	3,354	4,020	Pennsylvania	130	142
			New Jersey	109	122
The Northern Plains			Maryland	153	163
North Dakota	875	930	Delaware	163	182
South Dakota	917	997			
Nebraska	596	634	**Appalachian**		
Kansas	544	574	West Virginia	153	188
			Virginia	149	165
The Southern Plains			Kentucky	122	128
Oklahoma	407	434	Tennessee	114	124
Texas	691	668	North Carolina	97	107
The Corn Belt			**Southeast**		
Iowa	219	329	South Carolina	144	177
Missouri	222	236	Alabama	164	188
Illinois	225	242	Georgia	215	234
Indiana	166	173	Florida	380	394
Ohio	146	154			
			The United States	352	390
Delta States					
Arkansas	207	260			
Mississippi	163	221			
Louisiana	167	232			

Source: United States Census of Agriculture, 1969.

Orange County, Florida, or a ranch producing cotton, grapes, and enough alfalfa hay for a 450-cow dairy in the San Joaquin Valley in California.

Farm appraisers, whenever they get together to pool their ideas, are often intrigued with the various patterns of land use and many different types of farming that exist in the United States. Yet, they are also surprised that in spite of the differences, their appraisal problems are much the same. There is no pattern as far as the individual farm is concerned. Yet the principles of farm appraisal are equally applicable the country over.

ORIGINS OF FARM VALUE

Various persons buy or own farms for many different reasons. In general, they hold or own farms because they can thus obtain certain satisfactions, which they could not otherwise enjoy. These satisfactions are oftentimes income-inspired. Yet they also stem from satisfactions other than the opportunity to make money. At some income level, and this varies widely, additional income becomes competitive with other satisfactions. In other words, there are multiple desires, multiple sources of satisfaction, and hence multiple reasons for farm ownership. What are the origins of value?

1. A farm is a means of making a living. The typical commercial

Each appraisal assignment is unique. This small ranch headquarters is located in West Central Montana.

farmer—owner-operator—buys or owns a farm, and he, along with the members of his family, operates it as a business. Income or earnings may result from the sale of grain, certain specialty crops, livestock, or livestock products. Whatever the case, the opportunity to earn this income, is a major origin of value. The farm appraiser takes this income and capitalizes it into the value of the farm.

However, prospective buyers are often willing to pay for things other than the opportunity to earn a given income. It is for this reason that the average aggregate long-term dollar returns in agriculture tend to be low. Furthermore, even the commercial farms are not always valued in proportion to their earnings. The commercial farm typically includes not only land, certain farm buildings and improvements, but a home and other related features.

2. A farm is a place to live. Many persons who buy or own a farm place a high value on the farm home and its many features. The home itself is a major source of satisfaction and, hence, value. With the possible exception of the absentee-owner or investor, the farm and the home are inseparable.

The farm home is a place to rear children, and to utilize certain family resources that may have little or no other alternative opportunities. It is a place to do things. There are hobby and recreational advantages. Thus the home and its intangible features—that thing called pride of ownership—is a major origin of value.

Farms owned by persons with outside income are hybrids in a sense. They have some of the farm characteristics, yet in addition, they derive value from some of the same considerations which affect the values placed on residential properties. Location is especially important, for it affects not only the desirability of the farm as a place to live, but also the accessibility to outside income.

Where the farm is primarily a place to live, the investment in such is often related not to the earnings capacity of the farm but instead to the income (non-farm income) of the owner. The farm is a place for the owner to invest his savings. The value of the residence is thus a major part of the total value of a residential farm, and a large part of the total value of the part-time farm, as well as an important part of the value of the commercial farm unit.

3. A farm is an investment. The absentee-owner often buys or owns a farm which he rents to an adjoining owner-operator, to a tenant-operator, or a manager with hired help. The unimproved tract, minus any buildings or improvements, is a particularly desirable unit, for the owner of this farm typically obtains the same amount of rent

as does the owner of an improved tract of land. The owner of the unimproved tract doesn't have the expense of maintaining the buildings or improvements. The dollar return on the investment and the present value of future benefits are both major origins of value. In fact, in these instances the absentee-owner typically expects a higher return on his investment than does the owner-operator.

The investor seeking safety of principal, a reasonable degree of liquidity, a minimum of management, and high returns can often find a more appropriate investment. Yet farm properties are often purchased or financed with a minimum of equity and a maximum of borrowed capital.

One doesn't have to be in a very high income bracket today to be more interested in capital appreciation than in income. In these in-

There is no pattern so far as the individual farm or ranch is concerned. A dry land ranch in the Wallowa Valley in Oregon.

Courtesy, U.S.D.A.

THE ORIGINS OF FARM VALUE

Farm Income or Earnings

From the sale of crops, livestock, and/or livestock products.

Most likely owner may be an owner-operator, interested in tangible dollar income.

Land is the basic resource, yet buildings and improvements are an important means of increasing farm size and efficiency.

The farm may be a headquarters unit with additional land being rented. In this case the subject property may be over-improved.

The owner often places a high value on improvements including many intangibles.

A Place to Live

Many intangible features provide psychic income.

Considerable pride of ownership in the dwelling or home and other resources.

Consumption and family activities lead to more satisfactions than farm production or employment.

Location in relation to off-farm employment opportunities, community services, and recreational facilities is a major factor.

The farm may be primarily a place to invest savings.

Dollar Return from an Investment

With the returns received as cash rent, or in the form of a share of the crops, livestock and/or livestock products sold.

Most likely owner is an absentee-owner with a tenant-operator, resident manager, or hired man.

Land is often the more important resource with buildings and improvements being unnecessary, in fact, sometimes unwanted.

Present dollar returns may be more important than future income, although not always.

Accessibility to other sources of income—minerals, oil, coal, gravel, a lease or a right-of-way, etc. may also exist.

A Hedge Against Inflation

The right(s) to future benefits and income overshadow present dollar returns.

A change in land use, future development, and increasing land values are anticipated.

Must sell or cash in property in order to win; in the interim depreciation and other expenses may provide tax offsets.

stances, the owner's objective is for his equity to increase faster, hopefully considerably faster percentagewise, than the farm's total value. This occurs whenever farm real estate values are rising.

The buildings and improvements on these farms sometimes become an ownership benefit in the form of a tax deduction or offset. The buildings and improvements may not contribute much to the market value of the farm, yet provisions for depreciation can be established in the owner's books.

Some investors have paid more for a farm than could be justified on the basis of current earnings. They have done so in anticipation of increased farm values in the future. They are desirous of maximizing income mostly in terms of long-term capital gains. The opportunity for capital appreciation is thus a major origin of farm value and particularly during periods of rising prices in the economy.

4. Farms often have other values, both tangible and intangible. Market prices are affected by the amounts of land for sale, by the cash resources and amounts of credit being made available to persons desirous of buying farms, and by the attitudes of both potential sellers and prospective buyers with regard to the future. There is often considerable pride of ownership. School facilities and other community features are often of considerable appeal. The part-time farmer may

The principles of appraisal are the same the country over, even in the diversified areas. Vegetable crops, sugar beets, and prunes being raised in the Santa Clara Valley in California.

Courtesy, University of California

place a high value on non-farm employment opportunities. The investor may be interested in a farm located in the transition area where there may someday be residential, commercial, and industrial development. Many persons attach strong sentimental values to farms. Grandfather may have owned the farm at one time; Mother may have been born there; or that house may have been the first tavern in Boone County.

The appraiser's job is to ascertain all the various sources of satisfaction that can be obtained by farm ownership, to ascertain all of the various origins of value, and to then explain all of this supportive evidence underlying the farm's present market value.

A FARM APPRAISAL DEFINED

A farm appraisal is a definite and usually detailed opinion as to the value of a farm property as of a given date. Such is typically written, although not always. The value ascertained by all appraisers is the farm's present market value.

The word opinion implies to the naive that an appraisal is merely a horseback, a windshield, or a seat-of-the-pants estimate arrived at in a fairly hasty fashion. Nothing could be further from the truth. Today's professional farm appraiser provides his client with a physical description of the farm, an estimate of the farm's productive capacity, and considerable economic data supporting his value figure.

The professional appraiser typically uses three approaches to value in order to assure his client of a highly objective value.

1. The earnings or income capitalization approach tends to establish a minimum value. An informed seller, free to act without haste or pressure, will not usually accept an amount of money less than the capitalized value of his farm based on whatever long-term earnings can be obtained from that farm, assuming an appropriate rate of return.

2. The sales comparison or market data approach tends to establish that value which most closely approximates the farm's present-day value in the market, providing recent, nearby, and comparable sales are available. Most appraisers spend many hours collecting and correlating comparable farm sales, each of which, when properly adjusted, leads the appraiser to his best estimate of the subject property's present market value.

3. The inventory or cost approach tends to establish a maximum value. An informed buyer, free to act without haste or pressure, will not usually offer an amount of money more than the cost of comparable land plus the cost of replacing all buildings and improvements (less their depreciation), or in other words, the cost of replicating or re-constructing a similar property in a similar area.

The use of all three approaches, whenever they are applicable, gives the professional farm appraiser a set of checks and balances, which in turn assures him that his final value figure is reasonably accurate. The professional farm appraiser then documents his conclusion by citing each of the various origins of value and by presenting considerable supportive evidence.

The appraiser's function is not to predict what the subject property's value *should* be. His role is not to determine value. The appraiser merely measures the market. He ascertains the value at which a change of ownership will most probably occur. His final value figure is thus determined by all buyers and sellers of farms. It measures the currently prevailing opinion as to the present worth of all of the satisfactions that can be obtained as a result of farm ownership.

THE PURPOSE OF AND REASONS FOR APPRAISALS

The appraiser's job begins with his client's problem. The appraiser and his client should have a clear, and preferably written, understanding as to the appraisal assignment, the purpose of, and the reason for or use to be made of the appraisal.

The purpose of an appraisal is to ascertain the present market value of the subject property. This is the No. 1 value. It is obtained by all appraisers. It is or should be the purpose of all appraisals.

The reason for an appraisal is to transfer ownership, to insure or to assess the property, to make a loan, or to condemn and take the property. The reason for an appraisal should have no effect on the property's present market value. The reason for or use to be made of an appraisal determines (1) the thoroughness of the farm inspection, (2) the amount of material to be included in the report, and (3) any value other than the property's present market value, which may need to be determined.

The typical appraisal course or set of instructions usually infers that a complete and thorough inspection of the farm or subject property is required. A more proper requirement perhaps is a complete investigation of all the major factors affecting value. The number of details which a professional appraiser investigates is difficult to appreciate. He seldom, if ever, gets all of his questions answered. He sooner or later has to quit, realizing, perhaps, that he is not quite done. However, his job is merely to investigate the major factors affecting value.

When the appraiser is on the witness stand and on cross-examination, an attorney may ask him certain irrelevant questions—for example, "What color were the kitchen cupboards?"—hoping, of course, to embarrass him and perhaps discredit his testimony. These questions are difficult ones. The appraiser's only recourse is to say that he investigated all of those factors which he felt had a major influence on value, that he didn't waste time on those factors which he felt were irrelevant. (As long as the kitchen cupboards were conventional in size and color their characteristics should perhaps have been ignored.)

The reason for or eventual use of an appraisal also determines the amount of material which should be included in the appraiser's report. An appraisal for a client who anticipates buying a farm will be more detailed than that for a lending agency. An appraisal for an attorney who expects to go to court will be more detailed than one for a tax authority.

Furthermore, appraisal assignments often request special values— the insured value of all buildings for an insurance company, the assessed value of the property for the local tax authority, a loan value or a probable liquidation price for a lending agency, or before and after values for a condemning authority. In all of these instances, present market value is always the No. 1 value. It is obtained first. It is then used as the basis for, or as a point of departure, to determine (not ascertain) some of these other values. In this fashion, the reason for an appraisal may determine the type of value required; however, it should have no influence on the process of ascertaining the present market value of the property.

Appraisals to Transfer Ownership: Most farm owners buy only one, two, or maybe three farms during their entire lives. Unfortunately they seldom hire a professional appraiser. This is a mistake. The professional farm appraiser looks at farms almost every day. He knows the area and the things to look for. He will typically spend several days checking various maps, walking the farm, probing the soils, checking irrigation and drainage facilities, looking at the crops, inventorying the buildings, and maybe visiting with the neighbors.

The professional appraiser usually obtains more cooperation from both the person selling the farm and the neighbors who live nearby than does a prospective buyer. He knows the right questions to ask and how to go about it. If, for example, a professional appraiser asks the owner about a wet spot, and in doing so, pulls a soil probe out of his car, the owner at that point is usually quite candid.

When a prospective buyer reads a professional appraiser's report he often learns more about the subject property than he would if he were to walk that farm himself. When a prospective buyer is shopping around an appraiser can help him evaluate his alternatives. For whenever a farm is for sale, the appraiser's ability to assemble, compare, and adjust recent farm sales in the area and relate each to the subject property is of considerable value.

In instances where a prospective buyer has partially decided on a farm, the professional appraiser may counsel with him with regard to price. The appraiser may suggest an offering price, realizing that his client doesn't want to make a ridiculously low offer, yet neither does he want to offer any more money than necessary. Thus, the appraiser may help a prospective buyer formulate a reservation price—the highest price he is willing to pay—realizing that during the final negotiations this figure may be modified.

The farm owner who desires to sell a farm is confronted with a set of questions which parallel those of the buyer. He doesn't want to offer his farm for sale at a too high price, for in so doing he may scare away some or all of the prospective buyers. (They seldom if ever come back even though the price may later be reduced.) Yet, the seller wants to sell his farm at as high a price as possible.

Many a farm owner has a friend in the real estate business. He says to this friend, "What do you think you can sell my farm for?" The real estate broker always has an opinion, however he doesn't generally walk the farm; and an opinion is oftentimes all he has. Furthermore, he has a vested interest. For the lower the price, within reason, the easier it is for that broker to sell the farm; and the sooner he sells the farm the sooner he receives his commission and the sooner he can go and sell another farm or property.

The farm appraiser doesn't work on a commission. He sells his expertise. The prospective buyer may hire him; the farm owner or seller may hire him. Either obtains the same information. The appraiser's report may inform a buyer. It may disclose to the owner or seller some facts that he didn't know, or at least, hadn't thought about. Again, the appraiser's ability to assemble, compare, and adjust recent farm sales and other economic data and relate each to the subject property is of considerable value.

The professional appraiser may also counsel a seller in terms of how he might best sell his farm—as a single unit, or as several tracts, and for cash or on contract. He may counsel a seller in terms of an asking price. If the owner is in no hurry, that price can be a fairly firm one; however, if he is desirous of selling soon, some sacrifice in price may be indicated. If the seller is willing to finance the transfer of ownership through a land contract, the most probable selling price may be increased. Thus, a qualified appraiser may be extremely helpful to either a buyer or seller.

Appraisals for Other Reasons: Farm appraisals are made for many reasons. Building valuations are made to underwrite fire and other casualty insurance. They assure the property owner that he has the correct amount of coverage; they provide proof of loss, and they facilitate the settlement of claims.

Insurance appraisals present a unique problem in that only the buildings are valued. On some farms the buildings are largely leftover ones—obsolete and empty, yet insured. On other farms the buildings are special purpose buildings, full of the newest and latest technologies. The latter may be extremely useful in terms of their ability to save labor and to increase the scope or volume of the farming operations. Yet their cost when built did not add anywhere near an equal number of dollars to the market value of the farm. Thus, oftentimes insured values more nearly reflect utility values in the farming operations

---

THE REASONS FOR APPRAISALS

1. To buy, to sell, to trade, or to transfer ownership.

2. To establish the bases for depreciating various buildings and improvements in subsequent tax schedules.

3. To settle a claim resulting from fire, wind, or other casualty.

4. To assess the subject property for real estate tax purposes.

5. To obtain the basis for federal estate or state inheritance taxes.

6. To extend credit to the owner, thus financing the purchase of the farm, using the farm as security.

7. To liquidate the property, using the asset's sale price to settle debts, liens, and other encumbrances.

8. To establish just compensation to the property owner in instances where a public agency is taking either all or part of the property for public use.

9. To appeal where compensation, assessment, or other values or amounts are thought to be in error.

than they do contributory values in the market. Nowhere are the problems of appraisal more evident than in farm building valuation.

Most farm properties are subject to ad valorem property taxes. These are based on assessments which traditionally have been the job of the township trustee, the assessor, or some locally elected official. Upon occasion the farm appraiser has been asked to help the tax authorities describe soil types, to develop land classifications, and to relate or assign various values to the different kinds of land. Upon occasion he has been asked to help update farm building costs.

Today a number of tax districts are recognizing the need for better appraisals per se. As a result some are hiring, at reassessment time, professional appraisal firms who then do a mass appraisal of all properties in the tax jurisdiction.

The laws of property descent and distribution along with certain legal instruments, such as one's last will and testament, determine the inter-generation transfer of property. Soon thereafter federal estate and inheritance taxes are due. Farm appraisals are often required in order to establish the bases for these taxes. The trust departments in many banks—both city and country—are called upon to appraise farms. The larger banks, with clients ranging over a wide area, tend to farm out their appraisals, hiring a fee appraiser located in and knowledgeable about the area, to do their farm appraisal work.

The farm lending institutions and the government loan agencies also make a large number of farm appraisals. These lenders are interested in the farm's value as security for a loan. They are interested in the farm's income, its debt-carrying capacity, and its resalability in case of default. The farm loan appraiser has typically used the income approach as the basic approach to a subject farm's value. The lending institutions, of course, are concerned primarily with the amount of income likely to prevail over the loan repayment period.

The most detailed farm appraisals are the eminent domain or condemnation appraisals. These are required whenever a public agency takes private property for public use—for a highway, a power-line, a pipeline, a reservoir, or an airport, etc. When the entire property is to be taken, the assignment merely requires a straightforward appraisal of the value of the subject property. However, in many cases only a part of the property is to be taken. The assignment then involves an appraisal of the farm before the take and a second appraisal after the take.

The unfortunate circumstance which complicates many of these appraisals is that many farms are severed and oftentimes diagonally. The residuals or remaining parcels are often unequal in size. The improvements may end up on the smaller residue rather than the larger. However, circuity of travel is not, in itself, compensable.

Condemnation appraisals require the very best skills on the part of professional farm appraisers. Fifteen to 20 percent of all cases often go to court. The appraiser then gets to present his appraisal before a judge and jury. He is examined and cross-examined, an activity enjoyed by only a few. At the same time, the best qualified appraisers are those who have studied their lessons long enough and know the appraisal process well enough so that they have no qualms about their appraisals being exposed to the public.

The varied nature of most farm appraisals often qualifies the farm appraiser to do specialized appraisals. The typical farm appraisal, unlike most residential, commercial, or industrial appraisals assumes that the farm's income will last indefinitely.[5] However, appraisal assignments occasionally include a source of income which will someday be used up; in other words, a source of income that cannot be projected into perpetuity. Thus, a professional farm appraiser is occasionally asked to appraise the present value of an income stream or the present value of an asset sometime in the future.[6]

FOUR OF THE PROBLEMS

Every farm appraisal is a special challenge. Farm-to-farm values, both total and per acre, are influenced by such things as the type of land, the extent to which the farm is improved, and the size of the unit. Farm values are also influenced by general price changes occurring in the economy. Over time, farm real estate appraisers have developed certain broad generalizations with regard to what good versus poor land, bare versus improved tracts, and large versus small farms are worth to prospective buyers and sellers of farms. However, their success as appraisers, no matter how skilled or competent they are, has been largely conditioned by the broad general swings in farm real estate prices.

---

5. This is because land, generally speaking, is considered to be indestructible. Buildings, on the other hand, wear out, hence are referred to as wasting or depreciable assets.

6. The present value of an income stream equals the present worth of $1.00 every year for the next N years. The present value of an asset available only in the future—a reversionary right—equals the present worth of $1.00 N years from now.

Good Versus Poor Land: The difference in the price per acre as between good land and poor land is usually insufficient. On a per-acre basis good land has a tendency to be under-priced and poor land has a tendency to be over-priced, assuming, of course, all other factors are equal (Table 3).[7] This relationship is largely a result of three factors.

First, most buyers and sellers do not completely recognize, nor are they able to accurately measure the actual differences in productivity. The favorable characteristics of good land are often recognized, yet not completely; seldom if ever can they be measured sufficiently accurate and thus converted to premium prices. Vice versa, the unfavorable characteristics of poor land are often recognized, yet not completely; seldom if ever are they sufficiently discounted in terms of price.

Table 3. Soil Productivity Ratings Related to Farm Sale Prices.
359 Farms, Central, Western, and Northern Illinois, 1971-72.

Soil Productivity Rating[1]		Number of Tracts	Tract Size (Acres)	Percent Tillable	Sale Prices per Acre	
Range	Average				Per Total Acre	Per Tillable Acre
Less than 75	66	75	136	76.3	$401	$526
75-89	84	73	137	87.0	538	624
90-96	93	40	118	97.5	692	711
97-102	101	171	117	97.8	$771	$788

Source: Tables 8 and 9. Landlord Earnings and Farmland Prices, Illinois A.E. 4301, University of Illinois, November, 1972.

1. This relationship is affected quite considerably by the percent of tillable and untillable land on the farm. Thus, the statement in the text relative to good land versus poor land is correct but only if it defines good land as that which is both high in tillable acres and high in soil productivity.

Second, many persons develop more price resistance and they do so more quickly when prices are high than when prices are low. It's quite natural to pay less (relatively speaking) for good land, mainly because price resistance tends to occur more readily when prices are high. It's quite natural to pay more (relatively speaking) for poor land primarily because the price appears to be low, even though maybe it isn't, actually.

---

7. The price of poor land also tends to fluctuate more than does the price of good land. When farm real estate values rise the price of poor land rises faster, percentagewise, than does the price of good land, and vice versa, again assuming all other factors are equal.

Third, good land tends to attract farm operators with above average to high levels of management, whereas poor land tends to attract the more marginal operator with less managerial skill. The better managers are more skilled in bargaining for and in acquiring various farm resources. They tend to do a better job recognizing differences in quality, they tend to shop around, and they tend to buy good land at high yet reasonable prices. The average manager is less skilled (by definition perhaps). He tends to have less bargaining power. He tends to bid on the cheaper, poorer quality farms. He tends to "get taken" occasionally, oftentimes without realizing it.

The professional appraiser is more aware of the differences between good land and poor land than is the man in the street. Yet he too tends to err. During the 1920's and 1930's farm loan appraisers often loaned too much on the poor land and perhaps too little on the good land. Foreclosure and loss ratios indicated such at the time (Table 4). Loss ratios were low on the good land yet they rose rapidly on average and inferior quality land.

Table 4. Soil Productivity Related to Land Values and Loan Foreclosure. 108 Foreclosures Out of 827 Loans, East Central Illinois, 1936.

Soil Productivity	Value per Acre	Amount Loaned per Acre	Loan Ratio	Loans Foreclosed	Losses per $1,000 Loaned
Inferior	$ 83	$33	39.9%	$20.7	$106.29
Average	117	44	38.3	11.7	45.99
Good	$207	$79	39.5%	$ 8.4	$ 16.10

Source: Illinois Agr. Exp. Sta. Bul. 468.

The local assessor almost always undervalues farm and other real estate for tax purposes. Empirical evidence may be lacking, yet the practice is well known. He, of course, is elected by neighbors and friends and perhaps for reasons other than his ability as an appraiser.

The fee appraiser may also undervalue good land and overvalue poor land. Hopefully he does so to a much lesser degree than does the typical buyer and seller. Of course the fee appraiser is obligated to reflect the market and there is a real tendency even in the marketplace to under-price good land and over-price poor land.

Bare Versus Improved Tracts: There also exists considerable variation in the extent to which various buildings and improvements contribute to a farm's market value. Generally speaking, buildings and
improvements are obtained more economically by purchasing them
with land than by purchasing them separately. However, one has to
assume, (1) that the prospective buyer wants or needs the improvements, (2) that the existing improvements are in balance with the
acreage purchased, and (3) that the improvements can be adapted to
whatever use is to be made of the farm.

The trends today are toward fewer farms, increased farm size, and
the consolidation of farm units. This has resulted in many leftover
farmsteads and farm buildings. Many farm buildings are also obsolete.
The new technologies have led to more efficient methods of handling
grain, feeding livestock, etc. The typical prospective buyer today is
often one desirous of purchasing additional land but not additional
buildings or improvements. Thus, in many areas, bare land sells for as
high a price per acre as do the improved tracts.

In many areas the typical investor prefers bare land, for the expenses
incurred in maintaining farm buildings are typically higher than the
income received as a result of owning the improvements. In some instances, a new owner can claim large amounts of depreciation even
though the buildings may have no use. The tax laws are often condu-
cive to ownership. By not maintaining the buildings the new owner
can perhaps come out money ahead. Yet what about the insurance
rates? What about the appearance of the subject property and its effect
on the value of surrounding farms?

When buildings and improvements are purchased separately, their
cost seldom if ever adds an equal number of dollars to the value of
the farm. The percentage added varies with the improvement. A large
application of fertilizer or drainage tile often adds little to the value
of a farm because such cannot be seen—except gradually and through
increased yields several years ·later. An investment in a pole barn,
machinery shed, or building which has several alternatives as to use,
adds more value than an investment in a specialized building such as a
Harvestore, a milking parlor, or a slotted-floor farrowing house. Yet,
the capital invested in an attractive fence around the farmstead may
add more to the market value of the farm than it cost, primarily because it adds to the farm's general appearance. The latter is an exception to the rule that (1) bare land often sells for as much as an improved tract, and (2) that an improvement seldom adds anywhere near
its cost to the value of the real estate.

Whenever farm ownership is transferred, the new buyer often desires something somewhat different in the way of improvements. Unfortunately, that which appeals to one farm owner seldom appeals to the next owner. The next owner may remodel the building, adapting its use to some other purpose; he may add onto an existing building, he may move such to a new location, or he may tear the structure down. Whatever money he spends, he seldom adds an equal number of dollars to the value of the property. Thus improvements add value only when they (1) are needed and useful, or adaptable to new uses in the future, (2) are in balance with the rest of the farm's resources (not over- or under-built), (3) are properly located, and (4) add to the farm's appearance.

Large Versus Small Farms: Large farms have some tendency to sell for a lower price and small farms have some tendency to sell for a higher price (relatively speaking). This is more apparent when sale prices are compared on a per-acre basis in the agricultural Midwest or on a per-cow basis in either the dairy areas or in the Great Plains than when only total sale prices are given. The phenomenon sometimes shows in aggregate data (Table 5). This tendency is a result of three factors.

Table 5. Farm Size Related to Per-Acre Farm Prices.
Agricultural Properties Only, United States, March 1973.

Acres per Farm		Dollar Price per Acre[1]	
Range	Median	Average	Additional
10– 49	30	$909	—
50– 69	60	665	−244
70– 99	80	586	− 79
100–139	120	525	− 61
140–179	160	430	− 95
180–219	200	436	+ 6
220–259	240	425	− 11
260–499	380	335	− 90
500–999	750	284	− 51
1,000 and over	—	108	−176

Source: U.S.D.A. Farm Real Estate Market Developments, C D 78, July 1973.

1. These values are for the entire United States; hence represent a combination of agricultural tracts with considerable variability in land quality and building investments per acre as well as different acreages per farm. Thus, the data do not represent strictly a cause-and-effect relationship between acres per farm and price per acre.

First, a fairly large number of persons are capable of bidding on the small farms or ranches. However, as total acres or total capital requirements (acres times per-acre value) increase, more and more persons encounter financial restrictions. As a result, there are fewer persons capable of bidding on or purchasing the larger farms. This is commonly referred to as the skewed distribution of capital resources. It is quite common among prospective buyers of different sized farms in practically all areas.

Second, the large farms usually have larger and better quality residences or homes than the small farms. However, on a per-acre basis the value of the typical house on the large farm is still less usually than the value of the typical house on the small farm. This is particularly true if one moves from a commercial, to a part-time, or a residential farm. The residence or home on the larger unit usually makes up a much smaller portion of the total value of the property.

Third, there is a tendency for farm size to influence those production costs which are fixed. Land is combined with other resources in variable proportions. As acres are increased the investment in the required machinery does not increase proportionately; instead this investment is spread over more and more acres. As acres are increased production costs per acre tend to decline. The larger farms also tend to have more and better farm improvements; however, here again as acres increase, the investment seldom if ever increases proportionately.

Farms can occasionally be too large as well as too small. When this is the case, the farm is typically divided and is then transferred or sold in two, three, or four separate tracts. This often creates an additional problem for the farm real estate appraiser. Every farm should be appraised, always, in terms of how it will most likely sell. If a farm will most likely sell as two or three separate units, then that farm should be appraised that way.

The appraiser's job is to sometimes decide how the subject property will sell. It is the appraiser's job, always, to ascertain the effect that a farm's size has on value. For as farms increase in size their values, on a per unit basis—per acre or per cow—often decline. This has nothing to do with the physical resources of the farm; it is instead a phenomenon of the market.

The Price "Cycle": Over time prices go up and prices go down. That is, most prices do. In fact, many of them rise and fall in fairly regular cycles. However, there are also long-term trends, seasonal price variations, sporadic price changes, and others, all of which tend to overshadow the regularity of a price cycle.

Farm real estate prices have never shown any particular cyclical tendency unless perhaps there is a 40- or 50- or 60-year cycle. However, farm real estate prices do tend to exhibit some of the psychological characteristics that accompany rapidly changing prices.

Price cycles are the result of man's over and under efforts, really his inability, to match production to demand. Man tends to first overproduce; he then tends to under-produce. It is also human nature to oscillate, to be either overly optimistic or overly pessimistic with regard to the future. Many persons tend to act differently at different points in a price cycle. When prices are rising people rejoice; when prices are falling they tend to lose confidence.

All people like to see prices rise; then they are happy. When prices continue to rise over a period of time people eventually become overly optimistic; they often think prices will continue to rise, and they sometimes get quite excited. In the extreme this is referred to as "speculative fever." Such is much easier to observe and study in the market for common stock than in the market for farm real estate. However, seldom do prices rise forever; they eventually level or plateau and sometimes, sooner or later, they decline.

When farm prices are rising or are extremely high, farm owners and others become enthusiastic. They tend to view farm land as an important hedge against inflation. As prices rise, farm real estate values often rise to the extent that they rise above any long-term value based on earnings. This is because present expectations with regard to the future appear to be excellent. Later, the neighbors (and sometimes some appraisers) may say, "That farm sold for more than it was worth." This statement is incorrect as far as the definitions of value and price are concerned, yet it relates a farm's value, based solely on earnings, to its sale price.

When prices decline, people are unhappy. They become pessimistic, oftentimes discouraged and sometimes overly so, for it looks as though prices will never recover. Yet, sooner or later, prices bottom out and they gradually work their way back up. Nevertheless, for those persons who have lived through the bottom of the cycle it takes considerable time to regain confidence and to realize that prices are now going up.

When farm prices fall farm owners and others tend to become discouraged. Sometimes they become exceedingly pessimistic. Farm real estate may then sell at lower and lower prices—prices which are often below any long-term value based on a given farm's earnings. This happened in the 1930's. It happened because the future expectations appeared to be very poor. A decade later the neighbors (and again some appraisers) said, "That farm sold for less than it was worth." This statement is again incorrect as far as the definitions of value and price are concerned, yet again, it relates a farm's value, based solely on earnings, to sale price.

Farm real estate prices do not appear to be subject to much price fluctuation. For the last 40 years they have risen—at first gradually and more recently rapidly. From 1933 to 1956 they exhibited an upward trend. Since 1956 there has been a fairly steep rise (Figure 1).

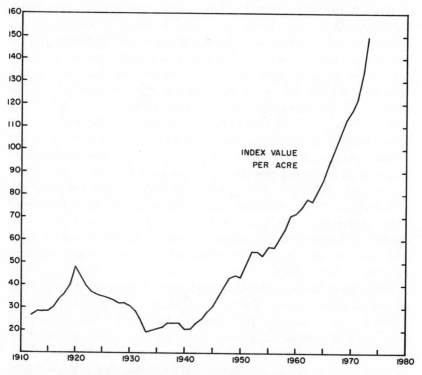

Figure 1. The Long-Term Changes in Farm Real Estate Values.
Index of Value per Acre, United States, 1912-1973.

This upward change reflects at least four factors.

1. A faster rise in the farm prices received by farmers than in the prices paid by farmers. This relationship is one which leads to very favorable farm incomes. This phenomenon occurred largely from 1932, through World War II, and up into the early 1950's.

2. A more recent, rapid, and largely successful adoption of agricultural technology. When a price-cost squeeze, as reflected by these same price indices, occurred, various new technologies led to increased farm productivity and to a sizeable reduction in farm costs—not necessarily in total but on a per-unit basis. This phenomenon occurred largely from 1955 on, however, the beginning of such varies by areas.

3. A decline in the value of the dollar. This has been and continues to be reflected in continued price inflation which affects practically every sector of the economy.

4. A continued increase in the availability of credit. This has resulted from continued, if not increased, activity on the part of the federal government along with changes in the method of transferring farm ownership. The government agencies have continued to sponsor, in fact, subsidize credit to farmers at quite favorable rates of interest. The shift from the conventional farm mortgage or deed in trust to the installment land contract with its low down payment and below-market rate of interest has also been a source of additional credit. Both of these have provided considerable impetus toward increased farm real estate prices during the last 40 years.

At times, the increase in farm real estate prices has been rapid; at times it has been slow. Occasionally farm real estate prices have leveled and declined a little. Any quick change appears to create real problems for farm appraisers. Whether or not farm real estate prices are really subject to a 40-, 50-, or 60-year cycle is difficult to say. If such a cycle does exist, it's not difficult to realize that the working lives of most persons may not be long enough to experience both the up and the down. The farm appraiser who entered the profession in the 1920's was none too successful. The farm appraiser who entered the profession in the 1940's—20 years later—has been. His success, to some extent at least, has been the result of increasing farm real estate prices.

THE QUALIFICATIONS OF A FARM APPRAISER

The farm appraiser's job is to investigate the major factors affecting value and to ascertain the present value of the subject property as of a given date. This requires a knowledge of things agricultural, a certain amount of economic judgment, and considerable time to assemble and present the data. The farm appraiser inspects the farm and assembles all of the pertinent facts; he analyzes, weighs, and combines the information in an organized fashion. Based on his findings he then ascertains the value of the farm.

The qualified farm appraiser must have considerable technical knowledge about all things agricultural. Usually he was born and reared on a farm; often he has an agricultural college degree. He has acquired and combined skills from agronomy, engineering, animal science, economics, law, and psychology. As he walks the farm he has a feel for the soils, topography, drainage, climate, irrigation, and the cultural practices influencing the crops raised in the area. He has a feel for the contribution of various buildings and improvements, and whether the farm's resources, as an operating unit, are balanced.

The qualified farm appraiser has to have considerable economic judgment or ability. He knows that most appraisals are made before any money changes hands and yet that no real dollar value is established until the change in ownership takes place. He knows the difference between present market price and present market value. The qualified farm appraiser has to have a feel for the farm real estate market and for the many factors—prices, costs, earnings, landlord-tenant arrangements, land contracts, mortgages, interest rates, taxes, government regulations—and the many idiosyncrasies of both buyers and sellers that influence the market prices of farms in his area.

The qualified farm appraiser has to have the ability to organize and to analyze. He has to have the ability to grasp various situations. He is inclined to believe nothing that he hears and very little of what he sees and maintain a certain mental poise in the process. He digs into each possibility, weighs each fact, and eventually, through a fairly thorough process, arrives at one final figure, which accurately expresses, in dollars, the present worth of all of the future benefits or satisfactions which accrue to farm ownership. The final figure presented in his report is perhaps an opinion. However, that opinion, accurate or not, useful or not, and respected or not, depends upon the number of facts and other details submitted as supportive evidence and upon how those facts and other data are presented. The factual information, the analysis of such, and the methods of presentation are what make an appraisal.

Lastly, the qualified appraiser has to be intellectually honest. He does not make or determine present market value. He is never an advocate of value. When he is asked to appraise a property for a given amount—for example, "Bill, your final value must be at least $175,000, or we can't make the loan," he supposedly "straightens out" his client or turns the job down. In other words, the worth or accuracy of an appraisal depends not only on his ability, skill, and expertise, but also on his honesty, integrity, and moral character.

THE OBJECTIVE OF THIS BOOK

The appraisal profession is a challenging one in that each farm is different; each appraisal assignment is unique. Not all persons, in fact not all appraisers, have the skills or the expertise required to appraise farm properties. Hence, the reason for this book.

The author's purpose has been to set forth the various appraisal principles (the first eight chapters), and then show their application in the various areas of appraisal activity—farm building valuation, appraisals for property insurance, ad valorem tax appraisals, appraisals for farm loans, and eminent domain or condemnation appraisals. An understanding of appraisal theory and practice does not require any extraordinary amount of intellectual ability; however, to properly apply such does require an extraordinary amount of time, patience, and perseverance.

Chapter II focuses in on the differences between value and price. It then develops the definition and assumptions behind today's present market value concept. The chapter leads one into the maze of basic farm value, normal market value, farm building value(s), insured value, assessed value, farm loan value, fair market value, and some 26 others.

Chapter III develops the "what is" in real estate versus real property. It sorts out the rights of the property owner and those of the sovereign. It looks at various legal concepts and definitions and at some of the law which governs the ownership of private property. It presents the basics of ownership transfer, how the evidence is recorded, and how real estate is described in legal fashion.

Chapter IV details the *modus operandi* of the farm appraiser, or the path he follows as he goes about getting acquainted in a given area and appraising a particular farm. The typical operator concept is presented, along with what an appraiser does both before and enroute to inspect a farm. The chapter guides one in the all-important client relationships as well as how to describe the subject property, estimate its productivity, and write an appraisal report. The further one wanders in this chapter the more one realizes there are things to do and not to do in a farm appraisal.

Chapter V assumes that the appraiser is just starting in a new area. It outlines a system for organizing the many reference materials one needs to have in an appraiser's handbook, or better yet the office files. Real organization is put to the system of collecting and keeping such mundane materials as the physical features of the area, agricultural trends in the economy, economic statistics—both nationwide and locally—the characteristics of the community, and all the other "stuff" which is referred to as "miscellanea compacta."

Chapter VI gets down to the methods of establishing value. The very basic earnings approach to value is presented. The traditional methods used to estimate farm receipts, expenses, and income are given. Two different techniques now being used to capitalize income into value are presented. The chapter also recognizes that not all farm assets should be capitalized into perpetuity. The present value of an income stream and the present value of an asset N years hence are both presented.

Chapter VII presents the sales comparison or market data approach to value and again is most helpful in terms of getting a farm appraiser organized. The collection of recent farm sales, their verification, inspection, and classification, and how various adjustments may be made is shown.

Chapter VIII presents the inventory or cost approach. This one sums the value of each kind of land and the value of each building and improvement. In this chapter, as elsewhere, cost is a necessity, yet not necessarily a value. In each of these three chapters—VI, VII, and VIII—the various areas of importance and use are specified.

Chapter IX tackles one of the tougher areas—that of farm building valuation. There are many reasons to value a farm building, and unlike a farm appraisal, the reason for the valuation affects the final value figure. The difference between reproduction and replacement cost and the different kinds and causes of depreciation are presented. Structural value, contributory value, value-in-use, and salvage value are each developed. Best of all, perhaps, thirteen illustrations are presented.

Chapter X follows most logically, presenting both some of the philosophy as well as some of the practice regarding farm building valuations for property insurance purposes. The indemnity principle is presented, thus setting the stage for the utility value concept. Cost, actual cash value, the face amount of the policy, and payment of the proceeds on a deferred basis are all there. For the first time the problem of equitability appears.

Chapter XI takes the appraiser into another area—that of the assessor. The general property tax and the assessor's job are each presented. The mass appraisal technique is given, along with problems relative to preferential treatment for agriculture. True cash value and assessed value are defined and questions relative to full versus fractional assessment are raised. Lastly, the equitability and equalization problems are both described.

Chapter XII turns to the job of the farm loan appraiser and looks at the problems of the farm mortgage lender. The chapter looks at normal market value, which now has historical significance only, presents the bench-mark approach to appraisal, and discusses both farm loan value and liquidation price. The latter leads to the question as to whether all the credit that is now available is really good for the agricultural community.

Chapter XIII tackles the role of the condemnation appraiser, beginning first with the law of eminent domain and then the property owner's problem. The definitions of just compensation and fair market value—before and after—are presented in detail. Guides to some of the many state-to-state, agency-to-agency, and court-to-court variations involving severance versus consequential damages, special versus general benefits, and other problems, some without solution, are detailed. The before-and-after appraisal technique is presented along with some of the strategies involved in testifying in court.

No one professional appraiser will perhaps ever agree with all of the concepts or statements presented in this book. Some of the material is aimed at forcing the reader to think; some of it consists of practical suggestions aimed at increasing one's efficiency as an appraiser. Most farm appraisers work and live from one appraisal to another, from one case to the next. This is not necessarily bad. Generalizations are often both difficult and dangerous to make. However, unless one takes time out to occasionally think about the organization of his day-to-day endeavors he often gradually reduces his total contribution to society as he plods his merry way. If this book helps the new, young, and perhaps eager appraiser, or the old pro, in getting his day-to-day activities better organized, then it's accomplished its objective.

REFERENCES

Crouse, E. F., and C. H. Everett, *Rural Appraisals,* Prentice-Hall, 1956.
"How to Find Out What Your Farm Is Worth," *Successful Farming,* April 1967.
"Journeys from Farmland," No. 66, Doane Agricultural Service, Christmas 1959.
Murray, W. G., *Farm Appraisal and Valuation,* 5th Edition, Iowa State University, 1969.
"Who Knows What Land Is Worth?," American Society of Farm Managers and Rural Appraisers (around 1963).

Agriculture Today

Bachman, K. L., and J. V. McElveen, "Trends in Kinds and Sizes of Farms," *Land: The 1958 Yearbook of Agriculture,* U.S.D.A., 1958.
Baughman, E. T., "Shall I Buy or Sell a Farm?," *Journal of American Society of Farm Managers and Rural Appraisers,* Vol. 17, No. 1, April 1953.
"Changes in Farm Production and Efficiency," U.S.D.A., Stat. Bul. 233, 1971.
"Concepts Involved in Defining and Identifying Farms," U.S.D.A., E.R.S., 448, June 1970.
Conklin, H. E., "The Farm Family and the Coming of Revolutions," *Journal of American Society of Farm Managers and Rural Appraisers,* Vol. 30, No. 2, October 1966.
"Do You Want to Live in the Country?," Oregon State College, Ext. Bul. 753, April 1956.
Elliott, F. F., "Generalized Types of Farming in the United States," U.S.D.A., Agr. Info. Bul. 3, February 1950.
Frey, H. T., et al., "Major Uses of Land and Water in the United States," U.S.D.A., E.R.S., Rept. 149, 1968.
Higbee, Edward, *Farms and Farmers in an Urban Age,* 20th Century Fund, 1963.
Loomis, R. A., "A Profile of Part-Time Farming in the United States," Department of Agricultural Economics, Michigan State University, A.E. 15, 1965.
Marschner, F. J., et al., "Land Use and Its Patterns in the United States," U.S.D.A., A.R.S., Agr. Handbook 153, April 1959.
McElveen, J. V., "Family Farms in a Changing Economy," U.S.D.A., A.R.S., Agr. Info. Bul. 171, 1957.
Nikolitch, Radoje, "The Adequate Family Farm: Mainstay of the Farm Economy," *Appraisal Journal,* Vol. 34, No. 1, January 1966.

"Our 100,000 Biggest Farms: Their Relative Position in American Agriculture," U.S.D.A., E.R.S., A.E. 49, 1964.
Sisler, D. G., and S. W. Warren, "A Regional Summary of United States Farming, Cornell University, A.E. Res. 292, June 1969.
U. S. Census of Agriculture, Dept. of Commerce, Bureau of the Census, 1969.

Origins of Farm Value

Rowlson, J. F., "Investment Property: An Analysis of Motivation," The Real Estate Appraiser, Vol. 33, No. 5, May 1967.

A Farm Appraisal Defined

"The American Society: What It Is, What It Does," American Society of Farm Managers and Rural Appraisers, October 1964.
Appraisal Terminology and Handbook, American Institute Real Estate Appraisers, 5th Edition, 1967.
Ellwood, L. W., "Appraising vs. Engineering—Which Is the More Exact Science?," Appraisal Journal, Vol. 23, No. 3, July 1955.
"Farm Land Appraisal Methods," Doane Reports, August 1957.
Frissell, R. N., "The Professional Appraisal and Market Value," Appraisal Journal, Vol. 34, No. 4, October 1966.
Hyder, K. L., "The Appraisal Process," Appraisal Journal, Vol. 4, No. 1, January 1936.
Keefer, E. D., "It Is My Opinion," Appraisal Journal, Vol. 25, No. 1, January 1957.
Murray, W. G., and Joseph Ackerman, "Appraisal of Farm Real Estate," Land: The 1958 Yearbook of Agriculture, U.S.D.A., 1958.
Ratcliff, R. U., "Appraisal: Is It Measurement or Prediction?," The Real Estate Appraiser, Vol. 38, No. 6, November-December 1972.
Ratcliff, R. U., "A Neoteric View of the Appraisal Function," Appraisal Journal, Vol. 33, No. 2, April 1965.
Shugrue, F. R., "The Nature of Real Estate Appraisal," Encyclopedia of Real Estate Appraising, Prentice-Hall, 1959.
"What to Look for in Appraisal," American Institute of Real Estate Appraisers, 1964.

The Purpose of and Reasons for Appraisals

Babcock, H. A., Appraisal Principles and Procedures, Irwin, 1968.
Falloon, W. J., "Appraisal Fundamentals and Appraisal Terms," Appraisal Journal, Vol. 19, No. 1, January 1951.
Johnson, J. W., "Appraising Today—And Every Day," Appraisal Journal, Vol. 17, No. 4, October 1949.
McDonald, A. F., "Fundamentals of Real Estate Appraising," Appraisal Journal, Vol. 20, No. 1, January 1952.

Murray, W. G. (Chairman), "A Preview of the Farm Appraisal Panel Meeting, Appraisal Section," *Journal of American Society of Farm Managers and Rural Appraisers*, Vol. 16, No. 1, April 1952.

Ratcliff, R. U., "A Restatement of Appraisal Theory: Ch. II The Economic Function of Appraisal," *Appraisal Journal*, Vol. 32, No. 1, January 1964.

Ross, B. R., "Use of Appraisals in Accounting, Investments and Taxes," *The Real Estate Appraiser*, Vol. 34, No. 7, November-December 1968.

Rural Appraisal Manual, 2nd Edition, American Society of Farm Managers and Rural Appraisers, 1967.

Four of the Problems

Ackerman, Joseph, and L. J. Norton, "Factors Affecting Success of Farm Loan," Illinois Agr. Exp. Sta. Bul. 468, August 1940.

Atkinson, H. G., "The Basis of Creative Brokerage," *Appraisal Journal*, Vol. 29, No. 2, April 1961.

Baughman, E. T., "Shall I Buy or Sell a Farm?," *Journal of American Society of Farm Managers and Rural Appraisers*, Vol. 17, No. 1, April 1953.

Behrens, Hans, "Impact of Technological Changes on Small Farm Acreages," Proceedings Minnesota Farm Managers and Rural Appraisers Meeting, February 1969.

Cole, R. H., "What We Can Learn from Appraisal Studies," *Journal of the American Society of Farm Managers and Rural Appraisers*, Vol. 5, No. 1, April 1941.

Dowell, A. A., "Effect of Size of Farm on Investment in Land," *Journal of American Society of Farm Managers and Rural Appraisers*, Vol. 9, No. 2, October 1945.

Dowell, J. M., "What Is an Economic Farm Unit?," *Journal of the American Society of Farm Managers and Rural Appraisers*, Vol. 7, No. 1, April 1943.

Dunlap, J. H., Jr., "What Is Cheap Land?," *Journal of American Society of Farm Managers and Rural Appraisers*, Vol. 7, No. 2, October 1943.

"Earning Value of Farm Land," *Doane Agricultural Digest*, p. 1009, (no date).

Gray, D. S., "What Is Cheap Land?," *Journal of American Society of Farm Managers and Rural Appraisers*, Vol. 7, No. 2, October 1943.

Morse, T. D., "What Is Cheap Land?," *Doane Agricultural Digest*, March 1943.

Reiss, F. J., "Landlord Earnings and Farm Prices," University of Illinois, A.E. 4231, January 1970.

Smith, Walstein, Jr., "The Appraiser and the Real Estate Cycle," *The Real Estate Appraiser*, Vol. 29, No. 3, March 1963.

"When Is Land High Priced?," *Doane Agricultural Digest*, October 1951.

The Qualifications of a Farm Appraiser

Alexander, R. H., "The Appraiser Under Pressure," *The Real Estate Appraiser*, Vol. 31, No. 2, February 1965.

"The American Society of Farm Managers and Rural Appraisers: What It Is, What It Does," American Society of Farm Managers and Rural Appraisers, October 1964.

Donogh, A. O., "What's Wrong with Real Estate Valuation?," *The Residential Appraiser*, Vol. 27, No. 8, August 1961.

Dowell, J. M., "Rural Appraisal: Foundation for Sound Progress," *Journal of American Society of Farm Managers and Rural Appraisers*, Vol. 3, No. 2, October 1939.

Free, R. L., "Pitfalls for the Condemnee's Appraiser," *Appraisal Journal*. Vol. 39, No. 4, October 1971.

Murray, H. T., "Appraisal of Farms and Ranches," *Appraisal Journal* Vol. 22, No. 2, April 1954.

Potts, W. T., Jr., "Problems of the Trainee," *The Real Estate Appraiser*, Vol. 29, No. 12, December 1963.

Ring, A. A., "Appraising: What It Takes to Be Expert," *The Real Estate Appraiser*, Vol. 31, No. 5, May 1965.

Smith, Walstein, Jr., "Selling Your Appraisal, but Not Your Integrity," *The Real Estate Appraiser*. Vol. 37, No. 4, July-August, 1971.

Trowbridge, C. R., "What Is a Review Appraiser?" *The Real Estate Appraiser*. Vol. 37, No. 2, March-April 1971.

CHAPTER II

The Concept of Value

Nowhere in the real world is the theory of value perhaps more difficult to apply than in the appraisal of farm real estate. In most neighborhoods farms and monies change hands rather infrequently. Not always are many persons knowledgeable. Not always are the transfers arm's length transactions. At some later date a neighbor may say, "That farm sold for more (or less) than it was worth!" To express an opinion, of course, is one's privilege; sometimes the statement is correct, however, not always.

Usually there are many opinions regarding a farm's value. Some are off-the-cuff or top-of-the-head opinions; some are based on a fairly thorough analysis of the market. A value based on the latter is usually similar to market price, yet not always. And likewise, the selling price of a farm may or may not be a real indication of its value.

The goal of the professional farm appraiser is to estimate the present market value of the subject property or what that property will most

For centuries, the problems of price versus value have intrigued economists. Modern economic theory perhaps started with Adam Smith, 1776 (upper left). He observed that the word "value" actually had two meanings. Sometimes it expressed the utility of some particular object, sometimes it expressed the power to purchase other goods. Thomas Malthus, 1798, (upper right) predicted that the human reproductive urge would out-strip the nation's resources, thus lower its standard of living. He dealt Smith's market economy a staggering intellectual blow in his essay on population. Karl Marx, 1867 (lower left), thought of value as a quality inherent in a commodity. It was the "crystalized human labor" congealed in production. In his materialistic interpretation of history, value was more ethical than factual. His labor theory exercised a tremendous influence on men's minds. Alfred Marshall, 1890 (lower right), re-examined classical economic theory, leaving the psychological ideas outside the world of economics. He said that at the margin, the forces of cost, or effort, or sacrifice, expressing themselves through supply, and the equally important forces of utility, or desire, or satisfaction, expressing themselves through demand, tended to balance out. He said that under some circumstances, price and value could vary widely, but that when supply and demand were in equilibrium, price and value would coincide.

Courtesy, Krannert Library, Purdue University

likely sell for. He supposedly does this on an objective basis. Yet he often considers his final figure to be an opinion. Furthermore, the farm does not always sell at his figure. A difference here does not necessarily mean that the appraiser was high, or low, or wrong. Yet, when this occurs, it bothers some persons, sometimes even appraisers.

Let's illustrate. Carl Mason purchased a 100-acre farm in a good land area in August of 1937. He paid $60.00 per acre. Carl was a tenant farmer, a good farmer, and he had just come through the droughts of 1933 and 1934 and hopefully the bottom of the Great Depression. The sale was a forced sale. The previous owner had not been able to meet his principal and interest payments, the mortgagee— in this case a life insurance company—had foreclosed. After the moratorium, the farm was advertised as "an excellent tract of land," which it was, and also, that it was "already financed." In other words, the insurance company not only wanted to sell the farm but would willingly take back a mortgage.

At the time, farmers had suffered not only declining farm prices but two severe droughts. It had been so dry that the latest rumor or story was "that the Baptists had started sprinkling, that the Presbyterians were using a damp cloth, and that the Episcopalians were giving rain checks." Most farmers were whipped financially. Since the 100-acre farm was some of "the-best-black-dirt-that-lays-out-of-doors," most of the neighbors felt that it would probably sell for more than they could afford to pay.

August 21, 1937, turned out to be the only day it rained that summer. Only one prospective buyer showed up. Carl and his wife had saved some money; he was prepared to bid up to $70 per acre, but he didn't have to. It was a buyer's market. He and Mrs. Mason helped the insurance company solve its problem. Several of the neighbors have wished ever since that they had also.

Carl stood around a while, then finally bid $50 per acre. The insurance company refused to accept it. However, he acquired the farm an hour later by paying down $2,500 in cash and assuming a $3,500 mortgage. The insurance agent and the neighbors both said, "That farm sold for less than it was worth." Whether or not this price was an accurate measure of the farm's value is a real question.

Thirty years later a man by the name of Phil Swenson was farming this 100 acres on a crop-share lease. He was farming it along with 420 acres, which he owned and on which he lived, just down the road. Phil had tried to purchase the 100 acres from Mrs. Mason several times.

However, she was now widowed, quite elderly, and the 100 acres was her only source of income. For this reason she had never wanted to sell.

On March 23, 1968, Mrs. Mason passed away. Following the funeral, Phil visited with two of the heirs. He told them he would like first chance to buy the farm and he made them a tentative offer of $500 per acre. The heirs thought about it, talked about it, but finally decided to have the farm appraised, along with a residential property in town. A month later they put the farm up for sale to be sold to the highest bidder.

The 100 acres consisted of 95 acres of cropland, a 3-acre knoll with a smattering of large oak trees, where the farmstead used to be, and no improvements. A professional farm appraiser—a stranger to the neighborhood—came in, walked the tract and afterwards stopped by Phil Swenson's farm. He introduced himself and inquired as to the cropping history, the fertility practices, and the crop yields. Mr. Swenson quickly learned that he was from out-of-town. When Mr. Swenson inquired, the appraiser wouldn't tell him the farm's value; he recommended instead that Mr. Swenson check with the attorney who would be selling the tract.

Phil Swenson did, but only to learn that the appraiser had placed a value of $650 per acre on the 100-acre tract. He was shocked. He swore. He told the attorney, and later his wife, that it was not worth one bit more than the $500 per acre, if that. Yet, two weeks later the tract sold for $72,500.

This illustration raises several questions. Mr. Swenson, a local successful, and experienced farmer had confided to several of his neighbors before the sale that that out-of-town appraiser had appraised the 100 acres for far more than it would ever sell for. After the farm sold, Mr. Swenson and his neighbors all agreed, "that farm sold for more than it was worth."

However, Phil Swenson and his neighbors were thinking about farm prices and the income that could be derived from farming. Phil, the neighbors, and the appraiser all knew about the two wet spots in the southwest corner; the buyer, it turned out later, didn't. The knoll with 16 to 20 huge old oak trees had no appeal whatsoever to Mr. Swenson or his neighbors. They perhaps valued those three or four acres at the going per acre value of farmland minus the cost of removing the trees. Yet, the 100 acres was less than 10 miles from town— a community with considerable non-farm employment opportunity. The appraiser had placed some location or residential value on the

3.6-acre knoll; Mr. Swenson had not.[1]

When the farm sold there were five or six parties interested in it. It was a seller's market. The actual bidding, however, slowed down at around $60,000 and came to a standstill at $67,500. The buyer then made his first and final bid—$72,500. He jumped the bid purposely. He thought that that would eliminate all the competition. It did. He and his wife had fallen in love with the 3-acre knoll. They wanted to build a house there, and later did, and the knoll alone was worth the extra $5,000 to them. Hence, the buyer paid more for the 100 acres than would any of the other six or seven bidders, and he did so willingly. Mr. Swenson and several of his neighbors thought he was "nuts." The appraiser, who later learned of the $725 price, yet did not hear about the bidding, was somewhat unhappy. He concluded that maybe his appraisal was low.

VALUE VERSUS PRICE

All things in the world fall into one of two categories—either they are free or they have value. To have value an item or asset must meet three criteria:—such must be either useful or desired, such must exhibit some degree of scarcity, and such must be under the control of man.

Value is not inherent in an item by itself. Whatever a thing or its qualities, it must be desired. It must be useful. Furthermore, utility has three parameters—form, place, and time. A thing must exist in some form; it must exist at some place, and it must be available at some given time.

---

1. Several other differences were also involved. First, Mr. Swenson's per-acre value on the 100 acres was the same as the per-acre value he would have placed on his 420-acre farm. He failed to recognize the fact that more persons are capable of bidding on the smaller farms or tracts of land due to the skewed distribution of capital availability. Second, Mr. Swenson had seen farm prices increase for some 25 years, and he "just knew" they couldn't go up forever. However, the buyer had at one time owned several government bonds which he had sold for 78 cents on the dollar. To him farm land was a hedge against further price inflation. Third, Mr. Swenson realized that farm prices were declining, and that 100 acres was not an economic unit. He thought that anyone, other than his two neighbors and himself, who would purchase such, would soon go broke. However, the buyer had a nephew starting farming on a rented unit five miles away. The two had already agreed as to how they would farm the 100 acres.

However, value does not depend wholly on usefulness or desirability alone. Value also depends on the extent to which various amounts of that item are available. If the item is available in relatively unlimited quantities, its value per unit may be quite low. If the item is relatively scarce, its unit value may be quite high. Hence such value depends on the relationship between the amounts of a particular item that can be supplied, within a given period of time, and the desirability of or demand for that particular item during that same time period.

Man must further have control over the item—either its ownership or its transfer. Man accomplishes this either through production or with purchasing power. As an entrepreneur man may create or bring an item into being; he may thus own various quantities of the item. Production is profitable whenever the market value of the item is greater than the costs of its production. This is the supply half of the equation. At the same time, man may own a second commodity or item which he is willing to forego in order to acquire ownership. This power or ability to purchase is the demand half of the equation.

When some medium of exchange, such as a certain number of dollars is used to acquire a particular item and a transfer of ownership takes place, a market transaction is said to have occurred. The amount of money that changes hands is the consideration or price of the item. Generally speaking, price is equal to value; however, not always.

Webster's Dictionary gives several guides as to the definition of both value and price.[2] Value or price is . . .

1. The quality of being more or less useful, desirable or important, worthy of esteem, and for its own sake,

2. The power or ability of an item to satisfy a need, a want, or a desire,

3. An equivalent, fair or proper, of one item in terms of another, or in terms of some medium of exchange, and

4. The amount of money asked for, offered, or given for a particular item.

The first definition is one of value; the last is one of price. The transition from value to price occurs when the item is either swapped for or exchanged for another, or for a given amount of money. This exchange indicates (1) that ownership has been transferred and (2)

---

2. *Webster's New World Dictionary.*

that money has changed hands. Hence, the difference between value and price is largely one of whether or not a transaction has occurred in the market place.

Unfortunately, this distinction has led to the conclusion (1) that value is subjective, in other words, an opinion influenced largely by one's personal feelings or the characteristics of the mind, and (2) that price is objective, in other words, derived in the market in a detached and unprejudiced fashion. Neither is necessarily the case.

Value is often idealistic, sometimes speculative; whereas price is a phenomenon of the real world. However, value can be ascertained in an objective fashion. A price paid in the market place can differ considerably from real value.

Let's illustrate. Grandfather died during the Great Depression. Among other assets, he owned a tall mahogany clock with Westminster chimes. When an inquiry as to its value was made Grandmother said it was "priceless." This word didn't mean that the clock wasn't worth anything. It meant, to Grandmother at least, that the worth of the clock was too great to be measured in dollars. She later said, ". . . that clock is worth $1,000 to me." This was her personal opinion; and it was only her opinion.

The clock, of course, was worth more to Grandmother than to anyone else. The very thought that that clock might someday "go" to someone outside the family was unmentionable. Hence, the figure she came up with was not based on what the clock might bring if sold. It was not based on what a new clock, similar in type and size, and less depreciation, might cost. Grandmother's figure was merely a pure and simple and subjective opinion. It was the clock's value to her. It was not based on a market analysis.

Three years later Grandmother died. The clock was sold at a farm auction. The auction was well advertised. The day of the auction was sunshiny and bright. Farm folk, generally speaking, had most of their work done and they came from miles around. Several inquired about the clock. The auctioneer's comment was, ". . . if it goes for $100 I'll be surprised." Yet, the old clock sold for $237.50, which, according to many persons was more than it was worth.

It was a seller's market. Two unhappy granddaughters were there. Neither one particularly wanted the clock, yet neither one wanted the other party to have it; and they each had more money than judgment. Strong sentimental feelings helped determine market price. Yet, the $237.50 was not an accurate measure of value, for about a year and a half later, the sister who acquired the clock sold it to an antique dealer for $90.00. Two months later, the antique dealer sold it to the other sister for $110.00.

The Definition of Value: Value is what some person thinks something is worth. It is not inherent in the item itself. It is created, it exists, it is maintained, it is modified, and it is destroyed, but only in the mind of man. The value or worth of an item is an opinion. That opinion may be a personal one in which the person making the judgment largely ignores the real world; or, that opinion may be a well-researched one in which the person making the judgment draws heavily on an analysis of the market.

In the first instance, value is the worth of an item to one person alone rather than to society in general. It is influenced by the past events in the life of that person. Sentimental attachments may be strong. It is influenced by one's present circumstances and by whatever alternatives are currently available to him. And finally, it is influenced by the present use or uses being made of the item. The outside world is typically ignored. Hence this opinion is a highly personal one, and subjective. Value in this instance tends to parallel what the scholarly economists have referred to in the past as utility value or value-in-use.

In the second instance, value is the worth of an item to all persons who might be typical owners or sellers or buyers of that item. Here the person making the judgment hopefully removes himself from any personal interest whatsoever in the item.[3] The value ascertained is defined. Certain assumptions are established. Various game rules developed over time and generally acceptable are followed. Hence, the final opinion is a professional one arrived at in an objective fashion. Value in these instances more nearly represents what economists refer to as market value or value-in-exchange.

The Definition of Price: The price of a thing is the amount of money that is required to transfer the ownership of that particular thing from one person to another, at a particular time, and at a particular place. The price is the amount of money which changes hands, the amount

---

3. The farm appraiser typically uses a disclaimer clause. For example, "We the undersigned, hereby certify, that we have no present or contemplated interests in this property, or in any of the surrounding circumstances which would affect the statements we have made in this report or the value which we have ascertained."

the buyer foregoes, and the amount the seller accepts in an actual market transaction. Thus, price represents a mutual, in fact contractual agreement, between buyer and seller.[4]

Prices vary of course. The nature of the variation differs with the type of market—more particularly the number of sellers and buyers, the nature of the commodity—its homogeneity and its relative availability, and the relative repetitiveness of the various transactions.

In some markets sellers and buyers are numerous. The sellers have for sale almost identical items exhibiting a high degree of homogeneity. There are other items which can substitute for or replace the commodity in question and accomplish the same purpose. The quantities that are available are relatively satisfactory even where the item may be consumed or used fairly rapidly. The number of transactions are large.

In this kind of a market sellers and buyers come and go freely. Artificial restraints are either limited or none. In fact, no single individual, seller or buyer, appears to have any real or lasting influence over price. Some bargaining occurs but mainly over price and oftentimes over mere fractions of a penny. Prices and quantities are reported in the newspaper and over radio and television daily, if not hourly. Price changes tend to be gradual. This type of market is a purely competitive one. Market price and value tend to coincide. The market for farm commodities is a good illustration.

In other markets, however, the number of sellers and buyers are limited; they are sometimes few in number. The sellers have for sale items which are unique or differentiated, items for which there are no good or close substitutes. The quantity available may be limited. In fact sometimes there is only one. The item may also be consumed or used not immediately but over a period of time. In this kind of a market the transactions tend to be both sporadic and irregular.

To negotiate a bona fide market transaction it typically takes a little longer, sometimes considerably longer, than in the competitive market. Each transaction tends to differ from the previous one. Providing the seller is in no hurry he tends to control price; however, the item may "hang over" the market for some period of time without being sold. When the seller is in a hurry, the buyer tends to control

---

4. Common usage also tends to accept the word "price" in terms of both asking prices and offering prices. In this respect both seller and buyer have entered the market, and these so-called "prices" reflect the strength of their intentions.

price; this is particularly so where the buyer has the feeling that the seller is in a forced action situation. Final negotiations often concern things other than price—many times the method of finance. Prices are not always reported. Even when they are, they may be misleading. Price change tends to be erratic, sometimes sizeable, and not particularly meaningful.[5]

This latter market, with its fewer participants, its product differentiation, and its price jurisdiction is an imperfect market. Market price and value may be equal, or, they may differ considerably. This is due in part to the ability of a given seller or buyer to exert considerable control over price.[6] One of the best illustrations of this imperfect market is the market for farm real estate.

THE FARM REAL ESTATE MARKET

A parcel of real estate is typically a large economic unit, requiring a relatively large amount of money in order to effect a transfer of ownership. Farms in particular are unique. They differ in size, productivity, degree of improvement, and location. No two parcels of

---

5. Economic theory sometimes appears to infer that there is no such thing as a bargain in the marketplace; that no informed seller is inclined to sell for less than what the traffic will bear. Vice versa, the college textbooks appear to infer that there is no such thing as being took; that no informed buyer is inclined to pay more than is required. Yet the real world does not operate this way. A skilled or shrewd seller may command a premium price, particularly when he faces an eager buyer, and on the surface at least, he creates the impression of being an unwilling seller. A skilled or shrewd buyer, on the other hand, may command a discount, particularly when he faces an anxious seller who is forced to sell. That buyer may wave all-the-cash-I've-got and give the seller a low-ball bid. The overly anxious seller may or may not later realize he was took.

6. The time period involved in bringing about, creating, or producing additional quantities of a good is also a major factor. In the short run, the quantity of a particular commodity that is available cannot be materially changed or altered. Hence, demand tends to be the dominant factor in determining price. With additional time, more quantities of a commodity or good can be produced, the limit being the capacity of the present facilities. Again with additional time, this capacity can be increased by adding to the investment in production facilities. The supply factor now plays a larger and larger role in determining price. In the long run, price equals the cost of production; yet one has to assume that all over- and under-efforts to match production to demand are in balance and that equilibrium has been reached. In the very long run, technology can change, new products can be developed, and changes can occur in the composition of the population, in the desires and tastes of people, and in the legal and economic frameworks governing society.

land are alike; never are two sets of improvements identical. Wherever a farm is located there it stays. It cannot be moved from a poor area to one of higher productivity or from a slow area to one of greater real estate activity. Hence, farm real estate often tends to sell both slowly and with difficulty.

There is no such thing as an organized farm real estate market— nationally, regionally, or locally. Most markets are very disorganized. Farm sales, when they occur, are widely scattered, both geographically and over time. Most sellers and buyers enter the market rather infrequently, and often with a limited knowledge. Rarely are farm sales comparable.

Farm real estate transactions are also notorious for being private in nature. Farm sellers and buyers often hesitate to discuss the real reasons for selling or for buying. They are often reluctant to disclose either the price or the terms of their agreement. Personal values often enter into real estate transactions. A bargain to one farmer may be an overpriced luxury to his neighbor; yet neither will admit to such, or talk about it. Considerable bargaining over the means of finance and matters other than price sometimes occurs. These other matters are often the key to the sale.

In many communities the good farms are "held in strong hands." There is, in other words, a social cohesiveness which makes farm owners reluctant to leave farming, or the community, and particularly if it means selling the farm to an outsider. Multiple sources of satisfaction, supplementary income in the form of government subsidies, and non-farm opportunities near an urban center often allow a farm to be farmed on an avocational basis.

The belief that the best place to have your money is in land, probably because once it's there it cannot be spent, along with the almost congenital optimism that land values will continue to rise, and other hopes—for example, the discovery of oil or minerals which may some day lead to windfall gains—tend to freeze farm real estate into static patterns of ownership.

Investors, speculators, and just plain uninformed persons sometimes contribute greatly to the farm real estate market. This is particularly true during periods of price inflation. The desire and ability to satisfy the urge to own land may also create a seller's market. To the prospective farm buyer or owner this is a difficult situation, for he may expect farm earnings and farm earnings alone to justify the value of the farm he hopes to someday own.

Another phenomenon is the behavior of the exceptional buyer or seller in the near ideal market. A prospective or potential buyer, who does not need to immediately buy, sometimes drives through various agricultural areas and makes offers on farms, offers which he assumes most informed sellers will not accept. He enjoys this sport, is pleased with himself, and is cordially loathed by farm real estate brokers. However, every now and then he meets a non-average seller who is not well informed, and who, for some reason or other, wants to sell his farm fairly soon. Thus, a sale takes place between two atypical individuals.

The exceptional seller personifies the property owner who puts a price on his property—a price above any expectation of immediate sale—yet hopes to someday get it. Hopefully, an atypical buyer will come along, one whose farm perhaps has been taken for public use and who not only has money, but according to the current tax laws, is forced to reinvest that money in a similar property within 12 or 18 months. Immediacy is important. This buyer ignores the average price. He may quite willingly pay more for the farm than necessary, and thus establish, empirically speaking, an unrealistic price.

The theoretical market structure ordains that buyers and sellers move at random, and that they tend to cluster. It assumes that the market consists of buyers and sellers, some of whom are eager and some of whom are in distress, some of whom are reluctant and some of whom are euphoric. It assumes that non-average buyers and sellers cannot alter market values. Yet in the real world they do, and particularly in the case of farm real estate.

In the more complex situations bi-modality sometimes emerges among market participants. This is illustrated most easily in a case of auctions. First, there is a group of bargain hunters that exchange bids up to a certain point. When their play is exhausted they drop out, and the more serious bidders take over. Later, perhaps a previously inconspicuous person, one with a barely audible voice, raises the bid still further. He wants it more than anyone else. He has a specialized use or desire, and this may justify his paying more for the property than anyone else. However, he will not obviously do so unless he has to. If there is but one buyer who foresees or can use some specialized feature, he's likely to get quite a windfall. However, this buyer is quite different from the naive person who, through either impatience or ignorance, pays too much for a farm in the more nearly normal market.

Lastly, there is the classic sitter. He clings stubbornly to his farm which he could sell at almost any time for considerably more than it's worth to him, agriculturally speaking, mainly because of a change in land use. This owner is typically an older person who has considerable pride of ownership in the old homestead. He may be a relatively poor individual who has no place to go, and/or he may lack the ability to foresee the trade offs, the solution to the tax problem, or the problem of finance. He may want to stay in a location familiar to him, even though others want it for a more intensive use; and he sometimes wants to stay there regardless of the cost in terms of a foregone alternative opportunity.

The value of a property designed to fit the specific requirements of one particular owner is sometimes referred to as value-in-use. In some instances there may be little or no interest in the property on the part of other prospective buyers or owners. If so, there appears to be an almost non-existent market. In other instances, a prospective buyer may be overly eager. The seller may say, "Either you pay me for what you want, or go without. Take it or leave it." Because of the tract's location, the inability to duplicate such, or for some other reason, the buyer may pay a premium rather than go without.

Finally, the farm real estate market is measured in terms of money—in the United States in terms of dollars. These dollars themselves are not stable.[7] In fact the money market, even in a "free" economy, is often a manipulated one. Any change in value may thus be the result of a change in the supply of or demand for real estate, or the result of a change in the supply of or demand for money. The appraiser of farm real estate may be a fortunate individual. With farm real estate values expressed in dollars, he can be reasonably assured that every now and then these values will change. This leads again and again to the question, "What is this farm worth?"

---

7. Money is anything generally accepted in a particular society as a means of payment. However, money has four functions:—as a medium of exchange, a standard of value, a store of value (savings), and a standard of payment. Any estimate of value made in terms of money is often subject to change due to changes in the unit of measurement or in the value of the money itself.

PRESENT MARKET VALUE DEFINED
(The Basis for All Appraisals)

The appraisal profession is most meticulous in its use of certain generally accepted definitions. These definitions tend to vary and they occasionally change over time. Yet, all of them are attempts to reconcile the various concepts of value with market phenomenon, namely price.

The most commonly desired value, the one ascertained by all farm appraisers, is what the subject farm will sell for on today's market—its present market value. This is the No. 1 value. It is ascertained first and always, and regardless of the appraisal assignment, the reason for the appraisal, or any other value which may be subsequently developed. Hence, the farm appraiser must have a firm knowledge of the definition of present market value and all of its underlying assumptions.

Present market value is the most likely price at which a given farm can be sold or transferred from a willing and informed seller to a desirous and informed buyer, with an acceptable downpayment changing hands, and with the change in ownership taking place within a reasonable period of time. It is the most probable price which a given farm will bring in an open and competitive market, under all conditions requisite to an honest sale, and resulting from negotiations between a seller and a buyer, each of whom is reasonably well informed, each of whom is acting prudently, and neither of whom is under any undue stimulus or pressure to sell or to buy.

The use of this definition obligates a farm appraiser to estimate present market value under certain specific conditions. A number of assumptions underlie the definition.

1. There exists a number of farm owners who have offered and sold similar if not identical farms in the past, owners who are willing to offer such farms today, and who can be expected to offer them again in the immediate future. There also exists a number of prospective buyers who have bid on and purchased similar if not identical farms in the past, buyers who are capable of bidding on such farms today, and who can be expected to bid on them again in the immediate future.

2. These sellers and buyers are each reasonably knowledgeable about the farm real estate market. They are each reasonably well informed about the natural, the legally permissible, and the most probable alternatives for which the subject farm property may be used in

the immediate future. They are each reasonably capable of considering or weighing in their minds the many factors that may influence that price over which they are negotiating.

3. The typical seller and typical buyer are each free to participate on a voluntary basis. Furthermore, they are not only free, but each will act according to his or her best interest. The seller is willing, ready, and yet is not subject to any undue pressure or force outside of his control. The buyer is desirous, able to the extent that he has the necessary downpayment, and yet is not subject to any undue pressure or force outside of his control.

4. The farm or property has a combination of resources or factors of production which determine a most probable use to be made of it in the immediate future by the typical buyer and owner. The adjective "most probable" refers to that which is natural, practical, reasonable, legally permissible, and most likely. The adjective "immediate" refers to that time period within which certain acts or actions can reasonably be predicted. The adjective "typical" is the most likely or most frequent.

5. There exists a reasonable period of time within which a prospective buyer can be found or located, a buyer who already has the required downpayment and/or is capable of commanding satisfactory financing. Furthermore, this purchaser, desiring to buy, has sufficient time to take into account all considerations that might be brought forward fairly and be given reasonable weight in effecting the transfer.

6. The potential benefits or satisfactions available in the immediate future can be ascertained. The present worth of these future benefits can be objectively measured and included. Hence the subsequent transaction is void of any real or apparent finance problem. Thus, the final price is in no way related to the method of obtaining the capital or the financing.

The value is affected by both long-run and short-run implications. Yet logically there exists but one present market value. It is the price which a farm or property will command, the price which the owner or seller will accept, the price the buyer will pay. It is the No. 1 value ascertained by all appraisers all of the time.

FIFTY-ONE OTHER VALUES

No one calls an appraiser unless he has a problem. That problem often dictates the reason for or use to be made of an appraisal; that problem often necessitates a value other than present market value. In other words, one's client often asks for or requires more than one value figure in order to make whatever decision he has to make.

This fact is often ignored by appraisers. Many an appraiser, armed with the definition of present market value, estimates this value without considering his client's problem. Yet, the appraiser performs a service only when he directs his activities toward whatever problem led to the request for his services.

The farm owner planning to sell his farm is interested in the best price he can get. He first wants to (or should) know what his farm is worth, but he also wants to know what he should perhaps ask for it. The prospective buyer is also interested in the best price he can get. He also wants to (or should) know what a given farm is worth, but he then wants to know how much he should perhaps offer. What a farm is worth is a single figure. Yet asking and offering prices tend to differ.

The broker, insurer, assessor, lender, investor, speculator, and attorney are all interested in what a given farm is worth. However, they each have other interests and values in mind. They may be interested in the insured values placed on the buildings, the property's assessed valuation, the farm's loan value, or its fair market value. Hence, the reason for a farm appraisal is often to ascertain values other than, or more correctly, in addition to, the subject property's present market value.

Unbeknownst to most appraisers, an appraisal made for one reason is often used at some later date for some other reason. In these instances it is not always used correctly. This practice can usually be attributed to the lack of understanding as to the difference between (1) the purpose of and (2) the reason for (or use to be made of) an appraisal.

A professional appraiser should always explain to his client that his job, first and always, is to ascertain what the farm is worth on today's market. This is the fundamental purpose of all appraisals. He should then explain to his client that this value may then be used to develop or determine whatever other value is needed, thus recognizing that this other value may have been the reason for the appraisal in the first place.[8]

---

8. In many instances, there is a fairly definite or specific mathematical relationship between present market value and these other values. When this occurs, such relationship should be so stated in one's appraisal report.

In this way a farm's present market value is used as a point of departure or as the basis for determining any and all other values. Basic farm value, contributory value, insured value, assessed value, loan value, and fair market values are all related to if not based on the No. 1 value—the present market value of the subject property.

Basic Farm Value: Basic farm value is an ignored, if not forgotten, farm value today. It is based on the long-term farm earnings that can be expected under typical ownership or management. It is established using the income capitalization approach to value.

Basic farm value was developed during, and still reflects, the trying times of the 1930's. In the bottom of the depression many appraisers were driven to make desperate statements: "There is no market for farm land." "This appraisal is merely a guess." "During times like these, farms cannot be appraised." Such statements came from the older one-figure appraisers, and not from those grounded in the theory of value or those capable of arriving at farm real estate values through proper appraisal technique.

In the late 1930's the insurance companies, the Farm Credit Administration, and several farm economists joined forces to develop the American Rural Appraisal System.[9] The system disapproved of those persons who professed to know land values and began to seek and train appraisers to arrive at or establish land values by means of analysis and reason.

The American Rural Appraisal System placed major emphasis on income capitalization as the direct and primary approach to value. The system was developed largely in or for the agricultural Midwest, hence it relied heavily on the customary landlord-tenant arrangement, along with the crop-share lease, as the basis for calculating the landowner's share of the farm's receipts, expenses, and returns. This net income to a landowner was then capitalized into the farm's basic value. Adjustments for home use, location, and other economic features were then added to or subtracted from the earnings value.

Basic farm value was an attempt to measure a farm's inherent characteristics. Supposedly it was an intrinsic value that would exist over a long period of time. Special considerations regarding management were eliminated; instead facts and figures characteristic of a typical operation were requested.[10]

---

9. p. 84, Bowen and Mayer.
10. The word "typical" was later defined as "that which most frequently exists or occurs in the particular situation under consideration." P. 97, Bowen and Mayer.

THE CONCEPT OF VALUE

Agricultural earnings, under average conditions and typical management, were to be based on long-term crop yields and farm prices. Supposedly these earnings constituted a sound basis for a reasonably permanent value. Thus basic farm value was thought to be a more or less long-term value not subject to the whims of buyers or sellers. It was broad or general in scope, not specific, and unfortunately not too useful, except conceptually.

Yet basic farm value and many of the ideas it incorporates are still useful today. Most farm appraisers present in their reports the farm's productive capacity along with its probable earnings under a typical operator. Most farm appraisers still use the income capitalization approach to value even though they may not refer to the final figure as the subject property's basic farm value.

When properly developed, an earnings value essentially serves notice on prospective buyers, investors, and lenders that the typical earnings from this farm over a period of time will support only $_____ value. If a buyer or investor, or a lender wants to put more money into the farm he can do so, yet he must justify such on the basis of things other than the opportunity to make money.

An earnings value seldom if ever equals present market value. Usually it is less, and particularly during periods of price inflation. This is because there are origins of value other than the opportunity to make money. Many buyers of farms are willing to pay money for these other items as well.

Normal Market Value: Normal market value is another concept long forgotten and totally ignored today. It is the amount that a farm will sell for over a period of years rather than what it will bring during either a severe depression or a period of abnormally high or inflated prices. It is essentially a long-term norm around which farm real estate values fluctuate, hopefully an average of both the past and the future.

The normal value concept was also a product of the 1930's. It was developed and used by the same group of persons who developed the American Rural Appraisal System and primarily those who were interested in the making of farm loans. These persons were desirous of eliminating, or at least smoothing, the extreme fluctuations that seemed to occur in farm land values.

At the same time there were strong feelings that farms could not possibly be worth as much or as little as the market sometimes said they were. Comparative sale prices were thought to have caused appraisers to yield to the "strong magnetic influence" of first extremely high and then extremely low farm real estate values. Hence, the philosophy came into being that appraised values should never approach the extreme peaks or highs of the 1920's nor the troughs of the 1930's.

The normal value concept was an attempt to correct the tendency to overvalue and undervalue farm land. It was an attempt to eliminate the more violent land price fluctuations and to establish long-term norms, which during a period of depressed prices would be higher than, and which during a period of inflated prices would be lower than, actual farm real estate sale prices.

Normal market values were first established in 1937 when the Federal Land Bank was directed, by law as well as by policy, to (1) appraise farms using income as the principal factor and (2) base their loans on normal agricultural values.[11] Farm prices were depressed at the time; hence, normal values were well above present market prices. The normal concept thus gave the Federal Land Bank the legal right to refinance much of the farm mortgage debt at farm loan values that were above the then current farm real estate prices.

The technique of estimating normal agricultural value was and still is largely one of estimating long-term crop yields and farm prices.[12] In fact, normal values have meaning only to the extent that the appraiser specifies those conditions—both crop yields and farm prices—which he considers to be normal. A standard set of farm prices, along with a more or less stable set of farm costs, is assumed in order to estimate farm receipts and expenses. A given price period may be selected, or a set of weighted or adjusted average prices may be developed. Either supposedly allows appraised values to be estimated at or near an ideal trend line. Normal values thus swing gradually or conservatively. In contrast to merely recording the past, they hopefully anticipate the future.

The normal concept was excellent theory. If farm price changes over time were cyclical in nature the concept would have been most useful. Prices would be high at the top of the cycle, low at the bottom. To the extent that they rise above the trend line they could be expected to return and go below the trend line. This would be so regardless of whether the trend is horizontal, rising, or falling.

---

11. This latter was essentially a combination of basic farm value and normal market value.

12. Historically, farm product prices and farm real estate values have been closely related. Any change in farm prices has always had a fairly sizeable impact on the value of farm real estate.

However, instead of cyclical price change, agriculture began in 1955 to experience structural adjustments. Mechanized farming and new technology have increased the productive capacity of both the farm and farm family. There has, in addition, been a long, somewhat erratic, and yet continuous price inflation. As a result, farm real estate price changes have exhibited very little cyclical tendency since the middle 1950's (Figure 2). They have merely continued to go up. They could go down. There could, of course, be a 40- or 50- or 60-year cycle. Yet it would take a serious decline in farm values, along with a sizeable if not impossible change in the value of the dollar, to make a normal market value concept meaningful or useful today.

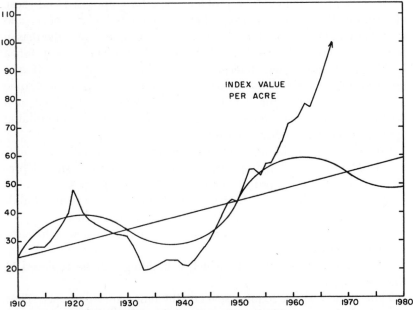

Figure 2. A Hypothetical 40-Year Price Cycle with a Built-in Upward Trend.

A normal value concept will work in the lower half but not in the upper half of a price cycle. When normal values are above market prices a loan equal to 65 percent of the farm's normal value makes a prospective borrower very happy. He then needs little or no equity. Yet, in the upper half of the price cycle where market prices supposedly are above normal values a loan based on 65 or an even higher percentage of a farm's normal value will not provide sufficient funds.

Normal agricultural value worked in the 1930's when prices were depressed. However, when farm prices rose, present market values soon rose above normal agricultural values, and adjustments were required. Long-term crop yields, along with the farm prices and costs specified by the various lending institutions and agencies had to be increased, not just once but several times.

The lending institutions or government agencies which were the first to make these adjustments—those with the highest "normal" prices —were the ones who made the most loans. Realizing this, the various participants not only increased their "normal" data; they soon attempted to shed or abandon the normal value concept.[13] The surprising fact is that the idea or concept lasted as long as it did.

Farm Building Values: The problems of a farm appraisal and those of farm building valuation often differ considerably both in theory and in technique. Unlike in a farm appraisal, the purpose of and the reason for farm building valuation are closely related. The reason for a building valuation often determines the value concept used. It also tends to influence the dollar value of that building. This bothers some persons; in fact, even the best farm appraisers are in somewhat of a dilemma when they are forced to recognize that a given farm building appears to have more than one value.

However, farm buildings and improvements are valued to . . .

1. Determine a building's book value so as to establish a depreciation schedule for record keeping and income tax purposes.

2. Indicate the basic physical condition or soundness of a building or its parts by estimating its structural or salvage value.

3. Ascertain the contribution that that building makes towards the market value of the farm.

4. Estimate the extent to which a building will be replaced in the event of a loss.

These four reasons require several different value concepts. They often lead to different dollar values. Each has its peculiarities, yet each is fairly readily accepted by society. Right or wrong, society readily accepts (1) cost, (2) structural value, (3) value to the farm, and (4) value to the owner. Several, if not all of these values, may be included in a detailed farm appraisal.

---

13. Several of the government agencies were legally required to use normal agricultural values as the basis for their appraisals clear up into the 1950's and 1960's.

In valuing farm buildings and improvements the one common denominator is cost. Cost tends to serve as an upper limit or as a maximum value above which the value of a building or improvement cannot
logically go. Two somewhat different concepts are used. One is reproduction cost; the other is replacement cost. The two concepts do not
have the same meaning, yet they tend to be used interchangeably, and
this often leads to confusion.

Reproduction cost is the cost of rebuilding a previously existing
structure with a new one using the same identical design or pattern,
the same materials, and supposedly the same workmanship. Replacement cost is the cost of replacing a previously existing structure with
its more modern version, namely, whatever is being built in its place
today—however, a building with the same economic capacity.

Many different values are placed on farm buildings and improvements. Generally speaking, this is a result of different philosophies,
different objectives, and different techniques. These various values
however, and there are four or five different ones, have meaning only
when they are defined.

1. Inventory or book value is the cost of a building or improvement less any calculated depreciation allowed or allowable between
the date of purchase and the date of valuation. The typical accountant
uses a fairly arbitrary formula (any one of three or four) to calculate
the annual amounts of depreciation and end-of-year remaining values.
These figures are used in financial statements and as a part of many
income tax returns.

2. Structural value is the cost of reproducing a building less any
and all physical deterioration. By placing a present-day structural
value on each building and improvement, the appraiser says to his
client, "This building does or does not have value as it stands. It is or
it is not sound. It can be used, as is perhaps, or, the depreciation to
date is curable. Thus this building can be added onto, expanded, or
remodeled without major difficulty."

Unlike book value, structural value is based not on the original
capital outlay or historical cost of the building; it is instead based on
the building's present-day replacement cost. Thus, compared to book
value structural value is a much more realistic figure.

3. Contributory value is the dollar amount that a building adds
to the market value of a given farm property. It too is based on the
building's present-day replacement cost. However, depreciation now
reflects not just physical deterioration, but functional inadequacy, and
economic obsolescence as well.

Contributory values are influenced by the economic trends occurring in the economy, the new technologies, and the various farm practices in the agricultural community. They are both created and destroyed through the over- and under-investment in capital improvements. The need for balance among a farm's basic resources, particularly the balance between land, buildings, and improvements must be fully recognized. When such is not realistic, contributory values tend to drop below the original capital outlay or historical cost of the building, sometimes by a considerable amount.

Thus, there exists a real dilemma between the cost of an improvement and its market value. Fundamental to all market value theory is the statement, "The cost of a new building or improvement seldom if ever adds an equal number of dollars to the market value of the farm." The minute a building or improvement is built or erected, its value, in terms of market or exchange value, decline to something considerably less than its cost.

4. Utility value or value-in-use is the present-day value of the building or improvement to the present farm operator and/or in the present farming operations. Most farm buildings and improvements are built in order to expand the size or volume of the farm business, or to increase the efficiency of the farming operations. They are built to be used and not for resale purposes. Thus a new building or improvement often contributes more towards the efficiency of the farming operations under the present operator than it contributes to the market value of the same farm under a typical operator.

Unfortunately for appraisers the decision to build a new improvement, particularly a specialized facility, is often influenced by the personal desires of the present farm operator. The present farm operator doesn't always recognize that the cost of the improvement will not add an equal number of dollars to the value of his farm, should he be forced to sell the farm. Hence, a value-in-use figure is often higher than contributory value.

In most farm appraisals the buildings and improvements are physically described. Not just one but several dollar values may be presented in this physical description. The appraiser's job is to understand, and, if need be show, in his report, the true meaning of each value, making sure that all building costs and values are properly related to one another. When done properly this tells a client something about the farm's buildings and improvements.

Insured Value: Insured values apply only to a farm's buildings and improvements—its depreciable or wasting assets. Insured values typically equal 80 percent of a building's replacement cost; however, they may vary from 40 to 80 percent of a building's actual cash value. Replacement cost is used as the basis in the case of a relatively new building or improvement. Actual cash value—actually its contributory or present-day market value—is used as the basis in the case of an older building or improvement. The latter supposedly equals or is measured by the building's reproduction cost less whatever depreciation—usually only physical deterioration—has occurred to date.

Today there is a tendency to substitute utility value in place of actual cash value. In the case of a new building this often leads to an insured value figure which is higher than the building's contributory value. The extent to which this occurs indicates the extent of the building's usefulness in the current farming operations. A higher dollar figure essentially says, "If this valuable building were to burn down or blow away it would be rebuilt to this level even though its replacement cost today would not be fully reflected in the market value of the farm."

The purpose of all insurance, of course, is to indemnify a property owner for whatever financial loss he has suffered. The purpose is not to make him a profit. This indemnity principle often leads one to insure a building at its value to the present owner or operator even though such is above its contributory value. Such a practice raises the moral hazard problem.

When insured values are above contributory values and a dishonest property owner finds himself in financial difficulty, the insurance company may find itself in a vulnerable position. Because of this, insurance companies sometimes place deferred payment provisions in their contracts. In the event a building burns, blows away, or is otherwise destroyed (under an insured risk) the property owner is fully indemnified, yet on a piecemeal basis. He may, for example, be indemnified to the 40 percent level immediately, then receive the other 60 percent of his claim when the building or improvement is rebuilt or replaced.

The professional appraiser may thus present in his physical description of the subject property structural, contributory, and insured values on each farm building and improvement. In this way, he tells his client as much as he can about the property. Furthermore, if his client has, either immediately or at some later day, the problem of insuring his farm buildings and improvements against the risks of fire, wind, or other peril he can then make his own decisions.

True Cash Value: True cash value, fair cash value, full cash value, and value-in-exchange are terms used in various states to describe that value to be used by the assessor. The various state constitutions and statutory provisions employ many terms, yet the courts have consistently interpreted each of them to mean value-in-the-market.

The majority of property owners are subject to the general property tax. This tax is based on the total taxable wealth in the community, and in the past, at least, it has paid for most local government expenditures. In order to administer the tax, every taxable parcel of real estate in each tax district must have some value placed upon it. True cash value is the typical term. Legally, such supposedly equals present market value. However, in actual practice, it tends to be a conservative value, and a value below present market value. The assessors and township trustees in the rural areas are typically elected public officials. When their values are below the market these values are much more palatable politically.

Furthermore, regardless of the market, true cash values do not always equal assessed values. Some states assess all taxable property at its full cash value. This is commonly referred to as full-value assessment. However, other states assess property at some fraction of full value, for example, one-half or one-third. In other words, assessed values, which are the final values placed on each parcel of taxable real estate, are related to true cash values, yet the mathematical relationship varies between states. The ratio between assessed and true cash value is frequently referred to as the level of assessment.

One of the fundamental objectives of the general property tax, of course, is uniformity. All types of property and all property owners are to be treated on an equitable basis. In a purely technical sense, uniform assessment is all that matters. It is of little consequence to the individual property owner whether his real estate is assessed at full value or at some fraction thereof. As long as a uniform ratio (assessed to present market value) prevails throughout the entire tax district each property owner pays the same (proportional) amount of the taxes. In theory, the question of full versus fractional assessment is mathematically irrelevant.

Yet the problem is to avoid both overassessment and underassessment, either one of which leads to inequities among the taxpayers. Property owners who happen to be overassessed, of course, promptly move to have their assessment reviewed. Those who are underassessed rarely if ever complain. The property owner who thinks he is underassessed typically reasons he is better off than his neighbors. However, he may be deceived. For his neighbors may also be underassessed and even more so than he. This is because fractional assessments often bear little or no relation to anything in the real world so far as the average property owner is concerned. The absentee-owner, the estate trustee, the widow, the uninitiated, and the naive are often unfamiliar with how assessments are determined. In fact, the figures are sometimes such a mystery that there is no basis for thought or discussion.

Property owners thus often tolerate overvaluation unknowingly. Their property's value appears to be conservative. Overassessment is not readily apparent. Such a possibility is often overlooked if not ignored. And for this reason, many elected public officials recommend fractional assessments. Even in states where the tax laws specify full-value assessment, the various officials do not always follow the laws. This is because fractional assessments make it easier to live with the typical taxpayer. He reacts much less vigorously to any change in his property's value. Yet, unknowingly, that same property owner may be paying more than his fair share of the property tax burden.

The solution is obvious yet difficult. The solution is full value assessment and full public disclosure. These tend to remove not only overassessment but underassessment as well. They tend to force public officials to adopt the more professional appraisal techniques.

Farm Loan Value: In the past, the basic farm value and normal market value concepts have been combined into a normal agricultural value for purposes of making farm loans. The various lending institutions and government agencies have then established a farm loan value which, historically at least, has roughly equalled 65 percent of the farm's normal agricultural value. More recently, the various value definitions have been changed, appraised values have been substituted for normal values, and farm loan values or ratios have been increased. Today a farmer can typically borrow anywhere from 75 to 100 percent of a farm's present market value depending on the lending institution or government agency.

The farm loan appraiser's job is to ascertain the farm's value using whatever legal definition of value, whatever crop yields, farm prices, etc., are specified by the lending institution or agency for whom he works. The farm's loan value, or the loan ratio, is, generally speaking, determined by law or by lending policy. It is not the appraiser's job.

The loan appraiser's job is a broad one in that he not only looks at the farm or the security, he not only estimates its productive capacity or income-producing ability, he also interviews the loan applicant, and assesses his personal character as well.[14] His success, as an appraiser, is often confused with what is really the lending institution's major problem—and that is whether farm real estate values will continue to climb upwards or whether they will perhaps level or decline at some point of time during the loan period (usually the next 20 or so years). What happens to farm prices and farm real estate values over the loan period tends to be the factor which will most likely determine success on the part of the farmer, the lending institution, and even the appraiser. The role played by the lender is unique mainly because, over time, farm loan values remain fixed. If property values rise the lender does not necessarily stand to gain. However, if property values decline the lender may be affected, sometimes adversely.

Equity values, on the other hand, rise and fall with changes in farm prices and farm property values.[15] When the latter increase, equity values increase, both in total and even more so percentagewise. However, when farm values decline, equity values decline an equal amount, dollarwise. In each case, farm loan values remain constant (except for the principal repayments). Rising land values thus lead to equity leverage. Declining land values, on the other hand, if they go far enough, lead to real problems, particularly if property values drop to the extent that the owner's equity is wiped out.

The higher the buyer's beginning equity in a property the more honest he is likely to be. When his equity is below 20 or 25 percent, he is more or less apt to look at his principal and interest payments as rent. When this is the case, financial difficulty may cause a property owner to fail to meet his payments. In these instances the law allows a mortgage to be foreclosed or a land contract to be extinguished. Unless some compromise can be worked out, the farm may then be put up for sale. The amount for which the farm is sold is its liquidation price.

A liquidation price typically recognizes any and all of the more unfortunate circumstances which may have taken place—drought, poor crop yields, declining farm prices, and usually, a lack of earnings. Liquidation price often emphasizes these past circumstances some-

---

14. In some areas the appraiser and the loan officer are one and the same person. This dual role sometimes makes it difficult for the farm loan appraiser to adhere strictly to appraisal principles.

15. In the simplest of terms the equity an owner has in the property is the difference between the cost or present value of the property and the amount of the loan that is still outstanding. Where a deed is transferred and a mortgage assumed, the owner's equity in the beginning is what he paid for the property minus the amount of his loan. Where an installment land contract is used the owner's equity in the beginning is the downpayment. At some later date equity values equal present market values minus the amount of the loan or mortgage still outstanding, or the amounts of principal payments still due.

times quite heavily. It tends to discount the future potential of a farm property usually quite severely.

The assumptions "willing seller" and "reasonable time period" are no longer applicable. The characteristics of the "willing buyer," who is usually knowledgeable about the circumstances, is changed. The typical "willing buyer" will lower his offer or bid. He knows, usually, that the seller is in a disadvantageous position. Thus, when farm properties are sold at these inopportune times, forced sale or liquidation prices often range from 70 to 85 percent of present market values. There are, of course, both appraisers and authors who would argue that whatever price a given farm sells for, that is its worth or value.[16]

Fair Market Value: Fair market value is "the highest price, estimated in terms of money, which a property will bring if exposed for sale in the open market allowing a reasonable time to find a purchaser who has knowledge of all the uses to which it is best adapted and for which it is capable of being used."[17] The words "with neither the buyer nor seller acting under duress either to buy or to sell" are sometimes added. This definition was set forth by the Supreme Court of the State of California in 1909 and has been widely accepted as authoritative[18] It has been adopted by many appraisers; however, primarily by those who do eminent domain or condemnation work.

Under the law of eminent domain private property may be taken for public use; however, the property owner must receive just compensation. In the case of an entire taking, just compensation is the fair market value of the property. In the case of a partial taking it is the difference between the fair market value of the property *before* the taking and the fair market value of the property *after* the taking.

The statutory provisions sometimes vary and particularly over time. However, the adjective "fair" is often used. This adjective has been imposed upon society, not by economists or appraisers, but instead by the legal profession. It appears to be desirable. It adds ethical content. Yet for all practical purposes it is meaningless. Its use has served only to confuse the courts, most juries, and sometimes appraisers.

Academically speaking, present market value and fair market value are one and the same. In actual practice they differ. In the courtroom,

---

16. Yet in arriving at a value through the use of comparable sales most appraisers do not use forced sales as comparables. See Chapter VII.

17. p. 131, *Appraisal Terminology and Handbook.*

18. The Sacramento Case involved the Southern Railroad Co. (respondent) versus Louise R. Heilbron, (appellant): 156 Cal 408: 104 Pac 979.

and particularly in front of a jury of 6 or 12 men or women, the fair market value of a tract of real estate being condemned is 10 to 25 percent higher than its present market value. As a result it usually, if not always, pays a property owner being condemned to go to court. This is particularly true in cases where only part of the property is being taken and where damages are involved.

It is unfortunate, but there is sometimes considerable variation among the opinions of appraisers. Many persons, even some appraisers themselves, attribute this to a lack of professional ethics. However, much of the variation in fair market values—much of the difference between present and fair market value—can be attributed to a lack of understanding with regard to the two definitions, the assumptions underlying each, and the extent to which these assumptions are applicable.

In condemnation cases fair market value is often higher than present market value for any one or more of the following reasons:

1. In the taking of private property for public use the property owner is helpless. The property owner or seller is an unwilling seller. He cannot prevent the taking of his property. Most appraisers, attorneys, courts, and juries recognize this. Their fair market values tend to reflect this fact of life.

2. Most juries, composed of laymen and women, have no real knowledge of the legal foundations underlying the law of eminent domain. They seldom realize and they are seldom instructed specifically, as to the definition of just compensation, what it does and does not include, and particularly in partial-taking cases, where the measure of just compensation is the difference between the market value of the property *before* and the market value of the property *after* the taking. When private property is taken for public use many persons feel that the property owner should be indemnified, fully, for whatever he has in the property, including all of his costs. To many persons cost equals value. Without specific legal definition and with all sorts of claims and all sorts of damages—both compensable and non-compensable— waved before them, most juries are forced to use their own best judgment with regard to both the value concept and the dollar figure.

3. The fair market value definition requests the highest price and infers best use of the property. This has led to a highest-and-best-use concept. Highest and best use is that use which will produce the highest income, both in terms of money and amenities over a given period of time, or in the case of an improvement, over its remaining life.[19] Such use is not based, nor should it be based, on what the property

owner is doing with his property now. However, neither is it based on, or necessarily equal to, the property's most probable or typical use. It is instead based upon consideration of every possible use to which a property may be adapted, naturally, and every possible use which will perhaps enhance its value in the future.

Most condemnation appraisers are admonished to use the highest and best use concept. In using such, the benefits most likely to accrue to typical or ordinary buyers and sellers are stretched as far as possible. The highest and best use concept thus tends to include benefits, which only an all-wise mystical man with a perfect crystal ball might foresee, discern, or conceive of, not only in the immediate future, but into infinity.

Typical and best are not the same. The typical use concept, which underlies present market value, and the highest and best use concept, which underlies fair market value, are not equal. To some persons they supposedly lead to similar conclusions. But in the real world the two concepts lead to decidedly different values.

In the transition areas where a farm or two have been purchased for residential, commercial, or industrial development, there tends to be wide discrepancies in both contemplated use and value. All farms, under condemnation, immediately take on all of the characteristics of the adjoining fully developed properties, even though they could not possibly all sell at their appraised values.

4. In a free enterprise society, defined here as a society in which the individual is more important than the State, the "under-dog" typically, if not always, receives "the-benefit-of-the doubt." When some doubt arises, most conscientious appraisers resolve the question in favor of the property owner. It makes no difference whether the appraisal is being made for the condemnor, or taking agency, or whether such is for the condemnee, or property owner.

On the witness stand an appraiser is occasionally asked to place himself in the position of the property owner, and to ask himself if he would willingly accept the compensation he has just recommended to the court if he himself were the property owner. This is a good and yet tough question.

The appraiser's job is to ascertain a value which is fair to both the property owner and to the taxpayers who pay for the property taken.

---

19. p. 44, *Rural Appraisal Manual.*

In accepting a condemnation assignment the appraiser is often aware that he and the property owner may someday meet face to face and look at one another eyeball to eyeball.[20] This type of meeting will never occur with the taxpayers except in a very general fashion. Hence, in a condemnation appraisal fair market values are often above present market values, and in spite of the fact that the reason for or use to be made of an appraisal should never influence the value ascertained.[21]

Many Others: Present market value, basic farm value, normal market value, farm building values, actual cash value, insured value, true cash value, assessed value, farm loan value, liquidation price, and fair market value—all of these can be defined. What could possibly remain? An incomplete list might still include the following:

Amenity Value	Intrinsic Value
Antique Value	Junk Value
Capitalized Value	Leasehold Value
Capricious Value	Nuisance Value
Commercial Value	Plottage Value
Depreciated Value	Potential Value
Earnings Value	Real Value
Exchange Value	Rental Value
Face Value	Replacement Value
Full Value	Sales Value
Improved Value	Warranty Value
Inheritance Value	. . . and Others[22]
Intangible Value	

Not always are these values specific. Nor are they easily defined. When a farm is sold, its ownership transferred, and the money has changed hands, that figure at which the farm was sold is its present market price. The sale may have been an arm's length transaction; or, it may have been a chance in a lifetime, a sacrifice, a bargain, a mistake, or a steal. A whole host of adjectives can be used to reflect one's opinion. Furthermore, the price at which the farm sold may or may not have been equal to the farm's present market value. This fact or thought shouldn't confuse the professional appraiser. However, it sometimes does.

---

20. While fair market values are often above present market values, they are often still below the values which the property owners themselves place on their properties.

21. In estate tax appraisal, fair market value is often 10 to 40 percent below present market value.

22. McDonald, A. F., "The Meaning of Value."

The No. 1 value first ascertained is always the subject property's present market value. All appraisal assignments require this figure. After a property's present market value is obtained it may then become a point of departure for determining many other values. Once the professional appraiser realizes this and adopts this philosophy, his appraisals will best serve his clients, the problems they have, and the decisions they have to make.

REFERENCES

Value Versus Price

Babcock, F. M., "Valuation Process and Appraisal Purpose," *The Real Estate Appraiser*, Vol. 31, No. 4, April 1965.

Bowen, J. R., "Land Prices Versus Land Values," *Journal of American Society of Farm Managers and Rural Appraisers*, Vol. 11, No. 1, April 1947.

Church, Bryon, "What Good Is an Appraisal?," *The Residential Appraiser*, Vol. 27, No. 5, May 1961.

Dunn, Dominick, "Can Real Estate Have More Than One Value?," *Appraisal Journal*, Vol. 5, No. 2, April 1937.

Denton, J. H., "Market Theory in Real Estate Appraising," *The Real Estate Appraiser*, Vol. 29, No. 9, September 1963.

Hanson, Peter, "The Meaning of Value," *Appraisal Journal*, Vol. 1, No. 4, July 1933.

McDonald, A. F., "The Meaning of Value," *Encyclopedia of Real Estate Appraising*, Prentice-Hall, 1959.

Mayer, L. B., "Farm Appraisal in a Period of Declining Prices," *Journal of American Society of Farm Managers and Rural Appraisers*, Vol. 13, No. 1, April 1949.

Murray, W. G., *Farm Appraisal and Valuation*, 5th Edition, Iowa State University Press, 1969.

Paarlberg, Don, *Great Myths of Economics*, New American Library, 1968.

Parvin, R. G., "Asset Valuation," *Appraisal Journal*, Vol. 22, No. 4, October 1954.

Quintana, Isidoro, "Coming to Terms," *Appraisal Journal*, Vol. 10, No. 1, January 1942.

Ratcliff, R. U., "Neoteric View of the Appraisal Function," *Appraisal Journal*, Vol. 33, No. 2, April 1965.

Ring, A. A., "The Labyrinth of Value," *Appraisal Journal*, Vol. 33, No. 1, January 1965.

Schulte, A. B., "Some Observations on Factors Affecting Price and Some Sound Value Concepts," *Appraisal Journal*, Vol. 22, No. 2, April 1954.

Smith, Walstein, Jr., "Appraising for Probate and Estates," *The Real Estate Appraiser*, Vol. 35, No. 3, July-August 1969.

Smith, Walstein, Jr., "Value—Verified or Vilified," *The Real Estate Appraiser*, Vol. 31, No. 9, September 1965.

Swan, R. E., "Appraisal Terminology and Its Use," *The Real Estate Appraiser*, Vol. 31, No. 6, June 1965.

Taeuber, K. C., "An Argument in Favour of the Acceptance of the Doctrine of One Value for All Purposes," *Appraisal Journal*, Vol. 24, No. 4, October 1956.

Troxel, J. C., "No Sale Without a Purchase," *The Real Estate Appraiser*, Vol. 36, No. 1, January-February 1970.

Webster's New World Dictionary, World Publishing Co., College Edition, 1956.

The Farm Real Estate Market

Sargent, F. O., "Land Market and Price Analysis in an Agro-Industrial Economy," *Appraisal Journal*, Vol. 27, No. 3, July 1959.

Various Authors, *The Farm Real Estate Market*, University of Minnesota Land Tenure Seminar, July 1959.

Wenzlick, Roy, "The Fundamental Differences Between Real Estate and Other Commodities," *The Real Estate Analyst*, Vol. 34, No. 7, March 1965.

Present Market Value Defined

Appraisal Terminology and Handbook, 5th Edition, American Institute of Real Estate Appraisers, 1967.

Davis, W. D., "What Is Market Value?," *Appraisal Journal*, Vol. 28, No. 1, January 1960.

Frissel, R. N., "The Professional Appraisal and Market Value," *Appraisal Journal*, Vol. 34, No. 4, October 1966.

Huck, Robert, "The Use of Real Estate," *Appraisal Journal*, Vol. 33, No. 2, April 1965.

Kazdin, S. E., "The Zone of Reasonable Doubt," *Appraisal Journal*, Vol. 30, No. 4, October 1962.

Lum, Y. T., "Basic Considerations of Appraisal Concepts and Value Factors," *The Residential Appraiser*, Vol. 28, No. 2, February 1962.

No Author, "Willing Buyer, Willing Seller, and Market Values," *Appraisal Journal*, Vol. 14, No. 1, January 1946.

Ratcliff, R. U., "The Neoteric View of the Appraisal Function," *Appraisal Journal*, Vol. 33, No. 2, April 1965.

Ring, A. A., "The Labyrinth of Value," *Appraisal Journal*, Vol. 33, No. 1, January 1965.

Smith, Walstein, Jr., "Is There More Than One Market Value?," *The Residential Appraiser*, Vol. 28, No. 9, September 1962.

Taeuber, K. C., "An Argument in Favour of the Acceptance of the Doctrine of One Value for All Purposes," *Appraisal Journal*, Vol. 24, No. 4, October 1956.

Troxel, J. C., "To Market, to Market . . . ," *Appraisal Journal*, Vol. 32, No. 2, April 1964.

Fifty-one Other Values

Appraisal Terminology and Handbook, 5th Edition, American Institute of Real Estate Appraisers, 1967.

Bowen, J. R., and L. B. Mayer, "The American Rural Appraisal System," *Journal of the American Society of Farm Managers and Rural Appraisers*, Vol. 10, No. 2, October 1946.

Brooker, M. A., "Problems of Normal Value with Rising Prices," *Journal of Farm Economics*, Vol. 34, No. 5, December 1952.

Colvin, Carl, "Factors in Establishing Prices and Costs for Normal Value Appraisals," Paper presented at the Farm Appraisal Conference, University of Illinois, June 1948.

Crouse, E. F., and C. H. Everett, *Rural Appraisals*, Prentice-Hall, 1956.

Davis, W. D., "What Is Market Value?," *Appraisal Journal*, Vol. 28, No. 1, January 1960.

Dolman, J. P., "Some Reflections on Terminology," *Appraisal Journal*, Vol. 31, No. 3, July 1963.

Engberg, R. C., "Federal Credit Agencies as an Influence upon Land Values," *Journal of Farm Economics*, Vol. 29, No. 1, February 1947.

Englehorn, V. A., "The American Society Approach to Various Kinds of Value," *Journal of American Society of Farm Managers and Rural Appraisers*, Vol. 24, No. 1, April 1960.

Frissel, R. N., "The Professional Appraisal and Market Value," *Appraisal Journal*, Vol. 34, No. 1, April 1960.

Hollebaugh, C. W., "On Definition Accuracy," *Appraisal Journal*, Vol. 30, No. 4, October 1962.

Hubbard, D. F., "Research for Farm Appraisals," *Journal of American Society of Farm Managers and Rural Appraisers*, Vol. 23, No. 2, October 1959.

Huck, Robert, "The Use of Real Estate," *Appraisal Journal*, Vol. 33, No. 2, April 1965.

Lostetter, E. K., "The Four-way Test," *Appraisal Journal*, Vol. 31, No. 4, October 1963.

Mayer, L. B., "Farm Appraisal in a Period of Declining Prices," *Journal of American Society of Farm Managers and Rural Appraisers*, Vol. 13, No. 1, April 1949.

McDonald, A. F., "Fundamentals of Real Estate Appraising," *Appraisal Journal*, Vol. 20, No. 1, January 1952.

McDonald, A. F., "The Meaning of Value," *Encyclopedia of Real Estate Appraising*, Prentice-Hall, 1959.

Morse, T. D., "The American Rural Appraisal System," *Doane Agricultural Digest*, March 1943.

Morse, T. D., "The Gyroscope of Rural Appraisals," *Journal of American Society of Farm Managers and Rural Appraisers*, Vol. 1, No. 1, April 1937.

Murray, W. G., *Farm Appraisal and Valuation*, 5th Edition, Iowa State University Press, 1969.

Murray, W. G., "A Review of the Farm Appraisal Panel Meeting; Appraisal Section," *Journal of American Society of Farm Managers and Rural Appraisers*, Vol. 16, No. 1, April 1952.

No Author, "Farm Appraisals" (Reprint from Agricultural Engineering), *Journal of American Society of Farm Managers and Rural Appraisers*, Vol. 5, No. 2, October 1941.

Norton, L. J., "Some Fallacies of Normal Values in Farm Land Appraisals," Farm Appraisal Conference, University of Illinois, June 1948.

Nowland, R. E., "Price Versus Value," *Journal of American Society of Farm Managers and Rural Appraisers*, Vol. 3, No. 1, April 1939.

Ratcliff, R. U., "A Neoteric View of the Appraisal Function," *Appraisal Journal*, Vol. 33, No. 2, April 1965.

Ratcliff, R. U., "The Economic Function of Appraisal," Ch. II, *Appraisal Journal*, Vol. 32, No. 1, January 1964.

Ring, A. A., "The Labyrinth of Value," *Appraisal Journal*, Vol. 33, No. 1, January 1965.

Rural Appraisal Manual. 2nd Edition, American Society of Farm Managers and Rural Appraisers, 1967.

Sanders, C. A., "The Reasonable Range of Value," *The Residential Appraiser*, Vol. 28, No. 5, May 1962.

Stewart, C. E., "The Concept of Normal Value in Farm Land Appraisal," *Journal of American Society of Farm Managers and Rural Appraisers*, Vol. 11, No. 2, October 1947.

CHAPTER III

American Real Property Law

The religious beliefs of the English colonists who first settled in North America led to the creation of certain property rights and responsibilities belonging to and of the individual. The right to own property has been a powerful incentive ever since. It has been a strong motivating force behind much human activity; it has led to a productive nation. In fact, the ownership of private property is one of the cornerstones of the American economic system.

The ownership of private property and the rights of the property owner are both determined and protected by law. The property owner is protected by the United States Constitution and its Bill of Rights, by considerable statutory law enacted by various state legislatures, and by much common law based on the many cases or court decisions which have been handed down through history. The purpose of all law, of course, is to define and assert certain legal rights, and as collateral thereto, to prevent and punish certain legal wrongs.

REAL ESTATE VERSUS PROPERTY VERSUS PERSONALTY

Property consists of all things which have value or which go to make up wealth and which are the subject of ownership. Every species of interest and every right is included. The appraiser, of course, is primarily interested in the distinctions between (1) real estate or realty, (2) real property, and (3) personal property or personalty. To distinguish between them is sometimes difficult.

Real Estate: Real estate refers to or consists of the earth's crust and all things of a physical nature which have been built upon, which are growing out of, or which have been affixed to such; in other words, all tangible, corporeal, visible, or physical things.[1]

The Fifth Amendment to the Constitution of the United States states that "No person shall be . . . deprived of life, liberty, or property, without due process of law. . ." At the same time, man does not have absolute title to land. He never has had in fact.

Courtesy, U.S.D.A.

The appraiser deals with two distinct entities:—(1) land and (2) improvements. Land embraces the surface of the earth's crust and all things attached or affixed thereto by nature—the rocks, the minerals, the soil, the water, the meadows, the streams, the woods, etc. Land also persists; it is for all practical purposes physically indestructible.

Improvements include such things as buildings, fences, permanent conservation, water control and irrigation systems, tile drains, and such things as trees, shrubs and perennial crops planted by man. Improvements differ from land in that they may be created, in that they are subject to depreciation, and in that they can be destroyed both by nature and by man.

Improvements are typically conveyed as a part of the real estate. In actual practice, whoever owns the land usually also owns (although not necessarily) the improvements. Typically these latter are so connected, both physically and legally, that by the rules of law, they pass as appurtenant to and by the same conveyance as land.[2]

Whoever owns the land usually also owns all things below and all things above (again not necessarily). Minerals, oil, gravel, and timber assets are not improvements exactly, yet they are similar, in that they also can be used up. These latter assets as well as buildings and improvements are commonly referred to as depreciable or wasting assets.

Real Property: Real property refers to the many rights and restrictions that may be attached to real estate. These rights include all of the intangible, incorporeal, or invisible things which arise out of or are endowed by virtue of ownership. Rights may issue out of, be annexed to, or be exercisable within land. They, or the lack of such, are divisible, definable, and enforceable; and they too pass as incident to land by virtue of ownership.

The term *fee simple,* as applied to ownership of real property, signifies the largest estate, or the highest quantity of ownership, or most extensive interest that can be enjoyed in land, in other words, an

---

1. The terms *real estate* and *realty* are often used interchangeably. They are sometimes said to consist of all the interests anyone has in lands, tenements, and hereditaments and varying from absolute and full ownership down to naked possession. This is not exactly correct for real estate refers primarily to the physical asset.

2. The same is also true of property owner rights. Whoever owns the land usually also owns (although again not necessarily) certain rights. Typically they are so connected, that by the rules of law, they also pass as appurtenant to and by the same conveyance as land.

ownership and interest free from most if not all restrictions. A fee simple absolute is an estate limited absolutely to a man and his heirs and assigns forever, and without any limitations or restrictions whatsoever. The term indicates that the property is free and clear of any and all conditions, that such is descendible to the heirs in general, whether male or female, lineal or collateral. The fee simple owner thus has a maximum of rights.

At the same time, the fee simple owner does not have a 100-percent unrestricted right to do whatever he wishes. His rights are still subject to the superior rights of society, based on the furtherance of the welfare of the general public. A property may also be encumbered or further subject to certain liabilities through legal means or through the purchase or sale of an individual right.

An encumbrance is any interest in, or right to a property which subsists elsewhere (in another) and to the diminution of its value, yet which is still consistent with the passing of the fee. An encumbrance may be a mortgage, a judgment, a lien, an attachment, an inchoate right of dower, a restriction in the deed, an encroachment of a building, a lease, an easement or right-of-way, or the unpaid taxes.

Personal Property: Personal property (personalty) consists of all things which are personal, movable, and not affixed to or a part of real estate. Personalty may be carried onto land, and various articles may be taken into buildings, yet such do not become an integral part thereof. Hence, an article of personal property is in contrast to any accessory to the real estate. Such cannot consist of a chattel attached to realty, or anything which is part and parcel of realty, and hence ordinarily the property of the owner of the realty.[3]

The enjoyment or use of an article of personal property sometimes requires it to become attached or affixed to real estate. When this occurs the article thus becomes, or is considered to be, a fixture. When this occurs the distinction between realty and personalty often requires some decision by an appraiser. That decision must be both logical and practical.

When the owner of both the real and the personal property is one

---

3. Examples of personal property are autos, trucks, machinery, livestock, livestock equipment, harvested crops, feed, supplies, household goods, clothing, jewelry, securities, and cash. Items that often raise questions include cut timber, fence posts, wire, and lumber; portable buildings and equipment; machinery attached to buildings but which could be removed without injury to either the machinery or the building; growing crops; and miscellaneous farm supplies, such as straw or manure.

and the same person he is free, within limits, to use his property however he desires. The property owner is at liberty, usually, to attach
and detach personal property to the real estate at will. Under these
circumstances, there is no particular problem as to whether the attached property remains personal or has become permanent (a
fixture).

However, questions are raised when the real estate is sold and when
there are no exceptions or reservations as to articles excepted from the
transaction, or reserved by the seller, and so specified in the contract.
In these cases a fixture is, generally speaking, a part of the real estate.
Oral exceptions or reservations are ineffective; such, in order to be enforceable, must be in writing.

In agriculture the problem sometimes arises between landlords and
tenants, and particularly where farm resources and living accommodations are both involved. Most landlords and tenants agree in advance
as to who contributes what, and how the ownership of various items
of personalty are to be shared. However, not always is the lease
written.[4] If one of the parties dies, the heirs are then forced to accept
the word of the other party as to who owns the various items of
personal property.

Domestic and ornamental items, of course, are often attached to a
home for purposes of making it a more comfortable and attractive
place to live. In these cases, most courts favor the tenant and hold that
he may remove such property providing it can be detached without
injury to the premises. If the article replaced is an older one, present
at the beginning of the lease, the article may not be removed (again
unless there was an expressed agreement beforehand) except in instances where the older article has been saved and can be reinstalled
without injury.

In determining whether an article or fixture is real or personal, the
following guides are useful:

1. What was the original intent of the person or party who affixed
the article to the property in the first place? Probably no one thought
about it at the time. Hence, today the question becomes one of what
is fair and reasonable? Whatever facts are available must be recognized. The circumstances surrounding the problem, both originally
and now, must be considered, along with the customs of the community.

---

4. In many areas an unwritten lease is not as unacceptable a practice as it may
appear, for leasing practices are often quite standardized.

2. Was there any previous agreement between the parties involved; for example, an agreement stating precisely that the article could first be attached and then later be removed or detached?

3. Was the article affixed strongly and in such fashion that removal would seriously injure or destroy either the article itself or the structure to which it was attached? Was the article obviously attached so that it could be detached later, fairly easily, and without injury to either it or to the real estate?

4. Was the real estate in any way remodeled or otherwise adapted to accommodate the article of property in question, and/or was the article (the personal item) fitted or fashioned to fit the purpose and use of the real estate to which it was attached, and in such fashion as to enhance the value of the realty? Will removal of the article lead to a diminution in the value of either the personalty or the realty?

Farm appraisers are occasionally called upon to make these decisions. Furthermore, they are sometimes called upon to appraise personal property. These appraisals may be made as a basis for setting up depreciation schedules, for settling estates, for ascertaining both insurance coverage and claims, and occasionally for estimating damage in a condemnation case.

The values ascertained should be present market values. The appraisal report should include an itemized list of all property along with the description, age, condition, size, and value of each item. Small items are often grouped. Current prices are usually referred to when it is possible. The remaining life of each item is typically estimated. The prevailing values in the community are then presented.

THE RIGHTS OF THE PROPERTY OWNER

The basic fundamental rights and freedoms that all citizens of the United States enjoy are outlined by the Constitution of the United States along with the Bill of Rights. Of particular interest to appraisers is the Fifth Amendment to the Constitution which states that "No person shall be . . . deprived of life, liberty, or property, without due process of law; nor shall private property be taken for public use, without just compensation. . . ."[5]

This is one of the more important provisions of the Constitution. It expresses the idea that man's life, liberty, and property are not

---

5. p. 131. "The United States Constitution," World Book Encyclopedia.

subject to the uncontrolled power of government. At the same time, man does not have absolute title to land. In fact, he never did have. Certain rights were reserved or retained by the government. Furthermore, man, as a citizen, has, in addition to these rights, certain responsibilities. He must support and defend the Constitution which makes the inherent rights of the property owner in this country possible. Without such constitutional guarantees—both federal and state— the security of the property owner would be null and void. His property would be valueless.

Rights of a Physical Nature: The property rights most generally associated with ownership are those which are physical in nature— namely, those of peaceful possession and quiet enjoyment. There are three rights of this nature.

First: "the right of possession—peaceable entry upon and use of the parcel of land and the fixed improvements thereon." Title to real property is always related to a specific description of a portion of the earth's surface. A fee simple title carries with it the ownership of all fixed improvements situated thereon and recognizes the precept that with the construction of improvements there is a unity with land.

Second: "the right to possession and use of the subsurface materials that make up the parcel of land or are available for use at the site." The conversion of mineral or gravel deposits to use illustrates this right.[6]

Third: "the right to possession and use of the air space above the surface of the land." Until recently, little thought was given to this right and as to whether or not such is tangible or valuable. However, the use of air rights, as separate from and for a use different than that of the surface of the land, has led to increased recognition of air rights as a separate entity.[7]

Rights of a Legal Nature: There are seven principal property rights which are legal in nature. They are closely related to those above, in that they arise from land, yet they are considerably more intangible in character. These legal rights are actually separate from one another. Each one's use and enjoyment is distinct. They stem from law or a combination of laws which enables each to be considered as a separate entity yet at the same time a component part of property ownership.

First: "the right to transfer (convey or sell) all or part of the

---

6. When minerals or gravel through use are separated from land, they cease to be real property and become personal property.
7. Adapted from Smith, L. C., "The Bundle of Property Rights."

other property rights for a specified term or in perpetuity." Deeds, easements, and leases are evidences of the exercise of this right.

Second: "the right to demand and to receive or not receive monetary or other consideration for the transfer of all or part of the other rights." Payments for property conveyance by deed or easement, rents, and interest are received under the exercise of this right.

Third: "the right to pledge all or part of the other property rights as security for a debt." The vast mortgage loan business relies on the use of this right. The practice of mortgaging property is so old and so general that little more needs to be said. However, all of the fee need not necessarily be subjected to the lien of debt. Only one right, or only a part of one of the rights, may be pledged.

Fourth: "the right to have all rights held at (the time of) death of the owner to pass to his legal heirs." If a man dies intestate (without a will), his property rights then pass to his heirs according to the laws of property descent and distribution.

Fifth: "the right to bequeath part or all of any right or rights to specified legatees." The execution of a will is the exercise of this right.

Sixth: "the right to recapture part or all of any right or rights at the expiration of the term in an instrument of transfer, or, upon default, in compliance with any of the provisions of such an instrument." An example is an owner regaining through reversion the rights previously granted in a lease at the expiration of the leasehold, or upon failure of the lessee to conform to the covenants expressed in the agreement.

Seventh: "the right to refuse to exercise any property right." The absence of compulsion to use any right merely rounds out and makes complete the freedom of will in the enjoyment of property ownership.[8]

These property rights are transferred from one person or party to another through written agreement. The first person or party merely promises (1) the existence or non-existence of a given state of things relative to a particular parcel of land and (2) the performance or non-performance of a certain act or acts, within a given period of time.

All rights may be conveyed (for example, the land and a fee simple title may be transferred by deed) or, only certain rights may be conveyed. Certain rights may be transferred for only a particular period of time (for example, the right of occupancy for one year) or, they may be transferred in perpetuity.

---

8. *Ibid.*

THE RIGHTS OF THE SOVEREIGN

At one time the Federal government owned all of the land in the United States. Much of this land has either been sold or transferred by grants to various individuals or parties. Yet in transferring such, the government retained certain rights, and today all property is still subject to these rights.

Hence, under the United States form of government, legal title to land (fee simple title) is not absolute. Property ownership rights are, in part at least, restricted. It is the property owner's responsibility to recognize and to conform strictly to the exercise of the sovereign powers of the government. There remains little or no choice on the part of the property owner with respect to the use of the following powers.

First: "the responsibility to conform faithfully to the terms of any lawful agreement or legal undertaking for the pledge or transfer of any property right or part thereof." Deed restrictions are an illustration. These latter are more or less an area of choice by the owner and purchaser, yet the courts force any and all responsibilities upon any individual or party who attempts to evade such.

Second: "the police powers for the protection of society, its general welfare, health, safety and moral character." This responsibility is more forced than voluntary and failure to conform usually results in some penalty or punishment. However, only when society in general is protected, is the individual or the property owner protected. In other words, it is a two-way street. The very acceptance of certain lawful acts by the citizenry who hold sacred their devotion to the ownership of private property is what holds intact the forces which continue to preserve the rights of the property owner.

Third: "the power of taxation to provide the public monies needed for such things as . . . " a military force to protect the nation, the services required to establish and maintain justice, along with a police force, all of the public institutions which are of benefit to society in general and yet cannot be efficiently or profitably provided by individuals—such items as public roads, post offices, facilities which regulate the money supply, commerce, and trade, along with those institutions which provide education to defend the dignity of the sovereign.

Fourth: "the right of eminent domain or the power to appropriate or take (really to resume possession of) private property, either temporarily or permanently, providing such is for public use and with just compensation to the owner." This right, which was held or retained by the sovereign, provides the basis for all eminent domain or condemnation appraisal.

Fifth: "the right of escheat, or the reversion of property back to the sovereign government, if the taxes on such are not paid, or in consequence of the lack of any individual capable of inheriting the property."[9]

Property owner rights thus consist of all the interests which a person has in property and to the exclusion of all other persons or parties. The owner's rights are not mere physical attributes; they instead represent a number of rights and responsibilities. In his book on real estate law, MacChesney adopted and developed the concept that property was a "bundle of rights"—like a faggot of sticks, each representing a different opportunity for use or for action by the owner thereof.[10] The property owner's rights are thus many in general. Twelve general categories were presented above. They are exclusive. Certain rights can be retained, given away, sold, or mortgaged. Yet they are not absolute. The government extracted and reserved certain ones when the Bill of Rights was written.

LEGAL CONCEPTS AND DEFINITIONS

Appraisers are not attorneys (at least not very often), yet their activities often involve a working knowledge of some of the legal concepts and terms used in real property law. The following are summary versions of definitions, adapted largely from Black and Webster.[11]

Abandonment. An owner may relinquish all title, right or claim to and/or possession of property with the intent of not reclaiming or resuming ownership, possession or enjoyment. There must be a concurrence of act and intent, in other words, the act of leaving the premises or property vacant.

Agrarian Law. Law which has for its object the distribution of land constituting the public domain by public authority and among the

---

9. *Ibid.*

10. MacChesney, N. W., *The Principles of Real Estate Law.*

11. Black, H. C., *Black's Law Dictionary,* and Gove, P. B., (Editor-in-Chief), *Webster's Third New International Dictionary.*

people. This law is frequently applied to expropriation and to the subdividing of large properties for purposes of increasing the number of landholders. The law is frequently aimed at obtaining a more equal division or distribution of landed property.

Alienation. The voluntary and complete transfer of real property and possession of lands, tenements, or other items of property from one person to another, as distinguished from passing it by law.

Appurtenance. That which belongs to or is annexed to another more worthy thing such as land and hence passes as incident to it—for example, a building or improvement, or an easement or right-of-way.

Assigns. Those persons or parties to whom property shall have been transferred. The term is seldom used today except in the phrase "heirs, administrators, and assigns" which may appear in deeds and wills.

Bill of Sale. A written agreement whereby one person or party transfers to another person or party his interest in or right to a given item of personal property.

Chattel. An article of personal property; a term typically extended to include animate as well as inanimate property.

Corporeal. Property which has material or physical existence and hence is perceptible by the senses of sight and touch.

Deed. A legal instrument whereby the owner of real estate (the grantor) conveys some right, title, or interest in or to the same, to a new owner (the grantee) in writing.

Deed of Trust. An instrument used in many states, taking the place and serving the uses of a common-law mortgage, by which the legal title to real property is placed in the hands of one or more trustees as security for the repayment of a sum of money or the performance of some other condition.

Easement. A non-possessory interest one person or party holds in the land of another and in which the first person is accorded partial use of such land for a specific purpose. An easement restricts the rights of the fee owner to the use and enjoyment of his land, yet does not deprive him of those rights. It is intangible and does not carry with it any rights or interest in the corpus or body of the land. An easement may be an appurtenant (goes with the land) or in gross (granted to or goes with an individual person or party). It may be affirmative or negative.

Eminent Domain. The power or right of society or of the sovereign to take private property, either temporarily or permanently, providing such is for public use and providing just compensation is paid the property owner.

Encroachment. The intrusion or invasion onto or into the property of another to the extent that there is displacement of an existing use, a diminishing in area, or a diminution in the value of the property. In the law of easements such may consist of an additional restriction or burden. However, the displacement of the present residence by persons of a different social and cultural background or of a lower economic status is referred to as infiltration.

Escrow. A scroll, writing, or deed, delivered by the obligor, promisor, or grantor, into the hands of a third person, to be held by the latter until the happening of a contingency or the performance of a condition, and to then be delivered by him to the obligee, promisee, or grantee. This third person is the escrow agent. The grantor may be the seller; the grantee may be the buyer of property.

Estate. The degree, quantity, nature, or extent of the interest which anyone has in property, real or personal, and which varies from absolute ownership down to naked possession. Estates in land are typically divided into two classes: (1) freehold estates and (2) leaseholds—the distinguishing characteristic being both quantity and duration.

Fixture. A chattel or item of personal property, which either has been or is attached to realty with the intent, or in such fashion, that it has become an accessory to and a part and parcel of the realty.

Freehold. An estate in land or other real property which is for life, in fee, and yet of an uncertain duration. An estate to be a freehold estate must possess two qualities:—(1) immobility (in other words, the property must be either land or some interest issuing out of or annexed to land) and (2) indeterminate duration.

Grantee. The person or party to whom a grant is made, namely, the buyer.

Grantor. The person or party by whom a grant is made, namely, the seller.

Hereditaments. Things capable of being inherited, real or personal, corporeal or incorporeal, including heirlooms, which by custom descend to the heir with land.

Joint Tenancy. A united, undivided, and yet not distinct interest in property and one in which the surviving tenant(s) or party(s) takes all. At the time of death, in other words, the survivor(s) receives all of the property. When joint tenants are husband and wife, as they often are, their relationship in many states is called tenancy-by-the-entirety and has certain special characteristics.

Judgment. A personal liability imposed upon a person, which may be satisfied out of any of that person's property which is within reach of due process. For example, in a mortgage foreclosure suit there may be a personal judgment against the mortgagor or the borrower for a deficiency that remains after sale of the mortgaged premises.

Lease. An agreement in which a contractual arrangement permits exclusive possession or control of the premises (all lands and tenements) by the lessee for a determinate period of time and with reversion of said property to the lessor at the end of the lease. The tenant or renter is the lessee in the relationship; the landlord is the lessor.

Leasehold. The tenant's interest in or his right in realty which is held by him, the lessee, as a result of the lease.

Lien. A hold, claim, or encumbrance one person has upon the property of another for the lack of performance of some duty or obligation, such as the payment of a debt. A mechanic's lien, for example, is a claim created by law for the purpose of securing priority of payment for materials furnished and/or work performed in erecting or repairing a building.

Life Estate. An estate in land which is limited in duration to the life of the owner or to the life of some other person. It is a freehold estate; it is not an estate of inheritance, but instead terminates on the happening of some future uncertain event.

Mortgage. A conveyance, which in many states is considered to be merely a lien, but which pledges as security a particular property for the payment of debt, or the performance of some other obligation, and which becomes void when a certain act or acts are performed in agreement with the stipulations prescribed at the time.

Mortgagee. The person or party who loans the money and takes or receives a mortgage on another's property.

Mortgagor. The person or party who borrows the money and who, having some or all title to the property, pledges such as security for the debt incurred or loan he receives.

Right-of-way. The most simple and fairly common easement in which one person or party has the intangible right to pass or cross another's land.

Riparian Right. A right which exists solely by reason of the location of the land with respect to the water supply. Such is acquired by acquiring title to riparian land. Furthermore, unless specifically restricted, the owner of land contiguous to, or which borders, a natural stream or lake is entitled to take water from that source for use upon that contiguous land.[12]

Squatter. One who settled on another's land, particularly on public land, and without legal authority.

Tenancy-in-Common. Where two or more persons have distinct yet undivided interests in the same estate in property. There is, however, no right of survivorship between them. Like joint tenancy, tenancy-in-common can be created by deed or by will. Unlike joint tenancy, however, it is frequently brought into being by the laws of property descent and distribution and in the absence of a will.

Tenant. A person or party who holds temporary possession in or has temporary occupancy and use of realty owned by another person, usually called the landlord, the duration and terms of his tenancy being fixed by the lease.

Title. The evidence of ownership of property and the means whereby the owner has just possession. A clear title, and a good and merchantable title are synonymous, meaning free from all apparent defects, grave doubts, and litigious uncertainties. Such title will be accepted by a reasonably prudent person with full knowledge.

Water Right. A property right, granted by law, to take possession of water occurring in a natural water supply and to divert such water putting it to a beneficial use on or in connection with land.

THE TRANSFER OF REAL PROPERTY BY CONVEYANCE

The United States is one of few countries in which the free alienation of property is held to be to the best interest of its society. The right of alienation is the right of the property owner to freely convey property ownership, either all or in part, to another person or party. Such a right is of outstanding importance in a free society.

The instrument in writing, whereby the owner of real estate (grantor) conveys some right, title, or interest in or to the same, to a new owner (the grantee) is called a deed. According to Lusk, "The drafting of deeds demands the highest skill and greatest care. Carelessness, sloppiness, or ignorance in handling a real estate transaction may result in an expensive lawsuit, or in costly action to quiet the title, or at best an inconvenience and expense to clear the record of technical defects."[13]

---

12. p. 7, Hutchins, W. A., *Irrigation Water Rights in California.*
13. pp. 117 and 118, Lusk, H. F., *Laws of the Real Estate Business.*

The more commonly used deeds are classed as warranty and as quit claim deeds.

1. A warranty deed purports to convey property. In addition, it contains certain covenants whereby the grantor makes certain representations to the grantee, namely, that (a) he, the grantor, possesses good and merchantable title, (b) he, the grantor, has the right and power to convey such title, (c) that with exception, the property is free from all liens and encumbrances, and (d) upon failure of title, he, the grantor, will remain personally responsible, and will, either in whole or in part, reimburse the grantee for whatever losses are sustained.

2. A quit claim deed does not purport to convey property. It instead conveys only the grantor's right, title, and interest therein. A quit claim deed is most frequently used to clear a title, or cure a technical defect in the chain of title. Where property is sold using an installment land contract (with the deed to be delivered at some later date), the grantor usually signs a warranty deed, the grantee often signs a quit claim deed, and both deeds are then placed in the hands of an escrow agent with the understanding that both instruments will be delivered to the appropriate person or party upon the performance (or non-performance) of a certain act or acts. In the event of default the quit claim deed passes to the grantor, and the grantee thus relinquishes all right, title, and interest to the property.

To carry out a valid conveyance of real estate a deed must meet certain formal requirements. These requirements are not uniform throughout the United States; however, the following are, generally speaking, the basics.

1. The Grantor. The person or party selling real estate must have both legal existence and legal capacity to convey the real estate. The signature of the grantor is all important. The grantor's name shall be spelled correctly and exactly the same as it was spelled in the deed or will whereby he acquired title to the property. In executing a deed, both husband and wife must usually join as grantors although this legality varies among states.

2. The Grantee. Every deed must have a grantee and he must be so named or indicated in such a way that identification is possible.

3. A Granting Clause. The grantor must indicate his intent to convey his present interest in the real estate in order to transfer title to the property. Words commonly used are "to grant and to convey to _____," or "to convey and warrant to _____ _____, and to the heirs and assigns forever."

4. The Consideration. A clause reciting the consideration is most

generally included in any acceptable deed. The practice of inserting "One dollar and other good and/or valuable consideration" is common. A good consideration proceeds from love and affection and the like, and has no pecuniary value. A valuable consideration is monetary in nature and does have value.

5. Legal Description. An adequate description is required in order that the property—actually the real estate—can be located and identified. This must be not only technically precise but legally sufficient. Land location and measurement methods are presented later in this chapter.

6. The Warranty. The warranty, of course, is an essential element in a warranty deed, however, not in a quit claim deed.

7. Appurtenances. Real property is typically conveyed along "with all the appurtenances, and all the estate, and all the rights of the grantor in and to said premises." In other words, all things which belong to the property and which are necessary for full enjoyment are typically conveyed without specific mention. Also, that which is appurtenant to a parcel of land is appurtenant to every and all parts thereof. For example, a right-of-way which goes with a particular tract of land that is later subdivided is conveyed with each and every separate parcel that is sold at some later date.

8. Exceptions. When certain defects against a parcel of land are known to exist, the grantor may include in the covenants of the warranty, certain provisions excepting them. For example, if there is right-of-way over part of the premises and if the property is also subject to a mortgage, a warranty deed would contain provisions to the effect that the grantor was granting good title free from all liens and encumbrances, except (a) an easement (described) and (b) the property is subject to a mortgage (giving the name of mortgagee, original amount, unpaid balance, and the place where such is recorded). This same clause will usually state whether or not the grantee assumes the mortgage and agrees to pay the debt.

9. Reservations and/or Restrictions. A reservation in a deed retains or withholds certain rights in the real estate. These rights remain in the grantor; they do not pass, or in other words, are not conveyed to the grantee. The grantor may also place restrictions in a deed. A restrictive covenant may specify how the grantee is to use the real estate, or it may limit the grantee's right to use the real estate conveyed. This occurs most often with regard to residential property.

10. Delivery. Lastly a deed must be dated. It must be signed (in some states in the presence of witnesses). It is customary to ac-

knowledge the execution of such before an attorney or some official such as a notary. Finally, the deed must be delivered. A deed is not legally operative until it is delivered, thus indicating that the intent of the grantor is that the instrument is to become legally effective.

There are no fixed rules which can be applied in all cases. Furthermore, physical transfer alone does not satisfy the delivery requirement. The fact that such delivery actually was or is the intent of the grantor has to be present. Delivery, in order to be effective, generally requires that:

1. The grantor must surrender all right to or control over the deed. Such cannot be recalled at some later date.

2. The grantor must make such delivery during his lifetime.

A grantor may execute a deed and place such in a safe deposit box, along with the direction that the deed shall pass at the time of his death. Such does not constitute delivery. However, a grantor may execute and deliver a deed to an escrow agent or third party, who holds said deed on behalf of the grantee, and who then delivers it to the grantee when the occurrence of some future event such as death takes place. This latter does constitute delivery, even though the deed is not delivered to the grantee until the occurrence of the event.

THE RECORDING OF THE EVIDENCE OF TITLE

In all states a permanent and public record of all interests in and titles to realty is maintained. The recording of a deed is the responsibility of the grantee (or his attorney). The act of recording the evidence of title serves constructive notice to all persons—the public at large and society in general—as to the contents of the deed and of all the rights of the persons or parties who are now in possession of the property. The grantee not only has proof of ownership, he has put that proof on display for all the world to see.

Deeds and mortgages should be recorded promptly; for most, if not all, courts hold that he who first records his deed has priority. For example, if a grantee should, for some reason, procrastinate in getting the deed to his newly acquired property recorded, a judgment against the previous owner, the grantor, could, in the meantime, become a lien against the real estate.[14]

---

14. Likewise he who holds the first recorded mortgage holds precedence over any subsequent mortgage in most states. For example, if the mortgagee who holds a mortgage does not record such promptly the public at large is not served notice and the owner may acquire an additional loan using the same property as collateral.

All instruments pertaining to realty are recorded in the designated office in the county in which the land is located. The office goes by a variety of titles: the Office of the Registrar of Deeds, the County Recorder's Office, etc. In most counties, deeds, mortgages, mortgage assignments and discharges, and deed releases, along with installment land contracts, long-term leases, mechanics liens, and other instruments, may be recorded. The early records consisted of handwritten copies. Later they were typed. Today most counties photostat the original after giving it a book number and page number. Many are now being placed on microfilm.

Any person can usually find any recorded instrument he may wish to examine by consulting an index. Two types of indexes are in use:— (1) a cross index in which the names of the parties to the instrument are listed in alphabetical order (the names of the grantees, or mortgagees, are indexed in one column; the names of the grantors, or mortgagors, in another) and (2) a tract index in which a separate page is kept for each tract of land in the county.

Prior to January 1, 1968, the Federal government imposed a revenue tax on all real estate conveyed for an actual cash consideration in excess of $100. Revenue stamps, purchased at the post office and amounting to $0.55 for each $500 or fraction thereof of value, supposedly had to be attached to the deed before a deed could be recorded.[15] This law expired in 1967, and many states imposed similar transfer taxes. Typically the grantor pays the tax, although not always.

The recording officer who receives the instrument generally endorses thereon the date, the hour, and the minute such was received or recorded, whichever the case may be. Typically the grantee (or mortgagee) pays the recording costs. The persons or parties who have purchased or mortgaged property both in good faith and for value are thus protected.

The records, of course, are accessible to the public, and as a result, they tend to be used by other persons and parties.

1. Abstractors use the records in examining titles and in bringing them up-to-date. Every person purchasing a tract of land usually, but not always, gets with that land an abstract of title. This abstract is a condensed history of the real estate with mention of all liens or liabilities to which it may be subject.

---

15. Actually the stamps did not have to be attached to the deed; all the original statute required was that the stamps be purchased at the time of the sale of the property. (See p. 147, Lusk, H. F.)

2. City, county, and township assessors use the records to keep an up-to-date list of all property for purposes of property assessment. The list typically contains the name of the owner, the kind of property, and its value.

3. Various banks, lending institutions, and credit agencies use the records to develop credit ratings on their clientele.

4. Appraisers use the records to keep up-to-date on the various sales of real estate in their areas. These sales are often used as the bases for comparison in appraising various properties.

LEGAL DESCRIPTION[16]

Every formal appraisal of real estate requires a legal description of the property. In fact, an adequate legal description is an essential part of many legal instruments—deeds, land contracts, mortgages, wills, etc.

Unfortunately legal descriptions vary, both in form and in completeness. An adequate description is one which enables a surveyor to locate the tract of land without question. The metes and bounds system and the rectangular survey system are the two most commonly used systems to describe farm real estate.

The Metes and Bounds System: The metes and bounds system was originally used in surveying land on the Atlantic seaboard. The system is the primary one in effect today from Maine to Georgia and also in Kentucky, Tennessee, West Virginia, and Pennsylvania. The system was also used in Texas before that state was annexed to the United States, and hence the system is still in effect in that state today. And, the system of course was used and is in effect today in all parts of the United States where certain peculiar local conditions require such— for example, where rivers, lakes and in some instances, highways form a part of the boundary.

The metes and bounds system describes land according to its measurements and its boundaries.

1. The Starting Point. Any and all legal descriptions have a point

---

16. Much of the material in this section has been based on Elson, J. J., *Legal Descriptions of Illinois Real Estate.*

Every appraisal requires a legal description of the property—technically precise and legally sufficient to locate and identify the real estate and all attached property rights.

Courtesy, U.S.D.A.

of reference or starting place. A metes and bounds description then continues specified distances along given lines called courses until the tract has been circumscribed and the point of the beginning is reached. The calls or recitals of distances and the directions supposedly describe an enclosed tract. If they do, the description is said to close; however, this doesn't always happen.

The Principal Meridians

The first principal meridian forms the boundary between Ohio and Indiana. The second principal meridian is located a little to the west of the center of Indiana. The third principal meridian runs through about the center of Illinois. The base line of the second principal meridian crosses that line in the southern part of Indiana. It is known as the Petersburg base line and is extended westward to the Mississippi River, crossing the third principal meridian near Centralia, Illinois. The fourth principal meridian crosses Wisconsin and a part of Western Illinois. This principal meridian meets its Illinois base line near Beardstown, Illinois and is projected westward across Missouri. The fifth principal meridian crosses eastern Iowa, Missouri, and Arkansas. The sixth principal meridian crosses Kansas and Nebraska and is used either wholly or in part by Kansas, Nebraska, Colorado, and Wyoming. Meridians other than these are the Choctaw and Chickasaw meridians in Mississippi, the Indian meridian in Oklahoma, and the Mt. Diablo meridian in California. The entire system, including the Fairbanks and Copper River meridians in Alaska, consists of 35 meridians.

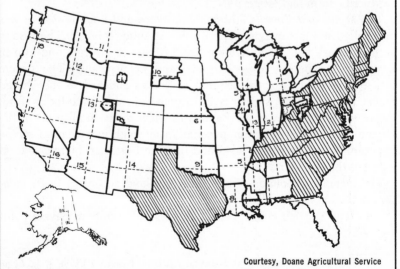

Courtesy, Doane Agricultural Service

The Principal Meridians are identified by number as follows: 1—First; 2—Second; 3— Third; 4—Fourth; 5—Fifth; 6—Sixth; 7—Michigan; 8—Louisiana; 9—Indiana; 10— Black Hills; 11—Principal; 12—Boise; 13—Salt Lake; 14—New Mexico; 15—Gila and Salt Rivers; 16—San Bernardino; 17—Mt. Diablo; 18—Willamette; 19—Copper River; 20—Fairbanks; 21—Seward.

Metes and bounds descriptions sometimes use topographic features as starting points. Trees, stones, rivers, or lakes, which are referred to in this connection, are called natural monuments. Corner markers, fences, and highways are called artificial monuments. These monuments, natural or artificial, of course, are sometimes moved, obliterated and/or destroyed over time.

2. Courses and Distances. Courses are lines identified by direction; distances are linear measurements along these lines. A course is generally described in terms of its angular relationship to the point of reference or to the meridian. Such a course is also called the bearing of the line.

A circle is composed of 360 degrees, which means that such has 360 equal parts. Each part is made up of 60 minutes. A north-south line and an east-west line divide a circle into 4 equal quarters or parts. Each quarter contains 90 degrees. In a metes and bounds description directional lines are typically given in terms of the number of degrees each varies east or west from the north and south starting points (Figure 3). In describing an angular course, the angle formed at the point of reference is given. A course in a northeast direction might be described as North, 13 degrees and 53 minutes East, meaning that the course is 13 degrees 53 minutes east of the true north-south line. A description might read in part, "Starting at the big oak tree, the point of the beginning, thence north, 13° 53′ east, a distance of 387 feet, thence, . . ."

Many units of measurement are used to describe the distances along a line. Miles, feet, and rods are the more common ones, although chains are frequently used. A legal chain is 66 feet long and is composed of 100 links, each of which is 7.92 inches in length. Actual chains, having 50 links, were used in much of the early surveying. These chains, called two-pole chains, are half as long as the legal chain.

Some of the more commonly used measurements and their equivalents are as follows:

1 mile . . . . 8 furlongs; 80 chains; 320 rods; 5,280 feet;
1 furlong . . ⅛ mile; 10 chains; 40 rods; 660 feet;
1 chain . . . 4 rods; 66 feet; 100 links;
1 rod . . . . . 25 links; 16½ feet;[17]
1 link . . . . . 1/100 chain; 7.92 inches.

---

17. The term *rod* is derived from the use of a pole 16½ feet long. Such is also called a perch.

3. Irregular Boundaries. Not all tracts of land have regular boundaries. Land bordering on lakes or rivers are in this category. Descriptions of lands bordering on such irregular boundaries are likely to include such phrases as ". . . to _____ river, thence along _____ river to. . . ." Unless the deed expressly states otherwise, the description is usually interpreted to mean a tract with one boundary at the center line or thread of the stream. This means the middle line between shores without considering the location of the channel. In the case of navigable rivers or streams, the ownership of the stream bed is burdened with the right to navigation on behalf of the public.

Highways and streets are often used as boundaries, especially if the highway forming the boundary is curved or irregular. Descriptions of land abutting public highways are generally interpreted to include a portion of the right-of-way, unless the wording makes it clear that the tract does not include such.[18]

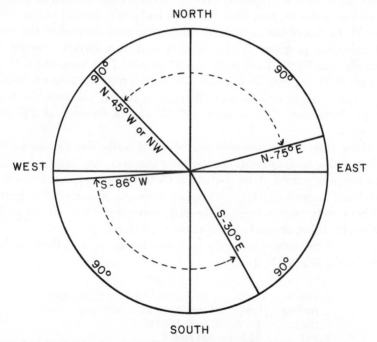

Figure 3. A Circle Showing the North, South, East, and West Directions and Four Illustrations Describing Angular Courses.

---

18. The public may own the right-of-way in fee simple absolute. This is usual when a city street is involved. Whenever city property is platted (mapped), title to the streets typically vests in the city.

4. Exceptions and Quantities. If a certain portion of a tract is not to be included, the description will frequently contain an exception. A description of the larger tract will be given and after the word "except" a description of the smaller portion will be presented. Care must be exercised in drafting exceptions to avoid ambiguity. The acreage of the tract typically is given following the description.

Where conflict exists, the courts have held that the natural boundaries or monuments are more reliable than artificial ones; that the monuments are more reliable than courses or distances (bounds take precedence over the metes); and that the quantities (acreages) are the least reliable.

The Rectangular Survey System: In many areas of the continental United States, farm land description is by rectangular survey. This system is primarily an American institution, as no other nation contributed to its development or perfection, and no other nation, with the exception of Canada, has ever used the system.

Land is described according to its distance from two fixed lines, each at right angles to the other (Figure 4). One line is a true north-south line and is called a Principal Meridian. The other is an east-west line and is called a Base Line.

1. Meridians. Contrary to popular understanding, the principal meridians are not located on geographic longitude. They were established to meet the surveying needs in a given area by government surveyors who often determined them with reference to natural objects.

2. Base Lines. The base lines are latitudinal lines, yet again, like the principal meridians, they also were established by government surveyors on an arbitrary basis. There is at least one base line for each meridian.

3. Correction Lines. Due to the curvature of the earth's surface, the meridians, if extended far enough, would converge at the North Pole. Hence, at various distances from the principal meridians and base lines, government surveyors established correction lines in order to keep their measurements accurate. Correction lines for the principal meridians are called guide meridians; those for the base lines are called standard parallels. In many areas these correction lines occur every 24 miles. Unfortunately, sections located on opposite sides of a correction line do not always have corresponding corners. Evidence of this exists today in the form of a jog in some country roads.

4. Townships. A township is a unit of land 6 miles square and containing 36 square miles. This is a Land Office or Congressional Township. It is not to be confused with the civil townships which are

political subdivisions of greater or lesser size. (Neither do township and range lines coincide with county boundaries.)

5. Rectangular Survey Lines. Rectangular survey lines are established every six miles from each meridian and from each base line. The east-west lines (township lines) form the north and south boundaries and the north-south lines (range lines) form the east and west boundaries for individual townships. Thus, the townships are six miles on each side. They are described according to their distance from both the meridian and the base line in terms of township and range numbers. For example, a township located between the base line and first township line north of the base line is said to be in Township 1 North. A township located between the third and fourth range lines west of the principal meridian is said to be in Range 4 West.

To locate a single township, both township and range readings are needed. Thus, a township located between the second and third township lines south of the base line and between the second and third range lines west of the meridian is described as Township 3 South, Range 3 West. A township located between the first and second township lines north of the base line and between the third and fourth range lines west of the meridian is described as Township 2 North, Range 4 West.

The principal meridian involved should be included in the description. If the second principal meridian is involved, for example, the latter part of the description of the second township in the example above would be Township 2 North, Range 4 West of the Second Principal Meridian. The county and state may also be given.

6. Sections. Each township is divided into 36 sections of land, each section of which is 1 mile square. To locate and describe the land within a township, it is necessary to identify the section in which it is located. Federal law established a 1-through-36 numbering system in which the sections are numbered consecutively, beginning with Section 1 in the northeast corner of the township and proceeding west to Section 6. Section 7 is located immediately below (south) Section 6. Then the numbering goes back and forth until it reaches Section 36 in the southeast corner of the township (Figure 5).

Theoretically a section of land contains 640 acres. However, due to the convergence of lines and due to surveying errors, not all sections contain this exact amount. To avoid having small errors in all sections all shortages or surpluses have been assigned to the north and west sections in each township. Thus, all shortages or surpluses in north and south measurements appear in the northernmost tier—sections 1

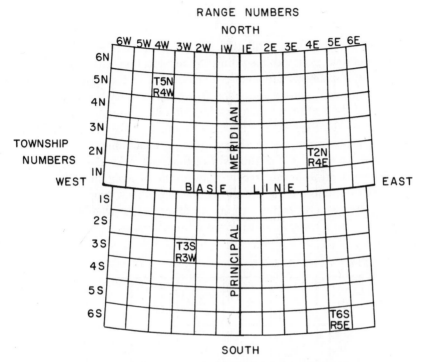

Figure 4. Township and Range Lines Showing Congressional Townships.

through 6; all shortages or surpluses in east and west measurements appear in the westernmost tier—sections 6, 7, 18, 19, 30 and 31.

Surveyors assigned these irregularities to the outer one-half of these sections. The procedures vary. However, the assignments were generally made by subdividing all sections on the north and west sides of a township (except Section 6) into two regular quarter sections and two regular half-quarter sections. The remaining four fractional quarter-quarter sections—approximately, however typically less than, 40 acres each—are commonly called government lots. Along the north and west edges of Section 6 there are 7 government lots.

7. Subsections. Since most tracts of land are the subject of a description smaller than a full section, the land within a section must also be described. Thus, each section is divided into regular quarter sections of 160 acres each (Figure 6). In the Midwest, markers were originally established at the three outside corners of each quarter-section (no markers were placed in the centers of each section). Each quarter section thus established is described according to its geo-

graphical position as the Northeast, Southeast, Southwest, or Northwest Quarter.

Tracts smaller than a quarter section are described according to their fractional part and according to their location within the quarter section. For example, the square 40-acre tract in the southeast corner of the southwest quarter of Section 23 would be described as Southeast quarter of the Southwest quarter of Section 23, or in abbreviated form, the SE¼ of the SW¼ of Section 23 (Figure 7). The west half of the southwest quarter of the southwest quarter, containing 20 acres would be described as the W½ of the SW¼ of the SW¼ of Section 24.

Whenever an appraiser receives an appraisal assignment he should attempt to obtain a legal description of the subject property from his client. The property owner's rights—in other words, whether the property is held in a fee simple title or as a life estate, as a leasehold or as a

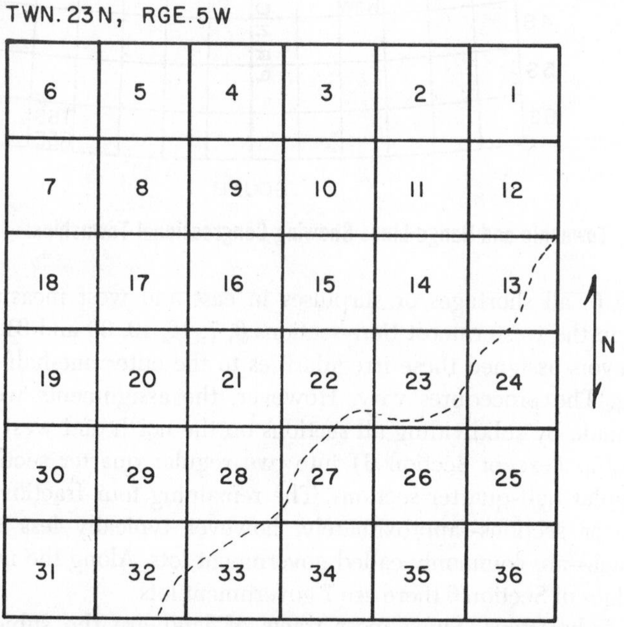

TWN. 23 N, RGE. 5 W

6	5	4	3	2	1
7	8	9	10	11	12
18	17	16	15	14	13
19	20	21	22	23	24
30	29	28	27	26	25
31	32	33	34	35	36

N

Figure 5. Township 23 North, Range 5 West, Showing the Numbering of the Various Sections of Land in a Congressional Township.

Unfortunately, legal descriptions vary both in form and in completeness. Title examination and land survey are both important parts of the ownership of real property.

mere easement—should be ascertained. Easements, right-of-ways, mineral rights, and all other exceptions, which may limit the use of the property, or which may grant certain uses to others, should be ascertained. If the client is not knowledgeable about such, then the appraiser may have to obtain these items by inspecting the deed, the abstract of title, or some other legal instrument directly related to the subject property.

The legal description which identifies a property should, of course, be verified by the appraiser by comparing it with the records available in one or more of the various county offices—the recorder's, the auditor's

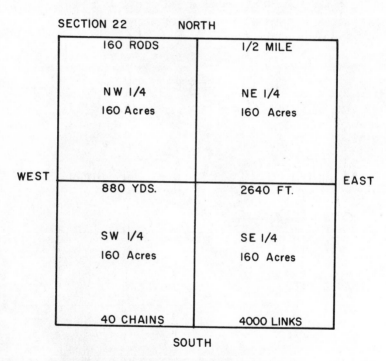

Figure 6. Section 22 Containing 640 Acres and Showing the Four Quarter Sections, Each Containing 160 Acres.

or the assessor's—and then with county ownership maps, and aerial photos. Such should also be verified on the farm as the property is inspected.

An appraiser is not concerned with whether the surveyor was right or wrong; he is concerned, however, with whether or not the farm is as represented. If a minor error is discovered, such probably will not affect the completion of the appraisal assignment. A note of explanation can be added to the appraisal. However, if a major error is discovered, the appraiser will usually want to consult with his client before proceeding further.

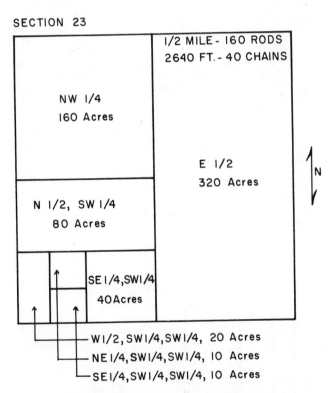

Figure 7. Section 23 Illustrating Several Divisions Within 640 Acres.

How to Read Land Descriptions Which Locate Tracts
of Land Using the Metes and Bounds Method

A metes and bounds description is one starting at a given point, running in a certain direction so many feet, then in another direction so many feet, etc., etc., back to the point of the beginning. To locate a tract of land, one needs to start from the point of the beginning and follow it step by step.

In a metes and bounds description the descriptions generally read from the north or south; however, sometimes they read from the east or west. For example, northwest is half-way between north and west; in terms of direction, northwest would read North 45 degrees West.

The following description describes a small tract. "All land located in the County of Tippecanoe, State of Indiana, Beginning at a point on the section line between Sections 23 and 24 in Township 23 North, Range 6 West, which is 594 feet North of the Southeast corner of said Section 23; thence North on said section line 223.8 feet; thence North 50°58' West 150.6 feet; thence North and parallel to the section line above mentioned a distance of 680.1 feet; then North 73°36' West 239.7 feet; thence, South 8°24' West 686.7 feet; then South 15°36' East 56 feet; thence South 52°02' East 78.8 feet; thence South 7° West 280.1 feet; thence East 342.5 feet to the place of beginning, containing 7.03 acres more or less." Book 276, page 210, **Book of Deeds,** Tippecanoe County Recorder's Office, State of Indiana.

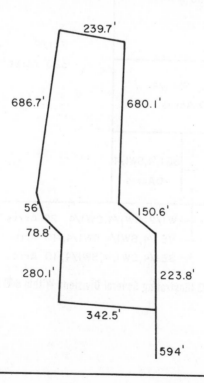

How to Read Land Descriptions Which Locate Tracts of Land Using the Rectangular Survey Method

Descriptions of land typically read from the north or the south first, such as NW, SE, etc. They are never WN, ES, etc.

With the rectangular survey system one determines a tract's location and ascertains its acreage by studying the legal descriptions backwards.

For example, a tract may be described as the E½ of the SW¼ of the SW¼ of Section 22. Reading backwards the last part of the description reads the SW¼ of Section 22. This means that the tract of land is located somewhere in the SW quarter of Section 22 which contains 160 acres. Proceeding backwards further one next finds the SW¼ again, which means the tract is located somewhere in the SW quarter of the SW quarter of Section 22 which contains 40 acres. Proceeding backwards again one next finds the W½ which means the tract is located only in the west half of that previously described and thus contains only 20 acres.

The following description describes a 100-acre tract.

"All land located in the County of Tippecanoe, State of Indiana, and in the Southeast ¼ of the Southwest ¼ of Section 27, plus the East half of the Southwest ¼ of the Southwest ¼ of Section 27, plus the Northeast ¼ of the Southwest ¼ of Section 27, Township 24, North, Range 5 West of the Second Principal Meridian and containing 100 acres more or less." Book 181, page 45, **Book of Deeds,** Tippecanoe County Recorder's Office, State of Indiana.

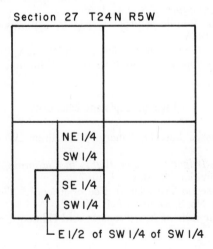

Section 27 T24N R5W

NE I/4
SW I/4

SE I/4
SW I/4

E I/2 of SW I/4 of SW I/4

REFERENCES

Real Estate Versus Property Versus Personalty

Beuscher, J. H., *Law and the Farmer*, Springer, 1953.

Church, Byron, "What's in the 'Bundle'?," *The Real Estate Appraiser*, Vol. 33, No. 8, August 1967.

Derbes, M. J., III, "The U. S. Land Tenure System: Origin and Development," *The Real Estate Appraiser*, Vol. 35, No. 5, July-August 1969.

Grange, W. J., and T. C. Woodbury, *Manual of Real Estate Law and Procedures*, 2nd Edition, Ronald Press, 1968.

Greenfeld, M. B., "Fixtures or Personal Property?," *Appraisal Journal*, Vol. 39, No. 2, April 1971.

MacChesney, N. W., *The Principles of Real Estate Law*, Macmillan, 1927.

Smith, C. H., *Survey of the Law of Property*, 2nd Edition, West Publishing Co., 1971.

Theiss, W. R., Editor, "Manner and Method of Determining Value of Fixtures," *Appraisal Journal*, Vol. 31, No. 1, January 1963.

Tiffany, H. T., *The Law of Real Property*, 3rd Edition, Callaghan, 1970.

The Rights of the Property Owner and the Sovereign

Ballin, F. A., Jr., "An Appraisal of Freedom," *The Real Estate Appraiser*, Vol. 34, No. 7, November-December 1968.

Clarenback, F. A., "The Use of Resources and Property Rights," *A Place to Live: 1963 Yearbook of Agriculture*, U.S.D.A., 1963.

Harris, Marshall, "How Our Rights in Land Came About," *Land: 1958 Yearbook of Agriculture*, U.S.D.A., 1958.

Smith, L. C., "The Bundle of Property Rights," *Appraisal Journal*, Vol. 24, No. 4, October 1956.

Unger, M. A., *Real Estate*, 2nd Edition, South-Western, 1959.

World Book Encyclopedia, Field Enterprises Education Corporation, Vol. 19, 1964.

Legal Concepts and Definitions

Black, H. C., *Black's Law Dictionary*, 4th Edition, West Publishing Co., 1968.

Hutchins, W. A., *Irrigation Water Rights in California*, California Experiment Station Circular 452, Revised, 1967.

Kibbey, G. S., "Second Trust Deed—Foe or Friend?," *The Real Estate Appraiser*, Vol. 30, No. 8, August 1964.

Tiffany, H. T., *The Law of Real Property*, 3rd Edition, Callaghan, 1970.

The Transfer of Property by Conveyance

Berston, H. M., *California Real Estate Practice*, Irwin, 1968.

Beuscher, J. H., *Law and the Farmer*, Springer, 1953.

Derbes, M. J., III, "The Consideration in Deed," *The Real Estate Appraiser*, Vol. 29, No. 3, March 1963.

Hannah, H. W., "Procedures Ordinarily Involved in Buying a Farm," *Journal of the American Society of Farm Managers and Rural Appraisers*, Vol. 11, No. 1, April 1947.

Kratovil, Robert, *Real Estate Law*, 5th Edition, Prentice-Hall, 1969.

Lusk, H. F., *Laws of the Real Estate Business*, Irwin, 1965.

Semenow, R. W., *Questions and Answers on Real Estate*, 6th Edition, Prentice-Hall, 1969.

Stewart, C. L., and S. W. Voelker, "The Mechanics of Land Transfer," *Land: 1958 Yearbook of Agriculture*, U.S.D.A., 1958.

Recording of the Evidence of Title

Grange, W. J., and T. C. Woodbury, *Manual of Real Estate Law and Procedures*, 2nd Edition, Ronald Press, 1968.

Hannah, H. W., *Law on the Farm*, Macmillan, 1950.

Semenow, R. W., *Questions and Answers on Real Estate*, 6th Edition, Prentice-Hall, 1969.

Legal Description

Clawson, Marion, *The Land System of the United States: an Introduction to the History and Practice of Land Use and Land Tenure*, University of Nebraska Press, 1968.

Elson, J. J., *Legal Descriptions of Illinois Real Estate*, University of Illinois, Agricultural Extension Service Circular 800, 1958.

Field, R. V., "Land Survey Systems of the United States," *Journal of the American Institute of Real Estate Appraisers*, Vol. 4, No. 4, October 1936.

Maley, L. W., "Legal Descriptions of Real Estate," *Appraisal Journal*, Vol. 22, No. 1, January 1954.

Murray, W. G., *Farm Appraisal and Valuation*, 5th Edition, Iowa State University, 1969.

Semenow, R. W., *Questions and Answers on Real Estate*, 6th Edition, Prentice-Hall, 1969.

Wall, N. F., "The Township Survey System of Land Identification," *The Real Estate Appraiser*, Vol. 31, No. 3, March 1965.

CHAPTER IV

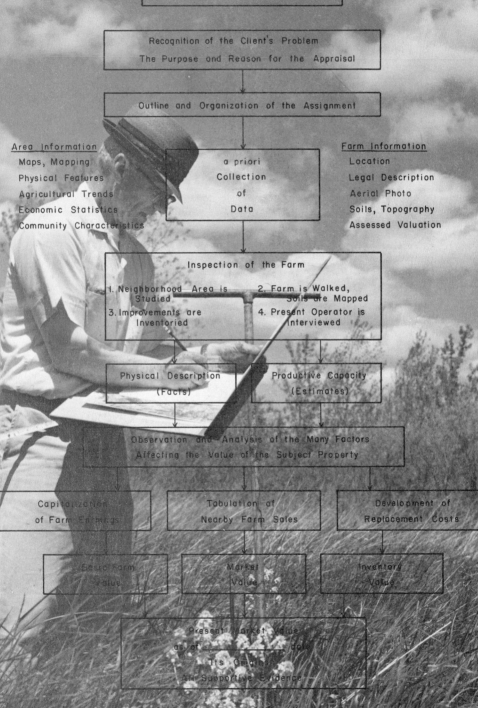

THE APPRAISAL PROCESS

Recognition of the Client's Problem
The Purpose and Reason for the Appraisal

Outline and Organization of the Assignment

Area Information
Maps, Mapping
Physical Features
Agricultural Trends
Economic Statistics
Community Characteristics

a priori
Collection
of
Data

Farm Information
Location
Legal Description
Aerial Photo
Soils, Topography
Assessed Valuation

Inspection of the Farm

1. Neighborhood Area is Studied
2. Farm is Walked, Soils are Mapped
3. Improvements are Inventoried
4. Present Operator is Interviewed

Physical Description (Facts)

Productive Capacity (Estimates)

Observation and Analysis of the Many Factors
Affecting the Value of the Subject Property

Capitalization of Farm Earnings

Tabulation of Nearby Farm Sales

Development of Replacement Costs

Basic Farm Value

Market Value

Inventory Value

Present Market Value
as of _____ date
Its Origin
All Supportive Evidence

Modus Operandi

The professional farm appraiser saves considerable time by developing and following a similar, if not the same, procedure each time he appraises a farm. Farms differ, of course, yet the appraisal process is the same. The job is a fairly specific one. It is to obtain the facts and to present them in a logical fashion so that any person, whether or not he has ever seen the farm, can read the appraisal report and visualize the property.

The job requires not just a knowledge of those things agricultural, not just economic judgment, but the ability to ascertain, to organize, to analyze, and to weigh the various factors affecting the value of the subject property. The professional appraiser thus develops not just certain technical tools but an analytical ability which, when skilled, allows him to proceed in an effective and efficient fashion. Needless to say, many appraisers never fully achieve this skill or expertise. However, most appraisers attempt to do so by performing, in order, each of the following tasks:

1. The client's problem is defined; the purpose of and reason for the appraisal are specified.
2. The work is outlined and organized.
3. The required *a priori* data are collected.
4. The subject farm or property is visited and inspected.
5. The property's physical resources are described.
6. The farm's productive capacity is estimated.
7. The methods used to find value are developed:
   a. Income is capitalized.
   b. Nearby sales are tabulated.
   c. All resources are inventoried.

The appraiser's job is (1) to prepare a physical description of the property, (2) to estimate the farm's productive capacity, and (3) to present his opinion as to the value of that subject property, along with all supported evidence and whatever line of reasoning he followed in arriving at that value.

Courtesy, U.S.D.A.

8. The various origins of value are ascertained.

9. The farm's present market value is finalized.

10. All supportive evidence is presented.

Organization is the key to the appraisal process. Providing one is organized, only one visit to the farm needs to be made. Enroute to the farm many details should be checked and recorded. While making the farm inspection, much of the appraisal report can be written.

THE APPRAISER'S JOB

For a number of years, Professor Stanley W. Warren at Cornell University best described the appraiser's job as consisting of three parts. First, the professional appraiser prepares a physical description of the farm. Second, he estimates the productive capacity of the property. Third, he presents his opinion as to the value of the subject farm or property, along with all available supportive evidence and whatever line of reasoning he followed in arriving at that value.

The Farm's Physical Description: The appraiser's first job is to describe the subject property. This physical description is based largely on facts. The following items are usually included.

1. The legal description of the farm:—its location and acreage.

2. A brief history of the farm:—previous owner or owners, sale dates, and amounts of money that changed hands; the present owner and/or operator, his tenure, length of ownership and/or rental arrangement; and such items as to whether the farm is in the process of being sold.

3. Location:—distance to the nearest shopping center, village, or community; kinds of roads, their general condition, accessibility, and amount of travel; schools, churches, recreational facilities; electricity, telephone, and other utilities.

4. The predominant types of farming in the area:—quality of farms, kinds of neighbors, tenure patterns, opportunities for off-farm employment, and the possibility of such things as residential development.

5. The suppliers of the more important farm resources:—financial institutions, local building and equipment dealers—and the markets for the more important farm products—grain elevators, milk plants, cotton gins, livestock yards, etc.

6. Climate:—the nearest weather station, its location and elevation; the rainfall, both the average annual amount, the amount ob-

tained during the growing season, and its distribution; the first and last dates relative to a killing frost; the length of the growing season (number of days); the possibility and frequency of drought, hail and other storms, flooding, etc.

7. The elevation at the farmstead.

8. Major soil types:—acreage of each in cropland and in pasture; parent material; texture; drainage, both surface and internal; productivity ratings, and native vegetation.

9. Topography:—the general lay of land; extent to which such is level, rolling, or hilly; the influence of such on the cropping practices, the tillage operations, travel to and from the farmstead, and items such as air drainage, etc.

10. Surface ditches, tile drains, and irrigation facilities:—location, condition, size, and adequacy.

11. Farm layout:—location of the farmstead, field arrangement, field shapes and sizes, travel routes, obstructions in various fields, and all other important land features.

12. Existence of growing crops, timber, gravel, oil, and minerals; right-of-ways, pipe lines, power lines, other easements, or leases.

13. Farmstead:—general appearance, ease of travel, convenience in terms of feed and manure handling; livestock management and efficiency.

14. Availability of water:—location of wells and windmills, their depth, and the extent to which the present water supply is adequate.

15. All houses:—present use, number of rooms, square feet; approximate age; general condition and appearance; foundation, siding, roof; general arrangement inside, basement, bathrooms, heating system, and other features; present-day replacement cost, depreciation, a structural value perhaps, and both contributory and insured values.

16. All barns, other buildings and improvements:—present use; dimensions, square feet; approximate age; general condition and appearance, foundation, siding, roof; general arrangement inside, floor, built-in equipment, other facilities; availability of water; flexibility or potential for other uses; present-day replacement cost, depreciation, again a structural value perhaps, and both contributory and insured values.

Most appraisers use a series of scale drawings—plats or maps to show various items. The location of the farm, along with the location of all nearby and recent farm sales, can be shown on a map of the area. All important land features can be shown on an outline map of the farm. Additional maps are often used to show soils, topography or slope, erosion, other detriments and hazards, drainage, fertility levels, and the present land use or crops being raised.[1]

A specific statement or two may also be made describing each of the more important physical features. However, many items—for example, soil characteristics and building descriptions—can be presented more quickly and more efficiently in tabular fashion.

Dollar values are sometimes used, even in the physical description, when they clarify or make the description more meaningful. For example, farm buildings are often described in terms of their present-day replacement costs, depreciation to date, a structural value based on present-day replacement cost less physical depreciation, and both contributory and insured values.

The structural values largely indicate whether each building is relatively old, pretty much worn out, and poor in physical condition and appearance, or whether it is fairly new and in good physical condition and appearance. Structural value is not the same as contributory or insured values. Contributory values indicate the extent to which the various buildings contribute to the market value of the farm. Insured values indicate the extent to which the buildings are needed or are being used in the farming operations, along with the probability of their being rebuilt or built back in case of fire, windstorm or other peril. Contributory values represent value in exchange. Insured values represent value-in-use or utility value.

In appraising every property, the appraiser has to decide how much time he can spend in making his inspection and how many details he should include in his report. One can never describe everything. Sooner or later the appraiser has to decide what's important and what isn't and then quit. One may inspect many items; yet the appraiser typically includes in his report only those items which are major and which thus affect value. Sometimes he includes a unique item or two that particularly stands out—an item which his client or some other person may purposefully check on later in order to ascertain if he did a thorough job.

---

1. To a certain extent, detriments and hazards are present on practically all farm properties. The appraiser may not refer to these per se, yet he may see such during the farm inspection and include such in his report. He should know the difference. A detriment is that which continuously or permanently injures or reduces the value of the subject property. It is reflected in lower yields and earnings and hence in a lower value. A hazard is that which causes loss or damage to a property or its products, recurring at irregular intervals, yet with sufficient intensity to destroy a portion of value. Detriments exist now; hazards may occur later.

The Farm's Productive Capacity: The appraiser's second job is to estimate the productive capacity of the farm. This is based largely on one's estimates relative to:

1. The type of owner or operator who may someday buy, own, or operate the farm.

2. The kinds of crops and livestock that will probably be raised, along with the most likely acreages and numbers of each.

3. The typical crop yields per acre, along with the typical rates of livestock production.

4. Estimates regarding farm receipts, farm expenses, and the residual returns to the subject property or to the owner.

In estimating the productive capacity of a farm the appraiser uses the typical operator concept. He decides what kind of a farm it is, who is most likely to be the owner, and what the typical operator is most likely to do on the unit. The typical owner may be (1) an owner-operator, (2) an absentee-owner with a tenant, or (3) a residential or part-time farmer.

If the typical owner is likely to be an owner-operator, the productive capacity of the farm will probably be based on (1) a fairly careful land use program (not necessarily intensive) and an above average level of fertilization, (2) a livestock enterprise or two and fairly large livestock numbers, and (3) substantial buildings and improvements—ones that are in good physical condition. The appraiser will, in general, find more value in the non-monetary origins of value, such as the home, and the more intangible items. The typical owner-operator is likely to have considerable pride of ownership.

If the typical owner is likely to be an absentee-owner or investor, then the appraiser will base parts of his appraisal on the typical landlord-tenant arrangements in the area.[2] The productive capacity of the farm will be based on the typical tenant-operator. Usually, although not always, it will be based on (1) somewhat lower fertilization levels and somewhat lower crop yields, (2) fewer livestock numbers (maybe none, but varying with the facilities), and (3) fewer improvements. The appraiser will, in general, find more value in the land resources and less value in the improvements. Usually there is less value in the home and in the non-monetary items.

If the farm is small, largely untillable, and located close to an off-farm source of employment, the typical owner is likely to be a part-

---

2. For a discussion of typical leasing arrangements see Chapter V on "Agricultural Trends."

time or residential farmer. In this case the farm appraiser may ignore the farm's productive capacity and spend most of his time estimating the value of the subject property as a residential unit. He will spend more of his time evaluating the home, the sources of satisfaction obtained from living in the country, and the trends in the community or area including the subject property's growth potential from the standpoint of development in the future.

Estimates of productive capacity are most important, of course, in the appraisal of commercial farm properties. These estimates generally include the following:

1. The typical or most likely acreage of various crops which will be raised on the farm in the future.

2. The typical per-acre yields that can be expected, and hence total crop production (acres of each crop times per-acre yields).

3. The typical numbers of livestock most likely to be kept, along with the typical rates of livestock production, and hence total livestock production.

4. The typical dollar receipts (under certain price assumptions), the dollar expenses, and the farm income that can be expected.

5. The typical costs of management, the cost of using certain amounts of non-real estate capital, and the residual return to the land, buildings, and improvements. This latter may be developed using the typical budget for a farm owned by an owner-operator, or using a standard landlord-tenant lease and the typical budget for a farm owned by an absentee-owner or investor.

The present cropping system and crop yields, along with the present livestock numbers and rates of livestock production, should be obtained from the present operator. These data may also be presented in one's appraisal report even though the present operator may or may not be the most likely owner or typical operator for the subject farm property. By including such, the appraiser challenges himself to analyze the differences between the present operator and whomever will most likely own or operate the farm in the future. He may present these differences in his report.

The Final Value Figure: ". . . An appraisal is an opinion . . . ," "It may or may not be accurate . . . ," "Its accuracy depends on many factors . . . ," "It is my observation . . . ," "Based on my experience . . . " These and many other statements have been made by appraisers without thinking. They are an insult to the appraisal profession.

The professional farm appraiser does *not* just state his opinion. He studies the area, walks the farm, looks at the soils, inventories the improvements, assembles all relevant data, and then, based on a fairly objective analysis of the many factors affecting value, develops a final value figure. The professional appraiser presents the subject farm's present market value, along with considerable supportive evidence indicating the origins of value, and the logic or line of reasoning he followed in ascertaining that value.

The professional appraiser thus develops sufficient detail in his appraisal report so that any intelligent person who takes the time required to read such can agree or disagree with the conclusions reached on the basis of the information which has been presented.

THE TYPICAL OPERATOR CONCEPT

Basic to all farm appraisals is the typical operator concept. The word "typical" refers to those characteristics which will most frequently occur or most likely exist in the future in the situation under consideration. The typical operator is the most likely person who will own or operate the farm, assuming the ownership of such is sold or transferred today. The typical operator is not necessarily the present owner or operator.

The typical operator concept is used for purposes of eliminating the influence of management in one's appraisal. It is used to separate the farm from the farmer. Sooner or later all appraisers master its application. For the best prediction, always, is that the farm in question—the subject property—will sell to the "most likely" buyer or owner and then be farmed by the "typical" operator. In other words, the farm's present market value is determined not by one person but by all prospective buyers and sellers who might have an interest in similar farm properties. Its value is not determined by the appraiser. The appraiser instead ascertains what the subject property's value is most likely to be if such were to be placed on the market.

Should the subject property be sold, there is little likelihood that a new owner will continue to use the property in the same fashion as did the previous owner. There is little likelihood that he will continue to use all of the same farm practices. Hence, the farm's value is based not on what the farm is producing under the present operator, but on what will most likely be done on the farm in the future.

On most farms the typical operator does not follow all of the practices recently recommended by persons newly-graduated from the college of agriculture. He does not always use the more up-to-date farm practices. Oftentimes he has some idle cropland. The stall barn, the farrowing house, and the feedlot may not be filled to capacity (many times this is not the farmer's fault). Typically some farm work is done late. The typical operator pays for his farm on the basis of what he thinks or expects he can accomplish, using not the present, the best, or the most recent technologies, but instead the methods he hopes or thinks will work for him.

The farmer or rancher with above-average management may, of course, be financially able to outbid his less capable competitors and pay more for a farm than they can. Yet, there is little or no reason for him to do so, primarily because he does not have to. The above-average farmer buys his farm (and generally speaking, all other resources) at the going market price. This is precisely why the above-average farmer or rancher makes more money than does the average farmer. He buys his farm at the going market price and then farms it better than his neighbors. Any extra income he makes tends to accrue to him rather than to the farm.[3] Thus a farm in the hands of a good operator is worth no more in the marketplace than if it were in the hands of a poor operator.

In a farm appraisal the typical operator concept is used to establish the subject property's farm organization and to estimate its productive capacity—the most likely cropping system and the most likely livestock enterprises. Unfortunately, there is a tendency to overestimate productivity levels. This is especially likely on farms with below-average land resources.

The various types and kinds of farms and their characteristics differ greatly. So do typical operators. The typical operator for "this farm" practically always differs from the typical operator for "that farm over there." This bothers many appraisers. This does not mean that there is wide variation in the typical operator concept. No indeed. The technique is the same from farm to farm.

In areas where the farms are mostly owner-operated and when the subject farm has above-average improvements, productivity estimates for the subject farm will be based on the typical owner-operator. In areas where the farms are mostly absentee owned and tenant-operated and when the subject farm "looks like" a rental unit, the productivity estimates for the subject farm will be based on the typical tenant-operator. The two operators are seldom if ever the same.[4] The dif-

---

3. The above-average farm operator may even bargain more effectively than the average operator, hence purchasing a good many resources at a discount.

ferences become greater as the newer technologies and non-real estate capital resources are increased, as more livestock are added to the acreage of crops raised, and as buildings and improvements are added to the land. Bare or unimproved land is fairly easy to appraise. Almost any appraiser can do so. However, when confinement livestock setups or feedlots, which depend only in part on the land or cropping base that goes with it, are added, the appraiser's job becomes more difficult.

Lastly, typical is not an arithmetic mean. It is instead a modal statistic—that which most frequently occurs. The typical operator is neither the best nor the worst farmer in the community. Excluding the very outstanding and the real failure he is almost any farmer. Hence, the concept is a challenging one, requiring the best from an appraiser.

GETTING ACQUAINTED WITH A NEW AREA

When a person lives for many years in one area he accumulates considerable knowledge concerning the farms in the area and oftentimes without making any real organized effort to do so. Farm appraisers and farm brokers both acquire such knowledge through observation and experience. As long as they stay in their local area they do a fairly good job of appraising farms.

However, every now and then an experienced appraiser is asked to appraise a group of farms in an area with which he is not acquainted. When this happens he does not have the time to acquire the knowledge he needs through experience alone. He now has to get acquainted in a straightforward and more efficient fashion.

Appraisal Technique: When an appraiser from some distance away is hired to appraise a local farm, the neighbors often laugh. They say, "What does he know about farms or land values in this area?" The truth is that he may soon know more about the farms and the values in their area than they do. The reason is that the professional appraiser who hasn't lived in a particular area all his life knows how to do the job. He knows how to get acquainted with the area. He knows the persons or parties he needs to visit with. He knows what questions to ask, and he often does all of this fairly rapidly.

The following techniques are ones an appraiser might well use in

---

4. Furthermore, the typical operator on a farm with a crop-share lease is seldom if ever the same as the typical operator on a farm with a crop and livestock-share lease.

order to get acquainted with a new area.[5]

1. Become well acquainted with the appraisal process— how one goes about (a) collecting information, (b) inspecting a farm, (c) analyzing data, and (d) ascertaining the origins of value.

2. Develop and keep an appraisal handbook of all the materials which are needed in the making of farm appraisals and in the writing of appraisal reports. Such a handbook typically includes the physical features of the area, current agricultural trends, certain economic statistics, the characteristics of the community, and other miscellaneous information. If properly organized such can be kept up-to-date fairly easily, and all of the various facts and figures can be referred to quite readily.

3. Collect and study all of the available maps of the area— county highway maps, plat books or maps showing land ownership, aerial photos, geological survey maps, soil maps, etc. Much of the information pertaining to an area can be recorded directly on a map. Thus, one can study the figures and at the same time become acquainted with the area's characteristics.

4. Visit several of the various persons who live in the area— particularly those persons who are acquainted with the agricultural community, persons who sell farms and/or make farm loans, persons who sell farm supplies and/or buy farm products, and, along with them, some of the top commercial farmers who are acquainted with the cultural practices being used and technological changes that are occurring.

5. Visit the county registrar of deeds, or the recorder's office and assemble all recent data pertaining to farm sales. Tabulate these data by areas—either congressional or civil townships. In doing so note any and all extenuating circumstances—deed restrictions, easements, family transfers, contract sales, sales subject to a mortgage, finance terms, sales including personal property, and, those which in some areas, may include the landlord's share of the crop.

6. Drive through and inspect the area observing the more recent farm sales. Stop and visit the new owners. Verify each sale relative to sale date, farm size, tillable acreage, extent to which the property was improved at the time of sale, the reasons for selling, the reasons for buying, and the sale price. Make and keep a record of the date of the visit, the person talked with, and any comments that were made.

---

5. This again is the approach used by Dr. Stanley W. Warren, Professor Emeritus, Farm Management and Farm Appraisal, at Cornell University.

Getting Acquainted with a New Area

**Persons Acquainted with the
Agricultural Community**

1. County Agricultural Agents or Farm Advisers
2. Vocational Agricultural Teachers
3. Soil Conservationists
4. Agricultural Stabilization and Conservation Service Employees
5. Area Planning Managers, Zoning Officials, Building Inspectors

**Persons Who Buy and Sell
Farm Supplies and Products**

1. Building Contractors and Farm Equipment Dealers
2. Farm Cooperative, Sales, and Service Representatives
3. Elevator, Milk Plant, and Livestock Market Operators

**Persons Who Sell Farms,
or Make Farm Loans**

1. Farm Real Estate Brokers and Salesmen
2. Federal Land Bank Loan Officers
3. Fieldmen for the Insurance Companies
4. Production Credit Loan Officers
5. Ag. Representatives for the Local Banks

Farm Managers and Others

1. Professional Farm Managers
2. Farm Operators, and Ranchers
3. County Assessors and Township Trustees

Generally there is little or no problem in visiting with a new farm owner. He often has some pride of ownership. He's usually glad the appraiser is sufficiently interested to stop and visit. He's usually willing to show an interested party what he bought, what improvements he has made, and what his plans are for the future. However, occasionally other appraisers have already stopped, and, with increased government intervention in agriculture, farmers are becoming more and more reluctant to discuss their business. All appraisers should have a course in psychology. For the approach, the interest shown, the questions asked, and how they are asked are most important in achieving results.

7. Classify the farm properties that have sold into various meaningful categories. Some appraisers refer to this as a market analysis. Farms may be classified as to:

a. Kind of farm organization—commercial, part-time, residential, or subsistence.

b. Type of farm—cash grain, dairy, hog, beef cow herd, feeder cattle, general livestock, etc.

c. Location—miles from town, type of road, predominant soils, or land use.

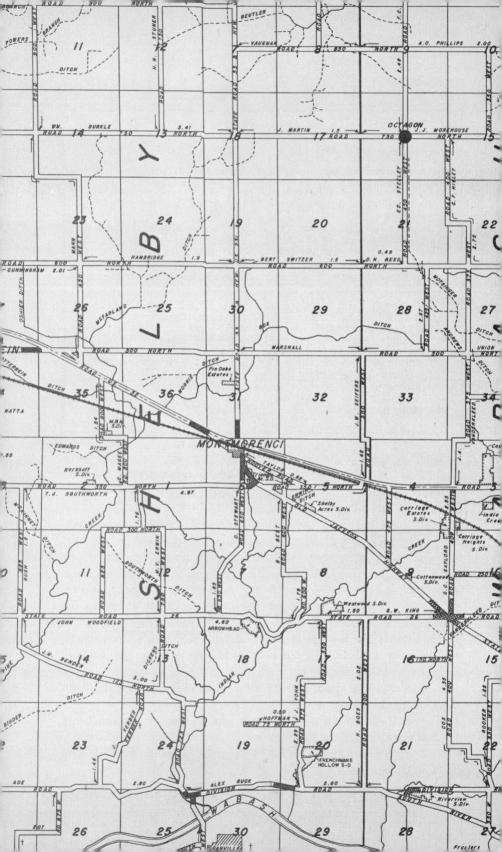

d. Farm size—total acres, acres of cropland, acres of corn, acres of a specialty crop, number of cows, number of sows, number of feeder cattle, etc.

e. Farm productivity—percent of tillable land, per-acre yields, etc.

f. Extent of improvements—home value, farm buildings, other permanent improvements.

The appraiser's real purpose, of course, is to ascertain the kinds of farm properties with which he will be concerned in the future. Only bona fide sales or arm's length transactions between seller and buyer should be tabulated. Furthermore, the modal or median sale price in each of the above categories is often more meaningful than the average sale price. The use of a mode or median tends to eliminate distortions due to extreme values.

8. Think about and evaluate the various origins of farm value that exist in the area and the various methods which may be used to establish these farm values.

9. Make an appraisal or two or three and check these with several of the better-informed, if not more experienced, local farmers or farm businessmen.

10. Make sure—doubly sure—the present market values reflect all of the origins of value and are in line with the various prices at which the ownership of farm real estate is being transferred.

Maps and Mapping: Very few persons are aware of the various maps and photos that are available or know how much information can be gleaned from them. The professional appraiser has a real advantage here in that he has usually learned to read and to study the many different types of maps and photos. The following are generally available.

1. County highway maps showing the main highways, both state and local, county roads, and approximate farmstead locations. On many of these, township and range numbers are given along the edges of the map, and section numbers can usually be determined.

2. County plat books showing the various tracts of land and land ownership. These usually show the shape of each tract, the name(s) of the current landowner(s), and the acreages.

County highway maps and plat books are both published upon

A county highway map showing state highways, county roads, and some of the natural drainage. Shelby Township, Tippecanoe County, Indiana.

GILBOA

Joseph & Marie Nelson 162.44 — 2

John F. Shea et al 169.33

Ella Stitz 30 — 1
Ella Stitz 2
E.S. Bressner 140

Chester B Biddle 160

Chas J. Biddle 154.35 — 6

Bertha Peters 80

Henry Koelliker 120

Balcom 200

Burling 240 — 5

Vinal & Lorraine Nichols 126.66 — 4

Joh Z...

Elizabeth Getz 90.76

B.L. Venable Inez Myers 160

Ethel & Elenor Elliott 160

Henry A. Gilkerson 160

Chester B. Biddle et. al. 80
Chester Biddle 80

Sam Kilgus 154

Arthur & Achsa C. Nussbaum 160

Earl J. & Eva Barling 241.50

A.N. Scheller 78.50

Elizabeth Getz 215

Sarah & Hazel Burling 105

B.A. Roth 40
Katie Roth 40

Diedrich & Anna Ubbinga 160 — 12

Geo. Weiss 160

Mary A. Blake 160

Robt. & Gertrude Girtz 154.7 — 7

Herman & Emma L. Beckley 398 — 8

Geo. W. & Anna 320 — 9

Ethel Elliott 80 — 11

Eva & Henry Dauphinee
Diedrich & Mine Ubbinga Co.

Annie L. Eilhard Fielcamp 180 — 14

Caroline Waibel 160

Theo. H. West 160

Arols & Mabel Cornwell 77.23
Theodore West 154.6 — 13

Thos. M. & Paul T. O'Connor 80
Herman & Emma Beckley 80

Geo. Weiss 160

Ruben & Louise Scherlach 160

Jas. & Catherine Irwin 80

Pearl A. Crow 120

Vincent Bryan 80

Joseph Schneider 235

Eli & Anna Schwamburger 160 — 18

Fern & Ethel Lough 120 — 17

Darrell S. Pampel
Mabel Pampel 240

Furman & Dorothy Pampel 40

Wm. S. Isham 80
E. & D. Faker 140

Jas. & Jos

Lydia Widmer

G I L B O A

Wm. S. Isham 100
W.C. Ferry 100

A. Roth 40
Ethel Elliott

Edmund & Doris Faker 161.98

Lester Pampel 140

Robt. & Mabel Pampel 80
Wilbur & Edna Roberts 80 — 19

Keith & Helen Butcher 77.24
Dora & Arthur Sparks 151.24

Edgar P. Basch 160

Edgar D. Basch 120

Pearl Pampel 80

Esther Widmer 80

Hazel Widmer 80

A.R. Paul

Amelia Anderson & Vivian Jelvert 120 — 23

Jacob & Amelie Peterson 120

Edward J. Wealing 100 — 24

Glenn Kinsell 200

Glenn Kinsell 80

Jas. O. & Minnie Hoagland 160

Daisy Ott Wall 200 — 20
40

Geo. F. Sweeney 160 — 21

Go

Dora & Arthur Sparks 80

Reason & Frances Biddle 76

Frank & Mary Lambert 180

Edward J. Wealing 319.50

Blanche & L. Baumgardt 154.54

Otis & Cora Stansfield
Blanche Louis Baumgardt 80

Jas. O. & Minnie Hoagland 160

Gertrude Biddle

Reason & Francis Biddle 80
159.9

Chester B. & Chas. Biddle 120 — 28

Earnest Merle Stillabower 240 — 26

Charles & Lorna Rass 160

Perry Montgomery 160

T. Montgomery Mary McIntyre
M.H. & Gertrldine Stanfield 100 — 25

Chester B. Biddle 152.04

Daisy B. Timmons 82.5 — 30
Robt. & Gertrude Girtz

Roscoe & Leona Elle

Clara E. Cresap 160 — 29

Myra H. Sheets L. Est.

Walter S. Wil

A. & F. Gardner 20
A. Anderson V. Jelfert 90

Marion Griffith 40

B.W. & L.A. Pratt 160

Loyd S. Atkinson 280

Roy E. & Alta B. Atkinson 120

Roy E. & Alta B. Atkinson 154.80

Fern & Louis R. Forry 80

Clara E. Cresap 80

Fred & Helen Dunker 160

Myra H. Sheets Life Est. 80

David & Lulu Phelps 220 — 33

Per G.

Lucille Pratt Johnson 120

Wm. Flemming 160 — 35
Joyce V. Eastburn

Claude Atkinson 199.14 — 36

Howard C. Washburn 399.64 — 31

Saylor & Leona Lamie 32.0 — 32

200

Ival F. Garri...

Joyce V. Eastburn 104.36

Bessie Hackley 310.11

Richard Mundy 200

Oral P. Kinsell 313.77 — 6

Stephen F. & N.A. Douglas 70.60
Charles Johnston

Stephen & M. Douglas 152.78

Alexander & M. Pirie 152.38 — 5

Julia C. B... 227.2

Vivian B. Pape 374.95 — 2

Richard Mundy 72.87

Leonard T. & Clara Moynihan 106.6

John J. & Edna Douglas 120

A. Pirie 40

Alexander Pirie 176 — 4

Florence Rae Hollingsworth 160

Warren 120

A. & Alma E. McCollough

Martha L.S. Smith et. al.

Charles
H. Ball 80

Dee

F.R. Hollingsworth 80

Mary Ellen Lehti 400 — 11

Stanley & N. York 80

Stanly & Nora E. York 200 — 12

William A. Fleming 305.16 — 7

Clara & Mary Bergen 120

Luita Curtis Churchman 320 — 8

M. Smith et al.

Charles H. Ball 79

Charles H. Ball 80

Dean M...

Vivian B. Pape 80

Vivian B. Pape 240

Agnes Nelson et. al. 80

Opal Nelson et al. 172.50

Warren & Jo Unger 160

Luita Curtis Churchman 80

Elijah G. & Ona McAshlan 60

E. & O. McAshlan 60

Harry & David Hall — 9

occasion by local banks and businesses who use them for advertising purposes. The county agricultural agent or farm adviser usually has a supply. However, they do get out-of-date. When this occurs the county surveyor, the county road commissioner, or the manager of the area planning office usually has a map that is up-to-date. Usually these can be borrowed or copied.

3. Aerial photos taken every few years by the Federal government are available from many federal, state and local agencies as well as from commercial firms. The County Agricultural Stabilization and Conservation Service Office has a county photo (or key) showing the flight pattern, date, and time each photo was taken. These serve as an index for ordering the aerial photos of a particular farm. Most county A.S.C.S. offices make these photos available to appraisers and others. Or, they can be ordered from the Eastern or Western Photo Laboratories. The forest service, soil conservation service, and local area planning offices also have aerial photos. (See Appendix for sources of information, maps, and other services.)

4. United States geological survey maps are topographic maps showing the physiographic features of an area. They are most helpful in identifying the more important land features. They show both the horizontal and the vertical positions of the various physical features of land on a flat plane and at a definite scale. The maps are usually printed in four colors, with the relief features—hills, mountains and valleys—in brown (shown by contour lines), the water and drainage features in blue, the permanent vegetation—woods and forests—in green or other colors, and the cultural features—roads, railroads, cities and towns, and buildings—in black. Excellent detail is available not only with regard to agricultural areas but metropolitan centers as well. These maps can be ordered from the state conservation departments, or from either the Washington, D. C., or Denver distribution section.

5. Soil survey maps are published by various agricultural experiment stations of the land-grant universities as well as by the soil conservation services. An excellent soils map for the United States appears in the back of *Soils and Men: The 1938 Yearbook of Agriculture* published by the United States Department of Agriculture.

A land ownership map showing the various tracts of land owned by various parties, approximate shapes, names of current owners and acreages. Gilboa Township, Benton County, Indiana.

Various state and county soil surveys are usually obtainable from the soils or agronomy departments in the various agricultural colleges, and county surveys can usually be obtained from the county agricultural agents or farm advisers.

These soils publications often contain a tremendous amount of information pertaining to the history and development of the various soils in an area, the major soil classifications, topography, drainage, soil productivities, climate, vegetation, land use, sometimes census data relative to the types and sizes of farms in the area, as well as soil mapping technique. The soil survey is most useful to farm appraisers.

Furthermore, the local soil conservation service office usually has soil conservation plans on some of the local farms. When available, an appraiser can usually photograph or copy the soils or land use capabilities map for the subject property. This saves considerable time. It also provides an appraiser with a means of checking on his own ability to identify and classify the soils in the area.[6]

6. In those cities or counties where area planning has been approved, city and county base maps and other information can be obtained from the area planning agency. These maps are particularly useful in the transition areas where residential, commercial, and industrial development is occurring around a metropolitan center.

7. Maps of many areas can be obtained from the local chambers of commerce and tourists' bureaus. These maps are often accompanied by some of the local history, the community's characteristics, and other cultural developments. All of this is very useful to an appraiser, particularly one just getting acquainted in a new area and even though his appraisals are concerned primarily with farm properties.

CLIENT RELATIONSHIPS

Many persons—prospective clients and others—have little or no knowledge of what an appraiser does, the materials he has available,

---

6. Furthermore, whenever a soil classification problem arises, there is an expert in the soil conservation office to provide assistance.

An aerial photo of a 400-acre farm located 4.0 miles west and 1.0 miles north of Romney, Tippecanoe County, Indiana, 1963.

or how he goes about appraising a farm. Hence, in his first contact with a prospective client an appraiser plays the role of a salesman as well as that of an appraiser.

His job is to sell the prospective client on a thorough appraisal of the subject property rather than a one- or two-page opinion. The appraiser must act as interested as possible in the prospective client's problem. He should ask a number of questions about it. And in the process he should impress his prospective client not with just his knowledge of the appraisal process, but with the need for the more thorough and objective approach to the appraisal of farm real estate today.

Rudyard Kipling's six honest serving men—their names, "What, and Where, and When" and "How, and Why, and Who"—serve very well in asking questions.[7] In the process, the appraiser attempts to obtain each of the following:

1. A basic understanding of the problem.

2. An identification of the property and a copy of the legal description.

3. The property owner's rights along with any property or property owner rights belonging to others.

4. The reason for or use to be made of the appraisal.

5. The value or values to be ascertained.

6. Lastly, the appraiser and his client should agree on the date of the appraisal, the approximate date the property will be inspected, and the date the report is to be delivered.

In the process of obtaining each of the above, the appraiser may briefly describe the appraisal process and what he does in appraising a farm. He may comment on the materials he has available, how he approached a similar problem in the past, and on the detail required to do a thorough job.

However, before proceeding further, an appraiser should obtain a firm commitment from his client, preferably a contract or agreement in writing. The easiest approach is to obtain an oral understanding and then send the client a letter of acknowledgement which outlines the purpose of and reason for the appraisal, the work that will be in-

---

7. p. 5, *Stories and Poems by Kipling.*

A geological survey map with a contour interval of 10 feet. Yeoman Quadrangle in the North-west part of Carroll County, Indiana, 1962.

volved, when such will be done, and the appraisal fee (either firm or within a given range). Two copies should be sent to the client—one for his files, and one to be returned to the appraiser with the client's approval so indicated by his signature. This letter of memorandum thus indicates that the client and the appraiser are in agreement as to the problem to be analyzed and the work to be done.

FIELD PROCEDURE

Most appraisers go about each appraisal in the same fashion; they do each job in approximately the same order. They may use an appraisal form prescribed by their company or client, or one they have developed themselves, or they may have a preliminary outline on which they record certain data or information as such is obtained. This form or outline is often organized in the same fashion as is the final appraisal report.

When the contract or agreement is signed the appraiser can then schedule or plan the appraisal. Hopefully several days exist between the date the assignment is received or acknowledged and the date the farm is to be inspected. This allows time to collect certain data without going out of one's way or making a special trip.

Prior Preparation: One can save considerable time by a little advanced planning. First, the appraisal assignment should be studied. Much of the basic information can be assembled beforehand. In fact, the following jobs should perhaps be performed before one makes any effort to inspect the area or the subject property.

1. The client's name, purpose of and reason for the appraisal, location of the farm, and its legal description can be recorded.

2. A map of the area can be obtained and studied, and all nearby and recent farm sales located.

3. An aerial photo can be acquired and several outline maps, which will be used eventually to show all important land features, can be drawn (to scale).

4. The soil map, topographic map, and any other map of the area can be pulled from the files; the soils and all physiographic characteristics for the farm can be studied.

5. Information on land use, climate, types of farming, leasing arrangements, and the characteristics of the community can be assembled. Any and all data pertinent to the farm itself—assessed valuation, property taxes, conservancy or irrigation district assessments, acreage allotments, zoning regulations, etc.—can be acquired.

In going to the field some or all of the following will be useful.

County highway map
Maps showing zoning
    and comprehensive
    plans
County plat book show-
    ing land ownership

Aerial photo
Topographic map
    (U.S.G.S.)

Clipboard (soils series
    may be glued on the
    back)
Tracing paper
See-through ruler and
    acreage template

Copy of appraisal report
    or outline

Soil auger or tube
Hand level
Altimeter and compass

Relief scale
Measuring wheel and steel
    tape (50 or 100 feet)
Tile probe
8-foot pole
6-foot ruler

Camera, lens
Flash equipment
Film
Photo schedule

Driving to the Farm: In driving to the farm one should drive and inspect the most frequently used road. However, before stopping, one should drive around the subject property and observe all other roads, along with the general setting. An accurate portrayal of the agricultural community and an accurate analysis of farms that are comparable to the subject farm is a very important part of any appraisal.

The neighborhood area surrounding the farm should be inspected. The appraiser should drive by and review the more recent farm sales, stopping to verify them if he hasn't already done so. Such may require as much time as the inspection of the subject property, particularly if one is unfamiliar with the area. And, even when one thinks he is familiar with the area, he should never fail to make this neighborhood inspection.

Inspecting the Land: A systematic approach to the inspection of the farm itself is also highly desirable. Most appraisers first like to walk the farm and study the land, then inventory the buildings and improvements, and then and only then, visit with the present operator and perhaps several of the neighbors.

Many appraisers walk the entire farm, unless, of course, the subject property is an extremely large acreage of low value land. An aerial photo and topographic map are often used as guides. A base map with some tracing paper may be used to check and record the present farm layout along with all important land features.

Four farm maps showing all important land features (including soil types) and illustrating the wide variations in farm layout.

Four farm maps showing all important land features (including soil types) and illustrating the wide variations in farm layout.

Important Land Features

Roads	Tile drains
Fields	Irrigation installations
Fences	Soil types
Streams, ditches	Land use
High spots, low spots, and slope	Condition of the crops
Gullies	Weeds, other infestations
Drainage ways	Trees, other obstructions
	Location of all buildings
	and improvements

Aerial photos reveal many of the more important land features and their location. Color differences on a land use capabilities map indicate differences in soils, in relief or slope, and in the amounts of top soil which have been removed by erosion. The acreages in each field can be estimated and the land use or crops being raised in each field can be ascertained. One plat can be used as an outline map, one as a soils map, one to show surface drainage, one to show slope or topography, and one to show land use. Easements such as utility lines and pipelines should also be shown. In those areas where the farms are small, a scale of one inch to 660 feet is ideal; one square inch thus equals 10 acres.

While walking the farm one should think about the typical cropping system and the typical crop yields—in other words, the most likely acreages and the most likely yields which will probably be obtained by the typical operator. One should notice and record wet spots, the weedy areas, and the idle acreages. There is a tendency, of course, and particularly on the part of an inexperienced appraiser, to set up an ideal rotation and to raise good crop yields, thus injecting management into one's appraisal. However, one should instead add only the tillable acres in each field and allocate this acreage—often an amount considerably less than total farm acres—to the various crops, which will most likely prevail over a period of time. One should consider the more recent crop yields in the area, yet weigh them in relation to the long-term average, including, of course, any upward trend. The probable

---

A Soil map for parts of sections 2, 3, 10, and 11 in the Southeastern part of Fountain County, Indiana.

effect of current technologies on future crop yields must be balanced against present production techniques and cultural practices.

Pasture carrying capacities are often expressed in terms of the numbers of various kinds and classes of livestock which can be grazed without detriment to the vegetative cover. Pastures vary from year to year and tangible measures of carrying capacities are not easily obtained. An appraiser may have to estimate the acreage of the various kinds of pasture—tillable pastureland, untillable pastureland, and woods pasture. He may then assign carrying capacities to each class of grazing land and compare these estimates to the numbers of livestock which can be carried.[8] Oftentimes he can obtain information by observing other pastures in the vicinity and by interviewing other ranchers in the area. Seasonality of use, availability of water, and type of vegetative growth are all important. Only through observation can an appraiser make realistic estimates.

Inventorying the Buildings: A fairly accurate scale diagram or sketch of the farmstead showing the location of each of the various buildings and improvements may be desirable. All buildings should be inspected, inside and out. Thus, each building is inventoried. The width, length, and height of each should be measured and the capacity or square feet calculated. The physical characteristics—type of construction, foundation, walls, roof, general condition, probable age, physical deterioration, the building's adequacy or usefulness, as well as the degree of obsolescence, along with all other important details, should be recorded. These details, along with a building's present-day replacement cost, depreciation to date, and structural value, should be recorded. This can usually be done most efficiently in tabular form.

The capacity, use, and function of each building should be given particular attention, for the toughest questions are those concerning the extent to which the various buildings contribute to the market value of the farm versus the extent to which they are being used in the present farming operations. On many farms there is a surplus of old and obsolete buildings. This is a result of farm consolidation. Hence, even though some farm buildings are in good condition they may have salvage value only.

The farm appraiser must also give considerable thought as to the

---

8. In the agricultural Midwest and in the East the appraiser thinks and talks in terms of acres per cow. However, in range country and in the far West, pasture capacities are measured in terms of cows per section.

balance between land and improvements while on the farm. All farms are typically appraised as units. This means that the land and the improvements should be in balance. Good buildings must have the land to support them. Good land should perhaps have certain improvements to go with it, yet not always are such necessary.

Interviewing the Present Operator: Before leaving the farm or area, the appraiser should visit with the present operator who has a knowledge of the current farming operations. Information that should be checked or obtained is as follows:

1. The farm's boundaries.

2. Any existing easements or right-of-ways.

3. Any personal property or capital improvements which are not a part of the realty.

A systematic approach in inspecting the farm itself is also highly desirable. Most appraisers first like to walk the farm and study the land, then inventory the buildings and improvements, and then and only then, visit with the present operator.

Courtesy, U.S.D.A.

4. The past cropping history and crop yields.

5. Fertilization practices.

6. Wells—type, depth, flow, and draw-down.

7. Irrigation equipment, drainage problems, and sewage systems.

8. Pasture carrying capacities.

9. Livestock numbers.

10. Detriments, hazards, and nuisances.

11. Weed and disease problems and control.

12. The typical leasing arrangements in the area.

13. Schools, churches, other community characteristics.

14. The available utilities—telephone, electricity, gas, water, and other.

15. An explanation of any unique feature observed while inspecting the farm.

The present operator may or may not be cooperative, depending on the reason for the appraisal, and the relationship between the client and the operator. An appraiser should always be both careful and diplomatic in asking questions. If he has walked the farm and the present operator knows this, the two of them can usually visit first about agriculture in general, then farm problems in particular, and eventually about the subject farm itself. If, however, the appraiser is the employee of the condemnor and the subject farm will be badly damaged, the present operator may refuse to answer any and all questions, sometimes on the advice of his attorney. In all cases the appraiser should be polite and accept whatever answers he obtains.

Unfortunately most farm operators keep poor records. In their absence many a farm operator is inclined to remember only the extremes. He is inclined to talk only about the good years. Hence, any information obtained from the present operator should be carefully evaluated along with all other available data. Crop yields per acre should reflect what can be expected in the future employing only those practices which are in general use.

Before leaving the farm the appraiser should check his outline or his appraisal report form to make sure all of the essentials have been ascertained. Some appraisers have inspection checklists. Upon leaving he should again take a careful look at the neighborhood. He should check on any farm sales not previously investigated.

The appraisal report should then be written as soon as possible, for there are a large number of details in the physical description of a farm. These should be written out immediately and while they are still fresh in one's mind, for the goal is to write that report so the client can visualize the subject property even though he has not seen or visited the farm.

THE APPRAISAL REPORT

The purpose of the appraisal report is to convey to the client whatever he needs to know in order to make his decision—to buy, to insure, to tax, to loan, etc. This information should be conveyed as effectively and as efficiently as possible and in such fashion that the client will have considerable confidence in the final value figure.

The real objective is to present the information in whatever form it can be presented as quickly and efficiently and effectively as possible. Whether various facts and figures are presented in a narrative or tabular fashion should be determined by this objective alone. Some information is best presented in narrative fashion—for example, the disclaimer clause. Certain data are best presented in tabular form— for example, soil characteristics and building specifications. Sometimes an additional explanatory comment is needed following a group of tabular data; oftentimes such is unnecessary.

Appraisal reports vary considerably. The type of report and the number of details included therein are determined in part at least by the reason for the appraisal—the client's problems, his wishes, and his knowledge about agriculture. Some appraisal assignments require a very thorough inspection of the subject property and a very detailed report. Others do not. Some clients specify the format to be followed, the style, and the amount of information to be included in the report. Some clients even provide their own appraisal forms. Others do not. They instead leave such decisions entirely up to the appraiser.

The reason for the appraisal determines the amount of time spent inspecting the farm and the amount of detail included in the report. The time spent in appraising a typical 240- to 320-acre commercial farm with one set of improvements and for several different reasons are presented in Table 6. The data represent the opinion of the author only. They are presented not to show what appraisers should do but instead to perhaps show the relationship between appraisal assignments and the amounts of time spent and lengths of various appraisal reports.

The first-time-only client often asks for only a letter—a one- or two-page opinion. A summary of one's appraisal may solve his problem. However, that client may or may not be particularly knowledgeable about agriculture. Hence, it is usually if not always advantageous to present him with a fairly detailed report showing the work that has been done, the techniques used, and all of the supportive evidence underlying the final value figure. Many times a farmer, a prospective buyer, or other client learns more by reading the report than he can by walking the farm.

The various lending institutions and government agencies often specify a given format or style. The lending institutions typically prefer much of the material to be presented in tabular form or in summary fashion. In fact, many of them provide their own forms, sometimes ones which are quite brief. These institutions and agencies want their reports to be look-alikes, so that their review appraisers, loan committees, or others who look at the various appraisals, find the same information in the same place in all reports. These reports are studied by persons familiar with the appraisal process. Seldom are they submitted to anyone outside of the organization for whom they are prepared. Hence, brevity and uniformity are a part of the job of conveying the necessary information to these particular clients in an efficient fashion. In these instances, the appraiser may keep many of the details in his own files.

Table 6. Thumb Rules as to the Amounts of Time That May Be Spent and the Probable Size of an Appraisal Report. Four Different Appraisal Assignments, Typical 240- to 320-Acre Family Operated Farm, Agricultural Midwest.

Appraisal Assignment	Amount of Time Spent in . . .		Number of Pages in the Report
	Inspecting the Farm	Writing the Report	
Appraisal for a Prospective Buyer[1]	1½ days	1½ days	24-30
Appraisal for a Farm Loan	½ day	2 hours	3-4
"Appraisal" by the Local Assessor	1 hour (or less)	15 minutes (or less)	2
A Condemnation Appraisal (Partial Taking)[1]	2½ + days	2½ + days[2]	36-48

1. An unimproved tract (no buildings) reduces these figures approximately one-third.
2. An additional day may be spent on the witness stand.

For many assignments the printed appraisal form is not efficient. A simple form is inadequate; a detailed one often hides the more relevant data. The appraiser often needs either more or less space to present the various facts and figures. Hence, a form report often requires considerable time.

Most fee appraisers have a specific outline or format that they follow. This serves as a checklist in the field. It helps to organize the writing of the report in the office.[9] Thus they standardize their work to the extent that a secretary can insert certification, definitions of value, instant paragraphs, limiting conditions, and sometimes even summary sentences. After some limited experience this saves con-

---

9. The author's own particular format and style is presented in the Appendix.

Information from an appraiser's field sheet may be checked against a soil survey map, a geological survey map, and when possible, a land use capabilities map.

Courtesy, U.S.D.A.

siderable time. The final report is more lucid. Furthermore, many clients are impressed with a personalized report and with the special attention it gives their farm properties.

In cases where 20 or more pages are submitted to a client, the good report writer will submit along with his appraisal report, a one- or two-page brief or summary. The client may read only the summary; or, if other activities are not too pressing, and if he wants to know more about the property, he may read the entire report.

Writing the Report: The job of writing the appraisal report begins with the appraisal assignment. If planned in advance, the writing is one-third to one-half done at the end of the farm inspection. An outline or checklist is highly desirable. Parts may be filled in, both prior to the visit and during the inspection. In other words, comments should be made and recorded and as much data as possible tabulated in a final and polished fashion as one goes about the appraisal task. This saves tremendous amounts of time.

All comments which are to appear in the final report should be dictated or written as soon as possible after inspecting the farm. This is because a detail is often missed or skipped in the farm inspection. The substance of a good many statements quickly scribbled in the field are not clear.

In writing the report most appraisers first complete the plats or farm maps. Considerable information can be presented on the maps. This allows the appraiser to review what he saw in the field. It gives him a check on any important or unique feature that might have been missed.

When an appraiser presents the farm's physical description, he should stick to the facts. The final value figure depends on the accuracy of this material. Any discrepancy regarding the facts, whether important or not, casts a tall shadow on the appraiser's capabilities.

Facts and estimates should be kept separately. Insofar as possible, all estimates should be so specified.

Furthermore, one should not hesitate to make assumptions as long as he admits to such. For example, a fee simple title is assumed. One should not hesitate to omit certain items as long as he again admits to the omission. For example, the ground was frozen; the soils were not probed.

The narrative parts of an appraisal report should be simple, brief, and to the point. Each statement with regard to each of the factors having some effect on value should be specific.

In most instances the appraiser will estimate the farm's income, he will select various comparable sales and adjust them, and he will inventory all of the farm improvements. There are a good many mathematical calculations involved. Each should be checked.

Present market value should be defined. The appraisal should be summarized, and such must be signed. And whenever the appraisal is for a new client, the professional appraiser usually includes a biographical sketch of his training, background, and experience.

The Essentials: The essentials of an appraisal report are as follows:

1. General Features. Name and address of the client, person or party authorizing the appraisal, the appraisal assignment, surrounding circumstances, the purpose of and reason for the appraisal, location and identification of the farm (both in general and specifically), an accurate description of the property including size, shape, occupancy, and use, the date of the appraisal, and the appraiser's signature.

The final dollar value is ascertained as of some date—today perhaps, or some other date in the past—for example, the date of death, the date of the take, the date of the claim, etc. The date of the value or appraisal and the date of the inspection should not be confused. Both appear in many appraisal reports. Furthermore, changes or improvements may have taken place or been made between the date of the appraisal and the date of the inspection. These should be noted.

2. The Affidavit or Appraisal Certificate. A statement as to certification, professional standards, assumptions or limitations, a disclaimer clause, the definition of present market value, the final value figure, the date, and the signature of the appraiser.

Depending on the client and the reason for making the appraisal, most appraisal reports include a statement or two as follows:

I, the undersigned, hereby certify, that I have inspected the above property on _____, 19___, that to the best of my knowledge the statements set forth in this appraisal report are true; that any and all estimates made in the report are identified as such; and that any opinions I have stated are based on both a full and complete and a fair and objective consideration of all pertinent facts; at the same time recognizing the following assumptions, limitations, or qualifying conditions:

1. _____

2. _____

3. _____

The undersigned further states that this appraisal has been made in conformity with those standards which have been generally accepted by all professional appraisers and in conformity with the laws of the State of _____; that he has no direct or indirect, present or contemplated interest in the property, or in any of the surrounding circumstances which might affect or influence any of the statements made in this report or the final value figure presented; that he will not reveal the findings or the results presented in this report to anyone other than the above named client, unless required to do so by due process of law, or until released from this obligation by letter, by public testimony, or other means.

After weighing all of the factors reported herein, it is my opinion that the present market value of this property as of _____, 19___, is $_____ total, or $_____ per acre.

Signature of the Appraiser

3. Legal Description, Brief History, and Pictorial Presentation. A map of the area showing the farm's location, an outline map of the farm showing all important land features, and various other maps including perhaps a sketch of the farmstead and one showing the location of nearby recent farm sales.

4. A Physical Description of the Farm. (See previous section.)

5. The Farm's Productive Capacity. (See previous section.)

6. The Income Potential. This may be based on an owner-operated or an absentee-owned tenant-operated farm. The income is based on the farm's productive capacity under a typical operator. It is capitalized into the farm's value, with the value of the home, its location and any other economic advantages added (see Chapter VI).

7. An Analysis of All Nearby Farm Sales. Farms that are either comparable to the subject farm, or comparable to the extent that certain dollar adjustments can be made thus making them comparable, are tabulated (see Chapter VII).

8. An Inventory of All Land, Buildings, and Improvements. The various types of land and the various buildings, along with a value on each, is typically presented (see Chapter VIII).[10]

9. A Brief Summary of the Appraisal. The final figure—present market value—is usually rounded to the nearest $100 (total), or nearest $5 (per acre).

10. Vita of the Appraiser.

The final report should be read carefully, making sure that each item has been weighed according to its relative importance and as objectively as possible, and that no important item has been omitted. Adjustments in the data should be made only once. Actually the fewer ad-

---

10. This assumes that all three methods of establishing value are used in the appraisal process. This is not always the case.

justments the better. All calculations should be double-checked. All typing should be proofed. The final report should be neat, well-typed, and attractive.

A color photo on the cover is excellent and is most advantageous in presenting the more detailed appraisals. If a client likes the photo or the report so well that he wants to leave it on the coffee table or show it to his friends, this does an appraiser no harm. And finally, the appraiser should keep a copy.

A Summary: The more comprehensive appraisals and the longer appraisal reports should be accompanied by an appraisal summary. This typically consists of several specific statements relative to each of the following:

1. The reason for the appraisal.
2. A brief history of the farm.
3. A description of the farm's physical resources.
4. The difference between present and typical operators.
5. The origins of value.
6. The methods used to establish the final value.
7. The final value figure.

In writing the appraisal report, most appraisers first complete the farm maps. The various facts and figures—for example, soil characteristics and building specifications —are then developed. The certification statement, disclaimer clause, limiting conditions, value definitions, instant paragraphs, and sometimes even summary sentences are then used in writing the report.

Courtesy, **Hoard's Dairyman**

These summary statements should be brief, factual, and to the point. Most clients do not have time to study all of the details that appear in one's report, and while they may appreciate a thorough analysis, they still may not want to read more than a few pages.

A transmittal letter attached to the report is also essential. It should include a brief mention of the appraisal assignment, an identification of the property, its location, the date the property was inspected, the final value figure, along with any other value that was determined, and the signature of the appraiser. One can also say certain things in a letter that should not be included in the appraisal report. Thus other items may also be included.

REFERENCES

The Appraiser's Job

"Farm Land Appraisal Methods," *Doane Agricultural Digest*, August 1957, pp. 1031-32.

Herzer, T. O. F., "Proper Appraisal Practices," *Journal of American Society of Farm Managers and Rural Appraisers*, Vol. 9, No. 2, October 1945.

Hyder, K. L., "The Appraisal Process," *Selected Readings in Real Estate Appraisal*, American Institute of Real Estate Appraisers, 1953.

Hyder, K. L., "Planning the Appraisal," *Selected Readings in Real Estate Appraisal*, American Institute of Real Estate Appraisers, 1953.

Murray, W. G., *Farm Appraisal and Valuation*, 5th Edition, Iowa State University, 1969.

"Rural Appraisal Standards," *Doane Agricultural Digest*, December 1944, pp. 1029-1030.

"What to Look for in an Appraisal," American Institute of Real Estate Appraisers, 1964.

The Typical Operator Concept

Brown, R. K., "Who Is the Typical Buyer?," *The Real Estate Appraiser*, Vol. 29, No. 4, April 1963.

Marshall, W. F., "Typical Operators," *Journal of American Society of Farm Managers and Rural Appraisers*, Vol. 3, No. 2, October 1939.

Seymour, C. F., "The 'Artillery' Theory of Market Value," *Appraisal Journal*, Vol. 23, No. 1, January 1955.

Getting Acquainted with a New Area

Avery, T. E., *Interpretation of Aerial Photographs,* 2nd Edition, Burgess Publishing Company, 1962.

Church, B. M., "Guides to a Successful Appraisal Practice," *The Real Estate Appraiser,* Vol. 29, No. 5, May 1963.

Crouse, E. F., and C. H. Everett, *Rural Appraisal,* Prentice-Hall, 1956.

Crouse, E. F., "Technical Tools of the Appraiser," *Journal of American Society of Farm Managers and Rural Appraisers,* Vol. 24, No. 1, April 1960.

Dill, H. W., Jr., "Information on Land from Airphotos," *Land: 1958 Yearbook of Agriculture,* U.S.D.A., 1958.

Field, R. V., "Land Survey Systems of the United States," *Selected Readings in Real Estate,* American Institute Real Estate Appraisers, 1953.

Kellog, C. E., et al., "Aerial Photo Interpretation in Classifying and Mapping Soils," U.S.D.A., S.C.S., *Agricultural Handbook 294,* October 1966.

Murray, W. G., *Farm Appraisal and Valuation,* 5th Edition, Iowa State University Press, 1969.

Rural Appraisal Manual, 3rd Edition, American Society of Farm Managers and Rural Appraisers, August 1969.

Pike, Herbert, "Good Five Cent Farm Plats," *Journal of American Society of Farm Managers and Rural Appraisers,* Vol. 1, No. 2, October 1937.

Client Relationships

Brabant, Davis, "Appraisal Contracts," *The Residential Appraiser,* Vol. 26, No. 8, August 1960.

Burt, Mary E. (Editor), *Stories and Poems by Kipling,* Curtis Publishing Co., 1900.

Morse, T. D., "Client-Personnel Relationships," *Journal of American Society of Farm Managers and Rural Appraisers,* Vol. 13, No. 1, April 1949.

Nelson, R. D., "Pitfalls of the 'Mini' Appraisal," *The Real Estate Appraiser,* Vol. 35, No. 7, November-December 1969.

Field Procedure

Crouse, E. F., and C. H. Everett, *Rural Appraisals,* Prentice-Hall, 1956.

Fiedler, A. C., "More Walking in Farm Appraisals," *Journal of American Society of Farm Managers and Rural Appraisers,* Vol. 6, No. 1, April 1942.

Mawhorter, D. M., "Invoicing Existing Tile Drainage Systems," *Journal of American Society of Farm Managers and Rural Appraisers,* Vol. 6, No. 1, April 1942.

McAnelly, E. E., "Information Needed in Making Appraisals Other Than That Which Is Secured from a Study of the Farm Itself," *Journal of American Society of Farm Managers and Rural Appraisers,* Vol. 5, No. 2, October 1941.

"Rural Appraisal Field Procedure," *Doane Agricultural Digest,* February 1947, pp. 1031-32.

Thorkelson, G. F., "Rural Appraisals to Meet Users Needs," *Journal of American Society of Farm Managers and Rural Appraisers,* Vol. 25, No. 1, April 1961.
Van Cleif, Eugene, "Maps for Appraisals," *Appraisal Journal,* Vol. 17, No. 2, April 1949.

The Appraisal Report

An Informational Guide for Appraisal Review. American Association of State Highway Officials, 1968.
Bennett, E. P., Jr., "The Appraisal Report and the Review Appraiser," *The Residential Appraiser,* Vol. 26, No. 10, October 1960.
Hall, H. C., "What Does a Loan Committee Want in an Appraisal Report?," *Journal of American Society of Farm Managers and Rural Appraisers,* Vol. 11, No. 2, October 1947.
Hollebaugh, C. W., "Watch your Language!," *Appraisal Journal,* Vol. 26, No. 4, October 1958.
Hulten, J. J., "The Appraisal Report," *Selected Readings in Real Estate Appraisal,* American Institute of Real Estate Appraisers, 1953.
McAnelly, E. E., "What Essentials Are Desired in an Appraisal by the Appraiser," *Journal of the American Society of Farm Managers and Rural Appraisers,* Vol. 12, No. 1, April 1948.
McSpaden, F. J., "Guidelines for a Narrative Real Estate Appraisal," *The Real Estate Appraiser,* Vol. 33, No. 12, December 1967.
(No Author), "Interpretation of Types of Appraisal Reports and of Letters of Opinion," *The Real Estate Appraiser,* Vol. 35, No. 6, September-October 1969.
Reese, Louie, "Instant Paragraphs—Short Cut to Better Appraisals," *Appraisal Journal,* Vol. 35, No. 2, April 1967.
Rogers, R. R., "Technique of Writing the Narrative Report," *Appraisal Journal,* Vol. 28, No. 4, October 1960.
Schmutz, G. L., "Writing Reports," *Selected Readings in Real Estate Appraisal,* American Institute of Real Estate Appraisers, 1953.
Smith, C. B., "How to Write a Poor Report," *Appraisal Journal,* Vol. 41, No. 2, April 1973.
Smith, L. H., "Appraisals for Highway Acquisitions," *Appraisal Journal,* Vol. 32, No. 2, April 1964.
Smith, Walstein, Jr., "Preface to Appraisal Report," *The Residential Appraiser,* Vol. 27, No. 6, June 1961.
Wright, C. W., et al., "California Society of Farm Managers and Rural Appraisers, Suggested Appraisal Outline," *Journal of the American Society of Farm Managers and Rural Appraisers,* Vol. 26, No. 2, October 1962.

CHAPTER V

The Appraiser's Handbook

Farm real estate values are created, maintained, modified, and sometimes destroyed by (1) the physical features existent in any given area, (2) the agricultural trends in the area, (3) the economic changes that forever occur in a free society, and (4) the customs and characteristics of the people who live in the community.

Farm appraisers often keep a comprehensive file containing much of this information. Their objective is to bring together in one place the maps, the aerial photos, and all of the data with regard to the various factors which influence farm real estate values in their area.

Collecting such is a continuous yet frustrating job; in fact, there is no such thing as a complete file. The amount of time spent in collecting various sets of data and the emphasis placed on each depend largely on the kind and number of appraisals made. Considerable time and effort is involved. However, when the "handbook" is properly organized, there is always a job for the secretary or a new man in the office. Various materials can be ordered, the files can be brought up-to-date, and graphic presentations can be developed.

It is impractical to attempt to present in this chapter everything that goes into an appraiser's files. Instead, the objective is to present a method of organizing an appraiser's handbook.[1] Various sets of data are presented to illustrate each of five areas: (1) physical features, (2) agricultural trends, (3) economic statistics, (4) community characteristics, and (5) miscellanea compacta. Some of the data are presented in tabular form; some are presented in graphic fashion.

---

1. A second and perhaps equally important objective is to show some of the differences that exist within agriculture and some of the changes that have occurred over time.

Many persons have little or no knowledge of what an appraiser does, the materials he has available, or how he goes about appraising a farm. The professional farm appraiser looks at farms almost every day. He knows the things to look for and the questions to ask. He collects and has in his files tremendous amounts of information.

Courtesy, U.S.D.A.

There are many alternatives as to organization. This is largely a matter of personal preference. However, organization is also a function of where the data come from and how they are to be used.

The organization should be such that one can immediately file any and all information as it becomes available. The organization should allow one to readily obtain various sets of data, refer to them, use them, and return them to the files in an efficient fashion. The various sets of data should be related to each of the reference sources so that when current data are missing, reference sources—persons, places, addresses, and telephone numbers—are readily available. Then and only then can the data be obtained and verified with a minimum of effort.

No amount of appraisal skill will substitute for the time required to obtain the data that are typically required in a farm appraisal. In fact, the ability to have certain information at hand, and to know, that if it's not in the files it probably isn't available, saves one tremendous amounts of time.

The system presented here utilizes three-integers. The left integer indicates the major classification, the middle integer designates the data, and the right integer refers to the data source.

Five major classifications have been developed in a 100, 200, 300, etc., series.

    100 – Physical Features
    200 – Agricultural Trends
    300 – Economic Statistics
    400 – Community Characteristics
    500 – Miscellanea Compacta

For each of these five major classifications information sets are filed in a 110, 120, 130, etc. (Physical Features); 210, 220, 230, etc. (Agricultural Trends), 310, 320, 330, etc. (Economics Statistics) series. For example . . .

    110 – Soil Formation, History
    120 – Soil Characteristics
    130 – Soil Surveys, Land Classifications

    210 – Farm Land, Number of Farms, and Farm Size
    220 – Kinds of Farm Organization and Ownership
    230 – Farm Population and Production

    310 – Market Activity and Farm Real Estate Values
    320 – Farm Prices Received by Farmers
    330 – Prices Paid by Farmers and Farm Costs

Much of the data with regard to agricultural trends and economic statistics can be tabulated and shown graphically. At the bottom of each table or chart the publication or reference source from which the data were obtained should be listed. On the front of each file the file number of the folders where the data sources or references are filed should be given.

Each publication or reference source is then filed in a 311, 312, 313, etc. (Market Activity), 321, 322, 323, etc. (Prices Received) series. For example . . .

> 311 – *Farm Real Estate Market Developments*
> 312 – *Agricultural Finance Review*
> 313 – Farm Land Price Studies
> 314 – Recent Land Value Outlook Articles

On the front of each folder (3 integer level) the institution or agency which publishes each publication—name, address, and telephone number, and sometimes a person who can be contacted—may be listed.

This particular system has been developed so an appraiser can ask his secretary, for example, for the File on Farm Prices (320). If it's not up-to-date, he can ask for File 321, 322, and maybe 325. If a more current figure is still desired the name of the agency issuing the publication is on the file folder's cover, and the appraiser can make a telephone call. In this fashion both the appraiser and the person called can readily identify the exact data series, as well as the publication, and be reasonably assured of data continuity.

No system is quite this simple, of course. Some publications or reports contain but a single series of data; hence, may be filed in the data folder. Others contain several to many series of data. The Land Value File (310), for example, may refer to 312; the Farm Costs File (330) may also refer to 312, and to others as well. The system presented here is presented in more detail in the Appendix.

PHYSICAL FEATURES

The physical features—soils, topography, and climate—throughout the United States determine much of the nation's agriculture. These natural resources tend to determine not only the types of farming—kinds and acreages of crops raised and kinds and numbers of livestock kept—but also the many farming methods and farm practices. Not always are the demarcation lines between types of farming sharply defined; often there are instead transition zones. A relatively small area may contain only specialized farms or it may contain many diferent types of farms.

Soils, topography or slope, and climate are the predominant features. There is an extremely high relationship between these physical features and the various types of farming. The principal dairy regions are the stony loams in the Northeast. The Corn Belt coincides closely with the grey brown and the darker prairie soils in the agricultural Midwest. The wheat regions are associated more with the lighter chestnut or brown soils which contain somewhat less organic matter and are located in an area of limited rainfall. The cotton areas are the reddish, yellowish, and alluvial soils. The fruit and truck crop areas are largely in the sandy areas along the Atlantic coast in Florida, and in the alluvial soils of the Pacific valleys.

Climate, of course, plays a major and a simultaneous role. In the humid East, where rainfall is not particularly limited, the agriculture varies with both soils and temperatures. Here the agricultural regions extend primarily east and west, following the temperature zones. However, in the West the agricultural regions tend to run north and south, being determined by the mountain ranges, the valleys, and the rainfall belts. And in the semi-arid West, where rainfall is limited, the agriculture varies more with the elevation or altitude and with the availability of water (for irrigation purposes).

Thus the pattern of farming is not haphazard. Soils, topography, and climate are each capable of establishing an upper limit. While man has erected a superstructure of economic and other factors, the natural or physical resources tend to remain comparatively static. Furthermore, once agriculture adjusts to its physical environment it seldom changes unless Dame Nature changes.

1. SOIL

Agriculture is unique in that it has an immobile and largely irreplaceable production plant. Agriculture's biggest basic asset is its soil. Soil is found on practically all farms and regardless of the rest of the real estate's characteristics. In the utility sense, soil is unstable. It has a tendency to be perishable. It can be destroyed. However, real estate tends to endure physically. It always has some value—if nothing more, location value.

The soil within any one agricultural area is usually the most important single factor determining the type of farming. Its natural and inherent powers underwrite the dollar returns to all other resources. Soils are related to the well-being of the farm family, to the safety of the capital invested, and to farm real estate values. In fact, all farm real estate appraisals are based on a knowledge of soils and their productive capacities.

The inexperienced appraiser sometimes takes soil more or less for granted, not thinking very much about "What soil is," or "What soil does." In fact, if one were to raise the question "What is soil?" this fellow might answer by saying, "A mixture of rocks and minerals and organic matter on which plants or crops grow."

This statement is essentially correct. Certain specific soil components are named and their function is specified. However, the answer is incomplete. It is not particularly a scientific description, nor is it a practical definition from the standpoint of the farm manager or appraiser. It does not say why different soils lead to different types of farming or to different farm real estate values.

Soil is a natural body. It is a mixture of fragmented and partly or wholly weathered rocks and minerals, organic matter, water, and air or gases in greatly varying proportions. It is essentially located on the earth's surface, covering much of the land as a continuum, and in many forms. It is mostly characterized by layers parallel to the earth's surface. In any one place, a soil's characteristics are modified by the combined influence of climate, vegetative practice, and living organisms acting upon the parent materials. These parent materials are conditioned by relief or topography over long periods of time. A soil's characteristics also reflect the effect of man and his cultural environment. Soil thus provides a natural medium for the growth of plants, and determines, in all areas important to agriculture, the crops that can be raised.

However, soil is not a mere mixture. It is relatively organized both in terms of form and function. The soils in various land areas have various patterns. They have certain attributes depending on (1) the nature of the materials from which they developed, (2) the intensity of the activity of the different soil forming factors, and (3) the length of time the various soil formation forces have been active.

Soil is dynamic in character. It undergoes constant change—physically, chemically, and biologically. After long exposure to certain natural conditions, a soil may reach a state of near equilibrium and then change but very little. However, time is important. As a

soil grows older, the more soluble elements tend to be leached out or removed. This is particularly true in a humid climate. Man can also affect soil fertility through use and misuse. He can gradually change a soil's physical condition, the crop yields that may be obtained, and the dollar values per acre.

The professional appraiser needs to have an appreciation for the various environmental factors which have led to the development of the soils in his area. He needs to have a knowledge of the various soil characteristics, particularly those which lead to soil differences and differences in productivity.

The Soil Formation Process: The soil formation process is the result of five principal factors: (1) the geological past with regard to a soil's parent material, (2) the climate and/or the environment, (3) the amount of vegetative and biological activity, (4) the lay of the land— its form, relief, or slope, and (5) time. These five factors are all interdependent, and each has a tendency to modify the effectiveness of the others.

1. Parent Material: Soils begin their history with the accumulation and exposure of rock materials. Rock forms the essential part of the earth's crust. It includes loose, incoherent masses such as a bed of sand, gravel, clay, or volcanic ash as well as the very firm, hard, and solid masses of granite, sandstone, and limestone. Most rocks are aggregates of one or more minerals, yet some are composed entirely of glassy material. Some are a mixture of glass and minerals.

There are three main rock groups: (1) igneous rocks, or molten materials often volcanic in origin, (2) metamorphic rocks, or those which are formed under intense heat and pressure, and (3) rocks deposited by glaciers (glacial rocks), by water (sedimentary rocks), or by wind (eolian rock or loess, which is really dust). These three groups vary in composition. Some are rich in minerals which provide nutrients for plant growth; others are not.

The various rocks may be granite, basalt, sandstone, limestone, or some mixture. No matter which, however, they are all gradually broken into smaller and smaller fragments or particles by physical

---

Each county Agricultural Stabilization and Conservation Office has several master photos showing the most recent flight patterns used in taking aerial photos of the county. These become the photo index for ordering the aerial photo of any given farm.

Courtesy, A.S.C., U.S.D.A.

weathering—the grinding of glaciers, landslides, avalanches, rivers, and scouring by winds. They are split by slow yet irresistible forces—the uneven expansions and contractions caused by temperature change, the wedging of ice and roots, and constant atmospheric exposure.

The various parent materials are, at the same time, being weathered both chemically and biologically. There is usually occurring some simultaneous change in the parent material's mineralogical and chemical composition. Some of the nutrients—potassium, calcium, and magnesium in particular—are constantly being dissolved. The leaching of these nutrients is then somewhat offset by growing plants. For plant roots continually pull the minerals in the water from the deeper subsoil layers and add them to the surface of the soil.

The parent material of a given soil may have originated in place, or it may have been transported into the area from somewhere else. A large proportion typically originates from the underlying bed rock—either from material laid down during a previous period of glaciation or from material weathered in pre- or inter-glacial times. This material remains where it was formed, hence is referred to as a residual material.

Occasionally a significant portion originates in one place and is then moved, sometimes a considerable distance, by glaciers, by water, or by wind. As a result, the following terms are often used to describe a soil's characteristics.

> a. *Residual* refers to that soil material formed from rock (granite, sandstone, limestone, or shale) and that which has remained in place.

Aerial photos obtained from the Agricultural Stabilization and Conservation Service show the fantastic variation in the nation's agricultural resources. From left to right on the next five pages.

1. The Tobacco and Vegetable Crop Region in Hampshire County, Massachusetts.
2. The Fruit and Truck Crop Area in Lorain County, Pennsylvania.
3. The Citrus Groves in Lake County, Florida.
4. The Level Broad Terraces in Eastern Arkansas.
5. The Deep Loess Soils in Tama County, Iowa.
6. A Strip Cropped Farming Area in Eastern Montana.
7. The Mountains and Carson Basin in Lyon County, Nevada.
8. The Palouse Prairie in Nez Perce County, Idaho.
9. The San Luis Valley in Rio Grande County, Colorado.
10. An Intensively Irrigated Area in the Imperial Valley of California.

Courtesy, A.S.C., U.S.D.A.

b. *Glacial till* refers to a mixture of unassorted and often jagged material, which has been deposited by glacial ice.

c. *Outwash material* refers to that material which is stratified, water sorted, and which has been deposited by glacial waters or more recent streams.

d. *Drift* is a general term which typically includes both glacial till and outwash material.

e. *Loess* is a very uniform wind deposited silt.

f. *Alluvium* is the sediment deposited almost continually by streams or flood waters.

In the initial stages of the soil formation process, most of a soil's characteristics are inherited. However, as a soil matures, more and more of its characteristics are influenced by climate—rainfall, sunshine or solar radiation, temperature changes, air movements, and the activities of man.

2. Climate: Climatic differences over extended periods of time tend to produce varying soil profiles even though the individual soils may have originated from the same parent materials. Rainfall and temperature are the more direct influences.

Rain and snow, both the amount and the intensity of such, govern, to a very large extent, the amount of moisture in a soil. Surface run-off, soil erosion, moisture infiltration, and the leaching of plant nutrients are related to the amount of rainfall, its seasonal distribution, and the rate at which it falls. Topography, vegetative cover, and soil permeability affect the amount or percent of rainfall that is absorbed by a soil.

The intensity and the extent of the soil formation process are both directly related to temperature, for as temperatures increase the chemical and biological activities in a soil speed up.

3. Vegetative and Biological Activity: The non-mineral or "living" portion of a soil (actually its organic matter) is determined by the amount of vegetation that grows on top of a soil and by the amount of biological activity that occurs within a soil. When plants die, the residues and roots contribute organic matter both at the surface and throughout the soil, with the latter depending on the depth and degree of the root penetration. Various micro-organisms—bacteria, fungi, protozoa, and others—are active both continuously and seasonally. These micro-organisms utilize certain raw materials and convert them to a form of organic matter or humus which is interspersed with the rock particles.

Native vegetation consists of conifers, hardwoods, various grasses, and desert shrubs. Trees produce substantially more organic debris, yet much of it falls on and remains near the surface where it is lost through oxidation and decay. Grasses contribute less debris or organic matter, yet a much higher portion is incorporated into a soil through its fibrous root systems.

There are a number of indirect effects. The roots which penetrate a soil tend to increase its permeability to both air and water. These same roots are instrumental in the upward transportation of water and minerals, which tends to counteract the leaching process. Some vegetative systems utilize nitrogen-fixing bacteria which add fertility to a soil by fixing atmospheric nitrogen in the soil in a form that such can be used by plants. These activities by roots also lead to soil aggregation with the organic residues contributing greatly to the stability of aggregates.

Climate, vegetation, and biological activity are all closely associated. The higher the rainfall the greater the production of organic matter; however, the higher the temperature the more difficult it is to maintain that organic matter.

4. The Lay of the Land: Lay of the land refers to land form, relief, topography, or slope. A geologist may further refer to a drumlin, an esker, an old plain of coalescing fans, a dissected terrace, an active flood plain, or the like.

Lay of the land tends to control both surface water runoff (external soil drainage) hence soil erosion, and internal soil percolation or moisture infiltration. The more rugged land forms contribute greatly to surface runoff as well as to the translocation of surface materials (soil erosion). Soils on the steeper slopes are generally young and shallow. Soils on the more level land are considered to be more mature in terms of soil development.

On the steeper slopes and where the water table is deep, oxidation tends to produce the lighter colored—sometimes yellowish or reddish-brown, soils. On the more moderate slopes, where the water table fluctuates, the soils are likely to be mottled—gray with brown streaks. In low areas, where the water table is near or at the surface, drainage is often imperfect. Due to poor aeration, the dull, gray soils are often predominant.

The high ground, the ridges, and some slopes are more susceptible to evaporation losses and sometimes wind erosion because they are exposed to air currents. The low ground and the depressions are more susceptible to poor drainage, in fact the latter are sometimes water-logged.

A moraine deposit in Western New York called a drumlin. These are long cigar-shaped hills made up of clayey till often 200 feet high and up to a mile long. Their axes run parallel to the flow of a former glacier.

At the same time, internal soil drainage is influenced considerably by the permeability of the soil and the material beneath it. On the very same slope, a soil may be either (1) well drained (due to its permeability), (2) imperfectly drained, or (3) poorly drained (due to a lack of permeability). Relief or slope thus has considerable influence on erosion, on the depth of the water table, and along with the permeability of the soil, on internal soil drainage.

5. Time: Under natural circumstances and depending on the parent material, it requires anywhere from 400 to 1,000 years to develop one inch of top soil. In many areas a century has been required; however, there is considerable variation. Over time all soils undergo definite stages. Rocks and minerals are broken into smaller particles, some to fine clays. Organic matter accumulates and nutrients

are released (for plant growth). Soil acidity gradually increases and permeability gradually declines. Nutrient removal may eventually exceed its release.

All of these changes occur slowly, yet when they are allowed to continue over a long period of time, a soil (particularly the surface layer) often becomes very different from its parent material. As a result, the changed portion varies all the way from a mere film to several feet in thickness.

Present-day Soil Characteristics. A soil is said to mature when it develops certain definite characteristics. However, soils differ greatly with respect to (1) profile development—depth, stratification, and arrangement, (2) texture, structure, and color, (3) relief, permeability, and drainage (both external and internal), (4) soil cover or vegetative growth and organic matter, and (5) mineralogical composition, lime content, and soil fertility. The farm appraiser eventually learns to relate all these characteristics to land use, to productivity, and to value.

1. The Soil Profile: As a soil matures, certain layers or horizons, more or less parallel to the earth's surface, tend to develop. These layers or soil horizons are the principal features used to identify, describe, and classify soils.

A soil's profile is really a cross-section of that soil (Figure 8). It shows both the organic layers which have developed on the surface and the genetic horizons—the parent material or layers beneath—both of which influence a soil's genesis and behavior.

The A-horizon consists of one or more surface mineral layers of maximum organic accumulation and a surface or subsurface horizon, somewhat lighter in color than the underlying layer, which has lost some of its clay minerals, its iron, and its aluminum, with a resulting concentration of the more resistant minerals. It is the horizon of maximum biological activity and the horizon subject to the more direct influences of climate, plants, animals, and other environmental factors.

The B-horizon is one of altered materials characterized by (1) an accumulation of clay, iron, or aluminum, with accessory organic material, and (2) a more or less blocky or prismatic structure, together with other characteristics, such as stronger colors unlike those of either the A- or the underlying horizons. The B-horizon is commonly called an alluvial horizon in that collodial material, which has been carried in suspension from the horizons above, is lodged in it.

The C-horizon is a layer of unconsolidated material, relatively little

affected by the influence of organisms, yet one presumed to be similar in composition—physically, mineralogically, and chemically—to the materials from which at least part of the soil above developed.

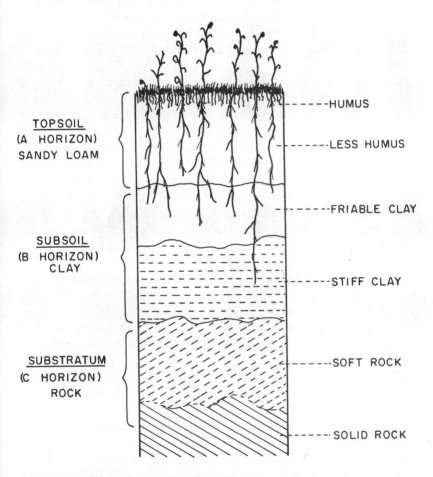

TOPSOIL
(A HORIZON)
SANDY LOAM

SUBSOIL
(B HORIZON)
CLAY

SUBSTRATUM
(C HORIZON)
ROCK

------HUMUS

------LESS HUMUS

------FRIABLE CLAY

------STIFF CLAY

------SOFT ROCK

------SOLID ROCK

Figure 8. A Typical Profile of a Sandy Loam Soil.

Four different soil profiles—Shelby silt loam, with a tight silty clay mottled lower profile (upper left), Bearden fine sandy loam with a fairly deep organic layer (upper right), "MO" silt loam, a lithosolic soil formed on chalk rock (lower left), and Holdredge silt loam, showing very definite A- and B-horizons (lower right).

Courtesy, Soil Conservation Service

2. Texture, Structure, and Color: Physically, soil is an aggregate of mineral particles ranging in size from those that can be seen with the naked eye to those which can be seen only with a powerful microscope. These mineral particles are classified into three principal groups—sand, silt, and clay. A soil's texture is based on the relative proportions of these different sized particles. In other words, texture refers to the size of the individual soil particles. It is not related to color.

The principal texture classes, in order of diminishing size and increasing silt and clay content, are: sand, loamy sand, sandy loam, silt loam, clay loam, and clay. Certain modifying words may be used, for example, fine sand, or very fine sand.[2] Various terms may also be combined, for example, a fine sandy loam or a silty clay loam.[3]

Classification is based on the relative percentage of each of the various sized particles by weight. The sand group must contain more than 80 percent sand. The clay group must contain at least 30 percent of the clay separate. A loam is a mixture of particles which exhibits the properties of both sand and clay in about equal proportions. It generally consists of 50 percent sand and 50 percent silt and clay (Figure 9).

Texture determination in the field is a skill largely acquired through the feel of soil in one's hand. A sense of touch is most important.[4]

Sand has a gritty feel. It makes a grinding noise on the auger or tube. Its particles glisten in sunlight and are apparent to the eye. Very fine sand may also have a gritty feel between the teeth. Thus it can be detected by the bite test. It is non-plastic.

Silt has a floury or talc feel when dry, and spindles easily when moistened. It is barely visible to the naked eye. Unfortunately, however, silt is often confused with organic matter.

The clay particles are not individually distinguishable to the eye. In fact, most of them are too small to be seen even under a microscope. Clay feels extremely smooth; it's highly plastic in nature. This characteristic is what makes a clay soil ball when wet. It becomes very sticky when too wet and very cloddy and hard when too dry.

---

2. Terms, such as *gumbo, black wax, stick,* and *adobe,* are often used to describe those soils which have a heavy clay content. The terms have various meanings. Usually they are useful only in a particular locality.

3. Texture, as indicated in a soil type name, refers only to the make up of the surface soil.

4. Texture can be checked by mechanical analysis in the laboratory.

The sand grains, because of their relative size, function as separate particles. However, these coarser particles are comparatively inactive. In fact, a sandy soil tends to be loose, pliable, or friable (easy-to-work), and well aerated. It is usually low in water holding capacity; and because of the large spaces between particles it is often too well-drained. However, these same sand particles do serve a function. They provide a supportive framework for the rest of the soil.

The same amount of space occupied by a grain of sand can be occupied by numerous clay particles (Figure 10). As a result, the clay particles have much larger total surface area. The chief component is colloidal in nature. Thus the clay particle is able to perform a complicated function. It serves essentially as a "bank" in which various plant nutrients can be deposited for future needs and from which they can be withdrawn when they are required by plants. The better clay colloids have large storage capacities.

A clayey soil also has a high absorptive capacity for water and gases. The kind and quantity of the material largely determines how much water can be held in the soil, especially in regions where rainfall is limited. But because of the smaller space between particles, as compared to sand, water and air tend to move much more slowly through a clayey soil.

A silt loam soil possesses the same properties of plasticity, cohesion, and absorption as does a clayey soil, but to a lesser degree. This is because the silt particles are larger. Thus texture, along with several other physical properties, may limit a soil's inherent productivity.

For example, a sandy soil often permits excessive moisture movement and leads to droughty conditions, unless, of course, the soil is irrigated. A very finely textured soil or a zone of clay accumulation often slows water percolation and root penetration. Thus, when climate and other physical characteristics are not limiting factors; texture may greatly influence the moisture and air relationships in a soil—important factors in plant growth. Texture may also limit the extent to which crop yields can be increased by fertilization. Thus texture may affect both productivity and value.

Structure is the arrangement of various individual soil grains or particles and the extent to which they are held together in aggregates of different sizes and shapes within the soil mass. The size, shape, and stability of such aggregates are closely associated with vegetative growth and with soil productivity. A granular, and hence crumbly, structure is most favorable for the growth of plants or crops. Such normally develops under a grass or other close-growing vegetation.

However, a crumbly structure may also be found in forest soil, particularly where there is a dense ground cover.

Soil structure or tilth is renewed by shielding the surface of a soil from the destructive forces of rainfall and by the granulating action of plant roots. It is impaired by vanishing organic matter, by the impact of rain on an exposed surface, and by compaction by tractors, tillage equipment, and livestock.

Color is one of the more obvious soil characteristics. However, it is of minor importance. Along with texture and structure, color forms much of the basis for differentiating the different soil horizons. Color also serves as an indicator of some of the other soil conditions that are extremely important.

In certain parts of the world color indicates productive capacity. Usually the darker colored soils are higher in productivity; however not always. This is because the darker soils are generally the result of pigments formed by decaying organic matter or humus. Usually the lighter colored soils are lower in productivity; however, again not

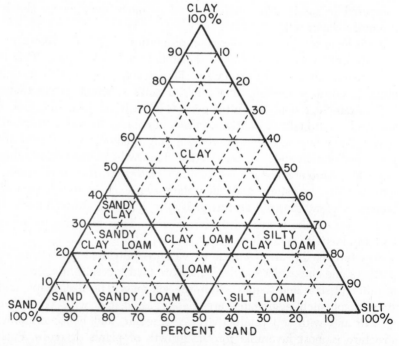

Figure 9. The Amounts of Sand and Clay in the Various Soil Textural Classes.

always. Gray, graying blue, and drab colors typically indicate a low organic matter content or a lack of sufficient oxygen. In the more arid regions these colors may be due to scanty vegetative growth. In the more humid regions they often indicate poor drainage. In either case the soil's inherent productivity is limited.

There are of course many color variations. Mottled subsoils normally indicate poor natural drainage. The yellow colors are dependent upon the presence of hydrated iron oxide. Mottling is the result of iron

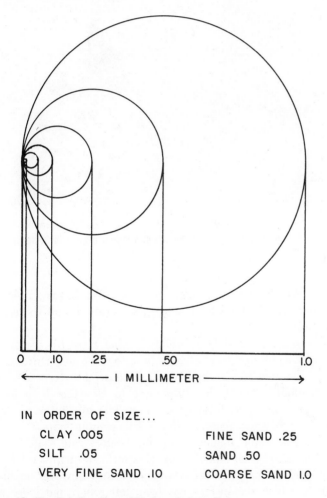

IN ORDER OF SIZE...

CLAY .005	FINE SAND .25
SILT .05	SAND .50
VERY FINE SAND .10	COARSE SAND 1.0

Figure 10. The Relative Size of Various Soil Particles.

A farm appraiser and a soil scientist examine the soil in a walnut orchard in Santa Barbara County, California.

concentrations which have not been oxidized. The brown, reddish brown, and red subsoils tend to denote good aeration, and therefore good natural drainage.

3. Relief, Drainage, and Permeability: Relief refers to the slope of the surface of a soil in a local area. It describes the major drainage profiles within the area and in the hydrologic sense. The term is often broadened to include all of the differences in elevation in a local area—the streams, the open-drainage ways, in fact all of the natural and physiographic features generally shown on a contour map.

Relief has considerable influence on the relative rate water runs off the surface of a soil each time it rains. This surface runoff is referred to as external soil drainage. Relief is a major factor; however, so also is the extent to which the surface has been left rough and loose by recent tillage operations and the vegetative cover.

Drainage refers to both the rapidity and the extent to which water is removed from a soil following a rain. Such results from both surface runoff and percolation through underground spaces. This latter characteristic is summed up in one word—permeability. It is that quality which permits the downward flow of excess water. It is determined by the height of the water table in relation to the amount of water added to the soil, by texture, by structure, and by the other physical characteristics.

Permeability enables a soil to transmit either water or air through itself. A soil's internal drainage can be excessive; it can be imperfectly or poorly drained. When a soil's internal drainage is excessive its permeability is high. The soil is often sandy in nature, the clay fraction (percent clay) is low and, therefore, ineffective in function.

A farm appraiser and a soil scientist compare two soils, one from the field next to the same walnut orchard.

Courtesy, Soil Conservation Service

One of the very productive Corn Belt soils, just freshly plowed, a bit wet perhaps, but in a very level area in Western Indiana.

The soil typically contains less organic matter than the medium textured soils, and hence has a lower moisture-holding capacity. Rain tends to be absorbed rapidly and to also drain right on down through the soil, thus leaching or carrying some of the plant nutrients with it. In fact, drainage may be so thorough and intense that plant roots are deprived of adequate moisture. This is a droughty soil.

When a soil's internal drainage is poor, its permeability is low. The sandy particles are less numerous, while the silt and clay colloids make up a larger part of the total. This soil often contains more organic matter, yet for some reason, the concentration of such may be restricted to a specific horizon. Usually it isn't very well mixed throughout the soil. Air and water cannot penetrate the various horizons uniformly. Hence, some soil particles are oxidized and some are not.

And, along with the basic soil color, there is definite mottling. This is a poorly drained soil.

4. Organic Matter and Lime Content: Soils vary greatly in organic matter and in the nature of its vertical distribution. Generally speaking, a large amount appears in the top or surface layer, and decreasing amounts appear in each of the horizons beneath. The amount of organic matter and the decomposition process is strongly influenced by climatic factors and by vegetation, particularly the more recent cultural practices.

In the tropical rain forests there is a great amount of litter, yet seldom more than an inch or two of it is incorporated into the soil. In the cooler, humid climates, the forested soils often exhibit a pre-

With adequate tile drainage some 10 additional acres of cropland could be obtained on this farm in Champaign County, Illinois. The typical drainage problem on the level, yet highly productive soils in the Corn Belt.

Courtesy, Soil Conservation Service

A tile drain installation in the process of being installed in Clackamas County, Oregon.

dominant layer of partially decomposed vegetative matter. In the temperate sub-humid climates the prairie grasses generate a large root system. The quantity and distribution of roots that die each year vary, yet these roots tend to provide a high and stable level of organic matter.

Humus is the fairly complex end product resulting from the decomposition of organic matter. It improves a soil's structure, increases its water-holding capacity, and adds to soil fertility. The decomposition process is greatly affected by the crops raised, by tillage practices, and by fertilization. Farmers have occasionally plowed down large amounts of plant residue. When such happens the material is often high in available carbohydrates and low in nitrogen. This tends to slow decomposition, tie up or immobilize the nitrogen, and as a result, crop yields are temporarily reduced. In areas where large amounts of crop residues are added to the soil annually, farmers have learned to apply fairly sizeable quantities of commercial nitrogen. This helps to keep the carbon-nitrogen ratio in balance.

Plowing and other tillage operations tend to distribute and mix organic matter throughout the soil and hasten decomposition. In certain areas the soils are tilled every other year by summer fallowing. This tends to destroy some of the organic matter, yet aid the carbon-nitrogen balance.

In areas where the more intensive cropping practices have developed, a soil can be partially destroyed or it can be gradually improved. Continuous cropping without the addition of fertilizer leads to a breakdown of soil structure, a decrease in productivity, and a decline in both crop yields and land values. With some crops, for example corn, continuous cropping and proper fertilization can improve not only the fertility level but structure as well. It can lead to

A farm worker irrigating strawberries in San Diego County, California.

Courtesy, Soil Conservation Service

increased productivity, increased crop yields, and increased farm land values.

The lime content of a soil is also directly responsible for the crops that can be raised. In soil classification, the lime content of a soil often receives special emphasis for it is used to infer other less easily ascertained soil characteristics.

Soil acidity or alkalinity is expressed as the pH of a soil. Soils vary from a little below 3.5 to a little above 9.5. A pH of 6.5 is, generally speaking, within the optimum range. At this level, the various plant nutrients required by most crops are most likely to be available.

In some areas the soil is alkaline, in fact so much so, that crop yields are depressed. In other areas the soil is acid, and again crop yields are low. The latter condition can be more easily corrected by applying lime.

5. Erosion: On some farms, soil erosion has removed a portion of the topsoil or A-horizon. Wherever this has occurred the parts that have been removed are usually the finer portions of the soil, the organic matter, and the portions highest in fertility. Soil erosion is frequently a gradual process, and like the soil formation process itself, it often occurs unnoticed. In fact, farmers have sometimes cultivated their fields unaware that part of the surface layer has been removed.

Broadly speaking, erosion is the wearing away of the earth's surface by the forces of water and wind. It is the removal and transportation of soil particles and certain leached materials. The process may be gradual or catastrophic, normal or accelerated. A normal rate removes soil from the surface at the same rate as the soil formation process penetrates downward. Erosion thus plays a major role in soil formation. An accelerated rate occurs when the earth's surface is wearing away more rapidly than is thought desirable. The latter is more serious, particularly from the standpoint of maintaining soil fertility. Soil erosion has been widely overexaggerated. However, in many areas erosion control is highly important.

There are two major types of erosion—water and wind. Water erosion occurs in the more humid areas where there is considerable rainfall. It is the result of heavy or torrential rains. It is the result of excess surface water runoff, which often moves rapidly across a field, carrying with it some of the soil itself.

Water erosion may be categorized into three phases. Sheet erosion is said to occur when a very thin layer of soil is removed fairly uniformly over the entire field. This often occurs unnoticed. In fact, an appraiser often has to use a soil auger and compare soil depth in the field with that in a nearby fence row or pasture in order to really estimate the amount of topsoil that is missing.

Rill erosion when the water becomes more concentrated in small rivulets. These rills are about the size of one's finger or forearm and are usually scattered fairly uniformly over a field. They are easy to recognize at first; however, whenever a farmer plows or cultivates, they disappear. In fact, usually very little significance is attached to rill erosion until a stream below begins to fill with silt.

Gullies represent the more advanced stages of water erosion. These are more easily recognized, for they range in size from small ditches, one foot or so in depth, to ones which are so large they cannot be crossed with tractors or field machinery.

Climate, the size of the watershed, the length and degree of the slope, the texture and structure of a soil, and the cropping practices all affect soil erosion. The major factor is the amount and intensity of rainfall. When a rain comes down gradually, as in a drizzle, the water has time to soak in, and very little erosion occurs. However, when a heavy or torrential rainfall occurs, as in a downpour, a cloud burst, or flash flood, the losses are considerable.

Alternative freezing and thawing during the winter months also speeds the process. When the ground is frozen two or three inches below the surface, yet is thawed on top and without cover—either snow or vegetation—a rain at that time often causes considerable erosion. This is because the water is unable to soak into the soil.

Erosion, of course, is both more severe and more difficult to control in the larger watersheds. The length and degree of slope both affect the velocity of the surface water runoff as it moves across an exposed surface. The greater the velocity the more the erosion. In fact, when velocity is doubled, the soil particle size that can be removed is roughly quadrupled.

The soil itself, including the parent material from which it developed, also has considerable influence. A glacial till or outwash material containing some of the larger and heavier soil materials is not as subject to erosion as is one composed of loess or windblown material. A stony or gravelly soil does not erode as easily as does a fine sand or silty clay soil. The materials that go into solution are leached out of a stony, gravelly, or sandy soil much easier than they are out of a soil containing more clay.

When water can penetrate a soil fairly rapidly there is less opportunity for it to collect at, or run off, the surface and carry soil particles with it. Hence, here again texture, structure, and permeability affect

both the erosion of the soil particle and the leaching of soil nutrients.

Wind erosion is caused by dry weather and wind. It is similar to sheet erosion in that usually only a thin layer of soil is removed. However, wind erosion is more noticeable, particularly during wind storms, as the air is often filled with small soil particles. Soil drifts may also collect in the fence rows.

Wind erosion is more serious west of the 20-inch rainfall line. The dust storms in the Great Plains during the 1930's are well-known. Texas, Oklahoma, Kansas, Nebraska, the Dakotas, Colorado, Wyoming, and Montana have always been more susceptible to wind erosion than other areas of the country even though these other areas have been more continuously cropped. This area, of course, has long had a high proportion of land in summer fallow.

However, wind erosion can occur in any area—particularly where the soil particles tend to be loose, for example, the sandy soils and the muck soils, and where the wind has a chance to sweep across wide and level areas.

Thus, many an inventory of erosion control practices and their probable effectiveness is an important part of a farm appraisal on many farms. Two types of control practices are common. Vegetative practices are concerned primarily with field layout, the crop rotations, and certain cultural practices, such as field strip or contour strip farming. Mechanical practices, while influenced by field layout, are concerned primarily with the fashioning of the soil itself into terraces and the building of earthen dams and concrete structures.

Soil Surveys and Land Classification: Beginning in 1899 the soil scientists began to make soil surveys. These surveys typically consist of both a soils map and a written report. They show the distribution of the various soil types in the area and describe most if not all of the various soil characteristics, usually in detail.

A soils map relates soil types to the more prominent physical features of the earth's surface. It shows the lay of the land, the natural drainage of the area, the depressions, the lakes, the amount of top soil removed through erosion, the location of farmsteads, roads, railroads, and present land use. The soil types are typically shown in colors or patterns designed to identify each area. The proper names for each

---

Four different stages of erosion.

Courtesy, Soil Conservation Service

soil type are listed in the legend. Individual maps are often used to show individual soil characteristics—depth, texture, slope, color, or combinations of several of these. Most are published on a scale of 1 inch to 1 mile.

A written report usually accompanies each map and describes the basic characteristic of each soil, along with the observable features relevant to its nature and behavior. This report typically relates all soils in the area to each other, and it often rates the various soils according to their relative adaptability to various crops and according to their productivity, either inherent or under a specific level of management.

The modern soil survey furnishes the farm appraiser with more relevant information than perhaps any other single publication. At the same time many appraisers learn to observe the soils in their area, to investigate on their own with a soil auger or tube, and to relate soil characteristics to both the crops raised and crop yields.

Soil classifications are commonly based on three categories. Soils are typically divided into soil series, series into soil types, and types into soil phases. A soil series is a group of soils which have developed from similar parent materials. The soil horizons are similar, both in external characteristics and in arrangement. With one exception, the morphological features of the profile—the texture, structure, color and carbonate and humus contents—are all similar. The exception is the texture of the A-horizon. The names given to various soil series are generally place names taken from whatever area the soil was first defined.

A soil type is a unique combination of both internal soil characteristics—texture, structure, color, chemical composition, and other properties which characterize the soil's profile—and a soil's surface features—for example, slope and stoniness. Any one type includes soils that are alike in terms of (1) the geological features of the parent material, (2) the physical, mineralogical, chemical, and biological features of the horizons, the characteristics of which are related to the nature and function of the soil, and (3) the geomorphological features in the natural landscape.

A soil phase is a further subdivision of a soil type which relates to

---

Four different solutions to the erosion problem.

any characteristic, or combination of characteristics, which is potentially significant from the standpoint of land use or management. Differences in slope, stoniness, or degree of erosion within a given soil type are commonly significant and thus are shown as soil phases. Emphasis is given to the features that are relatively permanent and those that influence response to management.

Soil types are defined the same way everywhere. However, soil phases are more narrowly defined where the agriculture is more intensive, and less narrowly defined where the agriculture is more extensive.

Most farms have several soil types. It is this combination that gives each farm its distinctive features and which limits a farm's productivity. At the same time many farm appraisers like to group all soils in a local area into very broad and general classifications, for example, high ground and low ground soils.

High ground soils are those formed where the rainfall runs off naturally and where the surface is left exposed to the air most of the time. The top soil is usually leached (to a certain extent). It is usually somewhat acid and somewhat lighter in texture than is the subsoil. Low ground soils are those formed in depressional areas. Here, rainwater tends to collect. As a result the land is often waterlogged during much of the soil forming process. The top soil typically contains considerable visible humus. It is usually fairly deep, sweet, and variable in texture. The subsoil does not have much humus; it is often mottled in color due to poor drainage.

Soils may also be grouped into catenas. A soil catena is a group of soils which have been derived from similar parent materials but which differ in profile development and in drainage due to differing relief and other physical characteristics. The typical catena extends across a number of relief positions and is a further guide to soil classification as well as an aid to remembering various soil characteristics (Figures 11 and 12). For purposes of quick reference, the beginning appraiser often glues the local soil catenas to the back of the clipboard he uses in the field.

Sooner or later the farm appraiser likes to generalize from the more detailed soil types to soil productivities, to land use, to cropping systems, and to the per-acre yields. One of the very best generalizations

---

Four areas for investigation by farm appraisers: an unproductive wet spot near Brookston, Indiana (upper left), a salinity problem near Delta, Utah (upper right), flooding near Jefferson City, Missouri (lower left), and wind erosion near Quay, New Mexico (lower right).

Courtesy, Soil Conservation Service

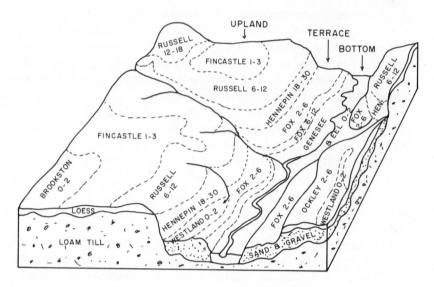

Figure 11. A Schematic Cross Section Showing the Topographic
Position and Natural Drainage for the Fincastle-
Russell (and Other) Soils Along the Wabash River.

is the land use capabilities information developed by the soil conservation service. Land use capabilities are based on (1) soils, (2)
relief or slope, and (3) the amount of top soil which remains. The
classification presents the various limitations on land use. It provides
guides as to crop rotations and cropping practices. It presents recommendations as to erosion control practices. All farm appraisers are
usually acquainted with land use capabilities.

Land use maps and other land classification studies are oftentimes
available. Some are based on vegetation, some on present land use
patterns, some on types of farming, and some on income levels or
economic programs, for example, drainage districts, or tax delinquency
areas. Many are more or less personal interpretations of various broad
and general cartographic classes of land use. The more accurate ones
make use of a basic soil survey and combine such with certain other
criteria which lead to a more general land classification.

No matter what information is available a farm's capacity to produce
is not easy to estimate. It is the result of not one but many factors.

A farm's natural productivity is supposedly based on the inherent and indestructible powers of its soils. For some appraisals this productivity level is the one desired. However, over time a farm's productivity can gain or lose depending on how it is farmed. Continuous cropping, along with poor cultural practices, may lead to declines in a soil's productivity. A good cropping system, the application of manure, the use of commercial fertilizers, irrigation, and other good management practices may improve a soil's productivity. Hence, most farm appraisals require a thorough study of a soil's present-day characteristics in order to estimate the subject property's long-run productivity under typical management.

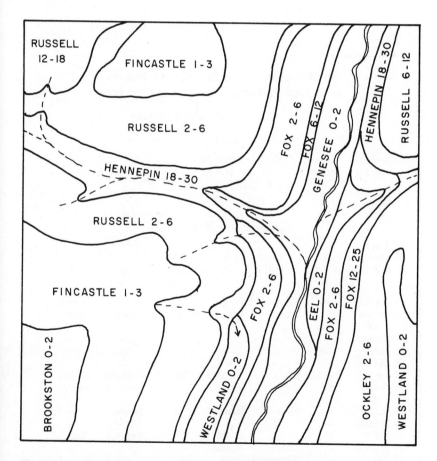

Figure 12. A Map of the Same Soils and the Same Physiographic Positions as in Figure 11.

2. CLIMATE

The climate in any given area has a tremendous influence on its agriculture. Climate is part of the soil formation process; it determines the type of vegetation. It affects the crops that can be grown, some of the methods of farming, and the crop yields per acre.

There is, of course, a tremendous variation in climate from one area to another. For example, in Central Iowa the farmers hope it will rain; in Central California they hope it won't. Every agricultural area is different. Each area has characteristics of its own.

An Illustration of How Soils May Be Grouped as to Their Predominant Slope in a Local Area

(Soils . . . in and Around Lafayette, Indiana)

S	Internal Drainage						
o	Well to	Well	Moderately	Imperfectly			
i	Excessive	Drained	Well	Drained	Very Poorly Drained		
l	Surface Drainage						
	Slow to		Moderately				
C	Rapid	Rapid	Slow	Slow	Intermittent		Ponded
a	Predominant Slope of Land Surface						
t	Flat to			Very		Depressional	
e	Sloping	Moderate	Slight	Slight	Very		
n	(0-25%)	(4-15%)	(2-4%)	(1-2%)	Slight	Slight	Deep
a	V	IV	III	II	VII	VIII	IX
14 Fox Kph	Miami	Celina	Crosby	—		Brookston	Kokomo
16 Warsaw Kph	Parr	Corwin	Odell	—		Chalmers	Romney
27 Hagener	—	—	—	—		—	—
47 Elston	—	—	—	—		—	—
49 Oaktown	—	—	—	—		—	—
37 Fox Kph	Russell	Xenia	Fincastle	Cope		Brookston	Kokomo
39 Warsaw Kph	Sidell	Dana	Raub	—		Chalmers	Romney
33 Fox	—	Ionia	Homer	—		Sebewa	—
34 Warsaw	—	—	—	—		—	—
44 Ockley	—	—	Sleeth	—		Westland	Abington
45 Longlois	—	Glenhall	Monitor	—		—	—
46 Wea	—	Tippecanoe	Crane	—		—	—
01 —	Genessee	Eel	Shoals	—		Sloan	—

A wind and snow break in Trail County, North Dakota.

The climate within any one agricultural area is remarkably uniform over time. It is commonly regarded as highly changeable, and it's sometimes suspected of cyclical tendency, however, scientific data collection has reversed both of these beliefs.

Climatological data, both monthly and yearly, can be obtained from the United States Weather Service and oftentimes from local weather stations. Most appraisers have a knowledge of the following with respect to their area.

1. The location of the local weather station, its elevation, and the length of its records.

2. The rainfall data—the 12-month average and range, the April-through-September average and range, monthly and sometimes daily distributions, along with the year-to-year variability.

3. The average frost-free dates—last frost in the spring, first frost in the fall—the latest and earliest frosts, the occurrence of occasional

off-season frosts, and the influence of such items as a large body of water. Temperatures here are typically specified as either 28° or 32°F., depending on the tolerance of the crops raised in the area.

4. The length of the growing season—both average number of days and range.

5. Temperatures—the average, the extremes, and the variations.

6. The frequency and regularity of certain climatic hazards—high winds, hail storms, tornados, hurricanes, droughts, and floods.

The extent to which each of these are mentioned or tabulated in an appraisal report varies with the client and the reason for making the appraisal.

AGRICULTURAL TRENDS

Some of the more fantastic changes occurring in the United States economy are those occurring within agriculture. Technological innovation, the increased use of capital, increased farm size and specialization, and increases in the managerial capabilities of farmers have had a tremendous impact on agriculture. A farm appraiser who does not keep up with these trends soon finds himself out-of-date.

Farm Land, Farm Numbers, and Farm Size: Every five years the Bureau of the Census enumerates the number of farms in each county, along with many of their characteristics. Considerable data relative to the trends in farm numbers, the variations in farm size, and the values of farm land are published in the *Census of Agriculture.* The data are not perfect, primarily because the definition of what constitutes a farm is changed every now and then.

Data with regard to farm size are approximations of the relative number of acres one farm family can handle in each area (Table 2, Chapter I.) The farm appraiser is interested in data for his particular county or area. Data for Humboldt County, Iowa; Cherry County, Nebraska; Addison County, Vermont; and Calhoun County, Georgia are presented here for purposes of illustration (Table 7).

Humboldt County is one of the smaller counties in the United States, covering nearly 280,000 acres in North Central Iowa. It lies entirely in the Clarion-Webster soils region. It receives an average of 30 inches of rainfall per year, 22 of which fall during the 150-day growing season. Most of the farms are cash-grain farms. The principal crops raised are corn and soybeans.

Cherry County is a large county covering nearly 6,000 square miles (3.8 million acres) in North Central Nebraska. Its population numbers less than 1.5 million and over 60 percent of these people live in town. The soils are Valentine, Nueces, and Dune Sand. Hence, the area is noted for its sand ridges and hummocky hills. The county straddles the 20-inch rainfall line, however 15 of the 20 inches typically fall during the 140-day growing season. The county is famous for its Sand Hills cattle.

Table 7. Farm Land, Number of Farms, and Farm Size.
Four Counties, United States, 1910 and 1969.

	Humboldt County, Iowa	Cherry County, Nebraska	Addison County, Vermont	Calhoun County, Georgia
Approximate Land Area (1,000 a.)	280	3,818	502	185
Land in Farms	278	3,640	253	123
Harvested Cropland	206	431	108	64
Number of Farms				
1910	1,476	2,187	2,690	1,509
1969	1,036	759	749	176
Average Farm Size (Acres)				
1910	182	933	164	74
1969	270	4,795	338	700
Number of Commercial Farms[1]				
1969	958	688	651	142
Average Farm Size (Acres)				
1969	282	5,249	372	841

Sources: **Thirteenth Census of the United States,** 1910.
United States **Census of Agriculture,** 1969.

1. Farms with sales of $2,500 and over (Economic Classes 1-5).

Addison County lies on the east side of Lake Champlain in Vermont. It's noted for its lake resorts, its rocky soils, and at one time, for having more cows than people. Near the lake are the Toledo and Vergennes soils. To the east the Dutchess and Nassau soils lie on the western slopes of the Green Mountains. The average rainfall is 35 inches per year; 20 inches fall during the 150-day growing season. Practically all of the commercial farms in the county are dairy farms.

Calhoun County is part of the Southern Coastal Plains in Georgia. It is part of the Old South. The soils are Greenville and Magnolia. The average annual rainfall for the area is over 50 inches. An average of 28 inches of rain falls during the 240-day growing season. The major crop is peanuts.

Kinds of Farm Organization: The *Census of Agriculture* classifies farms as to whether they are commercial, part-time, or part retirement farms. The commercial farms are further classified into six economic classes, according to the value of agricultural products sold. The kinds of farm organization and the agricultural products sold illustrate the skewed distribution of both farm resources and farm incomes. Data for the United States are presented in Table 1, Chapter 1. However, data for Scott County, Kentucky; Shannon County, Missouri; Ellis County, Kansas; and Pawnee County, Oklahoma are presented in this chapter. They illustrate not only the kinds of data that are available but the kinds of farms in each of these areas (Table 8).

Table 8. Number of Farms by Kind of Farm Organization. Four Counties, United States, 1969.

	Value of Farm Products Sold per Farm	Scott County, Kentucky	Shannon County, Missouri	Ellis County, Kansas	Pawnee County, Oklahoma
Commercial Farms					
Elite	$80,000 plus	7	—	11	16
High Income	60,000-79,999	11	1	6	8
Above Average	40,000-59,999	32	2	16	17
Average	20,000-39,999	106	15	78	37
Below Average	10,000-19,999	177	39	171	96
Sub-total		(333)	(57)	(282)	(174)
Low Income	$ 5,000- 9,999	225	90	244	157
Subsistence	50- 4,999	297	199	213	210
Part-time		195	140	127	168
Partial Retirement		104	42	24	76
Sub-total		(821)	(471)	(608)	(611)
Total Farms		1,154	528	890	785
Value of Agricultural Products Sold[1]					
Total for County ($1,000)		$11,059	$2,231	$17,605	$ 7,828
Per Farm		13,858	7,747	25,588	15,501

Source: United States **Census of Agriculture**, 1969.

1. Commercial farms.

Scott County is located approximately 10 miles north of Lexington, Kentucky where there is considerable off-farm employment opportunity, both in Lexington and in Georgetown. Hence, there are many residential and part-time farms. The county is located in the Central Kentucky Bluegrass Region. The major crop is Burley tobacco.

Shannon County is located in the heart of the Ozark Plateau in Missouri. A subsistence agriculture prevails. The area is most noted

for Round Springs, an underground river which comes to the surface in
the midst of this Clarksville and Lebanon soils area and for its Current
River float trips. The area is rocky and, agriculturally speaking, most
unproductive.

Ellis County is part of the Great Central Plains of Kansas. Hays is
the county seat and claims to be the Buckle-of-the-Wheat-Belt. The
predominate soil type is Hays. The area receives an average of 22 to 24
inches of rainfall, with 17 of this amount falling during the 170-day
growing season. It's a commercial farming area. The major source of
income is wheat.

Pawnee County is part of the Osage Plains which lie north and west
of Stillwater, Oklahoma. The reddish prairie soils—Zaneis and Renfrow
—predominate. The area receives an average of 36 inches of rainfall,
with 22 to 24 inches coming during the 210-day growing season. The
Bluestem and Indian grasses, which grow there naturally, lead to
livestock grazing. Small cow herds, pasture, some cotton, and wheat
are the principal sources of income.

Farm Ownership: The various agricultural areas also differ as to
land ownership. Yankton County, South Dakota; Piatt County, Illinois;
Clinton County, Indiana; and Cortland County, New York illustrate
some of the variation (Table 9).

Table 9. Number of Farms by Operator and by Type of Business Organization.
Four Counties, United States, 1969.

	Yankton County, So. Dakota	Piatt County, Illinois	Clinton County, Indiana	Cortland County, New York
Number of Farm Operators[1]				
Full Owners	314	160	366	317
Part Owners	362	281	353	174
Tenants	163	382	231	41
Acres Farmed (1,000)				
Full Owners	79	31	51	82
Part Owners	164	117	125	62
Tenants	51	128	65	11
Percent of Tenancy	19.4	46.4	24.3	7.7
Type of Organization				
Proprietor	722	675	706	460
Partnership	111	125	230	71
Corporation	2	6	8	—

Source: United States **Census of Agriculture,** 1969.

1. Commercial farms.

The farms in Piatt County, Illinois are mostly flat. A soil scientist would say "level." Most of them are cash-grain farms. Many of them are owned by absentee-owners and farmed by tenant-operators. The farms in Cortland County, New York are largely hillside farms and dairy farms. The majority of them are owner-operated.

Farm Population: Estimates of the current farm population, its distribution by age, sex, labor force status, and at times other characteristics, along with the components of annual change (births, deaths, and migration), are published in *Farm Population Estimates.* These data are for the nation. However, the farm appraiser is interested mainly in changes occurring in the counties where he is appraising. Hence, data for Lancaster County, Pennsylvania; Jerome County, Idaho; Orange County, Florida; and Maricopa County, Arizona are presented, again for purposes of illustration (Table 10).

Farm Production: A major statistical series emphasizing the changes in farm production and in farm efficiency both for the United States and for each of 10 major regions is published annually in a U.S.D.A. publication entitled "Changes in Farm Production and Efficiency." The data show the major trends occurring in agriculture (Table 11). They include the acreages of harvested crops, amounts of plant

Table 10. Population and Employment Data. Four Counties, United States, 1969.

	Lancaster County, Pennsylvania	Jerome County, Idaho	Orange County, Florida	Maricopa County, Arizona
Population, Total (1,000)	319.7	10.3	344.3	967.5
Rural Non-Farm	107.2	2.2	51.5	53.1
Percent	33.5	21.1	15.0	5.5
Rural Farm	39.2	3.8	6.2	10.8
Percent	12.3	37.3	1.8	1.1
Change in Population 1960-70 (Percent)	−0.2	−12.5	+30.6	+45.8
Employment, Total (1,000)[1]	136.7	3.9	126.7	362.2
In Agriculture	8.0	1.2	6.0	12.3
Percent in Agriculture	5.8	30.6	4.7	3.4
Number of Households (1,000)	97.8	3.3	108.6	302.6
Persons per Square Mile	338	17	378	105

Source: **United States Census of the Population,** 1970.

1. 16 years of age and over.

nutrients used, numbers of tractors and specialized machines on farms, and the man hours of labor used by various enterprises. Index numbers relative to total farm production, the major farm inputs, crop production per acre, and output per man hour are presented, along with the number of persons provided food and fiber by one farm worker.

Acres of Harvested Crops and Crop Yields: Estimates as to the acreages of various crops harvested, crop yields per acre, and total crop production are also available in the *Agricultural Census,* in *Agricultural Statistics* and in the U.S.D.A.'s *Crop Production* publication. These data can also be obtained from the Statistical Crop Reporting Service in various states. The data show the type of agriculture in each area. Data for Van Wert County, Ohio; Sunflower County, Mississippi; Rio Grande County, Colorado; and Fresno County, California are again illustrations (Table 12). By dividing the acreage of each crop raised by the total acreage of all crops raised the percentages

Table 11. Changes in Farm Production and Efficiency.
The United States, and the Southeast, 1950-1972.

	1950	1955	1960	1965	1970	1971	1972
The United States							
Acres Harvested Cropland (mil. a.)	336	333	317	292	293	305	296
Tons Plant Food (mil.)	2.8	4.5	5.6	8.5	12.8	13.7	13.8
No. of Tractors (mil.)	3.3	4.3	4.7	4.8	4.6	4.6	4.5
Hours of Labor (bil.)	15.1	12.8	9.8	7.8	6.5	6.4	6.2
Total Farm Output[1]	86	97	106	115	120	130	131
Crop Production per Acre[1]	83	89	106	120	123	135	137
Farm Production per Man Hour[1]	60	81	116	157	195	216	226
Total Population (mil.)	152	165	180	194	204	206	208
Farm Employment (mil.)	9.9	8.4	7.1	5.6	4.5	4.4	—
Persons Supplied by One Farm Worker	15.5	19.5	25.8	37.0	47.1	48.2	—
The Southeast[2]							
Acres of Cropland (mil.)	18.7	17.3	13.3	11.5	11.8	12.8	12.4
Tons of Plant Food (1,000)	214	327	393	483	674	692	729
Total Farm Output[1]	86	111	107	125	133	148	148
Crop Production per Acre[1]	80	104	117	154	146	157	164
Farm Production per Man Hour[1]	54	84	112	161	193	216	221

Source: **Changes in Farm Production and Efficiency,** U.S.D.A., E.R.S. Statistical Bulletin 233, 1972.

1. 1957-1959 equals 100.
2. Alabama, Georgia, South Carolina, and Florida.

of each can be obtained. These figures can then be used perhaps as guides to the typical crop rotation in the area.

Any trend or persistent change in these data over time may indicate a change in land use and perhaps in the type of farming. The appraiser, of course, must be knowledgeable about any features which limit crop production and those which occasionally lead to crop failure. He must check, adjust, and use these figures accordingly.

Table 12. Acres of Crops Harvested and Crop Yields per Acre.
         Four Counties, United States, 1969.

Major Crops		Van Wert County, Ohio	Sunflower County, Mississippi	Rio Grande County, Colorado	Fresno County, California
Acres of Crops Harvested (1,000 a.)					
Corn, Grain		62.6	0.9	—	7.6
Corn Silage		0.7	—	—	7.3
Soybeans		86.5	180.2	—	0.4
Grain Sorghum		0.1	1.0	—	12.4
Wheat		22.6	6.0	—	24.1
Barley		—	—	31.6	184.0
Oats		15.8	5.3	2.6	1.0
Alfalfa Hay		2.3	—	18.8	90.0
Other Hay		3.7	4.7	11.3	1.8
Cotton		—	114.7	—	172.1
Potatoes		—	—	19.8	0.9
Tomatoes		—	—	—	13.2
Vegetables		0.4	0.3	0.6	55.3
Orchards		—	—	—	256.4
Grapes		—	—	—	176.0
Acres Irrigated		—	22.7	113.2	1,033.4
Crop Yields per Acre					
Corn, Grain	bu.	91.4	68.4	—	84.1
Corn Silage	ton	15.0	—	—	17.3
Soybeans	bu.	29.8	15.1	—	48.8
Grain Sorghum	bu.	52.7	44.1	—	17.8
Wheat	bu.	44.5	26.2	—	49.0
Barley	bu.	—	—	62.7	55.8
Oats	bu.	75.2	43.6	50.5	53.8
Alfalfa Hay	ton	2.9	—	2.0	5.5
Other Hay	ton	1.7	2.0	1.5	2.3
Cotton	bale	—	1.0	—	2.1
Potatoes	cwt.	—	—	226	196
Grapes	ton	—	—	—	7.3

Source: United States **Census of Agriculture,** 1969.

Livestock Numbers and Rates of Livestock Production: Data on livestock numbers, inventory values, rates of livestock production, and total production are also available from the *Census of Agriculture.* Data for the United States, for individual states, and for each individual county can be obtained. Those for Deaf Smith County, Texas; Carbon County, Wyoming; Delaware County, Iowa; and Dane County, Wisconsin show the variation in numbers of livestock being raised in these counties (Table 13). Again any trend or persistent change over time may indicate a permanent change in livestock numbers and thus a change in type of farming.

Data with regard to crop yields and rates of livestock production are useful in keeping an appraiser up-to-date on the changes that are occurring in the area. Data for individual livestock enterprises and for the above-average commercial farms may be obtained from various university-sponsored farm-record-keeping projects and from crop and

Table 13. Number of Farms with Livestock and Livestock Numbers per Farm. Four Counties, United States, 1969.

	Deaf Smith County, Texas	Carbon County, Wyoming	Delaware County, Iowa	Dane County, Wisconsin
Number of Farms with . . .				
Livestock	506	238	1,582	2,855
Cattle and Calves	477	210	1,414	2,661
Beef Cows and Heifers	231	120	252	358
Milk Cows and Heifers	38	80	1,003	1,847
Farrowing Enterprise	51	7	1,258	999
Hogs and Pigs	98	15	1,358	1,327
Sheep	15	105	120	205
Poultry	65	39	465	721
Horses	193	181	233	634
Number of . . . per Farm				
Cattle and Calves	640	529	53	62
Beef Cows and Heifers	103	424	33	25
Milk Cows and Heifers	10	2	23	36
Litters Farrowed	31	3	45	22
Hogs and Pigs	78	17	211	110
Sheep	514	2,021	37	44
Poultry	96	39	831	438
Horses	3.8	16.3	3.2	4.4

Source: United States **Census of Agriculture,** 1969.

dairy herd improvement associations (Table 14).

Farm Practices: The farm appraiser must also have a thorough knowledge of the various farm practices in his area. These vary considerably. Not always are actual data available or published. However, by patiently digging one can usually find such. The farm appraiser typically has some of each of the following in his handbook.

1. Typical per-acre seed and fertilizer rates for each of the major crops raised in his area—for example, corn plant populations and the amounts of fertilizer applied per acre (Table 15).

The latter may be expressed in terms of N, P_2O_5 and K_2O or in terms of N, P, and K. In either case an appraiser may have need for the following conversions.

$$\text{Lbs. of } P_2O_5 \div 2.29137 = \text{lbs. of P}$$

$$\text{Lbs. of } K_2O_5 \div 1.20459 = \text{lbs. of K}$$

2. Typical feed requirements per head of livestock for each major livestock enterprise—for example, the typical amounts of corn and protein required per sow or per hog raised (Table 16).

**Table 14. Changes in the Rates of Livestock Production.
Various Areas and Sources, 1960-1972.**

	Milk per Cow			Pigs per Litter		Percent Calf Crop[3]	
Year	All Farms Indiana	Purdue Records	U.S. D.H.I.A.[1]	All Farms 10 States[2]	Iowa	Florida	Texas
1960-62	7,862	10,013	10,800	7.07[4]	7.12[4]	70	84
1965	8,950	11,245	11,685	7.23[5]	7.13[5]	75	82
1966	9,160	11,421	11,976	7.35	7.33	74	84
1967	9,300	11,378	12,127	7.32	7.37	69	86
1968	9,590	11,768	12,307	7.28	7.25	73	86
1969	9,880	12,103	12,397	7.23	7.05	78	89
1970	10,051	11,340	12,553	7.22	7.30	80	88
1971	10,466	11,483	12,750	6.99	6.95	84	91
1972			13,000	7.30	7.45		

Sources: **Indiana Crop and Livestock Statistics,** 1971.
Purdue Farm Account Summaries, Various Years.
Agricultural Statistics, 1972.
Hogs and Pigs, U.S.D.A., S.R.S.
Calf Crop, U.S.D.A., S.R.S.

1. Dairy Herd Improvement Association.
2. 1960-62 data for the Corn Belt.
3. Not strictly a calving rate. Figure represents calves born expressed as a percentage of the number of cows and heifers 1 year old and over on farms and ranches January 1.
4. December-May Litters.
5. December-February Litters.

Table 15. Some Typical Corn Plant Populations and Fertilizer Rates.
The Central Corn Belt, U.S.A., Early 1970's.

| | | Fertilizer Use (Lbs.) | | |
| | | Corn | Soybeans | Wheat |
State	Corn Plant Population	N-P$_2$O$_5$-K$_2$O	N-P$_2$O$_5$-K$_2$O	N-P$_2$O$_5$-K$_2$O
Ohio	18.2[1]	90-70-73	12-38-39	42-57-55
Indiana	18.3	113-76-94	10-29-42	52-56-53
Illinois	19.1	113-67-64	30-41-48	59-64-53
Iowa	19.2	—	10-34-45	—

Source: Field Crop Sheet, Indiana Crop and Livestock Reports.
1. Thousand plants, 1972 data.

Table 16. Some Typical Feed Requirements per Sow and per Hog Raised.
The Central Corn Belt, U.S.A., 1970's.

Typical Feed Requirements by Enterprise System	Bushels of Corn	Pounds of Supplement
Gilt or Sow, Through Weaning, 1-Litter	24.1	356
2-Litters	52.8	723
Per Hog Raised, 40-215 lbs.	10.6	84
Total, Sow and 1-Litter System		
7.3 Pigs Raised per Litter	101.3	969
Total, Sow and 2-Litter System		
6.3 Pigs Raised per Litter	183.5	1,721
7.2 Pigs Raised per Litter	204.0	1,908
7.8 Pigs Raised per Litter	217.7	2,033
8.2 Pigs Raised per Litter	226.8	2,116
8.9 Pigs Raised per Litter	242.8	2,262
Per Market Hog Sold (7.8 Pigs per Litter) (Includes Breeding Stock)	15.0	140
Feed Required per cwt. of Gain (Includes Breeding Stock)	380-400	60-78

Source: **Farm Planning Props**, Purdue University.

3. Typical space requirements per head of livestock (Table 17). Every year or so the *Doane Agricultural Service* publishes a set of recommendations. Every now and then some of the farm magazines do the same.

Table 17. Some Typical Building Space Requirements.
Per Cow, per Sow, and per Steer.

1. Dairy Cattle

Stanchion Barns		Loose Housing	
Total Floor Area	60-80 sq. ft.	Barn Space,	50 sq. ft. per cow
Feedway, Width	3'6"-4'6"		30 sq. ft. per heifer
Stall, Width and Length		Surfaced Lot	80 sq. ft. per cow
1,000 lb. Cows	3'9" x 5'0"		40 sq. ft. per heifer
1,200 lb.	4'0" x 5'4"	Freestalls, Width and Length	
1,400 lb.	4'3" x 5'8"	Heifers	3'0" x 6'0"
1,600 lb.	4'6" x 6'0"	1,100 lb. Cows	3'8" x 7'6"
Gutters, Width	16-18"	1,400 lb.	4'0" x 7'6"
Depth	10-16"	Alley Width	
Litter Alley, Width	8'0"	2-12 Stall Rows	8'
General		2-16 Stall Rows	10'
Dirt Lot	300-1,200 sq. ft.	2-24 Stall Rows	12'
Surfaced Lot	40- 100 sq. ft.	Bunk Space per Cow	
Shade	30- 40 sq. ft.	Silage, Free Choice	12"
Holding Pens	15- 25 sq. ft.	Limit Feeding	30"
Maternity	1-12 x 12 pen per 20 cows	Hay Bunk	10"

2. Hogs

Farrowing Facilities	Gilts	Sows		40-75	75-125	125-210
Stalls	22" x 6'	24" x 7'	Growing-Finishing	Lbs.	Lbs.	Lbs.
Conventional Pens	6' x 8'	8' x 8'	**Pasture**			
Long Pens	4.5' x 15'	4.5' x 15'	Head per Acre	20-35	15-20	10-20
	Before	With	Hogs per Foot	8-10	6-8	4-6
Sows	Farrowing	Pigs	Feeder			
Sleeping Space, sq. ft.	20-35	48-80	Shade, sq. ft.	5-6	6-8	8-12
Lot Space			**Semi-Confinement**			
Dirt Lot, sq. ft.		110-200	Lot Space, sq. ft.	8	12	16
Surfaced Lot, sq. ft.		20-30	Building Space, sq. ft.	6	7	8
Pasture		10-12 Sows per Acre	Pigs per Hole of Self-Feeder			
			Grain	5	5	4
Shade			Supplement	9	9	8
Before Farrowing, sq. ft.		20-30	**Confinement (Solid Floor)**			
With Pigs, sq. ft.		50-60	Pen Space, sq. ft.	4	6-7	9
			Other Space, sq. ft.	1	1	2
			Confinement (Slotted Floor)			
			Pen Space, sq. ft.	4	6	8
			Other Space, sq. ft.	1	1	2

(Continued)

Table 17 (Continued).

| | 3. Beef Cattle | | Cows and |
	Calves	Yearlings	Two-Year Olds
Feedlot Sq. Ft.			
Dirt	150-500	300-1,000	300-1,200
Surfaced	30- 50	35- 80	35- 100
Shade	15- 25	25- 35	30- 40
Open Shed			
Width Recommended	24-32'	24-32'	24-32'
Floor Area, sq. ft.	12-30	15-25	30-40
Covered Feedlot			
Solid Floor, sq. ft.	35	40	—
Slotted Floor, sq. ft.	15-20	20-25	—
Feed Bunk Space			
Limited Feeding	18″	20″	24″
Full Fed, Roughage	6″	6″	6″
Grain	4″	4″	4″
Height at Throat	24″	30″	30″

Source: **Doane's Agricultural Report,** pp. 209 and 210.

Leasing Arrangements: In the agricultural Midwest a good many farms are owned by absentee-owners and operated by tenants on a crop- or a crop-and-livestock-share basis. The farm appraiser in these areas must have a knowledge of the typical landlord-tenant arrangements—the typical share of the crop and/or livestock returns received by each party, the contributions made by each party, and the methods used to share various costs.

A landlord-tenant arrangement is essentially a bargain between two persons, one having a farm to rent, the other looking for a farm to operate. The desire of each person is to obtain the use of those resources owned by the other person as cheaply as possible. A landowner may, of course, make certain concessions in order to obtain a tenant whom he particularly wants. Vice versa, a tenant may make certain concessions in order to obtain a particular farm. The resulting arrangements vary widely. There are no patterns. However, the following are fairly typical of Central Indiana, Illinois, and Iowa.[5]

---

5. Many of these leases are verbal. Most are one-year leases, running from March 1 through February 28. Many are assumed to be renewed automatically unless either party notifies the other by September 1. Renewal is taken for granted when the tenant-operator sows wheat or begins to fall plow for the following year.

A Crop-Share Cash Lease: In a crop-share cash lease the landlord and the tenant each typically receives a 50 percent share of the crops produced.[6] The landlord contributes the land, all buildings, most of the permanent improvements (for example, the fences), and sometimes some equipment. He pays the real estate taxes, insurance on the buildings, and all upkeep on the buildings and improvements. The tenant furnishes all labor and all power and machinery. He pays for all hired labor, all machinery repairs, and usually all gasoline. The other operating expenses, such as seed, fertilizer, insecticides, and herbicides, are divided 50-50. In addition, the tenant may pay the landlord a fixed amount of cash or privilege rent for the use of the house, use of the improvements, and maybe use of the pasture.

A Crop-and-Livestock-Share Lease: In a crop-and-livestock-share lease the landlord and tenant own the livestock jointly. Each typically receives a share of the income from both the crops and the livestock (usually 50-50). The landlord contributes the land, all buildings, and most permanent improvements, usually one-half of the productive livestock and one-half of the livestock equipment (feed grinder, manure spreader, milk cooler, milking machine). He pays the real estate taxes, insurance on the buildings, and all upkeep on the buildings and improvements. The tenant furnishes all labor and all power and machinery, usually one-half of the productive livestock, and one-half of the livestock equipment. He pays all hired labor, machinery repairs, and the taxes and insurance on the property he owns. All other operating expenses—seed, fertilizer, feed, veterinary bills, and livestock expense—are divided 50-50.

ECONOMIC STATISTICS

The United States probably has the best economic statistics in the world. These statistics develop and show many of the economic changes which are of interest to farm appraisers. The data are comprehensive. The various statistics kept by an appraiser depend on the type of client and on the reasons for or uses being made of one's appraisals.

The appraiser should know what each statistic represents—the concepts and definitions used in its development. He should know what

---

6. This is true in the good land areas. Where the land is lower in productivity, landlords and tenants often share the crop, as well as some of the operating expenses, on a 60-40, 66-33, or 75-25 basis.

each series is, and what it does and does not measure. He should know something about how the data are obtained, tabulated, and analyzed, whatever is known about their accuracy and reliability, and how each particular series relates to others. Obviously it is not possible to discuss each of these questions in depth. Yet, all persons who use statistics must guard against misinterpretation. Different persons on different sides of the same argument often use the same statistics.

The first five sets of data presented here are kept by many farm appraisers. The last two sets are kept mainly by those persons who do farm loan work.

Market Activity and Farm Real Estate Values: The long-term economic position of agriculture may be measured by the relative amounts of farm real estate activity and by the changes in farm real estate values. These changes have broad implications for farm owners, for the prospective buyers of farm real estate, insurance agents, tax officials, persons making farm mortgage loans, and others.

Data on market activity and on farm land values are published twice yearly in *Farm Real Estate Market Developments* by the Economic Research Service. The figures are based on semiannual estimates made by the U.S.D.A.'s crop reporters.[7] In between times special surveys are occasionally sent to obtain supplemental information from real estate brokers, attorneys, bankers, and farm loan men. Every five years the figures are checked against each new set of data reported by the *Census of Agriculture*. Adjustments at this point are quite often made.

Activity in the farm real estate market is measured in terms of the number of farms sold per 1,000 farms in each area (Figure 13). This series is available for the United States and for all individual states. Five methods of transfer are generally recognized.

1. Voluntary sales and trades (excluding contracts but not options).

2. Mortgage foreclosures.

3. Sales due to tax delinquencies.

4. Sales resulting from inheritance and gifts.

5. Administrators' and executors' sales and others of a miscellaneous and unclassified nature.

Farm real estate values are also published semiannually in *Farm Real Estate Market Developments*. Data for each county and the changes for each county presented in Tables 7 through 13 are presented

---

7. Farm land is commonly transferred, and possession or occupancy is commonly given, as of March 1. Hence, the data are as of this date and October 1.

in Table 18. Every appraiser should have figures similar to these for every county in which he appraises farms.

Farm real estate values are also available on a semiannual basis for the United States, for individual states, and for various production regions. Two series are available: (1) dollar values, both per farm and per acre, and (2) index numbers of average per-acre values. The dollar value series is the more useful one for comparing the level of farm real estate values between or among various states or regions (Table 19). However, as a measure of change over time, the index series is preferable (Table 20).

The index measures the change in farm real estate values by expressing each figure as a percent of some base period. For example, a three-year base period—1957-59—is used in Table 20. The three-year index is set at 100 and the figure for each year, before or after, is then expressed as a percent of this three-year base. The index thus shows the relative changes that have occurred. The index can be used to estimate the current value of a subject property based on its sale price sometime in the past; or, it can be used to estimate the subject farm's value in the past based on a current sale price.

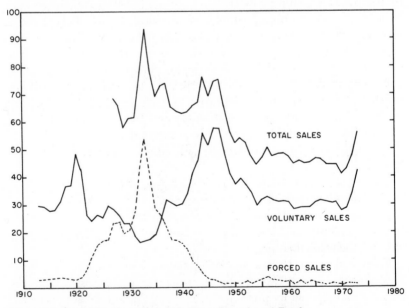

Figure 13. Farm Title Transfers: Voluntary, Forced, and Total.
Number of Farms Transferred per 1,000 Farms, United
States, 1912-1973.

Table 18. Farm Real Estate Values per Acre.
Various Counties, 1959, 1964, and 1969.

County	State	Dollar Value per Acre			Percent Change	
		1959	1964	1969	1959/1969	1959/1964
Humboldt	Iowa	358	388	551	53.8	42.1
Cherry	Nebraska	31	42	49	61.8	16.7
Addison	Vermont	95	130	235	146.5	80.0
Calhoun	Georgia	57	92	194	243.1	112.0
Scott	Kentucky	330	375	488	47.9	30.0
Shannon	Missouri	39	56	120	207.2	112.1
Ellis	Kansas	100	101	116	16.6	14.8
Pawnee	Oklahoma	74	144	174	135.1	20.6
Yankton	So. Dakota	135	146	226	67.6	54.4
Piatt	Illinois	510	562	742	45.3	32.0
Clinton	Indiana	361	404	515	42.9	27.5
Cortland	New York	90	102	164	81.5	60.4
Lancaster	Pennsylvania	494	603	924	87.0	53.4
Jerome	Idaho	285	249	321	12.5	28.7
Orange	Florida	778	1,132	1,213	56.0	7.1
Maricopa	Arizona	432	333	422	−2.5	26.5
Van Wert	Ohio	338	429	486	43.7	13.3
Sunflower	Mississippi	183	285	368	101.0	29.4
Rio Grande	Colorado	132	145	216	63.3	48.9
Fresno	California	482	572	586	21.5	2.4
Deaf Smith	Texas	132	198	233	76.4	17.4
Carbon	Wyoming	13	20	35	170.4	71.8
Delaware	Iowa	241	265	384	59.2	44.9
Dane	Wisconsin	233	289	460	97.5	59.0

Source: United States **Census of Agriculture,** 1959 and 1969.

The dollar values in the *Census* are aggregates. They are, by necessity, weighted according to the size, type, and quality of farms reported. Changes in the definition of a farm and in the methods of
obtaining the data are occasionally made. Hence, the *Census* measures
and reports changes in the values of a constantly changing composition
of farm real estate. However, in constructing its index, the U.S.D.A.
uses data sources and weighting procedures which attempt to hold
both the land base and the quality of land more nearly constant. This
minimizes the influence of change in each of these, which is inherent
in the dollar value series.

Unfortunately, the statistics on farm real estate values are none too
reliable. This is no fault of the data or their collection. It is largely a

Table 19. Farm Real Estate Values per Acre.
Select States, and the San Joaquin Valley, 1971, 1972, 1973.

| State or Area | Dollars per Acre, March 1 | | | |
	1970	1971	1972	Average
Select States				
New Jersey	1,171	1,364	1,599	1,378
Illinois	491	527	590	536
Wisconsin	257	278	336	290
Nebraska	157	171	195	174
Texas	155	172	194	174
Montana	63	68	76	69
Wyoming	42	47	54	48
The San Joaquin Valley in California				
Irrigated Orchard Land	1,795	1,950	—	1,872
Truck and Vegetable Crops	1,120	1,135	1,215	1,157
Intensive Field Crops	935	980	1,005	973
Non-Irrigated Cropland	405	420	430	418
Pastureland	340	375	330	348
Rangeland	225	250	205	227

Source: **Farm Real Estate Market Developments**, C D 78, July 1973.

result of the unique characteristics of the farm real estate market. The market is a local one, a sporadic one, and largely unorganized. No standards of quality prevail. The low incidence of transfer, the lack of comparability among farm units, and the many factors affecting both supply and demand make data collection and analysis difficult.

The data largely represent market values rather than market prices. They are based mostly on subjective opinions or estimates made by farm owners rather than farm transfers or farm sales. Ever since the 1930's, farm real estate values have been rising, at first gradually but more recently quite rapidly (Figure 1 Chapter I). Many persons assume today that this upward trend will continue indefinitely. This thought or idea has undoubtedly led to some upward bias in the data, with smaller, temporary, and year-to-year changes being somewhat ignored.

In using the data one needs to be aware of certain problems.

1. The *Census* includes in its data large numbers of part-time and residential farms. This is particularly the case in the transition areas around urban centers. For this reason the *Census* has not always provided perhaps a true indication of the values of the real estate used primarily for farming.

2. The U.S.D.A. series, both the dollar value and the index, refers to farm real estate, not farm land. This definition is adhered to in

order to approximate a composite of both land and the improvements associated with it—that composite which is traditionally bought and sold in the market.

3. The 16,000 to 20,000 crop reporters who make farm value estimates are primarily farm owners. There is a strong tendency for these owners to report asking prices or holding values rather than market prices. The market prices they quote are often the high ones they happened to hear about rather than the average. This is particularly the case when the number of farm transfers is small.

4. The sale price of a given farm property measures that farm's market value only to the extent that the sale is a bona fide sale or an arm's length transaction between seller and buyer. If the sale price was biased for any reason, that same bias carries over into any value estimated by the index.

5. The data series, the index in particular, indicates the overall changes which have taken place in each state as a whole, and may conceal significant variations in value within small or local areas. This, of course, is inherent in any average or index. Nevertheless, if the index is used in an area where land values have risen more rapidly than for the state as a whole, for example, in and around an urban center, the index will underestimate the changes which have

Table 20. Index Numbers Showing the Change in Farm Real Estate Values.[1]
Select States, 1960-1973.

Year	Pennsylvania	Illinois	Wisconsin	Nebraska	Texas	Wyoming	California
1960	111	106	107	110	117	113	116
1961	114	102	109	111	122	120	125
1962	118	105	113	117	129	125	131
1963	125	111	111	118	140	130	136
1964	131	116	115	128	147	136	148
1965	141	124	118	135	159	141	160
1966	150	139	125	145	165	148	171
1967	160	149	138	157	172	156	171
1968	171	156	146	169	184	164	180
1969	188	163	160	177	195	171	186
1970	214	161	174	180	204	180	186
1971	230	159	190	184	212	187	185
1972	251	167	205	199	234	203	196
1973[2]	300	191	249	228	265	237	197

Sources: **Farm Real Estate Market Developments.** July 1973.
Agricultural Statistics, 1961, 1966, and 1971.

1. 1957-1959 equals 100.
2. Estimate.

occurred in the values in that area. Similarly, it will overestimate the changes in the values in those areas where there has been a less-than-average change in farm real estate values.

6. Whenever the index is used to estimate changes in the value of a given farm over time that farm must have remained relatively the same physically. The index cannot, for example, estimate changes in the value of a subject property caused by erosion, or by new field tile, a new machinery shed, or a new farrowing house.

In spite of all these limitations the index of farm real estate values is a most useful tool for farm appraisers and others. It is used to adjust the sale prices of comparable farms, to make annual adjustments in farm inventory values, to update the rental rates in cash farm leases, and for many other purposes.

Size of farm, amount of tillable land, extent of improvements, type of seller, reasons for selling, type of buyer, intended use after purchase, complete unit versus farm enlargement, method of finance and many other factors affecting the land market are published in the U.S.D.A.'s *Farm Real Estate Market Developments*. When these data are related to market activity or to farm real estate values, the relationships developed are often of more interest than the rates of transfer or dollar values themselves. They often help to further explain the financial position of farm families.

Farm Prices Received and Farm Prices Paid: Farm appraisers are most aware of the influence that the general price level has on the economy as a whole, and of the influence that the relationship between farm prices and farm costs has on agriculture. The Bureau of Labor Statistics calculates a wholesale price index for all commodities in the United States. This index is published in both *Agricultural Prices* and *Agricultural Statistics*. It is commonly referred to as the general price level, and holds the longest record of any price index in the history of the country (Figure 14). The United States Department of Agriculture also calculates an index of farm prices received by farmers, and an index of the various prices paid by farmers (Figure 15). These two indices are closely watched by farmers, farm managers, and farm appraisers.

The dollar prices received by farmers are reported monthly in *Agricultural Prices* and annually in *Agricultural Statistics*. In the case of farm crops the data are usually summarized on a crop-year basis (Table 21).[8] In the case of livestock and livestock product prices, the data are typically summarized in terms of 12-month average prices (January through December) (Table 22).

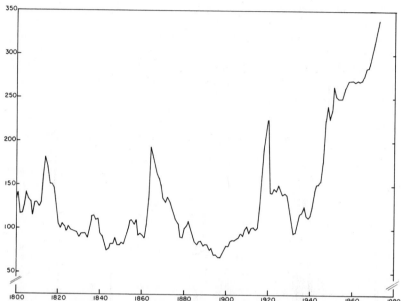

Figure 14. The General Price Level (Wholesale Price Index—1910-1914 = 100).
All Commodities, United States, 1800 Through 1972.

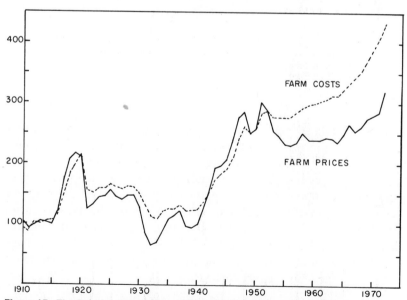

Figure 15. The Relationship Between the Index of Farm Prices Received
by Farmers and the Index of Farm Costs (1910-1914 = 100).
United States, 1910-1972.

The farm product prices received by farmers are used by appraisers to estimate the subject property's income which is in turn capitalized into the subject property's value. Farm prices thus play a sizeable role in appraising farms, for farm values are predicated on the probable income stream that can be obtained from a given farm.

Table 21. Farm Prices Received by Farmers for Various Crops.
Season Average Prices Each Crop Year, United States, 1963-1972.

Year	Corn	Soybeans	Wheat[1]	Oats	Alfalfa Hay	Clover-Timothy Hay
1963	$1.11	$2.51	$1.85	$0.62	$23.50	$24.70
1964	1.17	2.62	1.37	0.63	24.00	25.20
1965	1.16	2.54	1.35	0.62	24.00	25.80
1966	1.24	2.75	1.63	0.66	24.70	24.90
1967	1.03	2.49	1.39	0.66	23.60	23.60
1968	1.08	2.43	1.24	0.60	23.00	23.50
1969	1.15	2.35	1.24	0.59	23.90	24.30
1970	1.33	2.84	1.36	0.62	24.70	24.50
1971	1.26	2.94	1.36	0.63	27.10	25.28
1972	1.17^2	3.30^2	1.58^2	0.66^2	31.45^2	26.92^2
Average 1963-72	$1.17	$2.68	$1.44	$0.63	$25.00	$24.87
Average 1968-72	$1.20	$2.77	$1.36	$0.62	$26.03	$24.90

Sources: **Agricultural Statistics**, 1971.
Agricultural Prices, 1972.

1. Does not include value of marketing certificates—1964-1969.
2. Estimate.

The schedule of prices used by appraisers varies. Some appraisers use current farm prices, some use an average of the last 3 years, some an average for the last 5 or 10 years, and some an average for a particular price period. The major lending institutions and government agencies have often specified a particular price level as the basis for determining normal agricultural values. Most of the loan agencies thus have kept a running tabulation of farm prices received. Many of them have used average or most likely figures. Some of them have calculated 10- and 12-year moving averages, dropping off the oldest and adding the newest figure each year.

---

8. For some crops the marketing season is less than 12 months; hence, the average prices are summarized that way. Tobacco is an example.

Most important, perhaps, is that whatever schedule or level of prices is used, those prices should be presented in one's appraisal. The level of farm prices, the source of data, and the methods of calculating any average should be given.

Table 22. Farm Prices Received by Farmers for Various
          Livestock and Livestock Products.
          12-Month Average Prices, United States 1963-1972.

Year	Milk[1] 3.5%	Hogs	Calves	Feeder Steers[2] Calves	Yearlings	Fat Cattle[3]
1963	$4.53	$14.90	$24.00	$28.46	$23.71	$23.21
1964	4.58	14.80	20.40	24.14	19.71	22.21
1965	4.63	20.60	22.00	25.30	21.78	25.12
1966	5.17	22.80	26.00	30.31	24.83	25.69
1967	5.43	18.90	26.30	30.10	26.68	25.27
1968	5.67	18.50	27.60	31.26	27.92	26.83
1969	5.87	22.20	31.50	35.45	31.78	29.66
1970	6.05	22.70	34.50	38.76	33.70	29.34
1971	6.19	17.50	36.30	39.25	34.87	32.42
1972	6.40[4]	25.97[4]	43.90[4]	46.79	41.40	35.83
Average 1963-72	$5.45	$19.89	$29.25	$32.98	$28.64	$27.56
Average 1968-72	$6.06	$21.37	$34.76	$38.30	$33.93	$30.80

Sources: **Agricultural Statistics**, 1971.   1. Blend prices.
         Agricultural Prices, 1972.   2. Choice feeder steers, Kansas City.
         Livestock and Meat Statistics.   3. Choice slaughter steers, Omaha.
                                                    4. Estimate.

Prices paid by farmers are also collected and published by the United States Department of Agriculture. These costs are reported in *Agricultural Prices* quarterly. The index of all farm costs (commodities, interest, taxes, and wage rates), the index of the prices paid for goods and services used in farm production, and individual indices for farm building and fence materials, fertilizer, seed, farm wage rates, property taxes, and other costs are also available (Table 23). These indices are for the United States.

The farm appraiser typically wants costs of his area. First, he must decide on what he wants. Building construction costs, seed and fertilizer rates, custom rates, and wage rates are typically obtained. Second, he must decide how these costs will be used. They aren't always collected in their most useful form. Building cost data are often

Table 23. Changes in the Prices Paid by Farmers (Farm Costs).
United States, 1950-1972.

	Index (1910-14 = 100)						
	1950	1955	1960	1965	1970	1971	1972
Building and Fence Materials	312	356	393	391	469	505	548
Fertilizer	144	155	152	152	148	155	158
Seed	228	235	211	237	265	282	302
Wage Rates	425	516	631	728	1,083	1,140	1,203
Taxes	320	403	587	756	1,191	1,281	1,346
All Costs	255	276	300	321	390	410	433

Sources: **Agricultural Statistics,** 1953 and 1971.
Agricultural Prices, January 1972 and 1973.

converted into costs per square foot, seed costs into costs per-acre, and fertilizer costs into the cost per pound of plant food.

The best way to acquire these costs is to do so whenever the opportunity avails itself. Oftentimes this is when one sees a new farm building being built. The farm appraiser should perhaps now stop and go and ask questions. Unfortunately the job takes time. However, most farmers are proud of a new building and the fact that someone is interested enough to stop and look at it. An appraiser can usually look the building over, and inquire as to its dimensions and it's costs—both total and per square foot. The appraiser can then usually obtain from that same farmer all sorts of information about seed and fertilizer rates, custom rates, wage rates, etc.

These costs can also be obtained from other sources:

1. Farm building costs can be obtained from farm builders or contractors who are in the business. For illustration purposes building costs were obtained in West Central Indiana (Table 24).

2. Seed and fertilizer rates can best be obtained from farm suppliers. Seed costs (per bushel) and fertilizer costs (per pound) are reported each spring in *Agricultural Prices* (Table 25).

3. Typical custom rates for doing various farm jobs can be obtained most easily from the *Doane Report* which also is published each spring (Table 26). At the same time appraisers need to recognize that these rates sometimes vary from area to area.

4. Cash rents, farm wage rates, tax and interest rates are summarized in *Farm Real Estate Market Developments,* in *Farm Labor,*

and in the *Agricultural Finance Review*. These data are available for individual states as well as for the United States (Table 27). Local tax rates may also be obtained from the county auditor's or assessor's office in each county (Table 28). The current contract interest rates on loans, along with the prime rate, may be obtained from the *Federal Reserve Bulletin*, which is usually found in most libraries (Figure 16).

Most farm appraisers keep these costs and rates on file at all times. They use these various costs to estimate the farm expenses on the subject properties being appraised, and also to keep track of what is happening in the agricultural economy. The relationships between various sets of data often pinpoint a problem that may be developing. For example, there are times when property taxes are increasing rapidly. Most farm appraisers are aware of this. However, a chart showing the relationships, for example, the ones between certain farm product prices and real estate taxes point them out most vividly (Figure 17).

Table 24. Farm Building Costs.
West Central Indiana, Early 1970's.

Building or Improvement	Cost per Unit
Farm House, Ranch Style	
One-story	$18.00 to 20.00 per sq. ft.[1]
Two-story	20.00 to 24.00
Attached Garage, Insulated	6.00 to 12.00
Breezeways, Porches	3.00 to 6.00
Pole Barns for Storage	$ 1.50 to 1.75 per sq. ft.[2]
Machinery Sheds, Hay Barns	
Shop, Heated, Insulated	$ 2.50 to 3.00
Grain Storage, Corn Cribs, Double 8 ft.	$ 1.10 to 1.35 per bu.[3]
Pole Frame and Wire	0.60 to 0.75
Metal Bin	0.45 to 0.65
Livestock Facilities	
Dairy Cattle	$ 750 to $1,050 per cow[4]
Hog, Farrowing, Finish	750 to 1,050 per sow
Feeder Cattle	85 to 125 per steer

1. Rectangular shaped house over crawl space. Irregular shape add $3.00 to $5.00. On a concrete slab subtract $2.00. With full basement add $2.50. Brick veneer add 8%. Fireplace add $1,250. Air conditioned add $1,250. Extra bathroom add $600. Washroom add $400. Outdoor barbeque add $750.
2. With concrete floor add $0.45 per sq. ft.
3. Includes the typical grain dryer and handling facilities.
4. Varies considerably depending on the amount of labor saving equipment—mechanized feeding and liquid manure facilities—included.

Table 25. Seed and Fertilizer Costs. Nebraska, 1970-1973.

		Prices in April			
		1970	1971	1972	1973
Seed					
Hybrid Seed Corn	bu.	$15.70	$17.00	$21.00	$21.50
Soybean Seed	bu.	4.20	4.80	5.30	8.40
Milo	cwt.	20.00	21.50	23.00	24.00
Wheat (Sept. Price)	bu.	2.50	2.60	2.90	—
Oats Seed	cwt.	1.55	1.65	1.90	2.25
Alfalfa	ton	62.00	62.00	58.00	81.00
Fertilizer					
Ag. Limestone	ton	$ 7.10	$ 6.80	$ 6.90	$ 6.70
Ammonium Nitrate, 33.5%		58.00	62.00	64.00	71.00
Per lb. of N		0.086	0.092	0.096	0.106
Anhydrous Ammonia, 83.0%		71.00	76.00	75.00	84.00
Per lb. of N		0.043	0.046	0.045	0.051
Superphosphate 20.0%		47.00	49.00	52.00	58.00
46.0%		76.00	78.00	80.00	89.00
Per lb. of P_2O_5		0.083	0.085	0.087	0.097
Muriate of Potash, 55.0%		58.00	60.00	61.00	65.00
Per lb. of K_2O_5		$ 0.053	$ 0.055	$ 0.055	$ 0.059

Source: **Agricultural Prices,** April Issues, Various Years.

Table 26. Custom Rates for Doing Farm Work.
North Central United States, 1972.

Machine or Operation	Basis for Charge	Dollar Amount
Stalk Cutter, PTO	acre	2.10
Spreading Fertilizer[1]		
Bulk Dry	acre	1.00
Liquid	acre	1.20
Anhydrous	acre	1.85
Plowing, Moldboard Plow	acre	4.85
Discing, Tandem Disc	acre	2.10
Planting		
Corn, with Fertilizer	acre	2.60
Soybeans	acre	2.00
Drilling Small Grain	acre	1.90
Seeding Alfalfa	acre	1.85
Spraying[2]		
Fields	acre	2.00
Fence Rows	hour	7.00
Cultivating	acre	1.70
Combining		
Corn	acre	8.10
Soybeans	acre	6.40
Small Grain	acre	6.00
Crop Handling		
Dry Corn	bushel	0.08
Shell Corn	bushel	0.04
Custom farm		
Plow-harvest, Corn	acre	30.50
Making hay		
Windrowing, Self-propelled	acre	3.00
Baling, Twine	bale	0.12
Cut, Rake, Bale, Store	bale	0.34
Field Chop Silage		
Chopper and Blower[3]	hour	22.50
Silo Filling		
Upright	ton	1.80
Grinding Feed		
Corn, Corn and Cobs, Other	cwt.	0.16
Bulldozing	hour	19.00
Machine Tiling[4]	rod	3.00
Boring Post Holes	hole	0.21

Source: **Doane's Agricultural Report.**

1. Does not include materials.
2. Includes materials.
3. Includes 2 men, 2 wagons, 2 tractors.
4. Does not include the tile.

Table 27. Cash Rents, Wage Rates, and Taxes. Wisconsin, 1950-1973.

	Cash Rent		Farm Wage Rates		Hourly Earnings Production	Taxes	
Year	Per Acre Cropland	Per Head Pastured[1]	Month[2]	Day[3]	Workers[4]	Per Acre	Per $100 Value
1950	—	—	$129	$ 6.10	$1.47	$1.57	$1.78
1955	—	—	161	7.50	1.92	1.96	1.94
1960	—	—	198	8.80	2.37	2.50	1.88
1965	$14.55	$2.28	226	9.90	2.75	2.99	1.93
1966	16.70	2.45	252	10.50	2.87	3.24	1.98
1967	17.85	2.56	272	11.40	2.99	3.66	2.06
1968	18.45	2.71	295	12.20	3.18	4.13	2.17
1969	20.35	2.77	322	13.20	3.40	4.53	2.16
1970	21.20	2.60	346	14.00	3.61	5.03	2.21
1971	21.05	2.66	362	14.60	3.85[5]		
1972	22.35	2.56	387	15.70	4.11[5]		
1973	24.15	3.57					

Sources: **Farm Real Estate Market Developments,** Various Issues.
Farm Labor, Various Issues.
Handbook of Labor Statistics, 1971.
Agricultural Statistics, Various Years.
Agricultural Finance Review, January 1972.
Employment and Earnings, November 1972.

1. All Lake States.
2. With house.
3. Without board or room.
4. Average hourly earnings.
5. Estimates for September.

Table 28. Real Estate Tax Rates (Dollars per $100 of Assessed Valuation). Several Rural Townships, Tippecanoe County, Indiana, 1968-1972.

	Tax Rate Payable in				
Township	1968	1969	1970[1]	1971	1972
Jackson	$5.65	$6.21	$5.77	$6.88	$7.39
Perry	5.62	6.24	5.72	6.91	7.37
Sheffield	5.76	6.27	5.85	6.98	7.48
Shelby	5.51	6.09	5.74	6.81	7.22
Union	5.57	6.10	5.69	6.87	7.33
Washington	5.64	6.13	5.71	6.86	7.31
Wea	5.64	6.19	5.81	6.96	7.39
Average 14 Rural Townships	$5.59	$6.13	$5.74	$6.87	$7.32

Source: Auditor's Office, Tippecanoe County, Indiana.

1. All property was reappraised as of March 1, 1969, and the new basis lowered the 1969 tax rate payable in 1970.

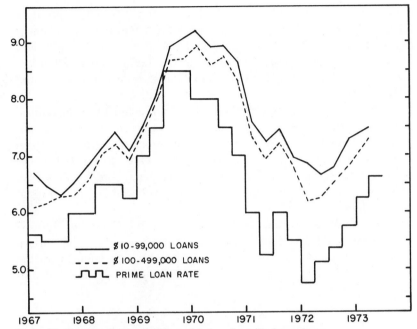

Figure 16. Average Contract Rates of Interest on Business Loans
          and the Prime Rate.
          Long Term Loans, 35 Business Centers, 1967-1973.

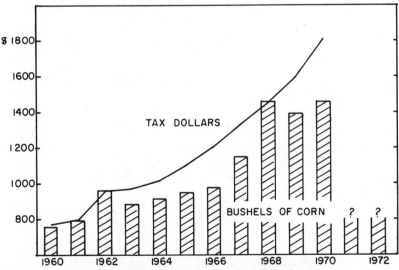

Figure 17. Bushels of Corn Required to Pay the Farm Real Estate
          Taxes on 320 Acres of Farmland, Indiana, 1972.

Farm Receipts, Production Expenses, and Incomes: Aggregate data relative to the cash farm receipts from farm marketings, government payments, farm production expenses, home consumption costs, and farm incomes are published annually in the *Farm Income Situation*. These data are available for both individual states and for the United States (Table 29).

Cash receipts from farm marketings are presented by commodities. Thus these data indicate, to some extent at least, the relative importance of the various crops grown and livestock raised in each state. However, there is one fallacy. Cash farm receipts do not reflect the amount of crops grown and subsequently fed the livestock enterprises. At the same time, these income figures tend to be related to farm real estate values (Figure 18).

Data for individual counties are available in the *Census of Agriculture* (Table 30). The farm appraiser can thus ascertain the various crops and livestock products being raised in his area, along with the importance of each, relative to the total value of all agricultural products produced.

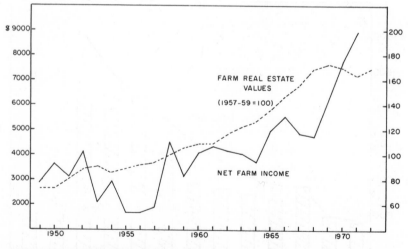

Figure 18. The Relationship Between Farm Incomes and Farm Real Estate Values. Kansas, 1949-1972.

Table 29. Cash Receipts from Farm Marketings and Farm Incomes.
Four States and the United States, 1971.

	North Carolina	Illinois	Texas	California	United States
Cash Receipts From Farm Marketings (mil. $)					
Corn	73	783	46	36	3,593
Soybeans	61	675	9	—	3,551
Rice	—	—	121	84	431
Wheat	11	54	47	31	2,081
Barley	1	—	1	77	345
Grain Sorghum	4	4	310	34	691
Hay	3	8	29	187	702
Cotton and Cottonseed	30	—	281	178	1,470
Peanuts	49	—	44	—	423
Tobacco	562	—	—	—	1,328
Truck Crops, Vegetables	53	32	159	901	3,024
Fruit, Nuts	19	10	36	1,038	2,358
Other Crops	59	58	49	475	2,612
Sub-total	(925)	(1,624)	(1,132)	(3,041)	(22,609)
Dairy Products	101	154	222	560	6,815
Cattle and Calves	62	439	1,543	942	14,972
Hogs	117	518	87	8	4,105
Sheep and Lambs	—	8	43	25	314
Poultry and Eggs	318	50	202	332	4,000
Other Livestock	3	5	25	16	248
Sub-total	(601)	(1,174)	(2,122)	(1,883)	(30,454)
Total Cash Receipts	1,526	2,798	3,254	4,924	53,063
Government Payments	41	177	468	113	3,145
Value of Home Consumption	49	22	29	14	731
Rental Value Farm Dwelling	126	152	162	144	3,118
Gross Realized Farm Income	1,742	3,149	3,913	5,195	60,057
Farm Production Expenses (mil. $)					
Hired Labor	103	87	264	939	3,809
Repairs	171	312	346	211	5,236
Seed	24	91	56	61	978
Fertilizer and Lime	96	199	133	131	2,522
Feed	226	259	619	738	7,956
Livestock	40	172	309	391	4,759
Depreciation	214	425	409	266	7,189
Taxes	36	236	149	522	3,093
Interest	36	80	132	217	1,849
Rent	32	220	36	15	1,328
Other	121	242	425	518	5,287
Total Farm Expenses	1,099	2,323	2,878	4,009	44,006
Realized Net Farm Income (mil. $)	643	826	1,035	1,186	16,051
Change in Inventory	10	139	96	2	1,346
Total Farm Income (mil. $)	653	965	1,031	1,188	17,397
Per Farm	4,243	7,780	6,112	20,837	6,049

Source: **Farm Income Estimates**, FIS 220 Supplement, August 1972.

Table 30. Cash Receipts from Farm Marketings and Farm Incomes.
Four Counties, 1969.

	Lancaster County, Pennsylvania	Jerome County, Idaho	Orange County, Florida	Maricopa County, Arizona
Land Area (1,000 acres)	605.5	380.5	582.4	5,859.2
Land in Farms (1,000 acres)	426.1	207.7	246.7	1,898.6
Percent in Farms	70.4	54.6	42.4	32.4
Farm Size (acres per farm)	80	240	202	1,006
Total Value Agricultural Products Sold (Mil. $)	152.6	28.8	77.3	263.4

Five Leading Commodities and Their Relative Importance (Percent)

Lancaster County, Pennsylvania		Jerome County, Idaho		Orange County, Florida		Maricopa County, Arizona	
Milk	27.5	Cattle	46.5	Fruit	48.9	Cattle	46.3
Cattle	24.8	Field Crops	19.4	Nursery	17.6	Cotton	10.4
Poultry	24.8	Grain Crops	16.3	Vegetables	15.1	Vegetables	10.2
Hogs	5.4	Milk	6.2	Poultry	7.5	Milk	9.7
Tobacco	5.0	Silage Crops	5.2	Cattle	6.1	Fruit	5.4

Source: United States Census of Agriculture, 1969.

Farm Record Summaries: Annual summaries of crop and livestock production, capital requirements, income analyses, and various measures of efficiency are also published by a number of universities with farm record projects. Many agricultural economics departments have farm account projects for various areas and various types of farming. These farm record summaries are most helpful in developing typical dollar receipts and expenses for the better commercial farming operations. The appraiser needs to make sure, of course, that the data are applicable to the property being appraised.

The typical farm organization on some 32 different types of farms in the major commercial farming areas are summarized annually and published in the United States Department of Agriculture's booklet entitled *Farm Costs and Returns.* Farm size, land use, livestock numbers, crop and livestock production, capital investments, cash receipts, cash expenses, cash farm income, change in inventories, farm income, interest on capital, and the returns to the operator are presented. These data tend to represent all commercial farms. Hence, in attempting to specify typical acreages, typical yields, and other data on the subject property, an appraiser should use these summaries with extreme care.

The Asset and Debt Structure: The total assets and liabilities of agriculture are presented in *The Balance Sheet of Agriculture* as though agriculture were one large enterprise (Table 31). The figures show agriculture's financial position. Inherent, of course, in any balance sheet are the dollar values placed on real estate, livestock, machinery, crop and other inventories, and other assets. These values tend to determine the dollar returns. *The Balance Sheet* calculates as a residual the percent return on the productive assets owned by farmers. This calculation is much the same as that used by appraisers to calculate the dollar returns to land.

Farm Mortgage Debt: Farm appraisers who work in the farm loan area often keep current statistics on the amounts of farm mortgage debt, along with the number and amounts of new loans (Figure 19). The amount of outstanding debt is also indicative of the financial condition of agriculture. Furthermore, when the data are related to the type of lender, they tend to reflect some of the policies of the lending institutions and government agencies (Table 32).

COMMUNITY CHARACTERISTICS

A farm's location is a major factor affecting value. This is particularly true when the farm is located near a metropolitan area, the county seat, or even a local community. In many cases, the farm is a place to live as well as an increasingly complex business. More and more families like to live just like the folks in town. Hence, most prospective buyers will pay more for a farm located on an all-weather paved road free of mud, dust, and snow. Distance is not as important as is travel time. As a result, the appraiser, when he visits the subject property, inspects all of the more frequently traveled roads. He includes in his report a number of items relative to the farm's location and the community in which it is located.

Agricultural Markets: The farming areas in which grain, livestock, and other individual farm products are raised are often determined, in part at least, by the shipping points, the available transportation, and the relative processing costs. Today, most farm products are processed off-the-farm. More and more resources are being supplied by off-farm producers or suppliers.

Several nearby markets for the principal crops and livestock raised on the subject farm are a definite asset to that farm's value. Duplication of market facilities is not always desirable; however, some degree of competition is usually beneficial. The grain elevators, the milk plants,

Table 31. The Asset and Debt Structure of the United States Farming Sector, Farmers' Equities, and the Dollar Return to Assets Used in Agricultural Production. United States, Select Years, 1950-1972.

	1950	1955	1960	1965	1970	1971	1972
Physical Assets							
Real Estate	$ 75.3	98.2	130.2	160.9	207.1	213.0	228.6
Non-Real Estate	41.3	49.4	55.2	56.9	75.9	78.3	85.8
Financial Assets	15.9	17.5	18.1	19.4	22.8	23.6	24.8
Total Assets	$132.5	165.1	203.5	237.2	305.8	314.9	339.2
Liabilities							
Real Estate Debts	$ 5.6	8.2	12.1	18.9	28.4	29.5	31.3
Non-Real Estate	5.1	7.2	11.5	17.2	27.0	29.7	33.3
Other	1.7	2.2	1.2	1.5	2.7	1.9	2.3
Total Liabilities	$ 12.4	17.6	24.8	37.6	58.1	61.1	66.9
Owner Equities							
Real Estate	$ 69.8	90.0	118.1	142.0	178.7	183.5	197.3
Non-Real Estate	50.3	57.5	60.6	57.6	69.0	70.3	75.0
Total	$120.1	147.5	178.7	199.6	247.7	253.8	272.3
Equity Ratios							
Real Estate	$ 92.6	91.6	90.7	88.3	86.3	86.2	86.3
Non-Real Estate	88.0	85.9	82.6	75.5	70.0	69.0	67.8
Equity in Production Assets[1]	$86,437	107,279	133,458	152,358	193,479	197,278	—
Net Income from Agri. Production[2]	$17,825	15,399	16,568	20,308	24,103	24,908	—
Return to							
Labor	$10,445	10,503	9,501	8,864	10,696	11,171	—
Management[3]	1,437	1,486	1,735	2,081	2,701	2,799	—
Borrowed Capital[4]	544	782	1,257	2,012	3,552	3,674	—
Net Earnings[5]	$ 5,399	2,628	4,075	7,351	7,154	7,264	—
Rate Earned (%)[6]	2.6	2.4	3.1	4.8	3.7	3.6	—

Source: **Balance Sheet of Agriculture,** January 1973.

1. Total equities less financial assets, crops in storage, operator's dwelling, household equipment, etc.
2. Farming, cash wages, perquisites of hired labor, interest, and rent to non-farm landlords.
3. Five percent of cash farm receipts including government payments.
4. Interest on both real estate and non-real estate.
5. Net income from agricultural production minus the returns to labor, management, and borrowed capital.
6. Net earnings divided by the equity in production assets.

the livestock yards, the tobacco auctions, the cotton gins, and other market facilities are often specified in an appraiser's report.

The extent to which various suppliers of farm resources—building contractors, equipment dealers, and others—are available in the local area may also be included. The extent to which certain specialty crops have unique demands for harvesting labor, for processing or selling may be mentioned, depending of course on the crops and the livestock which may be raised on the subject farm.

Community Facilities: The prospective farm buyer or owner and hence the appraiser should also consider the availability of various community services—local shopping centers, financial institutions, banks and loan agencies, schools and other educational opportunities, churches of various denominations, off-farm transportation facilities, public utilities—electricity, telephone, water, gas, and sewage—the availability of police and fire protection, public health facilities, hospitals, medical, dental and other professional services, the opportunity for off-farm employment, recreational facilities, and other community services. The farm appraiser should not only mention these services that are available and desirable in his report, but also those which may be objectionable or detrimental—a nearby major highway, a railroad, cemetery, gravel pit, city dump, or odor-producing business located nearby.

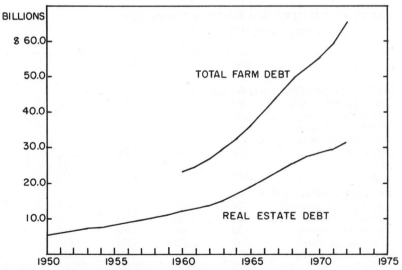

Figure 19. Farm Debt Outstanding: Real Estate and Total United States, 1950-1972.

Local Government Units: All farms are located in a particular political precinct and a particular taxing district. They may also be located in a special fire district, road district, or district related to irrigation or drainage, conservancy, reclamation, or pest control. The farm appraiser must be knowledgeable about any and all of these— their location, the agencies that attempt to control such, and their probable influence on farm value.

Organizational details vary a great deal. When a special district is established under the provisions of law, a special property assessment usually has the same legal status as, and it usually operates similar to, the general property tax. However, where the original financing was through bonds there may be bonded indebtedness against the property. Data relative to whatever assessment and/or indebtedness is involved should be obtained from the appropriate county or district office, along with information relative to any restrictions that affect the subject property, the cost of the indebtedness, and any and all benefits. The management and financial condition of these special districts often vary considerably. Due to the original method of organization or the present method of allocating costs, bonded indebtedness in particular is often difficult to ascertain.

Table 32. Farm Mortgage Debt Related to Principal Lenders.
United States, 1950-1972.

	1950	1960	1970	1971	1972
Farm Mortgage Loans Made or Recorded (mil. $)					
Life Insurance Companies	348	413	200	403	
Federal Land Banks	203	520	1,088	1,576	
Farmers Home Admin.	65	94	294	375	
Com. and Sav. Banks	472	541	1,064	1,517	
Individuals	569	1,001	1,094	1,242	
Others	—	—	1,345	1,666	
Total	1,656	2,570	5,085	6,779	
Farm Mortgage Debt Outstanding (mil. $)					
Life Insurance Companies	1,172	2,820	5,732	5,608	5,562
Federal Land Banks	906	2,335	6,660	7,128	7,862
Farmers Home Admin.	193	437	452	344	310
Com. and Sav. Banks	937	1,625	4,109	4,441	4,214
Individuals and Others	2,371	4,857	11,434	11,986	13,386
Total	5,579	12,074	28,387	29,307	31,334

Sources: **Balance Sheet of Agriculture**, January 1973.
Agricultural Finance Review, May 1973.

Planning Agencies: More and more farm properties are located near the larger urban centers and are being subjected to many zoning rules and regulations. Zoning is concerned with land use. The goal or objective is to get all property in a given area utilized to the best interest of all property owners, in fact all citizens, in general.

Many areas are zoned, of course, for the very same purpose which the average property owner might voluntarily choose himself. Land best suited for farming is zoned agricultural, property in a residential area is zoned residential, property around a shopping center is zoned commercial, and land in industrial areas is zoned industrial. However, problems arise whenever there is pressure to change. Commercial or industrial areas may be expanding and encroaching on residential areas or upon agriculture.

When the subject farm is located in an area "regulated" by a comprehensive planning or zoning authority the farm appraiser must investigate these restrictions as well. He should weigh the probable effect that the restrictions have on the marketability or salability of the property and its value.[9] Comprehensive planning and zoning is thus one more area for the appraiser to investigate as he studies the subject property and its future potential.

The Local Customs: Many agricultural areas have a few local, if not unique, customs all their own. Many a rural community is extremely proud of its traditions. This is usually the natural result of the ancestry of the people who settled the area.

The Pennsylvania Dutch in Lancaster County, Pennsylvania, for example, are descendents of German, Swiss, and Alsatian immigrants. They are now 8 to 10 generations removed, yet one might think they have just arrived from the old country. Their very distinctive barn architecture with its hex signs, the lavish seven sours and seven sweets that make dinner worthy of the name, and the blue front gate which the Plain people supposedly paint whenever they have in the house a daughter or daughters of marriageable age, make the area a very colorful one. While some of these traditions are undoubtedly kept to intrigue the tourists, the customs and beliefs in this area have a deep and strong religious significance not immediately apparent or understood by fancy people.

---

9. Zoning supposedly bears more heavily on the "I-Don't-Care-Property Owner" who is bent on exploiting his own situation regardless of the effect on his neighbors or on the rest of the community. However, in practice, zoning regulations may also deprive an owner of the right to use or to sell his or her property to his or her best advantage. Thus zoning restrictions may lead to lower values.

A farm appraiser must be aware of the racial backgrounds, social traditions, and current attitudes of those who live in any agricultural community. It's sometimes surprising, but they too have a real influence on farm real estate values.

The Changing Agricultural Scene: In most agricultural areas there is a trend toward fewer and larger farms, and hence a consolidation of farm units. In some areas this change is taking place fairly rapidly. The young people are moving out and numerous farmsteads are left-over. In other areas off-farm employment opportunities are increasing the numbers of small farms, both residential and part-time. Whenever these changes occur, some communities tend to grow old and weak. Others become larger and stronger, and perhaps more complicated.

In many agricultural areas there is a tendency to conform, to stand pat, and to resist change. Farm people feel that farm prices should be supported, that farmers should be paid or reimbursed their costs of production, and that the Federal government should protect agriculture. In these areas, farming methods tend to lag behind, and farm incomes are not always satisfactory.

In other agricultural areas there is a tendency to innovate, to try out new ideas. Farmers have expanded their businesses. They have added technologies, and have continued to invest capital. Their goal is to reduce their costs and increase their incomes. Their attitude towards competition is entirely different. That attitude is quietly reflected in the activities in the community.

The Local Community: The farm appraiser may keep in his files many local statistics—population, employment, number of households, school enrollments, assessed valuations, building permits, bank deposits, and others, for the trends in the community are sometimes an important part of an appraisal. The local industries may be expanding. Employment and population may be increasing. A knowledge of the actual figures is often surprising. The demand for local community services, of course, has made many a farm family complain about its property taxes. Yet, a carefully growing community—one which is developing new activities and new services—is one which becomes a better place to live. And all this influences farm real estate values.

A very colorful Pennsylvania Dutch Barn in Lancaster County, Pennsylvania.

Photo by Heilman.

MISCELLANEA COMPACTA

The appraiser's handbook typically ends with a collection of miscellaneous bits and pieces of data that are helpful if they can be found, hence best kept in one place. Somewhere in the back of the appraiser's handbook the following are typically available.

1. A table of land measurement.

2. Various scales, weights, and measures.

3. The places to send for aerial photos, maps, and other supplies.

4. Sources of current information.

5. Instructions for using the camera and sources of photographic supplies.

6. The scaling, style, and format to be used on all graphic illustrations. If all graphs are scaled alike they can be used as overlays and the relationships between various sets of data can thus be studied.

REFERENCES

Brown, M. R., and M. D. Trivette, "Farm-Ranch Management Literature," *Journal of American Society of Farm Managers and Rural Appraisers,* Vol. 36, No. 2, October 1972.

Dexter, W. V., (Compiler), *Guide to U.S.D.A. Statistics,* U.S.D.A., November 1972.

Donogh, A. D., "What Constitutes a Good Appraisal Library," *The Residential Appraiser,* Vol. 28, No. 8, August 1962.

Economics of Agriculture, Reports and Publications Issued or Sponsored by U.S.D.A.'s Economic Research Service, E.R.S., U.S.D.A., Supplement No. 3 to E.R.S.-368, June 1972.

Morse, T. C., "Standard Appraisal Data," *Journal of the American Society of Farm Managers and Rural Appraisers,* Vol. 14, No. 1, April 1950.

Periodic Reports of Agricultural Economics and Statistics, E.R.S., Statistical Reporting Service, U.S.D.A., Published Annually.

Warren, S. W., *Rural Appraisers Handbook,* Department of Agricultural Economics, Cornell University, 1963.

Physical Features

Austin, M. E., *Land Resource Regions and Major Land Resource Areas of the United States,* Agriculture Handbook 296, S.C.S., U.S.D.A., December 1965.

Buckman, H. O., and N. C. Brady, *Nature and Properties of Soils,* 7th Edition, Macmillan, 1969.

Bushnell, T. M., *A Story of Hoosier Soils*, Peda-Products, August 1958.
Climate and Man: The 1941 Yearbook of Agriculture, U.S.D.A., 1941.
Climatological Data, Various States, Annual Summary, Various Years, U. S. Department of Commerce.
Conklin, H. E., "The Cornell System of Economic Land Classification," *Journal Farm Economics*, Vol. 41, No. 3, August 1959.
Elliott, F. F., *Generalized Types of Farming in the United States*, U.S.D.A., Agricultural Information Bulletin No. 3, February 1950.
Hedge, A. M., and A. A. Klingebiel, "The Use of Soil Maps," *Soil: The 1957 Yearbook of Agriculture*, U.S.D.A., 1957.
Klingebiel, A. A., "Land Classification for Use in Planning," *A Place to Live: The 1963 Yearbook of Agriculture*, U.S.D.A., 1963.
Longwell, C. R., et al., *Outlines of Physical Geology*, Wiley, 1941.
Newman, J. E., "Climatic Influences on Agricultural Lands," *Journal of the American Society of Farm Managers and Rural Appraisers*, Vol. 32, No. 1, April 1968.
Nunns, F. K., "The Classification of Rural Land," *Land: The 1958 Yearbook of Agriculture*, U.S.D.A., 1958.
"The Origin of American Soils," *Doane's Agricultural Report*, No date.
Pavelis, G. A., and Karl Gertel, "The Management and Use of Water," *A Place to Live: The 1963 Yearbook of Agriculture*, U.S.D.A., 1963.
Pike, Herbert, "Soil Texture and the Appraiser," *Journal of the American Society of Farm Managers and Rural Appraisers*, Vol. 2, No. 2, November 1938.
Ruch, P. E., "Effects of Climate and Weather on Real Estate Values," *Appraisal Journal*, Vol. 22, No. 4, October 1954.
Select Climatic Maps of the United States, U. S. Department of Commerce, Washington, D. C.
Simonson, R. W., "What Soils Are," *Soil: The 1957 Yearbook of Agriculture*, U.S.D.A., 1957.
Smith, G. D., and A. R. Aandahl, "Soil Classification and Surveys," *Soil: The 1957 Yearbook of Agriculture*, U.S.D.A., 1957.
"Soil Origin and Formation," *Doane's Agricultural Report*, Vol. 30, No. 12-5, April 1967.
Soils and Men: The 1939 Yearbook of Agriculture, U.S.D.A., 1939.
Soils of Illinois, University of Illinois Agr. Exp. Sta., Bul. 725, August 1967.
Soils of the North Central Region of the United States, North Central Regional Publication No. 76, University of Wisconsin, June 1960.
Soil Survey Manual, U.S.D.A., Agricultural Handbook No. 18, August 1951.
Soil: The 1957 Yearbook of Agriculture, U.S.D.A., 1957.
Walker, E. D., and W. F. Purnell, *Understanding Soils*, University of Illinois Extension Service, Circular 758, April 1956.

Agricultural Trends

Agricultural Statistics, United States Department of Agriculture, Published Annually.
Changes in Farm Production and Efficiency, Statistical Bulletin No. 233, E.R.S., U.S.D.A., Published Annually.

Crop Production Annual Summaries, U.S.D.A., Published Annually.

"Farm Population," *Current Population Reports*, E.R.S., U.S.D.A., Series Census, P-27, No. 43, May 1972.

Handbook of Agricultural Charts, E.R.S., U.S.D.A., Published Annually.

Major Statistical Series of the U.S.D.A., How They Are Constructed and Used, Vol. 8, Crop and Livestock Estimates, U.S.D.A., Agricultural Handbook No. 365, May 1971.

Marshall, Douglas, "Grazing Capacity and Animal Unit Formulas for Managers and Appraisers," *Journal of American Society of Farm Managers and Rural Appraisers*, Vol. 35, No. 1, April 1971.

Midwest Farm Handbook, 5th Edition, Iowa State University Press, 1960.

Standard Appraisal Data for the United States, Revised, Doane Agricultural Service, Inc., 1956.

Straszheim, R. E., "The How and Why of Government Crop and Livestock Reports," *Economic and Marketing Information*, Purdue University, June 1968.

United States Census of Agriculture, U. S. Government Printing Office, Washington, D. C.

Wunderlich, Gene, and W. E. Chryst, "Farm Tenure and the Use of Land," *Land: The 1958 Yearbook of Agriculture*, U.S.D.A., 1958.

Economic Statistics

Agricultural Prices, U.S.D.A., Published Monthly.

The Balance Sheet of the Farming Sector, Agriculture Information Bulletin No. 356, E.R.S., U.S.D.A., Published Annually.

Farm Costs and Returns, Agriculture Information Bulletin No. 230, E.R.S., U.S.D.A., Revised Annually.

Farm Cost Situation, E.R.S., U.S.D.A., Published Annually.

Farm Income Situation, E.R.S., U.S.D.A., Published Biannually.

Farm Labor, S.R.S., U.S.D.A., Published Monthly.

Farm Mortgage Debt, E.R.S., U.S.D.A., Published Annually.

Farm Mortgage Lending, E.R.S., U.S.D.A., Published Annually.

Farm Real Estate Historical Series Data: 1850-1970, E.R.S. 520, U.S.D.A., June 1973.

Farm Real Estate Market Developments, E.R.S., U.S.D.A., Published Biannually.

Farm Real Estate Mortgages Recorded, 1971, Economic Research and Finance Division, Farm Credit Administration, November 1972.

Farm Real Estate Taxes, E.R.S., U.S.D.A., Published Annually.

Major Statistical Series of the U. S. How They Are Constructed and Used, Vol. 6, Land Values and Farm Finance, U.S.D.A. Agriculture Handbook No. 365, April 1971.

(No author), "Tax and Assessment Data," *The Residential Appraiser*, Vol. 27, No. 1, January 1961.

Community Characteristics

Elkin, A. D., "The Effect on Rural Appraisal Value of Government Acreage Allotments and Price Control," *Journal of American Society of Farm Managers and Rural Appraisers,* Vol. 19, No. 1, April 1955.

Given, C. W., and J. B. Mitchell, "Community Power Structure: A Methodological Analysis and Comparison," Ohio Research Bulletin 1046, Ohio State University, June 1971.

Libby, L. W., "Why Rural Planning and Zoning," *Michigan Farm Economics,* No. 336, Department of Agricultural Economics, Michigan State University, January 1971.

Libby, L. W., "Zoning No Panacea," *Michigan Farm Economics,* No. 343, Department of Agricultural Economics, Michigan State University, August 1971.

McDermott, J. K., et al., "Answers to Your Questions About Planning and Zoning in Indiana," Cooperative Extension Service, EC-208, Revised, Purdue University, 1970.

Meenan, H. J., "Impact of Technology and Government Programs upon Land Values," *Journal of American Society of Farm Managers and Rural Appraisers,* Vol. 21, No. 1, April 1957.

Mitchell, J. B., *Facts About Rural Zoning,* Ohio Cooperative Extension Bulletin 539, Ohio State University, July 1971.

Neuses, D. P., "The Rocky Road of Zoning," *The Real Estate Appraiser,* Vol. 32, No. 8, August 1966.

Stoevener, H. H., "Some Economic Aspects of Agricultural Zoning and Farmland Taxation," *Journal of American Society of Farm Managers and Rural Appraisers,* Vol. 30, No. 2, October 1966.

Solberg, E. D., "Old and New Principles of Zoning," *A Place to Live: The 1963 Yearbook of Agriculture,* U.S.D.A., 1963.

Solberg, E. D., "Planning and Zoning for the Future," *Land: The 1958 Yearbook of Agriculture,* U.S.D.A., 1958.

Miscellanea Compacta

Farmers' Handbook of Financial Calculations and Physical Measurements, Agricultural Handbook 230, Revised, E.R.S., U.S.D.A., November 1966.

Financial Compound Interest and Annuity Tables, 2nd Edition, Publication No. 176, Financial Publishing Co., 1960.

Richey, C. B., Editor-in-Chief, *Agricultural Engineers' Handbook,* McGraw Hill, 1961.

CHAPTER VI

The Earnings or Income Capitalization Approach to Value

Farm appraisers have traditionally developed and used three methods to establish farm real estate values.

1. The earnings or income capitalization approach in which value is based on the annual income stream that the farm or subject property will most likely produce in the future.

2. The sales comparison or market data approach in which value is based on the prices paid for other farm properties which are located in the same area and which have recently changed ownership.

3. The inventory or cost approach in which value is based on the sum of the values contributed by the various acreages of different quality land, as though unimproved, and by each of the buildings and improvements.

The professional appraiser typically uses all three approaches. However, in arriving at a final figure, any one of the three may be given more or less consideration or weight depending on the nature of the property, the reason for the appraisal, and the method providing the best supportive evidence. When the subject property is a commercial farm and the reason for the appraisal is to determine its loan value, the earnings approach is more important. When the farm is a residential unit and the appraisal will be used to estimate an asking price for probable sale, the sales comparison approach is more important. When the property is improved and the appraisal will be used to determine the insured values to be placed on each building and improvement, the cost approach is more important. There are many illustrations.

The earnings approach to value applies primarily to the commercial farming operations where the appraiser's job is to estimate the productive capacity of the farm and then project the income stream that can be obtained. Four decidedly different farming operations here are a ranch in Eastern Kansas (upper left), one in the San Joaquin Valley in California (upper right), a farm in Eastern Virginia (lower left), and one in Central Iowa (lower right).

Photos Courtesy of U.S.D.A., University of California, and J. C. Allen

The earnings or income capitalization approach is based on the assumption that those persons interested in buying or owning farms are interested primarily in the dollar returns that can be obtained on their investment. The income in itself does not impart value of course; the thing that counts is what the typical prospective buyer or investor is willing to pay in order to receive that income. The major determinant of value is assumed to be the anticipated income stream.[1] Thus the appraiser's job is to analyze the more or less systematic relationship between income and value and apply such to the subject property.

At the same time, the buyers of farms are often willing to pay for things other than the right or opportunity to receive that income stream. The subject property may have on it a beautiful home; there may be opportunity to obtain several additional sources of satisfaction of a non-monetary nature; it may have location value. The typical prospective buyer may anticipate the future income from the farm to increase substantially due to an output-increasing technology; or he may expect or hope for a relatively constant increase in the value of the farm itself over time due to inflation. When these factors are operative the typical prospective buyer will pay more for the subject property than its current earnings will justify. Thus, the appraiser's job is to estimate not just the farm's earnings but all of the reasons why various buyers may be desirous of owning a given farm.

Needless to say, the earnings approach applies primarily to commercial farm units. First, the farm's productive capacity has to be estimated (under a typical operator). Second, the farm's receipts and operating expenses have to be budgeted. Third, the income or residual return to the land must be calculated. The latter is then divided by the current rate of return required to get farm buyers or investors to buy or to invest in similar farm properties.

Most of the data—farm receipts, expenses, and capitalization rates —must be developed by the appraiser. In the agricultural Midwest where many appraisers also manage farms, they may use as guides the typical receipts and expenses from some of the farms they manage —assuming, of course, the farms they manage are comparable to the

---

1. This income premise is further based on the assumption that while the future annual income may fluctuate (sometimes quite widely), the average income can be budgeted with a fair degree of accuracy and that the average over a period of time will be level. In some non-farm property appraisals an income flow may have an upward trend or downward trend. This assumption has not been used in farm appraisals primarily because of the non-depreciable characteristic of land.

subject property. However, in many areas the appraiser has learned to rely on farm records and many other data sources.

One or more actual income statements on the subject property itself are sometimes available. If so, these statements may be scrutinized. However, the purpose for which various income statements are prepared often has considerable influence on the data therein. The business organization—whether it is a sole proprietorship, a partnership, or a corporation—often leads to differences in the method of handling income taxes. The cost of management, depreciation, and the handling of principal and interest payments on both real and non-real estate capital often vary considerably. Furthermore, most financial statements reflect not just the farm's productivity but the managerial ability of the operator as well.

THE FORMULA: ITS APPLICATION

Income capitalization requires the appraiser to ascertain the present worth or value of the income stream which can be produced over the economic life of the investment. In order to obtain this the expected annual income is developed. This figure is then divided by a capitalization rate. The process is mathematical, and for this reason, an earnings value is often called a formula value. The fomula is relatively simple.

$$\text{Earnings Value} = \frac{\text{Dollar Return to Real Estate}}{\text{Capitalization Rate}}$$

For example, the annual income or return to land on a 320-acre farm is estimated to be \$6,875 (\$21.48 per acre). If one desires or expects a 4.5-percent return on this kind of investment, the capitalized value of the farm is thus \$152,788 (\$477 per acre).

$$\frac{\$6,875}{4.5\%} = \$152,778 \text{ total; or, } \frac{\$21.48}{4.5\%} = \$477.43 \text{ per acre}$$

As the income level increases, the value of a farm goes up, and vice versa. As the capitalization rate is increased, the value of a farm goes down, and vice versa.

The above formula is the reverse of that used to calculate the return on a savings account or on some other investment. For example, if one has a \$5,000 corporate bond yielding 7.5 percent (the interest rate) he receives \$375 interest annually. This is his return.

$$\$5{,}000 \times 7.5\% = \$375$$

The same formula can be used to find the average rate of return on other farms which have recently sold. If, for example, another 320-acre farm in the area recently changed hands for $165,000, and its annual income is approximately $7,425, the capitalization rate is 4.5 percent.

$$\frac{\$7{,}425}{\$165{,}000} = 4.5\%$$

All of this is commonly referred to as straight or simple income capitalization. It is simple in that the income is expected to continue indefinitely. The income stream is said to be capitalized into perpetuity. In the appraisal of farm real estate, this is a fairly realistic assumption. A high percentage of the value of many farms is in land. Most farm buildings and improvements tend to be or are assumed to be maintained indefinitely. However, income capitalization is not always straight or simple (see "A Major Footnote: How—When Not in Perpetuity?").

The earnings approach to value was developed in the 1930's when many farm families were unable to meet principal and interest payments and a number of farm loans were foreclosed. The Farm Credit Administration, a number of insurance companies, and various interested members of the American Farm Economics Association combined thoughts to develop the American Rural Appraisal System. This was the first, really definite, logical step-by-step approach to farm appraisal.

The system led to a more careful scrutiny of the many factors that enter into a farm appraisal. It disapproved of those persons who "generally professed to know" land values and began to replace them with appraisers who were able to arrive at land values by means of analysis and reason. The real hope was that the farm's capacity to perform might constitute a sound base for a reasonably permanent value.

The farm earnings which could be expected over a period of time, assuming a typical operator, led to the concept of a basic farm value. It supposedly measured the characteristics inherent in the farm itself. It was somewhat of an intrinsic value which would exist over a period of time. It eliminated, hopefully, any and all special considerations regarding the present operator and required facts and figures characteristic of a typical operator.

This earnings value is still applicable today. It is a value based on a farm's productive capacity and its probable earnings. It is a value developed through a capitalization of income. As such, it is essentially a formula value rather than a market value.

However, farms don't always sell at prices which are in direct proportion to their current earnings. There is a tendency for farms that are small or near the margin to sell high relative to their capitalized values; there is a tendency for farms that are large or high in productivity to sell somewhat lower relative to their capitalized values.[2]

Furthermore, the buyers of farms are often willing to pay for things other than the opportunity to make money. A particular buyer may pay more than a farm's earnings value in order to gain the status of a landowner, to become a self-employed farm operator, to regain control of his original birthplace, to live in the country, to be near friends or relatives, to gain tax advantages, or to hedge against inflation or an urban expansion. The farm appraiser must recognize these other features—the home, the location, and the other sources of satisfaction achieved through ownership. After arriving at the farm or subject property's earnings value he may make adjustments for these other factors. Thus a farm's earnings value, plus or minus the value of these other factors, equals the farm's present market value.

One of the prerequisites of the earnings approach, of course, is that income must exist. Farm receipts must exceed farm expenses. This income is developed and then capitalized into value through the use of one of two techniques. One can assume . . .

1. An owner-operator as the most likely buyer, owner, or operator, and hence develop an income estimate on a total farm basis.

2. An absentee-owner as the most likely buyer or owner, a tenant-operator as the typical operator, and thus develop the dollar returns to the landowner on a crop-share, livestock-share, or cash-rent basis.

In most of the United States, the professional farm appraiser has to calculate the income on a total farm or owner-operator basis.

1. Total cash farm receipts are first estimated. These are based on (a) the farm's productive capacity—typical crops and livestock raised, (b) the typical crop yields and rates of livestock production, and (c) a fairly stable set of farm prices.

2. All cash farm operating expenses are estimated. These typically include a non-cash item—depreciation on buildings and improvements —yet they do not include principal and interest payments on the real estate itself.

---

2. The larger farms require and usually attract better-than-average management. Consequently they attain higher incomes. In some areas, and at times of course, there is a tendency to capitalize some of this income stream into the value of the real estate.

3. A cash balance is calculated by subtracting the cash farm expenses from the cash farm receipts. Unless the value of any unpaid family labor has been included as a cash expense, such is then deducted from this cash balance. The figure that remains equals the farm's income.[3]

4. Two items (a) value of the operator's time (labor and management) and (b) interest on all non-real estate capital are then deducted. Thus, the return to the capital invested in the real estate is obtained.

5. This residual return is then divided by a capitalization rate to arrive at the earnings value of the farm.

The formula is as follows:

$$EV = \frac{CFR - CFE - UnpdFL - VOpT - InNoReC}{Capitalization\ Rate}$$

EV   = Earnings value

CFR   = Cash farm receipts (total)

CFE   = Cash farm expenses (total)

UnpdFL   = Unpaid family labor

VOpT   = Value of operator's time

InNoReC   = Interest on non-real estate capital

In the agricultural Midwest a fairly high percentage of the farms are owned by absentee-owners and operated by tenants. A number of them are managed by professional farm managers. On these farms, the landowner is the lessor, the tenant the lessee. However, here the simile ceases. For while there are some cash leases, many landlord-tenant arrangements are on a crop- or crop-and-livestock-share basis. The landowner owns some of the personalty, pays some of the operating expenses, and receives either a share of the crops, or a share of the crops, the livestock, and the livestock products. He may also receive some cash or privilege rent.

The typical landlord-tenant arrangement provides the farm appraiser with a unique means of estimating the dollar returns to land and capitalizing these returns into value. The crop-share lease is a real shortcut in areas where these arrangements are common. The appraiser

---

3. Inventory changes are assumed to be equal to zero.

can reduce both the amount of work and the arithmetic involved. Even when a lease is not being used on the subject property itself, even where leases are not typical in the area, a typical arrangement may be "borrowed" from a nearby farm or area and used. This shortcut should be applied carefully. Its use and accuracy depend on the knowledge and skills of the appraiser.

1. Typical dollar receipts to the landowner are first estimated. These are based on the farm's productive capacity, yet adjusted for the typical landlord's share of crops sold, plus the typical landlord's share of any livestock or livestock products sold, plus any privilege or cash rent received by the landlord.

2. The landowner's expenses are then estimated. These include property taxes, property insurance, and all upkeep on the buildings and improvements, along with the landlord's share of the farm's operating expenses.

3. The dollar returns to the landlord are then calculated by subtracting his operating expenses from his dollar receipts. From this dollar return, the typical management fee and the cost of any non-real estate capital are deducted.[4]

4. The residual return is then divided by the capitalization rate to arrive at the earnings value.

The formula is as follows:

$$EV = \frac{\text{Lld Rec} - \text{Lld Exp} - \text{Mgt F} - \text{InNoReC}}{\text{Capitalization Rate}}$$

where . . .

$$EV = \text{Earnings value}$$

$$\text{Lld Rec} = \text{Landowner's receipts}$$

$$\text{Lld Exp} = \text{Landowner's expenses}$$

$$\text{Mgt F} = \text{Management fee}$$

$$\text{InNoReC} = \text{Interest on non-real estate capital}$$

---

4. The management fees in the agricultural Midwest are sometimes on a per-acre basis—$2.50 to $4 per acre, and sometimes on a percentage basis—5 to 10 percent of the adjusted farm receipts. Occasionally they are based on a combination of the two methods.

Estimating the landlord's receipts and expenses requires both fewer calculations and less time than estimating the receipts and expenses for the total farm. The residual return obtained is essentially a rental return representing that portion of the farm's income which accrues to the real estate.

The return may be based on a cash lease, a crop-share cash lease, or a crop-and-livestock-share lease. The cash rent approach is the easiest, for there is only one receipt and usually only two expenses—property taxes and upkeep.[5] However, the crop-share-cash lease is the more typical one used by many farm appraisers. In the agricultural Midwest, at least, the leasing practices are fairly well defined. The landowner's receipts and expenses are estimated fairly easily. In the dairy and livestock areas a crop-and-livestock-share lease may be used. However, the appraiser now has to estimate a larger number of receipts and expenses. He still has to separate the residual return to the real estate from the landowner's total farm returns. Furthermore, the income obtained on a dairy or livestock farm is often more closely related to the managerial skills of the operator than it is to the land and its productivity. Hence, there is considerable reluctance to use a livestock-share lease as a method of capitalizing incomes.[6]

ESTIMATING FARM RECEIPTS, EXPENSES, AND INCOME

The income approach has two foundations: (1) farm receipts and expenses and (2) a capitalization rate.

Cash Farm Receipts: Cash farm receipts are based on the productive capacity of the farm—the typical acreage of various crops raised, the typical yields per acre, the typical livestock numbers, and the typical rates of livestock production.[7] These figures lead to total crop and livestock production; on a rented farm they can be used to establish the share received by the landowner.

---

5. In recent years, more farms, in the agricultural Midwest at least, have been rented for cash. Tenant-operators have occasionally bid for these leases. They have sometimes bid the first year but not the second, thus indicating a tendency to bid cash rents too high. In other words, cash rents vary widely. A one-year figure is not always typical or useful.

6. Use of a livestock-share lease and its component parts is, of course, no more complicated than use of the total farm or owner-operator approach to income capitalization.

7. The word "typical" is perhaps overworked here, yet an appraiser cannot inject management into either his thinking or his analysis.

Needless to say, a high degree of accuracy is desired in estimating a farm's productivity. An error of 10 bushels in the per-acre yield of corn can lead to as much as a $100 difference in the per-acre value of the farm. (This assumes a corn price of $1 per bushel, a 50-50 crop-share lease, and a 5.0% capitalization rate.)

Total farm production must be multiplied by the farm product prices received by farmers. The appraiser should be neither overly optimistic nor overly pessimistic about the future of farm prices, for these prices essentially establish the level of income.

The commodity prices used often vary. In the past, long-term averages were used in order to give an appraisal some price stability. Various techniques such as weighted averages and moving averages were also used in order to establish normal agricultural values. Some clients, namely the lending institutions, specified the prices to be used. This led to more uniformity among appraisals. It provided a loan committee with the basis for comparing loans.

Today major emphasis is being placed on the prices which have been in existence during the most recent three to five years. This three- to five-year period is usually the same period or basis for which the typical crop yields and rates of livestock production were estimated. However, a three- or five-year arithmetic mean or mathematical average price should be examined carefully. A single year's price may be high or low due to abnormal variations in the weather or in the amount of the crop or numbers of livestock marketed. When this occurs that price of the commodity may need to be adjusted. In all instances, the farm appraiser should cite the farm product prices used in his appraisal.

The various quantities of farm production are multiplied by the various farm product prices, in order to obtain total cash farm receipts. These receipts are sometimes referred to as the gross income for the farm, the landlord's gross income, or the total income received before deducting any farm's expenses.[8] When a crop-share-cash lease is assumed, the farm receipts often include some cash or privilege rent. Where an extra house is available and is typically rented to a non-farm employee, the farm's receipts may include these rental payments.

Government payments may or may not be included. These payments are typically related more to the decisions of management than to the

---

8. In the appraisal of non-farm commercial properties the terms *potential gross income* and *effective gross income* are also used. The difference allows one to adjust for vacancy rates and credit or collection losses. These are not major items in a farm appraisal.

characteristics of the real estate. They are often said to be too uncertain to be considered a part of the long-term income stream. However, the present acreage allotments and/or the dollar payments received may be mentioned in one's appraisal report. They may or may not be a factor in the income stream, depending on the estimates made by the appraiser relative to the farm's productive capacity, and maybe other assumptions. When such are accepted as a part of the receipts, the appraiser must remember to make corresponding adjustments in the operating expenses.

Cash Farm Operating Expenses: All farm operating expenses, consistent with the farm receipts, should be estimated on a realistic basis regardless of what the appraiser himself thinks should be spent on the property. These expenses should represent what the typical owner-operator or typical absentee-owner will spend in order to maintain the property and produce the expected dollar returns.

Most of these expenses are budgeted using the quantities of each resource which are most likely to be used along with the farm prices which will most likely be paid. Many are related to or based on the per-acre resource requirements of various crops and the per-cow, per-sow, or per-steer resource requirements for each of the various livestock enterprises. The level of farm prices paid should be for the same price level or price period as the farm prices received.

Some of the various expenses and methods of estimating such are as follows.

1. Seed, fertilizer, and chemical costs are usually budgeted on the basis of seeding rates, fertilizer rates, and herbicide and insecticide rates, and in terms of the pounds of each required per acre. These rates are multiplied by the material costs per pound. Seed costs, for example, corn, are typically based on the number of acres one bushel will plant and the cost per bushel. Fertilizer costs are typically split into lime, nitrogen, phosphate, and potash. The typical application rates per acre, which vary with yield expectations, are then multiplied by the costs per pound for each type of plant food. The costs of application may be included as part of the cost of fertilizer or as a part of machine hire.

The farm appraiser must decide "What are the typical crops most likely to be raised and what are the crop yields most likely to be obtained by the typical operator for this particular farm?"

Courtesy, U.S.D.A. and J. C. Allen

2. Irrigation water is usually budgeted on the basis of the actual assessment. It may be based on (a) the typical number of applications, (b) the typical amounts of water applied each application, and (c) the cost per acre-inch of water. Overhead equipment costs are typically included only when that equipment is portable and not a part of the real property being appraised.

3. Harvesting expenses—combining, baling, drying, and hauling— may be budgeted several ways. On an owner-operated farm these costs are usually absorbed in the labor and machinery expense. On a tenant-operated farm typical custom rates may be used. The latter figures are usually available on a per-acre, sometimes on a per-bushel or per-bale basis. No matter what method is used, the cost data must correspond to the productive capacity of the farm and the typical amounts of farm products that will be produced.

4. Storage and handling costs in and out of storage vary with the facilities available, with the subject farm's typical operator, and some-times with the leasing arrangements in the area. On the owner-operated farm, storage costs are usually absorbed in building and improvement upkeep. Out-of-pocket costs are included only where the improvement or equipment is portable. On farms where there is a crop-share cash lease and storage facilities are non-existent, the landlord's share of the crop is assumed to be sold at harvest time and at some price discount. On farms where there is a crop and livestock-share lease, storage costs may be handled similar to those for an owner-operator with the exception that the tenant's share is kept separate.

5. Labor expense in some areas is based on the difference between the total labor or man work units required and the man equivalents of labor available, both operator and family. The extra labor required is multiplied by the farm wage rate per month or per day, depending on the amount hired.[9] Social security and workmen's compensation should be included.

6. Machinery expense on an owner-operated farm is typically based on thumb-rule investments and per-acre costs for similar farms

---

9. Some appraisers assume that all of the labor is hired. It is then included in the cash farm expenses. This technique eliminates the need to budget unpaid family labor and the value of the operator's time separately. It may or may not be more realistic depending on the type of farm and the practices in the area. Those who budget the unpaid family labor and the value of the operator's time separately typically base the unpaid family labor on current hired men's wage rates plus 10 to 20 percent. The value of the operator's time is based on current hired men's wage rates plus 25 to 50 percent.

located in the same area—data reported by farm record and farm machinery studies. Machinery expense on a tenant-operated farm is typically budgeted separately, using the custom rates in the area.

7. A feed balance in which crop production and feed requirements are compared is usually calculated with the resulting surplus or deficit providing a guide to either the amount of grain that can be sold or the amount of feed that must be purchased. The amounts to be purchased should be multiplied not by the farm prices received by farmers, but by the prices paid. The latter are typically 10 to 15 percent above those received, thus reflecting the marketing margin which includes transportation, handling costs, and commissions. Supplement costs are determined by the protein supplement requirements per head of livestock and the prices paid per ton.

8. Livestock expenses—veterinary and medicine, registration fees, milk testing, and death losses—are typically budgeted on a per-cow, per-sow, or per-steer basis.

9. The upkeep cost required to maintain all buildings and improvements in a proper state of repair is often based on a percentage of their replacement cost or a percentage of the total value placed on such, for example, 1.5 to 3.0 percent.[10] Individual items may be budgeted separately and, in this fashion, more accurately. For example, the maintenance of tile drains, irrigation ditches, and fences are often budgeted on a per-acre, per-mile, and a per-rod basis respectively. The upkeep or maintenance on the water supply or on an irrigation system may be budgeted separately.

10. Real estate taxes are typically based on current assessments and current tax rates, but with some consideration being given to anticipated changes in the future. Special assessments for roads, ditches, drainage, or irrigation should be included.

11. Insurance—fire, wind, and extended coverage—is typically based on the insured values placed on the buildings and improvements multiplied by the current insurance rates. Where liability, hail, crop, and other insurance is typical, the amount of coverage, the insurance rates, and the costs of these items may be included.

Other Costs—To Include or Not to Include: Several other costs—the management fee, in some instances depreciation, the cost of the non-real estate capital, capital outlays, and finance charges—may need to be

---

10. A reproduction rather than a replacement cost figure may be used as the basis for estimating this expense. The difference between the two is explained in Chapter IX.

considered. Sometimes some of these are included; sometimes they are not. The following items may present problems.

1. A management fee is typically included as an operating expense when the income estimate is based on a landlord-tenant arrangement. The common charge is the prevailing professional farm management fee in the area. This fee is applied to only the landowner's share of the total farm receipts. The charge for a farm rented on a share basis is more than for a farm rented on a cash basis. A management fee *per se* is not usually included when the income estimate is based on an owner-operated unit. This appears to be an inconsistency. However, in this latter instance, management is included, by definition, in the value of the operator's time. This latter is supposedly a payment for both labor and management.

2. Depreciation on farm buildings and improvements is not a cash farm expense. However, this cost is typically included as an operating expense in many farm appraisals. There are several reasons. In many farm appraisals the buildings and improvements represent a relatively small portion of a farm's total value. Most of them are maintained and used for one purpose or another indefinitely. Hence provisions for capital recapture are seldom made. Instead, farm appraisers tend to include depreciation in their upkeep costs on farm buildings and improvements.

3. The value of all unpaid family labor and the value of the operator's labor and management cannot be considered cash farm operating expenses. Yet these resources must be reimbursed prior to any capitalization of income. Hence, assumptions are made with regard to these costs and they are either included in the cash farm expenses or later subtracted from the cash balance (farm receipts minus farm expenses). Thus labor costs and management rewards, real or otherwise, are not capitalized into the value of the farm.

4. Capital outlays and principal and interest payments are not operating expenses. However, the cost of all non-real estate capital used in conducting the farming operations—actually an interest charge —should be subtracted from the farm's income in order to isolate the residual return to the real estate itself.

The farm appraiser must also decide "What are the typical kinds and numbers of livestock most likely to be kept, and what are the typical rates of livestock production most likely to be obtained by the typical operator for this particular farm?"

Courtesy, U.S.D.A.

5. An overdue and unpaid lump-sum assessment or bonded indebtedness against a property also occasionally occurs. The annual cost of such may be included as a part of the operating expenses or the lump-sum assessment may be deducted from the earnings value. Farms are occasionally sold subject to a mortgage. When this happens, the indebtedness is reflected in its sale price.

The appraiser's job is to select the budgeting method which is most realistic for the area in which the subject farm is located, the method most applicable to the subject property. This depends on the farm itself and the typical prospective buyer or owner. The appraiser's responsibility is to convert the subject property's earnings into value, using the most logical and most accurate method. In doing this, it is not the mechanics nor the degree of detail that determines the method used, but the area, the subject property itself, and the typical operator for the subject property. The job requires an intimate knowledge of practical farm and ranch operations.

The Dollar Return to the Real Estate: The income figure used in the earning's approach is the residual return which accrues to the real estate —the land, buildings and improvements—after paying all expenses.[11] Cash farm operating expenses are subtracted from cash farm receipts; the difference is the cash balance. Unpaid family labor, if not included as a cash expense, is then subtracted from the cash balance; the resulting figure is farm income. The value of the operator's time and the interest on all non-real estate capital are then subtracted from farm income; the remainder—the residual—is the dollar return to the real estate.

DEFINING THE CAPITALIZATION RATE

Income capitalization is a process of determining the present worth or value of the right or opportunity to receive a future flow of benefits in the form of an income stream. A key element is the selection of a capitalization rate which converts that future income stream into value. There is no magic formula for the selection or development of this rate. It instead requires the very best judgment from even the most experienced farm appraisers.

---

11. This is in contrast to most residential appraisals where gross rent multipliers are usually employed as indicators of value. The difference between gross and net rentals consists of (1) taxes, (2) insurance, (3) maintenance (heat, light, power, water, and repairs), (4) management, and (5) the recapture of capital.

Conceptually, the capitalization rate is the opportunity cost of money to whatever person or persons are the most likely buyers or owners of the subject property. The rate reflects that yield which could be obtained on a comparable investment by the most likely buyer or owner were he or she to invest, not in farm real estate or in the subject property, but instead in the next best alternative opportunity in the community. The alternatives find expression, of course, only in long-term investments with characteristics similar to the subject property.

The capitalization rate should reflect the current and competitive market as determined by the conservative yet informed judgments of the typical buyers and sellers of farm properties. The appraiser's job is to select that rate which will reflect the amount that the typical prudent buyer, investor, or farm operator will pay for the right to receive the income stream.

Mathematically, the capitalization rate is the ratio between income and value. Conceptually, it reflects many items in the financial community—the interest rate on borrowed money, the equity rate or return on a similar investment, and sometimes, in the case of a depreciable asset, a rate of recapture. Each of these reflects differences in types of property, the risks involved in ownership, the nature of the property transfer or contract, the terms of the sale, and the personal preferences of both sellers and buyers and such items as their tax brackets.

1. The interest rate on money is largely dependent upon (a) the supply of and demand for money, (b) the competitive returns on various alternative investment opportunities, and (c) the hazards of both property ownership and loan recovery. The interest rate is the price of money. It is expressed in terms of a percent, which the borrower pays and the lender receives for the temporary use of a certain sum of money over a given period of time. Expressed in dollars, the interest payment is the amount of money that changes hands in addition to each dollar of principal borrowed and returned.[12]

The principal and interest payments on a loan or investment are typically fixed in advance. They become due and are, generally speaking, paid or received each year regardless of the weather, the bugs, or other factors affecting the fortunes of farming.[13] For example, a farm

---

12. Interest is typically paid at the end of the borrowing period on either an annual or a semiannual payment basis.

13. Participating loans in which a lending institution acquires not just a fixed return on its loan, but in addition, a return based on a percent of the income, or profit, or capital appreciation are exceptions. Many lending agencies also have provisions releasing a mortgagor from a payment or two in case of emergency.

operator may borrow $100,000 at 7.5 percent interest and give the lender a 20-year mortgage. His semiannual principal and interest payment, to be paid on a level basis, would be $4,866 (Table 33).

2. The equity rate of return is the yield a farm owner receives on the capital he contributes or puts into the farm or investment. Like interest, it also is expressed in terms of a percentage. However, unlike the interest rate it is anything but fixed. The equity rate is the return on the risk capital and, as such, is highly variable. For example, the farm owner who borrowed $100,000 may have contributed $50,000 of his own capital. The return to that capital, after paying all costs including the interest on borrowed money, may vary, for example, all the way from $717, a poor year, to $16,471, a good year (Table 34). In the first case the return on one's equity is 1.3 percent; in the second case it is 38.5 percent.

Over the long run, interest rates and equity rates tend to be related. They are correlated to a considerable degree; they have a tendency to rise and fall simultaneously. However, this is not so in the short run. There are times when mortgage money may be relatively scarce and equity capital somewhat abundant. There are other times when mortgage money is relatively abundant and equity capital is relatively scarce. In many situations the equity rate is above the interest rate. However, with farm properties, the equity rate may be below the interest rate.

Table 33. The First Five Years of a Typical Farm Mortgage Repayment Schedule Along with Loan Balances.

$100,000 Loan, 20 Years, 7.5 Percent Interest, Semiannual Payments.

Year	Beginning Balance	Semi-Annual Payments[1]			Ending Balance
		Total	Principal	Interest	
1	$100,000	$4,866	$1,116	$3,750	$98,884
	98,884	4,866	1,158	3,708	97,726
2	97,726	4,866	1,201	3,665	96,525
	96,525	4,866	1,246	3,620	95,279
3	95,279	4,866	1,293	3,573	93,986
	93,986	4,866	1,342	3,524	92,644
4	92,644	4,866	1,392	3,474	91,252
	91,252	4,866	1,444	3,422	89,808
5	89,808	4,866	1,498	3,368	88,310
	$88,310	$4,866	$1,554	$3,312	$86,756

Source: Purdue University Farm Mortgage and Installment Contract Payment Schedule Generator.

1. Data have been rounded to nearest dollar.

Table 34. The Relationship Between Equity (Beginning-of-the-Year)
         and Equity Yields.
         $150,000 Farm, $50,000 Equity, Given Dollar Returns.

Year	Beginning-of-the-Year Equity	Payments This Year Principal[1]	Payments This Year Interest	Total Dollar Return	Equity Return[2] Dollar	Equity Return[2] Percent
1	$50,000	$2,274	$7,458	$13,564	$ 6,106	12.2
2	52,274	2,447	7,285	10,419	3,134	6.0
3	54,721	2,635	7,097	7,814	717	1.3
4	57,356	2,836	6,896	9,879	2,983	5.2
5	60,192	3,052	6,680	23,151	16,471	38.5
Etc.	63,244					
Average	—	—	—	$12,965	$ 5,882	12.6

1. Increase in equity.
2. Total return less interest payments.

Let's illustrate. When the typical buyer or owner is an absentee-owner or investor, he is often reluctant to purchase or own a farm unless he can get a return on his investment which is at least as high as the interest rate he has to pay on the loan. Otherwise he will not accept the risks of ownership. Yet, when the typical buyer or owner is an owner-operator, the property, to him at least, is a place to live as well as a place to farm. This typical buyer, owner, or operator will often willingly accept, all other factors being equal, an equity return below the current interest rate. He purchases or owns a farm for reasons other than the opportunity to earn money.

During periods of price inflation the investor will often willingly accept an equity yield below the current interest rate primarily because he expects the value of the property to increase in the future. Investors and others buy farms oftentimes not just to obtain a given annual income but to also obtain capital appreciation. Thus the many satisfactions obtained through farm ownership, both monetary and non-monetary, may exert considerable influence on the equity rate of return.

3. A recapture rate or return represents a rate at which certain prudent investors hope to recover a capital investment over the economic life of the asset. Remaining economic life is the period of time over which the asset is expected to be useful or the period of time over which it is expected to generate a competitive return. The idea or concept is applied primarily to depreciable or wasting assets rather than land. Recapture is actually the return *of* capital rather than a return *on*

capital. In the physical sense, a building or property is being used up. The return of the capital may thus represent depreciation.

In appraising family-operated farm properties, most farm appraisers do not usually include in their capitalization rate capital recapture.[14] Most purchasers of farm real estate do not include the recapture concept in their thinking. Instead they substitute depreciation, sometimes mortgage amortization, in its place.

Farm land, of course, does not depreciate. Farm income is assumed to be obtainable both continuously and indefinitely. This income is thus capitalized into perpetuity. However, farm buildings and improvements, gravel, oil, mineral, and other resources may be considered as wasting assets with fixed termination dates. In these instances provisions for capital recapture could be important.

TWO DIFFERENT TECHNIQUES

Today there are two different techniques being used in the capitalization of farm incomes. Much of the current vogue is to go to the market, find out what farms are selling for, estimate the current returns to the real estate, and then ascertain the ratios between these returns and sale prices. An alternative, somewhat old-fashioned perhaps, is to ascertain the opportunity cost of money in the community, develop an earnings value which reflects both directly and solely the productive capacity of the subject property, then adjust either the capitalization rate or the dollar values to reflect the other origins of farm value.

The first technique is an overall thumb rule, which may ignore some of the unique characteristics of the subject property. The second technique attempts to explain the origins of value—from both farm earnings and other sources. It requires considerably more judgment on the part of appraisers.

Going to the Market: The most popular technique today is to "go to the market." A detailed analysis of the dollar returns—receipts, ex-

---

14. This is in direct contrast to the appraisal of non-farm commercial properties where the business and the home are less connected and where capitalization rates sometimes combine an interest rate, an equity rate, and a recapture rate.

Livestock capacities for a given ranch or farm vary considerably and are often based, not just on the land resources, but also on the buildings, improvements, and feedlot facilities.
Courtesy, U.S.D.A., J. C. Allen, and A. O. Smith Harvestore Products, Inc.

penses, and incomes—which are being obtained on nearby farms which have recently sold is first developed. These individual returns are then divided by the sale prices paid for each farm, thus ascertaining a set of ratios between the dollar returns and the sale prices. The capitalization rate is thus based on all nearby and recent farm sales.

The appraiser's job requires a detailed estimate of the productive capacity of each of the nearby farms that have recently sold. The typical farm receipts, farm expenses, and residual returns to the real estate must be budgeted. In fact, the estimates of productivity and income on these comparable properties should be developed as carefully as on the subject property itself.[15] The appraiser also needs to verify the sale price on each of these farms. (Verification of sale price information is discussed in the following chapter.) The inexperienced appraiser may further find it helpful to verify some of the dollar returns he may have budgeted with the owners themselves. Thus the task of going to the market is a time-consuming one.[16]

The farms or sales selected should be comparable to the subject property. They should be comparable not only in terms of the date of sale, productive capacity, farm size, extent of the improvements, and factors such as location but also in terms of the non-monetary sources of value. In areas where the farms are fairly uniform and many of them are absentee-owned and tenant-operated the job is fairly easy. However, in areas where various farms exhibit unique characteristics and where many of them are owner-operated the job becomes more difficult.

Nevertheless, the real estate market is said to be an authoritative source. The approach is a most realistic one in that the capitalization rate obtained is that required to attract all of the capital necessary to transfer ownership. It assumes that the buyers and sellers of farms have considered all of the characteristics of the various farm properties, that the sale prices paid include all of the origins of value, and that the final

---

15. Some appraisers ignore this detailed analysis of farm sales. They use instead the overall long-run average dollar return to all of agriculture. This aggregate rate, published by the United States Department of Agriculture, is often quite low in that the rate includes or reflects the dollar returns being obtained on subsistent, part-time, and marginal farms as well as those in the commercial agricultural sectors. This overall aggregate rate does not represent any particular farming area. Neither does it recognize or reflect the peculiar characteristics of any one farm. Hence, an aggregate ratio is not really applicable in the appraisal of individual farm properties.

16. There has always been some question as to whether one's client can afford and will knowingly pay for the time and effort required.

rate is thus one at which all farm owners are being compensated. "Going-to-the-market" has thus gained widespread acceptance.

Explaining the Origins of Value: Use of a capitalization rate established in the market is essentially a thumb rule technique. Unfortunately it may be somewhat deceptive. It may ignore, in many instances, any or all of the subject property's unique characteristics. When only typical dollar returns and sale prices are examined, the first being divided by the second, the resulting ratio tends to cover up and ignore those origins of value other than earnings.

Farming is a way of life as well as a business. It is a means of living or a livelihood as well as a means of making that living. Unlike the ownership of non-farm commercial properties, perhaps, many persons buy and own farms for reasons other than the opportunity to obtain a given dollar income.

The appraiser may therefore attempt to sort out and explain the various origins or sources of value as they apply to the subject property. First, he ascertains an earnings value which reflects as realistically as possible the alternative investment opportunities in the community. He then adds (or subtracts) values which reflect the non-monetary sources of satisfaction and sometimes other factors as well. He then adjusts his capitalization rate for the long-term expectations—any inflationary or deflationary tendency. He may use two rather than one rate and thus attempt to show dollar earnings and values for different parts of the farm. He may adjust the capitalization rate to reflect the typical buyer or owner for the subject property.

This approach, when done properly, tells one's client considerably more about the farm and its present market value. It requires more thought and judgment on the part of the appraiser. Whether or not it leads to a more accurate final figure depends on the appraiser's expertise.

Explaining the origins or sources of value requires more knowledge of the money markets, considerable judgment as to the dollar value of certain non-monetary sources of satisfaction, and also an understanding of the mechanics of making adjustments—either adjustments in terms of dollars, or adjustments with respect to the capitalization rate.

1. The Opportunity Cost of Money. An asset purchased or owned for reasons of obtaining a given dollar income should be worth no less (or no more) than any other next best alternative investment opportunity in the community. If the owner of farm real estate did not have his money invested in his farm, what then would be his next best alternative opportunity? This is the opportunity cost principle.

If income is the whole reason for farm ownership—if it is the sole origin of value—the appraiser should thus base his capitalization rate on the behavior and characteristics of the money market. He should develop his rate, recognizing the ability of the typical purchaser or owner of the subject property. His job is to ascertain current rates on both farm and non-farm investments. His job is to be knowledgeable about the current interest rates on farm mortgages and installment land contracts, and about the band of investment and built-up rate theories. Each may have merit in selecting whatever capitalization rate best applies to the subject property.

In the 1930's, farm appraisers began to use the interest rates on farm mortgages as guides. The practice reflected the philosophy of the farm loan appraiser, and at a time when it appeared appropriate to capitalize earnings at rates equal to or perhaps slightly above those prevalent on farm mortgage loans. A slightly higher rate was based on the assumption that farm ownership had to be more profitable than lending—that unless it was, a farm or ranch owner would (or should) sell his farm and invest his money elsewhere.[17]

However, the farm or ranch owner's next best investment alternative is not necessarily in farm mortgages. Usually it is instead in a savings account in a local bank. The current rates of interest being paid on certificates of deposit come closer to most farmer's opportunity cost of money.

Furthermore, the rate of interest paid on a farm mortgage or installment land contract is not necessarily the same as that return which a farm owner or investor will willingly accept on his equity. The equity rate may reflect or include some of the non-montary amenities. It may include what the typical buyer or owner thinks is going to happen to property values in the future. Hence, the dollar return on a fixed debt is not the same as a capitalization rate.

The terms of a farm sale today vary more and more, with many sales based on installment land contracts as well as conventional deed transfers for cash. There are, as a result, many interest rates reflecting the financial positions of buyers, investors, and lenders as well as the preferences of sellers and their tax advantages.

---

17. At the time, farm loan appraisers used a uniform farm mortgage loan rate across a wide area. They did this so as to compare the risks of loaning money on various types of farms and in various areas. The idea had merit in terms of evaluating various types of farm properties, their long-term abilities to carry various loans, and in terms of determining the farms or areas where the company could most likely have their money invested with the least amount of risk.

A band-of-investment theory may be used to reflect the market struc-ture being used to finance a particular property. The capitalization rate may be based on a combination of equity and mortgage or contract rates, each of which are reflected in the money market. The rate is a weighted average or composite rate based on the amounts of each kind of capital required. Each rate represents a segment of the current market. For example, an installment land contract may consist of several parts.

Capital Portion	Asset Contribution	Rate or Return Required	Composite Rate
Downpayment*	15%	5.0%	0.75
Installment Contract	50%	6.0%	3.00
Balloon	35%	6.0%	2.10
Total Rate	100%	—	5.85

*This is comparable to savings or to equity capital. However, it may be a "grandmother" loan made to get a young couple started in farming.

The various portions are based on the ability of the typical buyer to obtain monies in various ways and on the current market cost of each kind of money. A weighted average satisfies all of the requirements of a capitalization rate based on the philosophy that the rate be one that is necessary to attract both the equity and the borrowed capital that is required to transfer ownership. The technique may include a silent loan, a second mortgage, or other sources of funding. With more ways of financing farm real estate, the problem becomes one of examining more and more financial arrangements.

A capitalization rate may also be a built-up rate based on various component parts, each of which reflects a particular risk or hazard. All investments are supposedly evaluated according to the risks assumed.

    a. The degree of safety measured, in part at least, by the certainty, the regularity (or the lack of), and/or the extent of the probable year-to-year variation in the future income payments.

    b. The extent to which the investment serves, provides, or is valuable as collateral; and, the extent to which it leads to, or, pro-vides an exemption or tax offset against other income.

    c. The ease of marketability or degree of liquidity, in other words, whether or not the investment can be liquidated before maturity and without shrink.

d. The size of the investment, its term or duration, and whether certain prepayment provisions (or penalties) and non-callable provisions exist.

e. The amount of management or supervision effort that may be required to collect the installment payments and, in the case of a participating loan, the management required to analyze and to either provide direction or some degree of control over the financial operations.

f. The attributes which may lead to capital appreciation in the future, in other words, the extent to which the investment provides a hedge against inflation.

Thus, a capitalization rate may be based on the actions of those persons who frequent the money market. The risk features or component parts are summed and a built-up rate is thus obtained.

For example, the various risks or hazards might be compensated as follows:

Risk Features	Rate of Return
The safe rate	3.0%
The risk rate	2.5
The non-liquidity rate	1.0
The management rate	1.0
The most likely rate of inflation	−2.5
The total built-up rate	5.0

The safe rate is typically based on long-term government bond yields and, as a result, is not difficult to obtain or defend. The risk rate reflects the elements of risk and uncertainty, along with the hazards which require a return above the safe rate before the typical investor will assume ownership. The non-liquidity, marketability, or salability rate reflects the length of time that may be required in order to convert a particular property into cash. The management rate reflects compensation for the burden of supervision. It is the rate required by the investment manager (not the manager of the property, but the manager of the investment). The most likely role of inflation is essentially a trade-off in which the prospective owner or investor indicates a willingness to substitute, for ordinary or current income, income from the

---

One of the large dairy feedlot installations in Northern Michigan.

Courtesy, Babson Bros.

sale of capital over the life of the investment (capital gains). For investors there is usually a considerable tax advantage.

Using this theory, the farm appraiser has to put himself in the shoes of the typical prudent investor and then assess the various yields, which are required in order to bring about the investment in this particular farm property.

Developing a built-up rate may be a make-believe antic. The various elements of risk and each corresponding cost seldom if ever exist as pure components in the money market. Nevertheless, appraisers and others could well spend some time thinking about the various risks associated with the ownership of farm real estate. As a pure investment, the risks in farm ownership are often greater than those assumed in other alternative investments—both non-farm real estate and non-real estate investments.

In theory, at least, the dollar returns from farm real estate should exceed the returns from treasury bills, savings accounts, and corporate bonds. However, real estate investments tend to be available in denominations that are not necessarily small. Relative to other investments the degree of liquidity is low. Farm properties are not readily marketable. Supervision in one form or another is often required. However, land has often been considered to be a "good" investment. It is assumed to be an excellent hedge against inflation. For this reason, the annual return on farm real estate has often been less than the returns from treasury bills, savings accounts, corporate bonds, and other alternatives.

Basically, the capitalization rate must represent what sellers, buyers, and investors require in terms of an overall rate in order to attract the capital required to transfer farm ownership. The rate must reflect the risks of ownership. It often reflects the future expectations as to capital appreciation. It often reflects the non-monetary sources of satisfaction which also result from ownership.

2. The Need for Variation. Most persons, in fact many appraisers, fail to realize the farm-to-farm, property-to-property variation in the rates of return which are necessary in order to attract the capital required to transfer farm ownership. Various properties command, and various buyers, investors, or owners require, widely varying capitalization rates.

Let's illustrate. The market for an additional acreage of land in a good land area may consist primarily of owner-operators interested in expanding their farming operations. There may be other potential buyers or investors. However, most of the adjoining farmers are desirous of purchasing additional land, adding it to their farms, thus spreading their fixed costs over a larger acreage, and thus making their existing units more efficient. These farmers will willingly accept a fairly low return on the additional acreage, and thus bid its price upwards.

The market for other farm properties, ones which the neighbors are not particularly interested in, may consist of only non-farm operators and absentee-investors. This type of buyer will buy, but only if he can do so with a low downpayment, a long-term contract, and a rate of return considerably above current interest rates. Why? This kind of a buyer will not assume ownership unless he can obtain a return considerably above that which he could obtain elsewhere. He will not otherwise risk his capital.

Assuming all other factors equal, a higher capitalization rate is required in the following instances:

    a. When the typical prospective buyer is likely to be an absentee-owner or investor rather than an owner-operator.

One of the large feeder lamb lots near Cheyenne, Wyoming.

Courtesy, Lamb Feeders Association

b. When a large portion of the farm's resources are income-producing and the future benefits, in terms of the non-monetary sources of satisfaction, are minor.

c. When the farm business includes a specialty enterprise or two which exhibits considerable year-to-year variation in income, and thus represents a high degree of risk.

d. When the investment precludes much opportunity for claiming depreciation, investment credit, or other tax offset.

e. When the cost of money or prevailing rates of interest are high due to either a short supply of available capital or a strong demand for money.

f. When the area or economy is no longer expanding and the terms of finance are being tightened.

g. When the dollar yields from alternative investment opportunities are high and when the future expectations of even higher yields are good. For example, common stock values are low, price-earnings ratios are low, and common stock prices appear likely to rise.

h. When farms or ranches are readily available and when additional land can be acquired fairly easily.

i. When there appears to be little if any desire on the part of investors to acquire capital gains in lieu of income or little if any need for a hedge against inflation.

Again assuming all other factors equal, a low capitalization rate is required in the following instances:

a. When the subject farm is a family farm, when the typical prospective buyer is likely to be an owner-operator, and particularly when the tract of land is one which will probably be added to an existing farm unit.

b. When the business aspects of the farm are relatively less important and a large part of the property's value results from several non-monetary sources of satisfaction, particularly those with emotional appeal.

c. When the farm business is a conventional one, located in a conventional farming area, hence a type of farming which leads to a fairly stable income from year to year or one which represents a fairly low degree of risk.

d. When the farm layout is above average—for example, large, long, and rectangular fields, when the amount of pastureland is low—hence, both livestock numbers and the need for unique managerial ability is less, when the number of buildings and improvements which have to be maintained are few in number, relatively simple, or both, and when the farm is located in one of the better land areas, or if nothing more, on an improved road.

e. When the cost of money or prevailing rates of interest are low, when the return on a small equity plus principal and interest payments are less than the probable annual dollar returns, and when the tax provisions provide considerable offset possibilities.

f. When the farm is located in a transition area where a change in land use is probable. An eventual change in use typically leads to higher land values in the future; it often attracts additional capital.

g. When the yields from alternative investment opportunities are low and when the expectations are that low yields will continue in the future. For example, when common stock prices appear to be excessively high.

h. When most farms or ranches are held in tight hands, when very few farms are changing ownership, and when additional farm land is difficult to acquire without a sizeable increase in offering price.

i. When there is considerable inflation in the economy, hence considerable desire on the part of many persons to have their money in land rather than cash.

In other words, capitalization rates, like typical operators, vary considerably from farm to farm. The capitalization rate is based on a number of facts gathered by the appraiser. It is not just an opinion.

3. The Occasional Use of Two Rates. Two capitalization rates, or a split rate, is sometimes more realistic than a single rate. Its use depends on the nature or makeup of the subject property and the origins of its earnings. Farm real estate can sometimes be divided into the natural and indestructible powers of the land, into buildings or improvements which decline in value over time, and into certain rights which may remain in existence, but only for a specific time period.

When a separate and distinct income stream from more than one of these assets or property rights can be defined, more than one rate of income capitalization may be used. Land may be capitalized at one rate, and the buildings or certain property or property rights may be separated out and capitalized at a second rate. In the case of land, the income may be capitalized into perpetuity. In the case of a wasting asset the income may exist only for a specified time period. In the latter case, the capitalization rate may include a recapture of as well as a return on the investment.

Different capitalization rates may be more difficult to explain—both in one's report and on the witness stand. However, a given subject property occasionally has some peculiar characteristics which make the use of a second rate most realistic. The use of a second or split rate provides an appraiser with considerable flexibility whenever the characteristics of a subject property indicate the need for its use. Illustrations are (1) a farm where the land may be rented or sold to one party and the buildings to a different party and (2) a farm where there are two separate income streams, one from farming and one from an entirely different origin. For example, a farm may have land that is farmed, yet some of that same land is frontage property and is quite likely to go to residential, commercial, or industrial development in the near future.

4. The Non-monetary Amenities. Many farm properties exhibit a unique characteristic or two, which does not directly affect its dollar income, yet which does affect the dollar value of the property. Unlike many appraisals, these non-monetary sources of satisfaction are usually recognized in a farm appraisal.

Many persons buy and own farms, not just for the opportunity of obtaining a given dollar income but for other reasons as well. These other reasons are also sources of value. They also need to be specified in one's report. Hence farm appraisers in the past have usually grouped or classified them as follows.

	Plus	*Minus*

1. Value of the Home
   Its size, attractiveness, physical
   features, recreational facilities,
   and scenic advantages.
	$ _____	$ _____

2. Location Value
   The road or highway, opportunity
   for off-farm employment, schools
   and churches, other community
   features, neighbors, and/or
   nuisances.
	$ _____	$ _____

3. Other Economic Assets or Liabilities
   Natural resources, mineral rights,
   physical features, unique build-
   ings, improvements, ownership
   rights (for example, leases), and
   indebtedness.
	$ _____	$ _____

These factors, both tangible and intangible, are not directly reflected into a farm's earnings. Hence, following the capitalization of the subject property's income, certain plus or minus adjustments may be desirable. (This depends on how the capitalization rate was developed and what it includes.) These adjustments may be expressed in terms of total dollars and applied to the total value of the farm, or they may be expressed in terms of dollars per acre and applied to the per-acre value of the farm.

A farm appraiser may thus develop several values in the income capitalization approach to farm value. He may develop an earnings value based solely on earnings. That earnings value may reflect only current and ordinary income, or the capitalization rate may have been developed to reflect or include capital appreciation. The farm appraiser may then adjust his earnings value for the value of the non-monetary amenities. He may also, if he has not already done so, adjust his value for whatever future expectations currently exist in the market.

Duplication is often difficult to avoid. Floods, drought, and other hazards that affect farm earnings may be considered in estimating a farm's productivity by either varying the crop yields or the operating expenses. If done accurately, that hazard does not need to be considered a second time by manipulating the capitalization rate or by making additional plus or minus adjustments. Such practice could easily penalize or undervalue a farm.

Hence, in recognizing the various origins of value, a farm appraiser needs to develop the earnings value of the subject property quite carefully. His job is to consider all of the major factors and ascertain the extent to which each affects the present market value of the farm. His job is to arrange or organize his work in a systematic fashion and avoid any overlap or duplication. The job is not easy.[18]

A MAJOR FOOTNOTE: HOW—WHEN NOT IN PERPETUITY?

The earnings approach to value is a method of estimating the present worth or value of a given income stream over the economic or pro-

18. Lastly, capitalization rates are typically developed to only one decimal point —e.g., 3.5, 4.0, 5.0 etc. When they are developed to 2 or 3 decimal places—3.54, 4.47, 5.23—this infers a high degree of accuracy, and to the naive at least, a superior knowledge on the part of the appraiser. However, to the person knowledgeable about the income capitalization approach to value, it presupposes a degree of false accuracy. Whether or not it is, it appears deceptive, and such a practice may do more harm than good to the appraiser's reputation.

ductive life of the property. When that income stream is expected to continue year after year, the income can be capitalized into perpetuity. A simple capitalization rate can be used. Primarily because land tends to be a physically indestructible if not inexhaustible resource, this technique is quite acceptable in the majority of farm appraisals. Theoretically at least, farm land does not depreciate. It supposedly persists indefinitely. Its income supposedly continues year after year.

The farm appraiser tends to treat farm buildings and improvements likewise. He typically includes an upkeep or maintenance item in the operating expenses. Conceptually, this is similar to, if not the same as, depreciation.[19] The farm appraiser thus assumes that the buildings will be maintained forever. In an appraisal where a large part of the property's value is contributed by land and where only a minor part is contributed by the improvements the assumption is perhaps acceptable.

However, a given subject property may, in some instances, include a unique asset—a building, an improvement, a mineral deposit, or a property right—which will eventually depreciate or wear itself out over time.[20] The income stream produced by this asset will, at some future point in time, cease to exist. This income should not be capitalized into perpetuity.

In these instances the appraiser is still interested in the present value of the income stream. However, his final appraised value must now reflect a flow of income that will someday dry up or be discontinued. His final value may also reflect an asset that may have value sometime in the future, however, not always. The asset may or may not have value at the end of the income period. The investor in this kind of a situation is desirous of obtaining not only a return *on* his capital; he wants to also obtain the return *of* his capital. In other words, he is desirous of recouping or recapturing his investment as well.

Let's illustrate: A 240-acre farm has a 35-acre gravel deposit. Northern Aggregates, Inc., is set up to remove approximately 185,000 cubic yards of gravel annually for which they are willing to pay the farmer $0.05 per cubic yard plus all his expenses. An engineering firm original-

---

19. Depreciation, a non-cash item, thus becomes a part of the cash farm expenses, which are then subtracted from farm receipts before the residual income is capitalized into value.

20. The non-farm commercial property appraiser refers to these resources as wasting assets. He typically assumes that they will, at some point in time, be replaced. To him, depreciation is the opportunity for recapture. He thus adjusts his capitalization rate to include a return *of* as well as a return *on* the investment.

ly estimated an 18-year supply of gravel. At the time of the appraisal, a
10-year supply remains. At the end of the 10-year period the land will
be of little or no value. Hence, the question "What is the present worth
or value of this asset, based on the income it will produce over the next
10 years?" This income stream will cease to exist at that time.

There are several key questions.

1. What is the remaining economic life of the asset? The rate at
which the investment is to be recovered or recaptured must first be
determined. In this case, the remaining supply of gravel will be exhausted in 10 years.

2. What is the going rate of return on other similar investments
in the community? For purposes of illustration this particular typical

The subject farm sometimes includes a unique asset—a building, an improvement, a mineral
deposit, or a property right. The income from this asset cannot always be capitalized into
perpetuity, for at some point in time that income may cease to exist.

Courtesy, U.S.D.A.

property owner's next best alternative investment is assumed to be capable of earning 6.0 percent.

3. What is the projected income stream? In this case it is $9,250 (185,000 cu. yds. × $0.05). The owner of the property could be paying real estate taxes, property liability insurance, or some other expense, which in these instances should be subtracted off the total return. However, in this case the $9,250 is assumed to be the net return or the income received after paying all expenses.

4. Will the asset itself still have value in terms of some other alternative use at the end of the period? In order to simplify this first problem the answer is "No."

The present worth or value of the gravel deposit on this farm (actually the remaining supply of gravel) may be budgeted at $57,812 (Table 35). This particular answer is based on a straight-line income capitalization method. The income stream—$9,250—is divided by a 16.0-percent rate, composed of two parts: (1) a 6.0-percent return on the capital invested and (2) a 10.0-percent rate of depreciation or recapture. The first part is the return *on* the investment (based on the typical owner's or investor's next best alternative in the community) and the second part is the rate of capital recapture or the return *of* the investment. Thus, the capitalization rate is not a simple rate.

The present value of an income stream may also be estimated using a second method. Instead of the straight-line method just presented, a compound interest method may be used. Using it, the remaining supply of gravel is worth not $57,812 but $68,091. This figure is obtained by multiplying the $9,250 income stream by 7.3601—a coefficient based on a 6.0-percent return or rate of interest over a ten-year period.

The compound interest method leads to a higher value. Why? It is based on the concept that there should be, in fact is, some penalty for waiting—namely interest on one's investment. Once a capital investment is made, that money is no longer available except as it is obtained or returned over a period of time. Thus the mathematical results obtained by the two techniques differ as to whether the income includes recaptured capital only (straight-line) or whether it also includes interest on that portion of the capital which is not returned or recaptured (compound interest).

The straight-line method is the more straightforward one. It is easier to understand. Part of the value ascertained is based on the amount of capital not yet recaptured divided by the number of years of remaining economic life. The method assumes that the amounts of capital recaptured remain constant or level over time. When the amounts are equal over time, the annual amounts of income decline.

The compound interest method is the more correct alternative. It calls for the same recovery of the capital itself, however, in addition, interest on that portion of the capital not yet recaptured. This method assumes that the income stream from the asset remains constant or level over time. (It's received or paid in equal amounts.) This is made possible because the amounts of recaptured capital are small in the beginning; however, as time goes on, they increase and are offset by smaller amounts of interest. In other words, the amount of recaptured capital increases each year as the amounts of interest paid on the still unrecaptured portions decline.

The compound interest approach is somewhat more complicated to understand mathematically. However, it is the more sophisticated method and the more accurate one. The calculations are no problem for the appraiser who keeps in his handbook a set of present-value tables. In fact, all appraisers should be familiar with two present-value tables.

1. The present value or worth of an income stream—the present value of one to be received or paid out each year over the next N years (Appendix Table A). This is actually the present value of an annuity.[21]

2. The present value or worth of an asset which will become available or revert back to the property owner in the future. This reversionary interest is the present value of one N years from now (Appendix Table B). It embraces a discounting process.

Table 35. The Present Value of an Income Stream or Depreciable Asset.
A 240-Acre Farm with a 35-Acre Gravel Pit.

The Asset	The Method	The Figures
The Basics 185,000 cu. yds. of gravel removed annually. The income is $0.05 per cu. yd. or $9,250 per year. A 10-year supply remains.		
Present Value of the Income Stream A. The Straight-Line Method, assuming a 6.0% return on one's investment and a 10% rate of recapture (ten years).		
	$9,250 ÷ 16.0% =	$57,812
B. The Compound-Interest Method, assuming a 6.0% rate of interest and a return over a 10-yr. period (Appendix Table A)		
	$9,250 × 7.3601 =	$68,081
Present Value of the Asset 10 years from now		0

Let's look at a second illustration: A 240-acre farm contains 10 acres which have been rented to the Commodity Credit Corporation for grain-bin storage. The Commodity Credit Corporation has a 15-year lease. The annual lease payment received by the farm owner each March 1 is $1,000. As of the date of the appraisal, the lease will run another eight years. Furthermore, at the end of the eight-year period the 10 acres will revert back to the farm owner and have value as farmland. Hence, unlike the gravel deposit, this land will have an alternative use and hence be valuable at the end of the lease period.

Two calculations are now required: one, to determine the present worth or value of the $1,000 income stream which will last eight more years, and a second, to determine the present value of the 10 acres, which, while it is not now available (because it is encumbered by the lease), will eight years from now become unencumbered or available for other use and have value at that time.

Using the compound interest method, the present worth of the eight-year income stream is $6,335 ($1,000 × the 6.3346 coefficient, Table 36). This assumes the $1,000 is a net return or income after paying all costs. The farmer could be paying some property tax or other expense. The present value of the 10 acres converted back to $600 farm land eight years from now (the value of the reversion) is $3,910 ($600 × 10 acres × the 0.65160 coefficient).[22]

Extending the economic life of the asset increases the present value of the income stream. It reduces the present value of the reversion. However, it increases the total present value of the property.

	8 Years	10 Years	12 Years
Value of the Income Stream	$ 6,335	$ 7,538	$ 8,618
Value of the Reversion	3,910	3,513	3,156
Total Value	$10,245	$11,051	$11,774

Increasing the capitalization rate reduces both the present value of the income stream and the present value of the reversionary interest.

---

21. The present worth of one per period is also equal to the reciprocal of the periodic principal and interest payment needed to amortize a farm mortgage loan.

22. The $600 figure is the present per-acre value of the farm itself (240 acres − 10 acres). The 0.65160 coefficient is the present worth or value of one dollar eight years from now. This particular coefficient assumes that if a given sum of money ($0.65) were invested today and if it were to earn 5.5 percent interest, compounded annually, that that sum would grow to one dollar in eight years.

Table 36. The Present Value of an Income Stream or Depreciable Asset and the Present Value of an Asset N Years from Now. A 15-Year Lease on 10 Acres.

The Asset	The Method	The Figures
The Basics Ten acres leased to the Commodity Credit Corporation for grain bin storage; annual lease payments are $1,000; and expiration date is eight years, at which time the land will revert back to the owner.		
Present Value of the Income Stream assuming a 5.5% return on comparable investments in the community and a return over an eight-year period.		
	$1,000 × 6.3346 (Appendix Table A) =	$ 6,335
Present Value of the Ten-Acre Tract available eight years from now and assuming a land value of $600 per acre.		
	$6,000 × 0.65160 (Appendix Table B) =	$ 3,910
Total Present-Day Value		$10,245

Hence it also reduces the total value of the property.

	5.5%	6.0%	6.5%
Value of the Income Stream	$ 6,335	$ 6,210	$ 6,089
Value of the Reversion	3,910	3,764	3,625
Total Value of the Property	$10,245	$ 9,974	$ 9,714

This same technique is used by non-farm commercial appraisers to ascertain the value of a lease. This kind of a problem is none too common in agriculture; however, again let's illustrate.

An elderly lady rented 232 acres for $40 per acre cash rent. Real estate taxes of $4.25 per acre were her only expense. She gave her tenant a five-year lease, keeping possession of the house and 2.5 acres. One year later the lady died. On the present-day market the land would sell for $650 per acre (unencumbered); the house and the 2.5 acres would sell for $24,000. However, what is the lessor's interest (the farm encumbered) and what is the leasee's interest (the lease itself) worth?

The lessor is the landowner (in this case the elderly lady's estate) who has conveyed or leased the right of occupancy and use of real estate to another person or party. The lessor's interest is the leased fee estate; it consists solely of title to the real estate, however, this is held subject to the lease, along with the right to receive certain rentals over the period of the lease. Ultimately, of course, the lessor repossesses the property. The lessee is the tenant or renter who has acquired the right to use the property. His interest is the leasehold estate. It consists of the right to occupy and use the real estate by virtue of the lease agreement.

In this illustration, the annual income stream for the next four years is $8,294 ($40.00 − $4.25 × 232 acres).[23] The present worth of this income stream, using a 5.5-percent rate of interest is $29,073 ($8,294 × 3.5052). This is the value of the lease. The present worth of the 232 acres four years hence is $121,726 ($650 × 232 acres × 0.8072). This amount ($121,727) plus the value of the lease ($29,070) is equal to $150,800, the total value of the 232 acres today.

Where a building, improvement, mineral deposit, or property right is unique and where that asset is a major part of the value of the subject property, the farm appraiser should appraise it as a depreciating or wasting asset. Eventually a building or improvement wears out. At some point in time the income from a mineral deposit or lease dries up. Thus, the farm appraiser should be capable of capitalizing income for given or fixed periods of time as well as into perpetuity. The present-value tables can be used to determine the present worth or value of an income stream, and the present value of any asset, which will become available or revert to the property owner in the future.[24]

Unfortunately, farmers and others often become lost in present value computations. The technique doesn't always appeal to prospective farm buyers or owners, and the farm appraiser has been much slower than his urban colleagues in using these techniques. However, the tables will be used more and more in the future when and where income such as the above cannot be capitalized into perpetuity.

---

23. In this problem one may use either the contract rent figure—the $40—or one may use an economic rent figure. Contract rent is the amount of rent called for by the terms of the present lease; it is the actual rent paid. Economic rent is the amount of rent that could reasonably be expected if the property were available for rent at this time. Contract rent may be above (the lessor has a good deal) or below (the lessee has a good deal) economic rent.

24. The straight-line and the annuity methods can both be taken one step further. The two methods, as presented in the text, assume that the recaptured capital is received annually and is then either spent or disbursed elsewhere. However, recaptured capital may also be deposited in a sinking fund, which in turn builds itself up by compound interest. In this case the return *on* the capital is available during the economic life of the asset; however, the return *of* the capital —the fund of money—is not available until the end of the period. Interest on this fund of money can thus add to the present value.

AREAS OF IMPORTANCE AND USE

The earnings approach to value is used primarily in appraising commercial farm properties. However, it works best only in certain areas. It works best where . . .

1. Soils and climate are largely responsible for crop yields and where fertilization and other cultural practices are well known and fairly uniform.

2. The system of farming is conventional, where new technologies are not being introduced. In these instances the typical operator can be specified fairly easily.

3. The income or dollar returns to land can be estimated quickly and easily; for example, in the cash-grain areas in the agricultural Midwest, where landlord-tenant arrangements are common, and where the crop-share cash lease is well defined.

4. The farms are large and largely commercial, and the so-called non-monetary features make up a small part of the total value of the real estate.

5. Farms are held in tight hands and where the farms, with the exception of estate sales and family transfers, are just not selling. In other words, when and where there is an absence of market data.

The earnings approach does not work as well where . . .

1. Management and the coordination of other capital resources are more responsible for the income from the farm than is the land or the real estate.

2. Livestock enterprises require a large capital investment in buildings and improvements and where these resources constitute a large share of the total value of the subject property.

3. Rapid change is occurring in the farming methods, or where certain specialty enterprises, for example, tomatoes, tobacco, or poultry provide the major source of income.

4. The farms are largely subsistence, part-time, or residential, and little or no farm products are sold, or where commercial farms are scattered in an area of largely marginal farms.

5. Agricultural opportunities are declining, relatively speaking, and the demand for land for residential, commercial, and industrial use is increasing, in other words, in the transition areas.

The earnings or income capitalization approach to value was developed in the 1930's largely by farm loan appraisers. Their observations then led them to a concept of value based on farm earnings. This earnings value, or basic farm value as they referred to it, was the more enduring portion of a farm's value. It dictated not only appraisal techniques but investment policies as well.

Today the approach continues to provide a guide as to whether or not a given farm will make money. The earnings approach serves an important function—that of separating the portion of value based on earnings from that portion of value based on the other non-monetary origins.

The appraisal which places major emphasis on the earnings or income capitalization approach to value is quite useful to investors, to farm loan men, and to farm appraisers themselves. The absentee-owner or investor may buy the farm and turn its management over to a professional farm manager. Immediately the farm manager has in the appraisal a plan for operating the farm. The typical cropping system has been developed. The dollar returns and operating expenses have been estimated. The farm manager's job is now to manage that farm in such fashion that its earnings are not just typical but are instead above expectations.

When there is little or no farm production, the farm appraiser may still do much of the basic analysis leading up to an earnings value. He should develop the physical description of the farm; he should estimate the farm's productive capacity. Then, by informing his client (1) the farm is not a money-making unit, (2) it probably never will be as it exists today, and (3) whatever value is there must originate from other sources, he performs a real service. Thus, the earnings approach may be quite useful, even though it doesn't come up with much income or lead to much value.

The earnings approach to value provides a strong test of the skills, ability, and tenacity of an appraiser. This is particularly so during periods of rapidly rising or rapidly falling farm prices, costs, and farm real estate values. The earnings or income capitalization approach requires a knowledge of all things agricultural. It requires considerable judgment and many calculations.[25] Many an appraiser has said, "the earnings approach is the toughest part."

The professional appraiser should always compare his final value figure based on earnings with those values ascertained through other approaches. Once an appraiser masters the earnings approach he be-

---

25. The mathematics involved are not always without error. In fact, most appraisers have learned to not only check but double check their arithmetic.

comes more confident. He is more likely to be honest—with himself, with his clients, and with others—and even when farms are selling for far more (or far less) than their values based solely on earnings.

REFERENCES

Bowen, J. R., and L. B. Mayer, "The American Rural Appraisal System," *Journal of American Society of Farm Managers and Rural Appraisers*, Vol. 10, No. 2, October 1946.

Crouse, E. F., and C. H. Everett, *Rural Appraisals*, Prentice-Hall, 1956.

Hudelson, R. R., "The American System of Farm Appraisal," *Journal of American Society of Farm Managers and Rural Appraisers*, Vol. 9, No. 1, April 1945.

Morse, T. D., "The American Rural Appraisal System," *Journal of American Society of Farm Managers and Rural Appraisers*, Vol. 2, No. 2, November 1938.

Murray, W. G., *Farm Appraisal and Valuation*, 5th Edition, Iowa State University, 1969.

Sackman, J. L., "Economic Approach to Valuation," *Appraisal Journal*, Vol. 34, No. 4, October 1966.

Stephenson, E. S., "Use of the Earnings Statement in Rural Appraising," *Journal of American Society of Farm Managers and Rural Appraisers*, Vol. 22, No. 1, April 1958.

The Formula: Its Application

"Capitalization Methods and Techniques," *American Institute of Real Estate Appraisers*, 1964.

Estimating Farm Receipts, Expenses, and Income

McConnell, E. J., "Verification of Income and Expense Items," *Journal of the American Society of Farm Managers and Rural Appraisers*, Vol. 2, No. 1, April 1938.

Morrison, E. R., "Establishing the Income Capitalization Value," *Journal of American Society of Farm Managers and Rural Appraisers*, Vol. 2, No. 2, November 1938.

Murray, W. G., *Farm Appraisal and Valuation*, 5th Edition, Iowa State University, 1969.

Defining the Capitalization Rate; Two Different Techniques

Appraisal of Real Estate, 4th Edition, American Institute of Real Estate Appraisers, 1964.

Bonner, J. T. Jr., "The Income Approach—Capitalization," *The Real Estate Appraiser*, Vol. 29, No. 1, January 1963.

Crouse, E. F., and C. H. Everett, *Rural Appraisals*, Prentice-Hall, 1956.

Dilmore, Gene, "New Direction in the Income Approach," *The Real Estate Appraiser*, Vol. 32, No. 5, May 1966.

Dorau, H. B., "The Capitalization Rate: Mirage or Will-o'-the-Wisp?," *Appraisal Journal*, Vol. 29, No. 1, January 1961.

Everett, C. H., "Estimating Market Value with the American Rural Appraisal System," *Journal of the American Society of Farm Managers and Rural Appraisers*, Vol. 24, No. 1, April 1960.

Fischer, R. M., "Economic Background of the Capitalization Process," *Journal of the American Institute of Real Estate Appraisers*, Vol. 5, No. 4, October 1937.

Gibbons, J. E., "Capitalization Rates," *Appraisal Journal*, Vol. 27, No. 2, April 1959.

Hitchings, T. C., "Fluctuating Terms May Affect Values," *The Real Estate Appraiser*, Vol. 35, No. 4, May-June 1969.

Lambert, L. D., "The Decline and Fall of the Mortgage Rate of Interest," *Journal of American Society of Farm Managers and Rural Appraisers*, Vol. 30, No. 2, October 1966.

McAnelly, E. E., "Discussion on Capitalization Rate," *Journal of American Society of Farm Managers and Rural Appraisers*, Vol. 7, No. 2, October 1943.

McLaughlin, F. J., "Proper Capitalization Rates," *Appraisal Journal*, Vol, 27, No. 4, October 1959.

Meyer, H. F., "Justifying Capitalization Rates on Farm Properties," *Journal of American Society of Farm Managers and Rural Appraisers*, Vol. 29, No. 2, October 1965.

Parcher, L. A., "Capitalization Rates for Rural Properties," *Appraisal Journal*, Vol. 30, No. 1, January 1962.

Pilmer, C. L., "The Earnings Approach, What Is It, a Formality or the Foundation for Value?," *Journal of American Society of Farm Managers and Rural Appraisers*, Vol. 30, No. 1, April 1966.

Smith, L. E. Sr., "Choosing the Cap Rate," *The Residential Appraiser*, Vol. 27, No. 3, March 1961.

Smith, W. J., "The Capitalization Rate as Applied to Rural Appraising in Canada," *Journal of American Society of Farm Managers and Rural Appraisers*, Vol. 7, No. 2, October 1943.

Stalcup, H. E., "Comparative Adjustments in the American Rural Appraisal System," *Journal of American Society of Farm Managers and Rural Appraisers*, Vol. 2, No. 2, November 1938.

Tredwell, J. C., "Selection of Capitalization Rates," *Journal of the American Institute of Real Estate Appraisers*, Vol. 6, No. 4, October 1938.

Weekes, R. E., "The Capitalization Rate," *Appraisal Journal*, Vol. 22, No. 2, April 1954.

A Major Footnote: How—When Not in Perpetuity?

Atkinson, H. G., "The Income Approach," *Appraisal Journal*, Vol. 22, No. 2, April 1954.

Cissell, Robert, and Helen Cissell, *Mathematics of Finance*, 3rd Edition, Houghton Mifflin, 1969.

Field, R. V., "The Mathematics of Valuation (The Six Compound Interest Tables)," *Selected Readings in Real Estate Appraisal,* Institute of Real Estate Appraisers, 1953.

Hollebaugh, C. W., "The ABC's of Capitalization Tables," *Appraisal Journal,* Vol. 23, No. 2, April 1955.

Hubin, V. J., "Some Further Remarks on the Nature, Meaning, and Use of the 'Cap' Tables," *Appraisal Journal,* Vol. 33, No. 4, October 1965.

Kinnard, W. N., Jr., "The Elwood Analysis in Valuation: A Return to Fundamentals," *The Real Estate Appraiser,* May 1966.

Parks, R. D., "Valuation of Mineral Property," *The Real Estate Appraiser,* Vol. 38, No. 3, May-June 1972.

Ring, A. A., "The Direct-Ring Method of Capitalization," *Appraisal Journal,* Vol. 28, No. 2, April 1960.

Schenkel, W. M., "The Effect of Leasehold Interests on Property Value," *The Real Estate Appraiser.* Vol. 38, No. 2, March-April 1972.

Schmutz, G. L., *Capitalization Tables,* Real Estate Association of California, 1936.

Shattuck, C. B., "Income Approach—Capitalization Processes," *Selected Readings in Real Estate Appraisal,* American Institute of Real Estate Appraisers, 1953.

Walrath, A. J., and W. L. Gibson, Jr., *The Evaluation of Investment Opportunities—Tools for Decision Making in Farming and Other Businesses,* Agricultural Handbook, No. 349, E.R.S., U.S.D.A., February 1968.

CHAPTER VII

The Sales Comparison or Market Data Approach to Value

The sales comparison or market data approach to value involves the use of other farms which have recently changed ownership. The bases for establishing the value of the subject property are the prices which have been paid for these farm properties in actual market transactions. The sale prices paid reflect all of the origins of farm value. They presumably include all of the factors affecting value.

Hence, the sales comparison approach to value is a most realistic one. Value is established by farmers themselves, by investors, and by other persons who have recently sold or purchased farms located in the same area. Each farm sale represents at least two other persons' judgment as to a given property's value. That judgment is supreme, for it is backed by either the property itself or by the money that has changed hands.

The sales comparison approach is based on two thoughts: (1) that an informed seller will not sell a given property for less than the dollar amount that other equally desirable properties are commanding in the market place and (2) that an informed buyer will not pay more for a given property than the cost of acquiring some other equally desirable property.[1] Bona fide sales of comparable farms thus become the basis for the sales comparison approach to value.

Unfortunately, perhaps, the prices paid reflect the many idiosyncrasies of farmers, neighbors, heirs, relatives, businessmen, investors,

---

1. In each case this represents an application of the substitution or opportunity cost principle.

The sales comparison approach to value makes use of any and all nearby farms which have recently sold. The appraiser's job is to inspect these properties and to also inquire into the reasons why the seller sold and why the buyer bought. Market prices are then adjusted for any dissimilarities in date of sale, location, farm size, productive capacity, and other factors so that those farms which have recently sold in actual market transactions are comparable to the subject property.

Courtesy, J. C. Allen

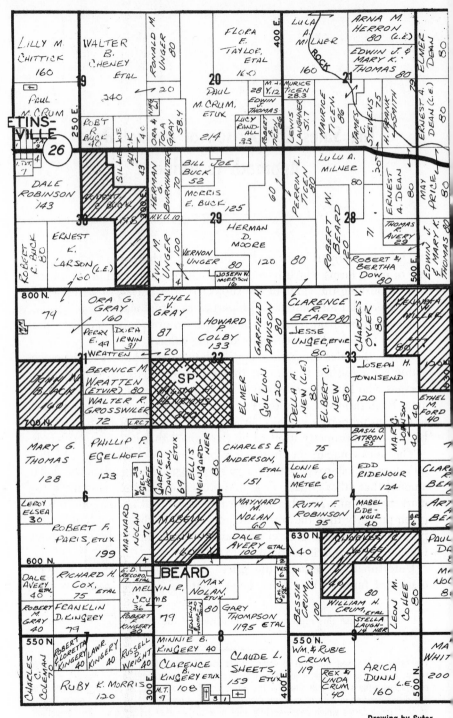

Drawing by Suter

A land ownership map showing the location of the subject property (SP) and its relationship to each comparable sale.

and other sellers or buyers, many of whom have varied interests or desires. For this reason, the appraiser's job is not just to inspect the various properties which have changed hands but to inquire into the forces
which motivated the sellers to sell and the buyers to buy. The behavior
of people is what creates the market. Hence, in measuring the market,
the appraiser must study the reasons why somebody sold and why somebody bought.

The professional appraiser can usually assemble and analyze considerable market data in a relatively short period of time once he makes
an organized effort to do so. At the same time, the job requires a certain amount of tenacity; it's tedious and painstaking. The appraiser's
job is to locate those farms for which reliable sales prices are known—
farms which are somewhat similar if not comparable to the subject
property. Once these farms are selected, their sale prices often need
to be adjusted to reflect some of the differences between these properties and the one being appraised. When their sale prices have been
adjusted for any dissimilarities, these comparable farm sales then give
the appraiser the bases on which to estimate his final value figure with
considerable confidence.

THE COMPARABLE SALE

A comparable sale is defined as a farm or property which resembles
the subject property being appraised as closely as possible in terms of
(1) kind of farm organization, (2) type of farm, (3) date of sale, (4)
location, (5) farm size, (6) productive capacity, and (7) extent of the
improvements. It is one which has recently sold in an arm's-length
transaction between a seller and a buyer, each of whom supposedly
represent, respectively, all sellers and buyers in the community.

No two farms are alike. Hence, the appraiser's job is (1) to have
available in his files all recent farm sales and (2) to select the three,
four, five, or so nearby properties which are similar to the subject
property. These farms are then compared to the subject property along
with the prices which were paid.[2]

At times it is difficult to find truly comparable properties for which
there was no compulsion on the part of either the seller to sell or the
buyer to buy, ones for which the date of sale is not too remote in time,

---

2. Asking prices by an owner and offers being made by prospective buyers may
at times be considered.

and ones for which no particular change has since occurred in the market. The inexperienced appraiser sometimes accepts any nearby property as a comparable one. He also assumes occasionally, and usually incorrectly, that there are no comparable properties in the vicinity. There are times, of course, when very few comparable sales are available. When this occurs the final value estimate can be made only with difficulty. But more often there are a number of available sales; the main difficulty is in finding them, verifying them, and sorting out those which are not comparable.

Comparability does not depend on any one single factor. Sales during the past three to five years are usually desired. However, sales six to eight years in the past may be highly relevant, particularly if, over time, the appraiser has tabulated all farm sales in the area and developed his own indices of changing values. Sales near the subject property are usually desired; yet sales several miles away may be highly comparable in terms of some unique feature—for example, a river bottom, an overflow problem, or triangulation of fields. Comparability as to soils may be emphasized in those areas where land values are highly correlated with soils—for example, in a cash grain area. Comparability as to buildings and improvements may be emphasized in areas where the improvements are major contributions to value—for example, in a dairy farming area. Thus, comparability does not depend upon a single factor.

Likewise, a dissimilarity or two does not necessarily eliminate the use of a particular farm as much as it may affect the weight of the evidence or testimony. A given comparable may be analyzed and used. However, the weight placed on its value as supportive evidence may vary. Lastly, as a matter of principle, the final present market value figure is not to be arrived at by calculating an arithmetical average. The final value figure should instead be based on the most frequent or modal sale price in the area.

SOURCES OF SALES DATA

Appraisers obtain sales data various ways. Many of them obtain the basic information from the office of the registry of deeds or a similar office in the county court house. However, farm brokers, farm loan officers, and other persons directly involved in, and hence knowledgeable about, various farm sales and farm loans in their area may be contacted.

The Office of the Registrar of Deeds: Whenever real property is sold or transferred by conveyance the subsequent recording of the evidence of title provides a continuous flow of property transfer information which is a matter of the public record. Many appraisers merely examine the deeds being recorded in the county court house.[3] Some appraisers do this themselves; others pay one of the clerks a per-farm fee to keep a record of all farm transfers. The appraiser may then check them himself later.

The basic information obtained usually includes . . .

1. The date of transfer.

2. The type of conveyance (the appraiser is typically interested in only warranty deeds).

3. The name(s) of the grantor(s) and grantee(s).

4. The location of the property (civil township and/or township, range, and section).

5. A brief description of the property, including acreage.

6. The documentary or revenue stamps which may be attached to the deed (in various states where such is the practice).

7. The amount of the consideration, actual if given; if not, an estimate based on the amount of the state's revenue stamps.

8. Any extenuating circumstance, such as the involvement of a third party, conveyance of only a partial interest, reference to an existing mortgage, a late recording (perhaps the result of a contract sale), and in some states, the source of title to the grantor.

10. The book and page numbers for future reference purposes (*Book of Deeds*).

All of this information should be recorded in a legible and organized fashion and also on the final form from which it will be used—so that the data does not need to be copied again at some later date.

Whenever the ownership of real estate is transferred, the customary practice is often to hide the price and to, instead, write into the deed some such comment as "for $1 and other valuable consideration." Thus, the problem of ascertaining actual market prices is sometimes a difficult one. Yet for years, appraisers and others have relied on various documentary or revenue stamps in order to estimate property values.

The first revenue act was the Federal Act of 1932 which required a stamp tax on all deeds of conveyance on properties exceeding $100 in

---

3. Local realtor boards, credit bureaus, and others sometimes publish property transfers in a weekly or monthly news sheet. An appraiser can usually get his name on the mailing list.

value. Revenue stamps were to be affixed to the deed in an amount not less than $0.50 per $500 (or fraction thereof) of value conveyed. In 1940 the rate was increased to $0.55 per $500 of value. However, the act was allowed to expire on December 31, 1967.

Many states immediately passed revenue acts of their own; however, the laws vary from state to state, and hence the federal practice in vogue prior to 1968 will be used here for illustrative purposes. A warranty deed for a 240-acre farm, for example, shows Federal revenue stamps in the amounts of $22.00, $22.00, $22.00, $5.50, $1.10 and $0.55 for a total of $73.15. Its value can be estimated at $66,500.

$$\frac{\$73.15}{0.55} = 133 \times \$500 = \$66,500 \text{ or } \$275+ \text{ per acre}$$

Comparable farms vary the country over, from the fertile valleys in Central New York to the orchard grass hills in Western Pennsylvania, from the eastern slopes of Virginia to the prairies in Western Ohio, and from the hills of West Virginia to the mountains in Montana.

Courtesy, U.S.D.A.

The tax stamps indicate a range in the amount of value conveyed; hence values can be interpreted two ways. One may assume that the midpoint is equal to the consideration, or one may use the upper limit as indication of value. For example,

Stamps Affixed	Range in the Amount of Consideration	Two Estimates of Value	
		Midpoint	Upper Limit
$72.60	$65,501-66,000	$65,750	$66,000
73.15	66,001-66,500	66,250	66,500
73.70	66,501-67,000	66,750	67,000
74.25	67,001-67,500	67,250	67,500
74.80	67,501-68,000	67,750	68,000

In general, there is a tendency for the amounts of consideration to cluster in the upper end of the range. Hence, the use of the upper limit tends to lead to more reliable estimates of value. In the preceding

Courtesy, U.S.D.A.

illustration the $66,500 figure would be the more accurate one.

Like all data, however, this one has a few quirks. One of them is that many laws require that the revenue stamps cover only the equity or the amount of cash conveyed. If the grantee assumes an existing mortgage, the value of the property as indicated by the stamps is low by the amount of the unpaid balance of the mortgage. Sometimes the unpaid balance, sometimes the original amount, and sometimes only the mere fact that a mortgage exists is shown in the deed.

When the unpaid mortgage balance is not given, one has to check the *Book of Mortgages* or mortgage recordings and estimate the amount that remains. The above 240-acre farm, for example, did sell subject to an existing mortgage and after some calculation, a balance of $58,663.14 appeared to still be outstanding. Thus, the total value of the farm was $66,500, the amount of money that changed hands, plus the $58,663 mortgage, or approximately $125,163. The actual sale price was perhaps

Courtesy, U.S.D.A.

either $125,000 or $126,000 (the latter is an even $525 per acre).

Lastly, there is no law against putting more stamps on the deed than necessary. In fact, the latter has been known to happen. An attorney or broker has, upon occasion, attached additional stamps, thus indicating a value above the actual sale price.

Persons or Parties Directly Involved: Once an appraiser has collected the basic information as outlined above, he should then contact one of the two or three persons who have a personal knowledge about the transaction and verify the actual price. The buyer or new owner is often the easiest person to contact. However, one may also visit with the seller, the realtor, the attorney, or whomever handled the farm mortgage loan. If the appraiser visits with the buyer he has the opportunity not only to verify price but also to inspect the property and perhaps obtain other information as well. One has to be polite and friendly of course.

Courtesy, U.S.D.A.

Farm Brokers, Loan Men, and Others: Farm real estate brokers, auctioneers, and loan men are often knowledgeable about farms that have recently sold, farms that are on the market, and farms that may be for sale in the future. These persons often have knowledge of the prices being asked and being paid.

Asking prices should be used only to establish the upper limits as to value. Asking prices and market prices are not the same, a possible exception being during a period when there is a strong demand for farms, and when farm prices are rising fairly rapidly. When farm real estate prices are high or appear likely to be declining, asking prices are often considerably above market prices. When this occurs, market activity declines and there are sometimes a number of farms on the market.

Some of the county assessors also maintain records as to property transfers and sale prices. Those records are usually available to ap-

Courtesy, U.S.D.A.

praisers; however, only occasionally are they reliable. Property values in the assessor's office, if not influenced by local politics, are often badly out of date.[4]

Actually, most professional appraisers collect sales data almost continuously. The court house records are merely a starting point. They do not tell an appraiser much about the farm or the property. The professional appraiser attempts to acquire this information whenever possible and from any and all sources. He then evaluates the many bits and pieces of information as he goes. He collects not only sales data, but also information on building construction costs, rental agreements, and financial arrangements. It's an interesting task.

---

4. In some states real property is assessed at its full value, in some at some fraction of its present market value. (See Chapter XI.)

Courtesy, U.S.D.A.

THE PRESENCE OR ABSENCE OF UNUSUAL CONDITIONS

Farm properties are bought and sold, of course, for many different reasons. Theoretically, the seller attempts to sell at the highest possible price; the buyer attempts to buy at the lowest possible price. When neither are under any compulsion to sell or to buy, these assumptions are reasonably valid. One can assume a bona fide farm sale and an arm's-length transaction.

However, most farm properties are unique. Sellers and buyers are even more so. Before an appraiser inspects a given property he often likes to first find out as much as possible about the market transaction. He likes to find out how the farm was sold, the motives of the seller, and the motives of the buyer. He likes to check for the presence or absence of any unusual conditions. Unless the transfer is an arm's-length transaction there is little or no reason to go further.

In the process of obtaining comparable farms, the following sales are often discarded.

1. Sales between related persons or members of the same family, unless value was established by competitive bidding or by a professional appraiser.

2. Sales in which the one party was obligated in some fashion to the other party, for example, a sale with a lease-back provision.

3. Bargain sales, or those made for purposes of obtaining a given amount of cash as quickly as possible.

4. Forced sales made by the sheriff (loan foreclosure) or by an executor, or administrator (estate settlement).

5. Sales made in a distressed market, for example, an area pending condemnation or an area in which present land use patterns have been frozen by zoning regulations.

6. Contract sales made with little or no down payment or with a rate of interest considerably below the market rate.

7. Sales which include some other extenuating circumstance which obviously influenced price.

These sales are not arm's-length transactions.

VERIFICATION, INSPECTION, AND CLASSIFICATION

Once the bona fide farm sales in an area are known they are usually spotted on a map or in a county plat book. Then, whenever the appraiser is appraising a farm in the area he can stop by the four, five, and sometimes more nearby farm sales, look them over carefully, and verify their sales prices.

Verification and Inspection: The sale price on each comparable sale used to appraise a farm should always be verified by someone with a personal knowledge of the transaction. The buyer is usually the easiest person to find, and with his permission, the farm can be inspected at the same time.

Most buyers are proud of the farm they have purchased; most of them are in the process of making some changes, adding improvements, etc. If properly approached, and if time permits, they will usually tell an appraiser a good bit about the farm, their plans for the future, and how and why they purchased this particular property. However, one does not motivate a new farm owner to tell much by quickly or immediately asking him what he paid for the farm. The job requires some finesse.

Most appraisers hesitate to take the time to inspect a farm—its soils, its productive capacity, its buildings and improvements, and its origins of value—until they are convinced the sale was an arm's-length transaction. Yet, this is often the best way of obtaining the information desired. For once the new owner realizes the appraiser is serious and that he is willing to take the time to inspect the property, he (the new owner) is more likely to be cooperative.

Unfortunately, three, or four, or more appraisers may have already stopped and bothered him. When this is the case, he will usually quickly decide either "This fellow knows what he's doing, he must be a professional" or "Here's another screwball asking me stupid questions I'm not about to answer."

The amount of time spent in inspecting a farm property depends on (1) the reason for appraising the subject property and (2) the extent to which the farm or sale is comparable to the subject. The appraiser who may some day appear in court usually takes time to inspect all of the comparables fairly thoroughly. Oftentimes he has an aerial photo. He obtains the tillable acres, an idea as to the land use, and an idea or two with regard to the farm's productivity or carrying capacity. If time permits he may note any and all important land features. He usually inspects the buildings, both inside and out. He usually makes notes so he can later classify the farm. He sometimes takes pictures which he may later include in his appraisal report.

However, the appraiser's real job is to verify the facts surrounding the transfer: (1) the date of sale, (2) the sale price, (3) whether the farm sold for cash or on contract, (4) if on contract its terms—the length of the contract, the size of the down payment, and the interest rate, (5) whether any personal property (for example, this year's crop) was included, (6) whether the buyer assumed an existing mortgage, any unpaid taxes, or assessments, and whether any government payments accrued to the buyer, (7) whether any other financial obligations were included in or affected the price of the property, and (8) the date of possession, along with the expiration date of any unexpired lease.[5]

Several bigger and even more important questions are: (1) Why did the buyer buy the farm? (2) Why did he pay that particular amount? (3) Was he informed? (4) What motivated him? (5) Did he buy the farm to get closer to his mother-in-law, or further away? (6) Did he buy the tract and add it to an existing farm unit? (7) Did he want the buildings; does he plan to use them or to demolish them? A number of questions have to be answered if an appraiser is to later adjust the sale price and thus make the farm comparable to the subject property being appraised.

Nobody sells or buys a farm except for good reasons. The appraiser has to learn to analyze the reasons why. For the various market transactions reflect the persons involved and their many idiosyncracies. Heirs, attorneys, farm auctioneers, lenders, and sometimes friends often play a large and important role in the transfer of a farm.

Neighbors often foresee a particular farm coming up for sale in the future. If it's a good farm and one they would like to someday own, an informal agreement is sometimes made with the heirs, and sometimes the attorney as well, ahead of time. When the farm comes up for sale it's not widely advertised. Only a few persons know about it. Eventually the farm sells, yet it's largely a private sale, and any previous arrangement cannot be documented.

The appraiser is interested in only those sales, the terms of which were well advertised beforehand, those sales in which the farm was offered to any and all interested parties, and those sales in which the charactertistics of the property were accurately portrayed.

These sales are sometimes difficult to obtain. For example, when a

---

5. The cost of transferring ownership, including sales commission, survey costs, legal fees, title examination, and insurance, often amounts to as much as 6 or 8 percent of the sale price. It is traditional for each of these costs to be paid by one of the parties. However, in the process of negotiating price one party may shift one or more of these costs to the other party. These items may thus lead to a difference in the true price of the farm or property.

farm is transferred to the next generation, the heirs often want as few persons as possible to know about the sale. They sometimes prefer that a particular person acquire the farm—one of the sons or maybe the present tenant. When this is the case the farm is not widely advertised. Only a small ad is placed in the local paper, and it appears there no more times than is required by law.

When one of the heirs lives on the farm and has farmed it for several years, the neighbors are often reluctant to bid against him. They may bid in some instances, yet refrain from running up the price. Friends, neighbors, relatives, and sometimes the owners themselves thus attempt to keep real estate prices at conservative levels. This is particularly true when the farm was purchased some years ago and when a sizeable increase in value has since occurred.

Yet the opposite sometimes occurs. When there are several outside heirs, the brothers and sisters may get together and decide, "If he wants it, he can have it, but he'll pay for it." Brotherly love and sentiment are placed on the shelf, at least temporarily.

Farmers, attorneys, and others sometimes put a farm on the market at the wrong time of year. They sometimes hesitate to wait for the market to absorb a sale. This is poor timing and it's often costly to the seller. It's usually due to a lack of knowledge about things agricultural; however, sometimes it appears to have been done purposefully.[6]

Attorneys often ask for sealed bids and they don't always disclose all of the terms of a farm sale in an understandable fashion. The practice of selling to the highest bidder over an indefinite period of time and accepting only sealed bids frustrates many buyers. "Whether or not my bid was accepted," "Whether or not I can raise the bid," and "What, actually, was the last bid?" are often unknowns.

What are the terms of the sale? How much earnest money is required? In what form is it desired? Is the property encumbered? Is the right-of-way properly described? Are the mineral rights included? Who pays for what and when? For example, this year's (last year's) taxes? Who gets this year's crop? What expenses are involved? If the farm is tenant-operated, how and when does the buyer obtain possession? These are questions which trouble many buyers, even though

---

6. The best time to buy a farm is in late summer or early fall (with January 1 or March 1 possession) when one can look at the current crop being harvested. However, a farm often sells best in late spring or early summer when the grass has turned green, when the crops are growing, and when all the wet spots and other defects are fairly well covered up. Furthermore, the relatively large farm or ranch may sell best if sold in several tracts.

according to the attorney, ". . . there is no problem!" The uncertainties are greater than generally realized. In fact, these items affect both the number of buyers and the price.

In areas where farms are sold at auction, the auctioneer sometimes plays a large role in determining the selling price. He may sell the farm too quickly, before all bidders have had an opportunity to appraise their resources, line up their credit, or work up to their final bid.[7] He may prolong the bidding and wear out prospective buyers. What's worse, he may overvalue a farm in the minds of neighbors or other prospective buyers and thus scare them away.

Farm mortgage lenders may influence real estate prices even though many of them consider themselves to be appraisers. They sometimes give a seller optimism, then turn around and encourage a well-qualified buyer to buy the property, when maybe no one else has even entered the market. This happens more often with residential properties than with farms. It happens more often with bankers than with professional farm loan personnel.

All this essentially says is that market behavior is not always predictable, that there is no organized market in farm real estate, that there are no grades or standards, and that often there is no single way of obtaining meaningful sale prices. The appraiser's job is to study the market.

Classification: The appraiser's job, of course, is not to do market data studies but to appraise farms. So he collects many bits and pieces of information representing various farm sales in various areas and over time. He often adds to his body of market data; however, only as time permits and only as required by various appraisals in various areas. Hence much of his information, initially at least, is incomplete.

The problem is to organize farm sales data from the very beginning, so that whatever data are available can be filed, referred to, and used efficiently, and so that whatever later information is obtained, it too can be recorded easily and without upsetting the system or copying the data over again.

Any system should be set up with the following thoughts in mind. Such should be . . .

1. Usable—in the court house, in the field, and in the office.

2. Printed—hence, similar information is recorded in the same place on each card (all cards and entries are uniform).

---

7. Neighbors and others should make their financial arrangements prior to the sale of a farm at an auction. However, failure to do so is a common mistake.

3. Sufficiently flexible—to accept any type of property, located anywhere, and at the same time, all salient features of the property and the sale can be coded.

4. One which will sooner or later absorb any currently existing system and permit future changes without becoming obsolete or necessitating a complete system revision.

5. Subject to quick hand-sorting, without the use of complicated codes so that given farms can be readily obtained.

6. One which does not require indices, cross references, double entries, or double codes.

One of the more efficient ways of classifying sales data is with the use of a 5 x 8 key-sort card. Each sale can be recorded on a separate card and that card can then be coded according to however many categories or classifications about which an appraiser wants to keep information in his particular area. The key-sort system involves a number of cards, one for each sale, with prepunched holes along each edge. A punch is then used for notching the cards, along with a sorting needle for sorting them and a conventional filing cabinet for storing them.

The cards are coded with a punch which notches the card, thus no longer leaving various holes intact. These notches along the edge make each card mechanically articulate. By running a sorting needle or piece of baling wire through hole number 18, for example, all cards or sales except those representing dairy farms are picked up. In other words, all of the cards representing dairy farms fall out. By running the sorting needle through hole number 23, for example, all cards on dairy farm sales, except those designating farms with over 50 cows, are picked up. In other words, all cards designating farms with over 50 cows fall out.

The system is thus hand operated. It could be computerized; however, few attempts have been made to do so in rural areas.

The key-sort system is compact, flexible, and capable of infinite expansion. The separate card used for each sale makes the data easy to collect and use. Classification can be done quickly and accurately and without copying. The basic objectives of readable data, coded classification, and direct sorting are achieved.

The appraiser, of course, has to determine the bases for his classifications—those that he wants to use in his area. Farm properties may be classified according to some or all of the following factors:

1. Kind of farm organization—commercial, part-time, residential, or subsistence farms.

2. Type-of-farming—cash grain, dairy, hog, feeder cattle, beef cow

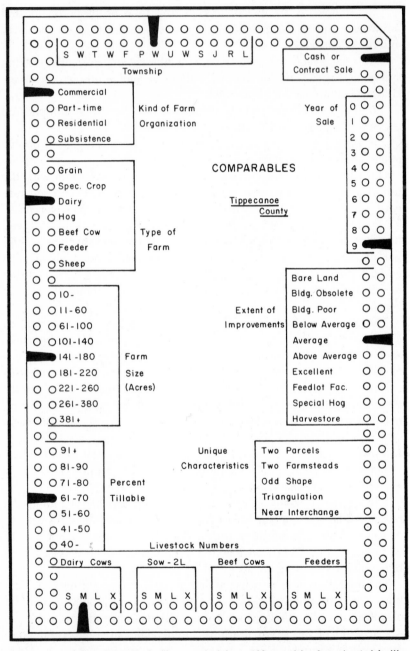

A key-sort card from the author's files, punched for a 160-acre dairy farm, located in Wea Township, 68 percent tillable, 44 cows, average improvements, a cash sale in 1969.

herd, or poultry farms.

3. Date of sale—year.

4. Method of selling—cash or contract.

5. Location—county and township, or township, range, and section number; sometimes type of road and distance from town.

6. Farm size—acres, number of dairy cows, etc.

7. Productive capacity—acres or percent of tillable land, crop yields, and livestock carrying capacities.

8. Extent to which the property is improved—bare land, obsolete buildings—poor, below average, average, above average, or excellent buildings and improvements.

9. Any and all other unique circumstances which prevailed at the time of the sale, for example, an irregularly shaped farm, triangular fields, or location near an interstate interchange.

ADJUSTMENTS FOR DISSIMILARITIES

An appraiser may find as few as 2 or 3 or as many as 15 or 20 sales in the area he is appraising. His job is to select those which are most comparable to the subject property. Not always is this possible. Thus the technique becomes one of selecting those farms which are as similar as possible, studying both the similar and dissimilar characteristics, and then adjusting their sale prices to allow for the latter.

Dollar adjustments are typically made for the six or seven major factors used to classify the sales, namely, (1) date of sale, (2) location, (3) farm size, (4) productive capacity, (5) extent of the improvements, and perhaps (6) others, such as the method of sale.

Plus or minus adjustments for each major factor are applied to the market data—oftentimes to each comparable sale. *They are not applied to the subject farm or property.* The adjustments may be applied to the total property values or they may be stated in terms of dollars per acre. In either case, the adjustments are expressions of the extent to which the comparable properties are dissimilar to the subject property.

The real estate market is imperfect. A farm's sale price seldom if ever fully reflects, in terms of dollars, the maximum difference in value due to any one major factor. Hence, the appraiser is forced to evaluate. He may calculate the maximum dollar difference, and then discount or reduce that figure, depending on the extent to which that particular factor may have influenced the sale price and depending on his judgment of the relative skills of the seller and the buyer of the property.

Date of Sale: The value of a comparable sale which sold several years ago can be adjusted up or down to reflect the increases or decreases in farm real estate values which have taken place between the date of sale and the date of the appraisal.

Ideally, only those sales during the last three to five years are used. Yet occasionally, the subject farm itself, or a tract of land adjoining the subject farm, sold 8 or 10 years ago, and in this case it's the same size, has the same productive capacity, and has similar improvements. When this older sale is well located, when the data are known to be reliable, and when few or no other adjustments are required, there is no reason why a farm sale 8 or 10 years old cannot be used. In other words, time alone should not be the determining factor as to whether or not a given sale is used as a comparable.

Let's illustrate: A 240-acre comparable sold eight years age (1992) for $150,000; the index of farm real estate values since the date of sale (1992 to 2000) has changed as follows:

Year	Index
1992	248
1993	246
1994	240
1995	242
1996	254
1997	268
1998	292
1999	301
2000	316

From the year 1992 to the year 2000—the index of farm real estate value has increased from 248 to 316 or 27.4 percent (316 ÷ 248). Hence, the value of the comparable sale today (year 2000), adjusted for the increase in value, is $191,000 ($150,000 × 127.4%). The per-acre value has increased from $625 in 1992 to $796 ($625 × 127.4%) in 2000.

This adjustment reflects the changes in value which have taken place in the farm real estate market between the year 1992, the year of sale, and the year 2000, the year of the appraisal. It reflects changes that have occurred in the general supply and demand for farm real estate and in the value of the dollar. It does not reflect changes that have taken place in the property itself.

The adjustment further assumes that farm real estate values in the community where the farm is located have changed at the same rate as those values on which the index was based. Not always is this correct. An appraiser may say, "Our data for the farms that have sold in this area alone indicate only a 21-percent increase in value. Hence, as far as we are concerned the comparable farm's value today is not $191,000 but $181,500 ($150,000 × 121.0%)."

Price changes may be indicated by:

1. Indices of farm real estate values for an entire state.

2. Changes which have occurred in the prices of a number of similar farm properties selling in a particular area over time.

3. Differences in the prices of properties which have been sold a second time within a given period.

Each of these indicators may be used. However, modifications to reflect technological changes occurring in agriculture, changes in farm commodity prices and farm costs, and/or current economic influences, such as a tight money market, are sometimes needed.

Location: Location adjustments are often ones of sheer judgment. However, farm sales along major county roads sometimes develop price patterns. The appraiser's job is to analyze his sales and ascertain if some such pattern exists.

Let's illustrate. An analysis of 16 farm sales indicates (1) that after the first 3 miles north of town (Brook, Indiana) there appears to be a $30 to $50 decline in per-acre land values, (2) that after the next 4 miles there appears to be an additional $150 to $180 decline, and (3) that beyond these 7 miles there is an additional $50 to $150 decline in per-acre values, depending on the relative amounts of sandy ridges and swampy ground on each farm (Figure 20). The changes in this particular instance are due primarily to changes in soil type. The first 3 miles are silty clay loam, the next 4 miles are sandy silt loam, and the next 5 or 10 miles are sandy loam, some of which are very unproductive.

The subject property in this case is located 5.5 miles from town. Four farms in the same area recently sold for $770 (A), $725 (B), $525 (C), and $400 (D) per acre. They are located 1.5, 4.5, 8.5, and 9.5 miles respectively from town. The subject property is located between comparables B and C. One of them is far enough north to be in a real sandy area. What are the probable adjustments? (See Table 37).

Farm Size: When farm size increases, sale prices also increase, but usually not proportionately. On a per-acre basis in particular, prices have a tendency to decline. Several reasons for this were presented in Chapter I. When all of the sales in a given area are classified, a relationship between size and price per acre can sometimes be developed.

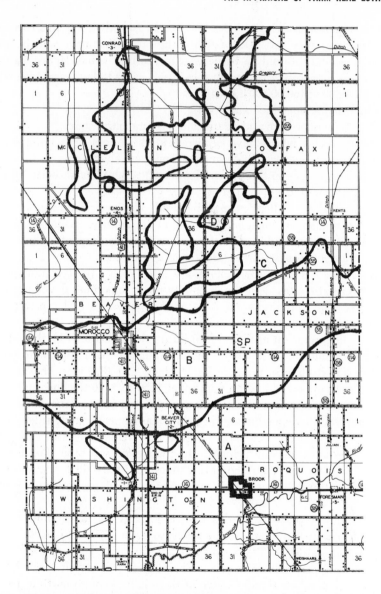

Figure 20. Farm Land Values Related to Location.

North of Brook, Indiana, Farm Land Values Range from
$750 to $800 per Acre, 3 Miles North from $710 to
$760, 4 Miles Further North from $540 to $590.
They Often Range as Low as $400 to $525 in This
Area Depending on the Number of Sand Ridges and
Low Swampy Land on the Farm.

Let's illustrate. Forty-five out of 210 sales are comparable, except for size, and have been tabulated (Table 38). Between 40 and 160 acres the per-acre sale price declines $53 ($631 — $578). However, to make the data useful one needs to calculate this decline in value on a per-acre basis. Between 40 and 80 acres the decline in value is $12.00 or $0.30 per acre, between 80 and 120 acres it is $16.00 or $0.40 per acre, etc.

The subject property consists of 120 acres. Three comparable farms recently sold for $600, $585, and $562 per acre. They range in size from 160 to 185 and to 240 acres. What are per-acre adjustments? (See Table 39.)

These adjustments assume that all other factors are held constant. The adjustments are sizeable; however, they are often offset by other factors in the final analysis.

Productive Capacity: Farms also vary in terms of the acreage of tillable land (or percent tillable) and in terms of productivity. In the more humid areas, farm land values vary with the relative amounts of level and rolling cropland. In the dry land areas and along various river valleys, ranch values vary with the relative acreages of dry and irrigated land.

Table 37. The Adjustment of Varying Sales Prices for Differences in Location. An Illustration Using Four Comparable Sales.

| | Comparable Farms | | | | Subject Property |
	A	B	C	D	
Sale Price per Acre	$770	$725	$525	$400	—
Location					
Miles from Town	1½	4½	8½	9½	5½
Miles from Subject Property	4	1	2	3	—
Sandy Ridges or Swamps	None	None	One	Three	None
Thumb-Rule Adjustments					
First 3 Miles	−50	—	—	—	—[1]
Next 4 Miles	—	—	+150	+175	—
Ridges or Swamps	—	—	+ 40	+150	—
Total	−50	—	+190	+325	—
Adjusted Sale Price					
Per Acre	$720	$725	$715	$725	$720

1. Adjustments are applied to the comparables; they are not applied to the subject property.

Let's illustrate: Four farms have recently sold for an average of $620 per acre. They are similar, in that they average 345 acres in size and are 86 percent tillable. Seven other farms have recently sold for $430 per acre. They also are somewhat similar; they average 375 acres in size, and yet are only 56 percent tillable. The differences have been tabulated as follows:

	Low Capacity	High Capacity	Difference
No. of farms	7	4	—
Acres	375	345	30 a.
Percent tillable	56	86	30%
Sale price per acre	$430	$620	$190

Going from 56 to 86 percent tillable the dollar value increases $190 per acre. For each 1-percent increase, the change is $6.33 per acre ($190 ÷ 30%).

Table 38. Sales Data Classified According to Size and the Relationship Between Farm Size and Price. Forty-five Farms, West Central Indiana, 1970.

A. The Raw Data Tabulated

Acreage Range	Acreage Mode	Number Farms	Sale Price per Acre	Decline in Price
30 to 55	40.3	10	$631	—
56 to 100	78.4	7	619	12
101 to 140	118.6	8	603	16
141 to 180	160.6	13	578	25
181 to 220	214.3	4	551	27
221 to 280	247.0	2	592	−41
281 to 480	—	0	—	—
481 to 1,075	1,075.0	1	$525	—

B. The Relationship Developed

Increase in Acreage	Number of Acres per Increment	Incremental Decline in Sale Price	Decline in Value per Acre
40 to 80	40	$−12	$0.30
80 to 120	40	−16	0.40
120 to 160	40	−25	0.62
160 to 215	55	−27	0.50
215 to 1,075	860	$−26	$0.03

Table 39. The Adjustment of Varying Sales Prices for Differences in Farm Size. An Illustration Using Three Comparable Sales.

	Comparable Farms			Subject
	A	B	C	Property
Sale Price per Acre	$600	$585	$570	
Size (Acres)	160	185	240	120
Differences Between Comparable Sale and Subject Property	40	65	120	—
Adjustments Per Acre	$+25^1$	$+37^2$	$+56^3$	—
Adjusted Sale Price Per Acre	$625	$622	$626	$625

1. 40 acres × $0.625.
2. 40 acres × 0.625, + 25 acres × $0.50.
3. 40 acres × 0.625, + 55 acres × $0.50, + 25 acres × $0.15.

The subject farm is a 320-acre tract, 72 percent tillable. One can now approach the subject's property's value, by "adjusting" these market averages.

1. $430 + (72 - 56\%) \times \$6.333 =$
    $430 +   \$101.33   = \$531.33.$

2. $620 - (86 - 72\%) \times \$6.333 =$
    $620 -   \$88.66   = \$531.34.$

In this illustration, market data are again used in place of the individual sale prices on several comparables. This merely illustrates that there are many ways of developing market data and making adjustments. In this illustration one can also adjust the sale price of a comparable. For example, a comparable farm recently sold for $665 per acre. It also is 320 acres in size, however, it is 93 percent tillable. The maximum per-acre adjustment is thus $133.00 (93 − 72 × $6.33). The adjusted value of the comparable is thus $532 per acre ($665 − $133).

These data can also be manipulated to obtain farm values on a per-tillable-acre basis.

$620 per acre ÷ 86% = $721 value per tillable acre.

$430 per acre ÷ 56% = $768 value per tillable acre.

These values can then be averaged and the value of the subject property or the value of a comparable may be based on these figures.

$$\frac{\$721 + \$768}{2} = 744 \text{ per acre.}$$

$744 \times 72\% = \$536$ (Subject Property).

$744 \times 93\% = \$692$ (Comparable Sale).

A weighted average may be more accurate.[8] However, the poorer land has a tendency to be priced upwards. The $692, based on the 93-percent figure is perhaps high, as the better land has a tendency to be priced downwards.[9] Thus, an element of judgment is still involved.

Extent of Improvements: Farms also vary in terms of the extent to which they are improved. In some areas farms are being consolidated. They are becoming larger and on some units there are leftover buildings and improvements. In other areas there is a squeeze play on land. Farms are expanding vertically, as contrasted to the adding of more acres, and as a result, in these areas there are a number of new buildings.

Let's illustrate: A given subject farm, 200 acres in size, has on it an obsolete ear corn crib which is no longer used and a house worth no more than $8,000. A nearby farm, which recently sold for $192,000 ($960 per acre), is also 200 acres in size. However, it has on it a relatively new 40,000-bushel grain-handling unit ($24,000) and a very attractive home ($32,000).

The maximum adjustment which could be subtracted from the price of the comparable farm, in this case, is $48,000, or $240 per acre. The arithmetic is as follows:

	Comparable A	Subject Property	Difference
House	$32,000	$8,000	$24,000
Grain Handling	24,000	Obsolete	24,000
Total	—		$48,000
Per Acre (200 Acres)			$ 240

---

8. [($721 × 4 farms × 345 acres) + ($768 × 7 farms × 375 acres)] ÷ 2 = $751 per acre.

9. The 93 percent is also above or outside the 56- to 86-percent range.

However, buildings and improvements are not readily saleable or marketable by themselves. Their cost seldom if ever adds an equal number of dollars to the market value of the farm. Hence, an appraiser should discount the above difference perhaps by as much as 40 to 60 percent. A more realistic adjustment would be $28,800 ($48,000 × 60%) or $144 per acre ($240 × 60%).

Other Adjustments: Farm properties often differ in terms of general appearance, field size or shape, acreage allotments, farmstead arrangement, length of driveway, mineral rights, or some encumbrance. Not always are these minor factors reflected in the market, yet several of them together may affect a given farm's salability.

An adjustment sometimes overlooked in the agricultural Midwest is the landlord's share of the crops. For example, a 240-acre farm sold in late summer. The price—$625 per acre—included the landowner's share of the corn crop. A total of 185 acres were tillable and 135 acres were in corn. The corn yield averaged 110 bushels per acre. The landlord's share of the crop was thus worth $7,425 (135 acres × 110 bu. × 50% share × $1 per bu.). This is the maximum total adjustment which could be subtracted from the sale price of $150,000.[10] Furthermore, this maximum adjustment may or may not need to be reduced, depending on whether or not the buyer "reimbursed" the landlord for his share of any seed, fertilizer, or other expense.

Another adjustment, seldom overlooked, however often highly confusing, is the sale of farm real estate on a contract basis rather than on a cash basis. Some of the arithmetic involved here is presented in the next section.

Lastly, while some appraisers go through some of the above gymnastics, many do not. The above illustrations are presented mainly to show that these kinds of relationships do exist. One cannot do a complete and detailed market analysis every time he makes a farm appraisal. However, if in a given area, or if over time, one does a number of appraisals, analyses such as those just illustrated can be developed.

In any single farm appraisal, a map of the area showing the location of the subject farm along with each comparable farm sale is quite helpful. A listing of each of these more important sales—grantor, grantee, sale date, location, farm size, and price—should be included in one's

---

10. Students often attempt to calculate these adjustments on a per-acre basis rather than for the total farm. This can be done (1 acre × 110 bu. × 50% share × $1 per bu. = $55.00). However, this figure needs to be adjusted for the percent of land in corn ($55.00 × 135/240 acres = $30.94).

report. An appraiser may also properly state that, in his investigation, he checked a number of sales in the area and that from this group— for example, 14 sales—he selected 5 which were particularly pertinent. This selectivity in itself is part of the appraisal process. Not always is one's client or a jury aware of such.

A brief description of each comparable farm sale, an analysis of the conditions surrounding each, and the adjustments pertaining to each should be presented in one's report. This can be presented in either narrative form or tabular fashion. The amount of detail included may depend on one's client and his level of comprehension.

In the making of adjustments the appraiser should be sure to use the proper plus or minus sign. He must remember he is adjusting not the value of the subject property but the price of each comparable farm sale.

Comparable farms are occasionally dissimilar as a result of changes that have occurred or improvements that have been made since ownership was transferred. A comparable sale with a low price may appear unrealistic. However, the woods may have been cleared and 80 acres may have been drained since the farm was purchased. The new owner may have built a new stall barn and milking parlor. The experienced appraiser often makes a note of these changes in his appraisal report. They often clarify questions which arise later. Furthermore, this practice is sometimes important whether or not a nearby farm was used as a comparable sale in one's appraisal.

Lastly, one needs to be careful not to adjust for the same item twice. Major emphasis should be placed not on the mathematical computations but on the thoroughness of the investigation, the logic of the analysis, and the clarity of various adjustments. One's analysis should show how each comparable farm is either superior, equal, or inferior to the subject property. Mathematical adjustments should be kept as simple as possible. The more complicated they are the more confusion is created, and oftentimes the overall perspective is lost. Any loss of perspective is to be avoided, particularly in courtroom testimony.

THE CONTRACT SALE

In recent years many farms have been sold using an installment land contract. This is largely the result of the more favorable tax treatment afforded sellers who are both able and willing to accept installment payments.[11]

A cash farm sale is one in which the seller is paid cash and in full. The property is deeded over to the buyer immediately.[12] A transfer on contract is one in which the seller agrees to sell and the buyer agrees to buy over a period of time with the seller usually receiving (1) a down payment, then (2) a series of installment payments, both prin- cipal and interest, over the life of the contract, and then (3) a balloon payment at the end of the contract period.

When a farm is "sold" on an installment basis the deed to the property does not immediately change hands. Instead, it is usually placed in the hands of a third party—an escrow agent, who agrees to hold such, giving it to the buyer, or returning it to the seller, whenever the buyer fulfills or fails to fulfill his obligations. A quitclaim deed is usually signed by the buyer and is placed in escrow at the same time. This quitclaim deed is then returned to the buyer when he fulfills his obligations, or, it may pass to the seller in the event the buyer defaults.

There is considerable confusion as to whether a contract sale should be used as a comparable farm sale. Some appraisers say the contract sale does not represent a bona fide market transaction. Some appraisers say it does not meet the definition of present market value, particularly the assumption that the buyer has an acceptable down payment. Other appraisers say the contract sale represents the highest price in terms of money, etc., etc., etc., and, that money can and should be defined to include the promise to pay, as well as cash.

The seller of a farm actually has three alternatives in the sale of his property.

1. He can find a buyer who has the down payment and the ability to borrow the remaining capital and thus provide the seller with cash. At this point the two parties may transfer the property by deed—the traditional method—or they may sign a contract.

2. He can find a buyer who has some cash but not much, and then sell the farm on contract, holding back the deed until a certain percent of the purchase price is paid, or until conventional financing can be obtained. In the meantime, he may keep the contract or he may sell it to a third party, for example, an investor.

3. He can sell his property to an investor who pays cash, and who then resells it on a contract. The property is usually sold at a somewhat

---

11. The various rules and regulations of the Internal Revenue Service have generally favored the selling of a capital investment over time.

12. This does not mean the buyer had the ready cash, for he may have given a mortgage to a third party.

higher price the second time. This latter is not as common with farm properties as it is with non-farm properties.

The prudent investor who purchases the contract, or who first purchases the farm and then sells it on contract, willingly accepts the lack of liquidity and the increased risk. However, he discounts the paper a certain percentage in order to obtain a dollar return similar to that which he could obtain in his next best alternative investment opportunity.[13]

An installment land contract is not money. Yet a contract can change hands, be transferred or sold, and in the process be reduced to its monetary equivalent. Sufficient market demand for such on the part of investors is all that is required. Hence, if a contract is marketable, that contract can be turned into cash. Oftentimes it is sold for less than its face value (or the amount of the unpaid balance), or, as the trade says, ". . . it is discounted."

Real estate contracts are often discounted 10 to 15 percent (sometimes more, sometimes less) depending on: (1) the current money market and whether interest rates have risen or fallen since the date the contract was executed, (2) the terms of the contract (green or unseasoned or new contracts are subject to larger discounts than older ones), (3) the farm (its productivity or condition as security or collateral), and (4) the probable ability of the buyer to make payments promptly.

Many farms are now sold on contract in order to minimize the income taxes. The owner may no longer want to farm. He may readily accept an income in the form of an annuity or in the form of principal and interest payments. The buyer may be a good credit risk. He may be a neighboring farm operator who will farm the property. The contract may be an easy way for him to purchase the farm already financed.

Some persons are now buying farms, sometimes excellent farms or tracts of land, on this basis. The down payment may be as high as 30 percent of the sale price. The real estate may be good security and readily marketable. Thus, the contract price may, for all practical purposes, be equal to the cash sale price. If the paper is later discounted, it is discounted but very little percentagewise.

Some persons buy farms on contract with an extremely low down payment, as long a term as possible, and with the idea that if the annual

---

13. The prudent investor may discount the contract price even further depending on (1) the buyer's reputation and (2) how badly the seller needs the cash, but not always.

income stream will cover the contract payments, that's all that's necessary. They may not need the income. Their purchase may be based
on the premise that the farm's value will rise in the future. These
buyers are often better informed than sellers relative to the probable
decline in the value of the dollar, growth in the local population or
the nearby urban sprawl, anticipated shifts in land use from agricultural
to residential or commercial or industrial, and even more immediate
factors, such as changes in the zoning regulations or pending condemnation for a new highway, with the cloverleaf to be built right
there.

However, some persons buy farms on contract because they lack the
cash. They cannot obtain adequate conventional financing. These persons buy on contract because their ability to pay is limited, by either
poor credit, low income, or both. They hope the farm income will be
sufficient to pay family living expenses, farm operating expenses, and
make the annual principal and interest payments (note the order).
These persons typically buy the marginal farms on this basis. The
seller is willing and desirous of selling it on contract oftentimes because only in this way can he get his asking price. This contract is discounted heavily if and when it is sold for cash at some later date.

Thus in attempting to equate a farm's contract sale price with its
probable cash sale price, the appraiser has to study the market. He
has to place himself in the role of the prudent investor, who typically
compares the contract rate of interest with whatever rate of return he
can obtain elsewhere, assuming equal risk.

Let's illustrate. A 240-acre farm is sold on a 20-year contract for
$20,000 down and a 6.0-percent rate of interest. The market at the
time indicated that typical farm mortgage rates were 7.5 percent. The
market also indicated that contracts on properties similar to this one
were being sold to investors at discounts of up to 10 to 15 percent.

If the seller were to sell his contract to an outsider at a discount of
10 percent, the contract price of $150,000 or $625 per acre would be
equivalent to a cash sale price of $137,000. This $137,000 consists of
the $20,000 down payment plus the $130,000 contract multiplied by 90
percent. The appraiser's adjustment would be $13,000 or $54 per acre.
If the same contract were discounted 15 percent, the equivalent cash
sale price would be $130,500. The adjustment would be $19,500 or $81
per acre.[14] A farm appraiser might thus change his farm price as

---

14. This is equal to the $20,000 downpayment plus the $130,000 contract
multiplied by 85 percent.

follows . . .

	Sale Contract Discount	
	10%	15%
1. Sale Price Reported	$150,000	$150,000
2. Down Payment	20,000	20,000
3. Contract Amount	130,000	130,000
4. Contract Discounted	117,000	110,500
5. Probable Sale Price, Total	137,000	130,500
Per Acre	$ 570	$ 544

The financial arrangements—terms, interest rates, and other economic provisions, which are a part of an installment land contract, are often much involved. One recently brought to the author's attention included a 10-percent down payment, no principal payments the first year and a half (until after the second crop), an interest rate 1.5 percent below the going market rate, a provision to delay up to three payments at any time adding them onto the remaining balance, and a term of over 50 years. The only item favorable to the seller was the price. However, he kept his taxes low and both he and wife had lifetime use of the home.

The farm appraiser needs to inquire quite carefully into the financial arrangements surrounding a contract sale. A number of details should be investigated—the seller and whether or not he was informed, the buyer's ability and his credit rating, the terms of the contract, and the condition of the property. When all of the surrounding circumstances have been studied the appraiser can usually discount a contract sale price fairly accurately. If need be, he can check with some of the investors who purchase real estate contracts. Usually these investors will discuss the extent to which similar contracts are being discounted in the market at that time.

The important thing is to have a full and complete understanding of the definition of present market value and to be able to convert the contract price, whether it be an excellent tract of land, a good farm, or a "dog," into cash. When the market does not provide adequate data, indicating current discount rates, the appraiser must then use his own good judgment in estimating the risks—this farm as compared to others in the market.

The appraiser who fails to consider contract sales as a part of his job today may be ignoring one-half to two-thirds of the market for farm real estate.

AREAS OF IMPORTANCE AND USE

The sales comparison or market data approach to value is perhaps the most essential part of every farm appraisal. As a method of establishing present market values on farm real estate, it is widely accepted as most authoritative. The prices at which other nearby farms have sold in the actual market transactions are values determined by the sellers and buyers of farms themselves, and by farmers, investors, lenders, and others.

In the past the market approach has been emphasized more in those areas (1) where farms are sold on a per-unit basis, as contrasted to a per-acre basis, (2) where the farms are largely owner-operated, as contrasted to absentee-owned and tenant-operated, and (3) where farm income is dependent more on the livestock returns and hence management, than on crop yields and the productivity of the land itself.

However, the professional appraiser in all areas today relies heavily on the market approach to value. There are difficulties of course. An appraiser occasionally find himself in an area where there are very few sales or where market activity is minimal. However, his appraisals are often no better than the market data included therein. The real challenge is to know the farms which have recently sold in the area, to analyze them, to make intelligent comparisons and adjustments, and to reach or develop a sound conclusion as to the present market value of the subject property. Most clients and most courts are impressed with the presentation of this kind of supportive evidence.

REFERENCES

Appraisal of Real Estate, 4th Edition, American Institute of Real Estate Appraisers, 1964.

Becker, George, "Market Data Analysis," *Appraisal Journal*, Vol. 23, No. 4, October 1955.

Campbell, B. P., "Methods of Obtaining and Presenting Sales Data in an Appraisal Report," *Journal of American Society of Farm Managers and Rural Appraisers*, Vol. 24, No. 1, April 1960.

Crouse, E. F., and C. H. Everett, *Rural Appraisals*, Prentice-Hall, 1956.

Easley, C. H., "The Market Data or Comparable Sales Approach: How Good Are Our Data?," *Journal of American Society of Farm Managers and Rural Appraisers*, Vol. 30, No. 1, April 1966.

Fisher, G. L., "On Sales Verification," *The Real Estate Appraiser*, Vol. 36, No. 1, January-February 1970.

Hamman, R. C., "Analyzing Comparable Sales in Your Farm Appraisals," Talk presented to the Illinois Society of Farm Managers and Rural Appraisers, January 1965.

Harter, H. I., "Use of Sales Data in Making Farm Appraisals," *Journal of American Society of Farm Managers and Rural Appraisers,* Vol. 18, No. 1, April 1954.

Lum, Y. T., "Comparison and Use of Market Data in Preparation for Expert Testimony," *Appraisal Journal,* Vol. 31, No. 2, April 1963.

Murray, W. G., *Farm Appraisal and Valuation,* 5th Edition, Iowa State University, 1969.

Murray, W. G., "Market Data in Rural Appraising," *Appraisal Journal,* Vol. 24, No. 3, July 1956.

Polley, J. H., "Simplified Comparable Sales Filing," *Appraisal Journal,* Vol. 34, No. 3, July 1966.

Potts, W. T., Jr., "Treatment of Contract Sales in Appraisal of Blighted Property," *Appraisal Journal,* Vol. 30, No. 2, April 1962.

Sackman, J. L., "Market Value Approach to Valuation," *Appraisal Journal,* Vol. 41, No. 1, January 1973.

Tontz, R. L., et al., "Reliability of Deed Samples as Indicators of Land Market Activity," *Land Economics,* Vol. 30, No. 1, February 1954.

Walrath, A. J., *County Courthouse Records: A Basic Source of Data,* Agricultural Experiment Station Bulletin 560, Virginia Polytechnic Institute, April 1965.

Weber, G. L., "Appraisal of Farms," *The Real Estate Appraiser,* Vol. 30, No. 4, April 1964.

CHAPTER VIII

The Inventory or Cost
Approach to Value

Land, buildings, and improvements are seldom if ever sold separately; instead, most farms are bought and sold as units. Hence, in the appraisal of farm real estate it is conventional to look at and appraise farms as total units. However, there are advantages in looking at each of the component parts of a subject property or at the various resources of a farm as separate entities. The inventory or cost approach to value does just this.

The inventory approach forces the appraiser to classify the various resources which go to make up a given farm property. It requires him to define the various types of land, measuring the value of each type against the comparable sales in the area, and to inventory the various buildings and improvements, weighing the value of each with one eye on its present-day replacement cost and one eye on its contribution to the market value of the property.

The physical description of the farm provides much of the basic data needed in the cost approach. Some of the information is already developed in the income approach. Some of it is already available in the market approach. The sale prices on unimproved tracts of land, for example, are often used as guides in valuing the various classes of land. Hence, the cost approach is not a totally independent approach to value separate from, or different than, the earnings or market approaches.

In the past, farm appraisers have sometimes been quite critical of

---

The inventory or cost approach to value is one in which the appraiser classifies the various resources that go to make up a given farm property and places a separate value on each. The different types of land are classified; the various buildings and improvements are then inventoried. However, the sum of the values of each of the parts is usually greater than the total value of the subject property. This is because the cost of a new improvement seldom if ever adds an equal number of dollars to the market value of the farm.

Courtesy, Purdue University

the cost approach. They have often relegated the approach to a minor role. This is because the sum of the values of each of the various parts of a farm is typically greater than the farm's total value. However, this third approach to value should be considered, if for no other reason than to provide a check against both the earnings and the market data approaches. Furthermore, the approach provides another check, in that the market value of the property cannot, under most circumstances, exceed present-day replacement costs.

THE SUMMATION PROCESS

The cost approach is one in which the appraiser inventories the various resources and places a separate value on each. The various types of land are classified and valued separately. The buildings and improvements are inventoried and valued separately. The values placed on each of the parts are then added together to get the total value of the farm.

In order to clarify what is and what is not included in the real estate, all items included in, affixed to, or arising out of the realty are mentioned, even though they may or may not contribute value. Portable buildings and other major items of personal property, of course, are not included as a part of the farm. An inventory of resources includes the following:

1. The various types of land. Tillable cropland is usually classified into excellent, above average, average, below average, and poor categories. Untillable land is usually classified as permanent pasture land, woods, and farmsteads, roads, and waste. The land use capabilities categories developed by the Soil Conservation Service may be used when available. The farm land is thus classified according to its typical or most likely use, its quality or inherent productivity in the case of cropland with soils being a major factor, and its carrying capacity in the case of range or pasture land.

In areas where cash crops are relatively important, the per-acre yields and per-acre land values are closely related. In areas where the more extensive types of livestock are fairly standard, per-acre carrying capacities and per-acre values are closely related. In range country, an animal-unit-carrying-capacity approach may lead to land values on a per-animal-unit basis.

Thus, per-acre values and total values are placed on each type of land. The well-documented appraisal report may show how these values were derived from the market. Wherever possible, the figures are usually based on recent sales of similar yet unimproved tracts. Hence, the inventory or cost approach and the market data approach to value are related.

2. All buildings and improvements. All buildings are measured and classified according to use. Each building is then studied to determine whether or not, and if so in what fashion, it might be replaced. Replacement costs based on the cost of present-day construction are estimated, along with depreciation to date and remaining values (cost less depreciation). Physical deterioration, functional inadequacy and obsolescence, and economic obsolescence are each considered in determining the amounts that the buildings and improvements contribute to the market value of the farm.

The extent to which all of the various improvements are inventoried depends on the reason for the appraisal and the values available in the area. Tile drains, driveways, shrubbery, and other items are not usually inventoried separately. In areas where most of the farm land is tiled, the land values usually reflect this tiling; hence there is no reason to inventory tile drain systems separately. In areas where most of the farms are fenced, the land values usually reflect the fencing; hence there is no reason to inventory fences separately. However, some appraisals require more detail than others, for example, when the data are to become the bases for depreciation schedules for income tax returns.

3. Other resources or rights. The subject farm may also have some additional assets that add to or detract from its value. For example, a right-of-way or a lease may have separate or distinct usefulness or value. Separate values are occasionally placed on these more intangible resources or property rights.

There are also instances when a capital asset has a negative value. An atypical enterprise, such as an apple orchard in the wrong area, or a fully depreciated set of buildings, which are no longer productive, are examples. In these instances the value of the property may be based on its present market value (assuming the improvements were not there) minus the cost of removing the improvements.

The summation process acquired its name because land values, building and improvement values, and all other values are added together. However, when this is done, that sum is often greater than the market value of the farm as a unit. The sum of all of the various components does not always equal, but is instead usually greater than the value of the whole. This sometimes places the conscientious ap-

Photos by Suter and Courtesy, U.S.D.A.

Tillable cropland is usually classified into excellent, above average, average, below average, and poor categories. Untillable land is usually classified into permanent pasture, woods, and waste.

praiser in a somewhat awkward situation.

There are several reasons for the tendency for the sum of the parts to be greater than the whole.

1. In many areas of agriculture, there is a strong demand for unimproved land. Hence there is a surplus of buildings and improvements. The new technologies in agriculture have increased farming efficiency and led to farm expansion and to farm consolidation. The trend toward fewer and larger commercial farms has meant fewer headquarter units and a surplus of usable, yet not always desirable, buildings and improvements.

Many existing farm buildings and improvements have become functionally inadequate or obsolete and/or economically obsolete long before they have become worn out physically. As a result of these changes, many an owner-operator would like to add land to his present farming operations. However, if additional buildings are needed or

desired he would much prefer these to be built new and at the headquarters unit rather than to be obtained through the purchase of an
adjacent tract of land.

The absentee-owner or investor would like to own unimproved land
which he could rent to a neighboring farmer. In the agricultural Midwest at least, he can usually rent this unimproved tract for the same
price—a 50-50 crop-share—as an improved one, and in doing so he can
avoid the upkeep expense on the buildings and improvements. Hence,
whenever the values placed on unimproved land and the costs of new
improvements are added together the total is typically greater than the
values placed on improved tracts in the same area.

2. The cost of a new improvement seldom if ever adds an equal
number of dollars to the market value of a farm. When a tract of farm
land is tile drained or if a fairly heavy basic application of fertilizer
is applied, such probably adds very little to the market value of the
farm, primarily because it cannot be seen. When a new and fairly
conventional improvement, such as a pole barn, is built, it probably
adds only 60 to 75 percent of its cost to the market value of the farm.

Photos by Suter and Courtesy, U.S.D.A.

Each type of land is described as to its typical or most likely use, its quality or inherent productivity in the case of cropland, and its carrying capacity in the case of range or pasture land.

When a new and somewhat unique technology, one not yet typical in the area, is added, one that the typical buyer or seller will not be interested in or recognize in the market, this investment won't likely add more than 40 or 50 percent of its cost to the market value of the farm.

There are of course exceptions. If one acquires a poor, run-down farm, spends money primarily to bulldoze out the fence rows and clean up the farmstead, and then builds a white picket fence, the opposite may occur. The picket fence and the white paint may add more to the market value of the farm than they cost, primarily because they make the farm much more attractive to the typical buyer.

3. New technologies often add to the volume of the farm business and to the efficiency of the farm family without making an equal or proportional contribution to a farm's market value. Most buildings are built and most improvements are made to increase the size of the

farm business or the efficiency of the farming operations. However, the purpose of practically all farm appraisals is to ascertain the present market value of the farm. While building and improvement values are considered, such values are based only on the extent to which they contribute to or enhance the market value of the property. The contributory approach may be a drastic limitation, considering the present-day replacement costs of most farm buildings and improvements. However, it is the only realistic approach to market value.

4. A number of investments in buildings and improvements are sometimes based on wants rather than needs. In other words, one's emotions as well as one's economics are sometimes involved. The present operator and a typical operator often differ as to their desires. The next buyer or owner is usually unwilling to fully compensate the previous owner or seller for his past decisions with regard to improvements. No matter how good or how rational the previous owner's decision, the next owner's desires are often different. Thus the cost of a new improvement seldom, if ever, adds an equal number of dollars to the market value of the farm. Inventory values based on present-day

costs of construction less depreciation often exceed values-in-exchange as reflected by the market. This may add confusion to the cost approach. It provides a real challenge to the farm appraiser.

COST IS NOT NECESSARILY VALUE

The idea that cost and value are equal is widely accepted by many members of society. However, in the world of appraisal the notion is ignored, largely because cost is a most uncertain evidence of value under most circumstances in a free economy.

To the producer or seller, cost is what it takes to create, to produce, or to bring a given thing into being. To the consumer or buyer, cost is what it takes to acquire or to own that particular thing, or, an acceptable substitute. Thus, cost derives its theoretical foundations from both the supply and the demand side of economics.

If one could assume perfect competition, and if that competition were to exist over a sufficiently long period of time, then cost of production and market value would be equal. The economist would say "equilibrium has been established." However, empirical observations relative to the rough and tumble of everyday economic life fail to substantiate the existence of conditions which even remotely resemble perfect competition.

In the farm real estate market, reasonable substitutes do not often exist. Each farm has unique characteristics of its own. The alternatives are either bigger or smaller or better or poorer, and therefore largely imperfect. Agriculture is forever subject to change, and so are the tastes —the likes and dislikes—of the typical buyers and sellers of farms. As a consequence, modern appraisal theory has largely abandoned the doctrine that cost of production and value in the market will reach equilibrium even in the long run.

Whenever a given item can be reproduced or replaced, the cost of acquiring that particular item, or an equally desirable substitute, does tend to establish an upper limit as to value. However, cost represents that upper limit only if several assumptions are made . . .

1. The existing item is one which can be replaced both actually and easily. It cannot be an old fashioned or an obsolete building. It must be one which can be replaced in modern fashion, with modern materials and equipment, and with modern techniques.

2. The item can be created, or a substitute can be acquired, without costly delay. In some instances, a buyer will pay more than the

cost of an item, and justifiably so, in order to own or have it now.

3. Following the creation of the asset no particular physical deterioration has occurred. In actual practice, of course, some is likely to occur, as this is a function of time which cannot be held constant.

Thus, cost, with reasonable and acceptable alternatives, tends to set an upper limit to the amount one might be expected to pay for a given thing. A buyer may pay more than its cost, but only when there is no acceptable alternative, only when he wants the property immediately, and only when he is no longer willing to wait. The rare buyer may also "fall in love" with the thing. When this occurs, he "just has to have it" at any price.

Most persons are assumed to be rational. If so, they will willingly pay no more for an item than the cost of an acceptable replacement or substitute. This is the replacement or substitution cost principle. It can be applied fairly readily to farm buildings and improvements; however, much less readily to farm land.[1] Buildings and improvements are replaceable. Land, generally speaking, is not.

Cost becomes a useful evidence of value primarily in valuing farm buildings and improvements, yet only when the buildings being built in the agricultural community are similar to those on the subject property. Present-day construction costs thus become the acquisition costs which represent the amounts which one can be expected to pay for various buildings or improvements. The buildings may be actual or they may be hypothetical. In either case their cost represents what various persons are actually willing to pay for similar improvements.

It is here that the principle of substitution exercises itself fairly automatically. The less costly building or improvement tends to replace or prevail over any and all other buildings or improvements of similar or equal want-satisfying ability. Thus, with the exception of the item that is highly desirable, and perhaps not immediately reproducible, cost represents the upper-value limit.

However, this does not mean that the typical buyer will always pay whatever a particular item costs. The prudent buyer will pay no more than he has to in order to acquire the ownership of any item. In fact, cost figures are meaningless unless they do also represent what various persons are actually willing to pay for specific items. Any item in order to have value must possess utility. It must satisfy a need. It must excite

---

1. For this reason the cost approach is more applicable in the appraisal of non-farm commercial properties than farm properties.

demand. If it is also somewhat scarce, this scarcity also helps create value. Differences of opinion between various persons often exist in this respect. Such differences are what lead to or establish the demand for an item.[2] Unfortunately, those persons who use the concept of cost often tend to ignore this fact.

Cost figures are also used in farm appraisals to make adjustments for qualitative differences between properties, again on the assumption that cost and value added are the same. In some cases this may be true, but not very often. For example, in order to remodel a milking parlor, it may cost $4,500, but the question as to whether or not a prospective buyer will willingly pay an additional $4,500 more for the subject property remains to be answered. "No" is the probable answer. Most appraisers will observe that no more than a $3,000 difference will probably exist. If so, then this figure should be used as an adjustment. Again cost sets the upper limit. However, the typical prudent buyer will not pay that amount if he can purchase such for less.

Hence, cost in any dimension never has, does not, and never will determine value. It only has a tendency to establish an upper limit.[3]

BUILDING AND IMPROVEMENT COSTS

Farm appraisers are usually well acquainted with the current costs of constructing new farm buildings and improvements in whatever area they work. Many of them keep a detailed list of thumb-rule costs in their appraisal handbook. Occasionally the farm appraiser is asked to analyze a farm or other building in more detail, looking at (1) the floor plan or layout, (2) one or more elevations, perhaps (3) a cross-section of the building, and sometimes (4) detailed specifications. Only occasionally, however, does the farm appraiser get into this much detail. This is because most of the value of the typical farm is in land rather than in buildings and improvements.

Thumb-Rule Costs: In the majority of farm appraisals, thumb-rule costs per square foot, per bushel, per ton, per cow, or per steer are

---

2. There is a time dimension on the demand as well as on the supply side. Over time, desires change and sometimes quite rapidly. Yesterday's desires, as reflected by yesterday's costs, do not necessarily reflect today's desires as reflected by today's values.

3. Value is determined by the combined actions of informed buyers and informed sellers in the market place.

used. In fact, many builder-contractors in the rural areas quote their prices or construction costs on this basis.

Accuracy, of course, depends on how well the appraiser stays up-to-date with regard to the new buildings and improvements that are being built in his community. This is often more important than the number of details he analyzes or puts in his report. In fact, whenever an appraiser is out in the country and happens to see a new building being built, he should take the time to stop and visit with the owner and collect data relative to its cost. If the farm appraiser does this, his thumb-rule costs are usually reasonably reliable figures. As compared to the more detailed quantity survey technique, they require much less time to develop and use.

However, in some areas there is a tendency to build highly specialized livestock facilities and include considerable companion equipment—free stalls, farrowing stalls, and other pens as well as automated feed-and-manure-handling systems—as a part of the building itself. When this occurs, a breakdown of various costs is desirable. Specialized components should always be noted. Their costs should be tabulated separately. Thus, the comparability of these newer facilities to those which exist on a given subject property, as well as their costs, can be more easily related. Any change in use can be evaluated.

Quantity Surveys: The quantity survey technique is used in appraisals where the building or improvement makes up the major portion of the total value of the property. The approach is essentially the engineer's approach. A blueprint of the building is used to identify and list, item by item, the quantity of all of the various materials required in its construction. These quantities are then multiplied by the local prices obtained from the local suppliers of building materials. Labor costs are estimated; so also are the costs of plumbing, wiring, heating, air conditioning, and other jobs that are typically turned over to sub-contractors. A builder-contractor can estimate these costs in detail. However, he is often reluctant to take the time to do so.

Farm building construction costs are generally available in any rural community. An intelligent appraiser should have no trouble in obtaining them with reasonable accuracy. Both the thumb-rule approach and the quantity-survey technique have some of the same inherent problems. Materials can be estimated in detail as long as time permits. However, sooner or later the costs of erection or the on-site costs have to be estimated. The costs of the jobs done by the subs—for example, plumbing and wiring—are often difficult to figure unless one is in the construction business.

All farm buildings and improvements are inventoried with various values—replacement cost, structural value, contributory value, and value-in-use—placed on each.

The responsibility of the appraiser is not to estimate construction costs in detail so much as it is to obtain whatever data best fit the types of property he appraises and the values involved. The approach he uses and the amount of detail he includes depend largely on the type of property being appraised and the proportion of value in the buildings and improvements relative to that in the land. The thumb-rule approach is used in many farm appraisals. The thumb-rule approach is perhaps less thorough. However, in the hands of the professional it is not necessarily less accurate.

DEPRECIATION AND VALUE THAT REMAINS

Building and improvement values are predicated not only on cost but also on depreciation-to-date. The appraiser and his client are interested in the present-day remaining values which the buildings and

improvements contribute to the market value of the farm.

The appraiser's job is thus to estimate not only present-day replacement costs but also approximate age, probable remaining life, and thus cost-less-depreciation or value that remains. This process appears to be a mathematical one. However, it is not. Considerable judgment is required.

To the layman, depreciation tends to be a physical thing based primarily on wear and tear, related primarily to age, and due primarily to use. However, in appraisal, the word has special meaning. Depreciation is the loss in the value of an asset due to all causes. That loss is the result of three items—physical deterioration, functional inadequacy or obsolescence, and economic obsolescence.[4] It may or may not be related to age. It may or may not be due to use.

In the market, depreciation represents the difference between the cost of replacing a building and the amount that that building contributes to the market value of the farm. In the earnings approach,

---

4. These three causes are defined in more detail in the next chapter.

depreciation is either a part of the farm operating expenses (most farm appraisals) or a part of the capitalization rate (most non-farm commercial appraisals). In the sales-comparison approach, depreciation is measured by the buyers and sellers of comparable farm properties and the sale prices of these properties. Hence, the loss in value is directly reflected in the earnings approach and indirectly measured in the market-data approach to value.

In placing a value on each farm building or improvement, the farm appraiser usually considers only total depreciation. He does not very often separate out or attempt to evaluate each of the various kinds of depreciation. However, in areas where specialized buildings and improvements are important, the different component parts of a building or improvement may be tabulated separately. The costs as well as the rates of depreciation for each may be used to establish the values placed on the various parts of these more specialized buildings.

Building values in the inventory or cost approach to a farm's value are thus based on cost less all types of depreciation. The values that remain represent the dollar contribution of the buildings and improvements to the present market value of the farm.

AREAS OF IMPORTANCE AND USE

The cost approach to value appears to be more useful in the following instances.

1. Where a farm, if it were to be sold, would be sold in several parcels or pieces.

2. In the more specialized livestock areas where buildings and improvements make up a large portion of the total value of the farm.

3. Where an investor or buyer wants to establish the value of any and all depreciable assets as bases for claiming depreciation in filing income tax returns.

4. Where neither the income approach nor the market-data approach to value is applicable.

In the transition area where agricultural opportunities are declining and other uses are expanding, relatively speaking, the various parts of a farm are sometimes sold separately. The house and two or three acres may be sold to one buyer, the frontage to another buyer, and the remainder of the farm held by or sold to a third party. Hence, not always are farms bought and sold as total units. In these cases the appraiser's job is to appraise each part of the property in terms of its most probable use and market value and then add the various values together. In this situation, the inventory or cost approach to value is usually the most realistic approach to value.

In the more specialized livestock areas, buildings and improvements often play a large role in determining value. Here, there is need for the more detailed inventory of all improvements—storage structures, livestock facilities, feed and manure handling equipment—along with a division between that which is permanent (part of the real estate) and that which is portable and thus personalty. When the buildings and improvements are a large part of the total, these depreciable or wasting assets often require a more thorough study of such items as depreciation. A recapture of this capital may be important. At this point the farm appraiser has to study the buildings and improvements in depth. His appraisal technique is somewhat different. However, he starts with the inventory or cost approach.

The investor's problem is one of allocating the purchase price or cost of a given property between depreciable and non-depreciable assets, thus establishing the bases for subsequent depreciation schedules. This is the result of the 1954 Internal Revenue Act. This appears to be an accounting rather than an appraisal problem. The farm appraiser is not often asked to place values on the various improvements for this purpose. Yet, unknowingly, his appraisal report is often pulled from the files at some later date, and his building values are then used to establish subsequent depreciation schedules, even though such was not the earlier reason for the appraisal.

Occasionally the earnings and the sales approaches to value are not applicable. By default, the farm appraiser has to rely on the cost approach. This does not happen in the appraisal of farm properties as much as it does in the appraisal of specialty properties. Non-profit institutions, churches, hospitals, schools, fire stations, and public utility buildings, country clubs, golf courses, art galleries, and other recreational facilities typically require the cost approach. Many of these properties do not earn an income. Very seldom are they bought or sold. Oftentimes they have no alternative use. There are few if any comparable properties. Sales data are impossible to obtain. Hence the cost approach, applicable or not, is the only basis for estimating value.

The cost approach is also used, sometimes quite widely, in appraisals for some of the governmental agencies and in condemnation work. The sovereign can decree that cost is equal to value. With or without proper legal ruling this Marxian dogma, that cost determines value, is widely accepted by some of the federal and state agencies. Some courts state that the award (to the property owner) should constitute market value in the broad sense, as opposed to market value in the strict sense. Some courts thus place the emphasis on value to the owner. These courts are concerned more with equity than with value. "Just compensation" may thus be interpreted to be the property owner's costs. However, when an appraiser interprets cost in this fashion it is usually a gross misuse of the cost approach. Value, in most instances, refers to the present market value of the farm.

THE FINAL STEP: REVIEW AND SUMMARY

No single approach to the value of a farm is likely to work best all of the time, or for all farms in all areas. A combination of the three methods—the earnings approach, the sales or market-data approach, and the inventory or cost approach—is instead most useful. In fact, most professional appraisers apply each of the three methods of approaching or establishing value in the same painstaking detail. If it's at all possible, they use each method, for the sole reason that each method serves as a check on all other methods before arriving at the final value.

Each method should be developed as independently from one another as possible in order to best serve as a check on each other. This is sometimes difficult, for many of the same fundamental facts are used in each approach. Building values, developed in the cost approach, for example, may serve as the bases for estimating certain farm operating expenses—depreciation and insurance—in the earnings approach. The ratios between probable dollar returns and sale prices in the market approach may serve as the bases for developing capitalization rates in the income approach. The sale prices on unimproved land in the market may serve as the bases for placing values on that kind of land in the inventory approach, and on, and on. Furthermore, all three methods rely heavily on the concept of opportunity cost and the principle of substitution. Hence, both in theory and in practice the three methods are almost inseparable.

The priority given, or the order in which the three approaches appear in an appraisal report (or for that matter in this book), is immaterial. The order depends on the appraiser and the circumstances surrounding each particular appraisal. Rather than follow some set pattern, an appraiser should develop whatever factual data he has available in a most convincing fashion and present it in such a way as to enlighten his client both quickly and effectively. At the same time, the following appraisal technique is highly recommended:

First: A fairly thorough physical inspection of the farm should be made. Its productive capacity should then be estimated. This step forces an appraiser to analyze the farm's basic resources and to estimate its productivity under both present and typical operators.

Second: The earnings capacity of the farm, which is one of, the more fundamental origins of value, should be developed, and the farm's value based on the capitalization of its income should be estimated. Earnings capacity is the basis for both ownership and the acquisition of additional capital resources through borrowing. Hence, the farm's earnings value should be established whenever it is possible. The value of the home, its location value, and the value of any and all other economic features may then be added to this earnings value to more nearly equal the farm's present market value.

Third: All farm sales in the area should be tabulated and analyzed. The present market value of the farm, based on all farm sales comparable to the subject farm, should then be established. The current market is the only realistic way of ascertaining what farms are selling for today. There may, of course, be a considerable difference between the value of the farm based on earnings and the present market value of the farm based on comparable sales. This tells an appraiser as well as his client something about both the agriculture in the area and perhaps the future expectations in the economy.

During a period of economic growth, the present market value of a farm may be considerably above its earnings value. This says that (1) farms in this area are currently overpriced relative to their earnings capacities, (2) there is a strong demand for land in this area due perhaps to both farm consolidation and absentee-owner or investor interest, and/or (3) farm land in this area is being purchased as a hedge against inflation. The prices at which farm properties sell during such a period are based not so much on past earnings; they instead reflect future expectations.

Fourth: All of a farm's basic resources—land, buildings, and improvements—should be inventoried. Comparable sale data and present-day construction costs should be used to develop the farm's value based on the cost of acquiring each of the various resources. The value placed on land of different types and uses should, if possible, be based on comparable sales of similar unimproved tracts of land. The values placed on the buildings and improvements should be based on present-day construction costs less depreciation, with the latter reflecting not only physical deterioration but functional inadequacy or obsolescence and economic obsolescence as well.

This cost approach typically leads to a value somewhat higher than either the earnings or the sale approach. It does not establish value in the market. However, it does tend to establish an upper limit to that value. It serves as a check against the other approaches. The cost approach, as applied to various components of a farm property, is most useful when the subject farm, if it were to be sold, would probably be sold in separate tracts and for separate uses.

Fifth: Any and all of the origins of value as they apply to the subject property should be reviewed and explained. The farm earnings, the value of the home, the location of the farm, and the value of any and all other economic features must justify and/or support the final value. The appraisal report should present all of this evidence. The summary should emphasize not just the origins of value but also the line of reasoning which led the appraiser to his final value conclusion. It is not just the facts, but the organization of those facts and the logic used in arriving at the final value which makes an appraisal.

Sixth: Each of the various approaches to value must be carefully weighed. The extent to which each approach has relevance must be considered in terms of (1) the property itself and its origins of value, (2) the reason for and/or the use to be made of the appraisal, and (3) the reliability of each set of data that contributed to the findings.

Appraisers have often used the word "correlation" to describe the thought process of analyzing the data, along with the results obtained using each of the three approaches to value, thus bringing them together in a single and sensible relationship. Technically, the word is incorrect. The job is really one of comparison.

Seventh: Farm appraisers, who have considerable appraisal experience in a particular area, often use a thumb-rule value—a value per acre, a value per bushel of wheat produced per acre, or a value per cow, or some other unit—for comparative purposes.

The Thumb-Rule Approach: Where there exists a large number of fairly uniform farms and where the use of the subject farm is quite probable, thumb-rule values are often applicable. Farms in the agricultural Midwest, particularly those in the good land areas where the major crops are corn and soybeans, often have fairly uniform per-acre values. The thumb rules vary, of course, with the type and the quality of the land and with the cropping system. Ranches where wheat is the major crop and summer fallowing is the general practice often have fairly uniform values per bushel of wheat produced per acre. The thumb rules vary sometimes with the government acreage programs. Farms in the dairy states are often referred to in terms of their carrying capacities—for example, the subject farm is a 60-cow or a 120-cow dairy farm—and the farms here often exhibit fairly uniform values on a per-cow basis. The same is true of areas in the Great Plains where brown grass and beef cow herds are the predominant, and oftentimes only, farm enterprise. Per-cow values are based on similar amounts of pasture per cow, similar amounts of meadow land per cow to raise the winter feed, and similar numbers of replacement heifers and yearling stock per cow.

These thumb rules vary mainly with changes in the value of the dollar. They apply only when a particular type of farming is the predominant type in the area. They apply only to farms which are sufficiently large and which have property values which are not affected particularly by the value of the dwelling. And, they apply only in those areas where the values placed on the farms do not vary as a result of location. With these limitations, thumb-rule values can be quite useful. However, they should never be used alone.

Actually no one method of establishing value is likely to be best for all farms. Most appraisers use a combination of methods.

Three or Four Values! Now What?: The competent appraiser uses all three or four approaches—the earnings or income capitalization approach, the sales comparison or market-data approach, the inventory or cost approach, and at times the thumb-rule approach. Supposedly they are developed independently of one another. This is a must; yet the data are used back and forth. Actually, the three or four methods serve as a bracketing technique.

In theory, the values should be similar. This assumes there were no difficulties in obtaining any of the data and that there were no apparent inconsistencies in the data. Similar values also assume that the appraiser had both the time and the skill to make perfect estimates of such items as (1) productive capacity under a typical operator, (2) receipts, expenses, and capitalization rates, (3) comparable sale prices and adjustments, and (4) costs and depreciation.

In actual practice it's somewhat of a happy coincidence if any two of the three values are similar. If the indications of value are reasonably close, the appraiser may give equal weight to each approach in arriving at his final value figure. This depends on the type of property, the reason for making the appraisal, and the reliability of data in each part of the report. When the values differ, of course, it's time to review each approach and to ascertain whether or not there are some obvious reasons for the discrepancies. However, when the values are similar, it's also time for an objective re-examination of each part of the appraisal.

Generally speaking, the various value estimates should be within a reasonable range of one another. When they are not, a critical review may bring the values closer together. Generally speaking, the earnings value is the lower figure, the market value is usually somewhere in the middle, and the value based on cost is often the higher one. This is not always true. This relationship perhaps exists mainly during a period of rising farm real estate prices.

The appraiser's job is to decide whether or not the spread is a reasonable one. When the spread is large it may indicate (1) that one or more of the approaches to value was not really applicable to this particular farm, due to an inherent weakness in the method itself, (2) that the appraiser did not have the tenacity to obtain all the facts, or that data he did obtain were not reliable, or (3) that the appraiser made major errors in applying one of the approaches to value.

Review and Summary: Review and summary is often the most incomplete and analytically inadequate portion of many farm appraisals. Yet review and summary is most critical. The appraiser must now pause and reflect. He must bring together all of the facts, organizing them, and combining them so as to develop a logical conclusion. The effect of all of the major factors affecting values, both individually and combined, must be placed in proper perspective. Such should be related to the trends surrounding the subject property. Only in this fashion can the farm appraiser arrive at a realistic and accurate final value figure.

A careful and conscientious review sometimes leads to the discovery of a ridiculously stupid, yet previously undetected mathematical or mechanical error. The professional appraiser, no matter how good he is, has to be constantly on guard against this. It is not improper, of course, to reanalyze the data or to form a new conclusion. However, such should be done as a result of previous oversights or errors of judgment, and not dishonestly.

Juggling the figures for the mere sake of juggling is not a part of the appraisal process. An appraiser should never manipulate the figures in any of the approaches merely to produce the desired result. It is better to attempt to explain the variation than to juggle the data.

The summary should not be a repetition of the facts and figures previously presented in the appraisal report. The final step is instead a review of the various approaches to value and the contribution that each made towards the final value figure. Providing the characteristics of the property, its origins of value, and the relative availability and reliability of data used in each approach are properly presented, the final value conclusion should be obvious.

If, for some reason, one of the approaches dominates the final answer, the appraiser should state the reason why. If, for any reason, an appraiser does not use one of the basic approaches, the reason should be presented. If the values deviate more than is thought desirable, a probable explanation may be given. The final conclusion is not an average figure. It is instead a value selected on the basis of the facts and the supportive evidence which best substantiates such a value. It is one arrived at impartially. It is one which is fair and reasonable. It is a conclusion which the person who reads the appraisal report will arrive at himself, if he has the time to study and to think through all the supportive evidence.

Unfortunately, there is a tendency among appraisers to sometimes be generous with the facts, yet stingy with their reasoning. The client (or review appraiser) must then bridge the gap himself between the factual data presented and the appraiser's conclusion. The appraiser's job is to lead his client, his supervisor, a review appraiser, or a jury to the same final value conclusion by presenting the property, the surrounding circumstances, the various approaches to value, and finally all of the supportive evidence in a logical and understandable fashion.

REFERENCES

Allison, N. F., "Fundamental Appraisal Thinking," *Appraisal Journal,* Vol. 32, No. 4, October 1964.

Armstrong, W. Y., "Is the Cost Approach Necessary?," *Appraisal Journal,* Vol. 31, No. 1, January 1963.

Babcock, H. A., *Appraisal Principles and Procedures,* Irwin, 1968.

Crouse, E. F., and C. H. Everett, *Rural Appraisals,* Prentice-Hall, 1956.

Edgerton, W. H., "Building Costs and Trends," *Appraisal Journal,* Vol. 35, No. 2, April 1967.

Featherston, J. B., "Correlation and Final Value Estimate," *The Real Estate Appraiser,* Vol. 34, No. 1, January-February 1968.

Healey, F. H., "Does the Cost Approach Suffer from Obsolescence?," *The Real Estate Appraiser,* Vol. 36, No. 6, November-December 1970.

Louie, C. F., "Depreciation and the Cost Approach," *Appraisal Journal,* Vol. 29, No. 4, October 1961.

Murray, W. G., *Farm Appraisal and Valuation,* 5th Edition, Iowa State University Press, 1969.

Nolan, J. J., "Cost Is Not Always Value," *The Real Estate Appraiser,* Vol. 31, No. 8, August 1965.

Orbaker, C. L., "The Cost Approach in Estimating Farm Value," *Journal of American Society of Farm Managers and Rural Appraisers,* Vol. 30, No. 1, April 1966.

Perthou, A. V., *The Cost Approach to Appraisals for Property Insurance,* Prentice-Hall, 1963.

Rural Appraisal Manual, 3rd Edition, American Society of Farm Managers and Rural Appraisers, August 1969.

Sackman, J. L., "The Limitations of the Cost Approach," *Appraisal Journal,* Vol. 36, No. 1, January 1968.

CHAPTER IX

The Valuation of Farm Buildings

Farm buildings and improvements are sometimes referred to as the "universal fudge factors" in an appraisal. At best, they present one of the more difficult problems, perhaps because farm building valuation differs from farm appraisal both in theory and in technique.

In most appraisal work a single value is placed on all of the real property. The land, buildings, and improvements are valued together, the same as they are sold. However, in the physical description of a subject property, a separate inventory of each type of land and each building and improvement is usually presented. In some instances, the appraisal assignment calls for separate values on each type of land and separate values on each building and improvement.[1]

Farm buildings and improvements are usually an integral part of a farm's total assets; however, not always. On some farms the improvements play a minor role. The buildings are largely leftover and obsolete resources. They may be used only for storage. On other farms, they may make up a sizeable portion of the property's total value. They may consist of or contain some of the more recent technological innovations and serve a very specialized purpose.

Appraisers and others often need to be reminded that farmers build farm buildings, not to add value to their farm properties but instead, to expand the size or volume of their farm businesses and to increase the efficiency of their farming operations.[2] Combined with certain other resources, namely, the present operator, some of the more modern

---

1. This is the case with both property insurance and most ad valorem assessment.
2. Exceptions are the operator's house, which is built for the comfort of the farmer himself, and perhaps a machinery shed or similar structure built for purposes of convenience.

Farm building valuation presents one of the more difficult problems in farm appraisal. This is because it often requires one to think in terms of several different value concepts. In fact, the farm appraiser may ascertain not one but several different values.

Courtesy, U.S.D.A.

improvements may lead to sizeable increases in the income to the farm family today. However, this income is not directly attributable to the buildings and improvements except perhaps through the use of some residual accounting technique.

Farm buildings and improvements are seldom purchased or sold separately from land or the rest of the real estate. A new building can be bought and built. However, once it is built, seldom is it sold in a bona fide market transaction. This places the farm appraiser in somewhat of a dilemma, for neither the income nor the market approach to value is very useful. The cost approach remains. However, the cost of a new building or improvement seldom adds an equal number of dollars to the value of the property.

In order to get out of this dilemma, one needs to admit that when farmers buy or build buildings these buildings often contribute more to the farming operations than they contribute to the market value of the farm. As a result, farm buildings have more than one value. Unlike farm real estate appraisal, farm building valuation requires one to think in terms of several different value concepts. It requires one to ascertain not one but several different values.

THE PURPOSES OF AND REASONS FOR FARM BUILDING VALUATION

The purposes of and the reasons for a farm appraisal have been largely separated. The purpose is to ascertain the present market value of the property. The reason for or use to be made of such does not have, or should not have, any influence on the value ascertained. However, the purposes of and the reasons for farm building valuation are more closely related. The purpose or reason for estimating a building's value often determines the value concept used. It tends to influence the dollar value figure. This bothers some persons; however, one needs to look at the various reasons for valuation.

Farm buildings and improvements are valued for purposes of . . .

1. Determining a given building's book value, so as to establish a depreciation schedule for record keeping and income tax purposes.

2. Recording the basic physical condition, soundness, and the structural value of a building.

3. Ascertaining the contribution that a given building makes to the present market value of the farm.

4. Estimating the extent to which a given building will be replaced in the event of a loss.

These four purposes are based on several different concepts. They lead to different values, each of which has its idiosyncrasies. However, each is readily accepted by society.

The first requires either the actual cost or capital outlay spent on the new building, or an approximation of that building's probable cost when land, buildings, and improvements have been purchased together.

The second requires a structural value which answers the question, "Is the building sound?" A detailed inspection of the building and each of its structural components or parts is required. The emphasis is on the building's physical features, along with its present physical condition. Location, use, and other factors are ignored.

The third requires a value which reflects the contribution that that building makes to the present market value of the farm. This exchange value is needed by prospective buyers and sellers, by those persons who are interested in security values for loan purposes, and sometimes by others as well.

The fourth requires a value-in-use figure which reflects the value of the building or improvement to the present owner and/or in the current farming operations. This utility value is used primarily by the insurance people who, for a fee or premium, are willing to indemnify farm owners for any financial and fortuitous losses that may occur.[3]

Right or wrong, society readily accepts for one purpose or another (1) cost, (2) structural or salvage value, (3) value to the farm, and (4) value to the owner. The appraiser's job is to recognize that each of these different value concepts are used, that such can be applied, and that such can be realistic. The appraiser's job may be to establish these values, to make sure each is properly related to one another, and to be able to explain their true meaning in his appraisal report.

PHYSICAL INSPECTION AND ANALYSIS

The appraiser is obligated to observe many structural details and to weigh several other phenomena before developing his dollar values. All important buildings and improvements on a farm should be identified, inspected, and described, first, by designating the type of each structure along with its present use; second, by presenting each building's overall dimensions, its shape and its size; third, by noting the

---

3. It is here that farm building values are often estimated with little or no appraisal of the rest of the farm's resources.

quality of its construction, both materials and workmanship; and fourth, by assessing both its present condition and its adequacy in relation to the rest of the farm. The amount of time spent on each building depends on its structural value, the amount it adds to the value of the property, and the role it plays in the present farming operations.

Structural Description: There are few items less interesting to write about or to read about than how to measure, inspect, and describe farm buildings.[4] Many structural details may be observed.

1. The excavation:—full or partial, dimensions, and surrounding soils.

2. Footings and foundation:—size, materials used, reinforcing, location of drainage tile, coating, surface slope, and runoff.

3. Framing:—type and spacing.

4. Outside walls:—materials used, size, thickness, insulation, doors, and windows.

5. Roof:—type, materials used, slope, insulation, flashing, eave troughs, and downspouts.

6. Floors:—materials used, thickness, finish, load capacity, and insulation.

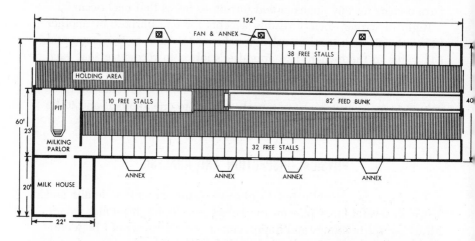

Courtesy, **Hoard's Dairyman**

Not always does the farm appraiser look at all of the detailed specifications with regard to a farm's buildings and improvements. The land resources are often more important. However, a knowledge of typical floor plans, cross sections, elevations, and building specifications is quite useful where the buildings and improvements are an integral part of the farming operations.

---

4. Maybe this is also why a lot of people do it incorrectly.

7. Inside partitions:—materials used and whether or not they are load bearing.

8. Electric wiring, plumbing:—type, location, and adequacy.

9. Heating, air conditioning:—type and control.

10. Built-in equipment.

The number of details inspected and included in one's report depends on the importance of each structure relative to the appraisal assignment. Many items can be presented in tabular fashion.

Several More Important Questions: Where land and buildings each make up an important portion of the property's total value, there are several more important questions which probe far beyond the physical description of the buildings and improvements.

1. Is the building in balance with the land and the farm's other resources? Is it properly related to the enterprise it serves—the crops that will probably be raised, the livestock which will probably be kept? Is the building overbuilt and overly expensive; or is it inadequate and lacking?[5]

2. To what extent does the building fit today's agriculture and the trends—increased farm size, farm consolidation, and the many new technologies—which are likely to occur in the future?

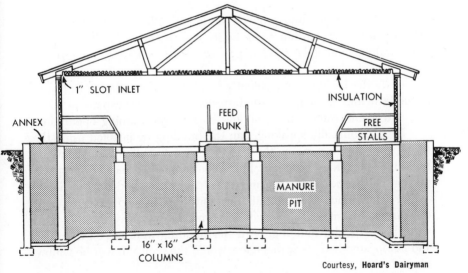

Courtesy, **Hoard's Dairyman**

A cross-section of an 80-cow free stall barn, with slotted floor, and liquid manure pit in Central Wisconsin.

5. This is the No. 1 and most important question. Its importance may in fact overshadow all subsequent questions raised in this section.

The 80-cow free stall barn on the previous two pages under construction.

Courtesy, **Hoard's Dairyman**

3. Was the building properly designed? Were quality materials and quality workmanship used in its construction? Is the building structurally sound today? What part or parts need repair or replacement?

4. Is the building conveniently located both in relation to layout of the farm and to the rest of the farmstead?[6] Is future expansion possible, and would such add to the efficiency of the farming operations?

5. Economically speaking, can the building be justified using the farm's probable income as the basis for investment? What about the building's remaining economic life? What about the income prospects during that period? Is further investment, such as remodeling, justified?

6. How much does the building contribute to the market value of the farm? How much more will the typical buyer pay for this farm with this particular building; or, if this building were not on this farm and not located here, how much less would the typical buyer be willing to pay?

---

6. A building improperly located may become somewhat of a liability in spite of any and all of its advantages.

7. To what extent is the building being used in the current farming operations? Does it serve a real function? Is the present operator using the building properly? Could it be adapted and used for a purpose other than its present use?

8. In the event of a loss due to fire, wind or other peril, will the building be replaced? If it burned, blew away, or was completely destroyed today, to what extent would it be rebuilt?

These questions are difficult to answer. They are difficult to present, even in narrative fashion, in an appraisal report. Yet these are the questions that lead to value.

Are the farm buildings in balance with the land and with the farm's other resources? Are they properly related to the enterprises they serve? Are the buildings on this farm overbuilt and overly expensive or are they inadequate and lacking? These and other questions probe far beyond the physical specifications, yet these are the questions that lead to value.

Courtesy, Granite City Steel

REPRODUCTION VERSUS REPLACEMENT COST

The one common denominator in valuing farm buildings and improvements is cost. Cost tends to serve as an upper limit or as a maximum value above which the value of a building or improvement cannot logically go. Ordinarily, no one will pay more for a new building than the cost of bringing it, or an acceptable substitute, into being.[7]

Two somewhat different concepts are used to specify farm building costs; one is reproduction cost, the other is replacement cost. The two concepts do not have the same meaning. They tend to be used interchangeably, and this sometimes leads to considerable confusion.

Reproduction cost is the cost of reproducing a previously existing building with a new one using the same identical design or pattern, the same materials, and supposedly the same workmanship. It is the cost of building a replica—a building of the same size and shape. Supposedly, the structure can be rebuilt as it was built originally—fancy or not, obsolete or not, and useful or not as far as the present-day farming operations are concerned.

Replacement cost is the cost of replacing a previously existing structure with its more modern version, namely, whatever is being built in its place today, however, one with the same economic capacity. It is the cost of an equally desirable structure having a similar if not the same utility, one with a more up-to-date design and more modern materials and workmanship. It need not necessarily resemble the original. It merely has to have the same economic capacity or perform the same economic function. Essentially, replacement cost is the cost of a substitute which has the same usefulness in the present farming operations and perhaps in the future.

Reproduction and replacement costs are each used as the bases for estimating farm building values. The two costs are somewhat similar where a farm building (1) has been built fairly recently, (2) is both adequate and well adapted to the present farming operations, (3) is conveniently located, and (4) where depreciation-to-date consists largely of physical deterioration. The two costs are decidedly different where (1) the building is an older one, (2) the building is obsolete or outdated in terms of present-day farm practices, and (3) the owner, in the event of a loss, would in all probability not rebuild such per se

---

7. Several exceptions to this statement were presented in the previous chapter.

but would instead replace it with something different. In the latter instance, the new building may be so unlike the original that reproduction and replacement costs defy comparison.

In most farm appraisals, the word "cost" refers to replacement rather than reproduction cost.[8] It is based on the present-day costs of new construction—materials, labor, etc. The appraisers who use the replacement concept thus raise the ugly questions: (1) to what extent would this building be replaced? and (2) with what and how will it be replaced? However, they save considerable time. First, they avoid estimating the costs of reproducing old buildings and second, they eliminate the need to estimate the various kinds of depreciation.

Cost is a relatively easy figure to estimate. At the same time, appraisers and others are often prone to ignore or miss some of the costs. Legal expenses, builder or architect fees, the costs of obtaining bids, preliminary survey costs, building permits, the cost of obtaining financing, insurance during construction, the cost of providing some supervision, and the builder's overhead and profit are often skipped by the inexperienced farm appraiser. Replacement cost should include all of these.

Many persons readily accept the cost of a building or improvement as being equal to the value of a building. The insurance agent and the county assessor accept a building's cost as its actual cash value (for insurance purposes) and as its true cash value (for tax purposes). This is because their objectives—to indemnify the owner in case of a financial loss, and to assess the property for tax purposes—are primarily concerned with what property the present owner owns and not necessarily with, or not always with, what the property would be worth were it to be sold.

Let it be said one more time, the cost of an improvement does not necessarily add an equal number of dollars to the value of the farm. The difference between the cost of a new building and its market value shortly thereafter is a real dilemma in appraisal. The minute the building is built, its market value declines quickly. Its contribution to the market value of the farm is often no more than 50 to 60 percent of its cost. Thus, cost becomes the basis for value only when such is combined with an extremely accurate estimate of that phenomenon called depreciation.

---

8. There is one major exception. Appraisals for property insurance purposes are often based on reproduction cost as a large number of the losses due to fire, wind, or other peril are partial losses. Also, specialized appraisals sometimes require values based on the cost of reproducing or rebuilding a replica of the original structure. An example is a structure to be restored for historical purposes.

KINDS OF DEPRECIATION AND CAUSES

In many farm appraisals the land contributes the major portion of the total value. Hence, farm appraisers, unlike their colleagues who do residential, commercial, or industrial appraisals, have often minimized, in fact oftentimes ignored, the intricacies of depreciation. Yet, the next step in farm building valuation is to estimate the amount of depreciation which has occurred to date and to then determine value-that-remains.

Engineers, accountants, and appraisers have used cost-less-depreciation guides for years. The engineers thoroughly believe in the concept. The accountants have accepted it. Yet, the good appraisers remain highly dubious. All of this is due to the inability of anyone to accurately measure the dollar amount of depreciation that occurs in the market.

Depreciation is not a simple phenomenon. The concept, the various kinds, and the various causes of such are not easily ascertained. Today, in fact, there are two entirely different theories in vogue.

1. Depreciation is an allowance for the decline in the value of an asset and as such represents the opportunity to recover the amount of a capital outlay over time. In this instance, the recovery period is usually as short at the law allows. It does not necessarily equal the economic life of the asset.

2. Depreciation is the decline or loss in the value of a capital asset over the period of its economic life, due to all causes—physical deterioration, functional inadequacy, and economic obsolescence. The hoped-for usefulness of the asset now determines its estimated economic life.

The first definition is used by most accountants and by the Internal Revenue Service. Depreciation is a non-cash item of expense on the income statement, a cash flow which, according to some accountants, becomes "available" and can be "put back into" the business. It is a deduction or tax offset on the income tax return. When depreciation to date (accrued depreciation) is subtracted from the original capital outlay, the difference is the asset's book value or value-which-remains.

The purpose here is to permit the owner or client to recover the original capital outlay (less some salvage value perhaps) out of current earnings and as rapidly as possible. The accountant is generally interested in whatever mathematical manipulation can be used to obtain the maximum amount of depreciation acceptable as a tax offset or as a deductible expense for income tax purposes. Faster and faster methods of write-off have been permitted, in fact recommended, by the Internal Revenue Service. As a result, the arbitrary methods now employed often lead to book or remaining values far removed from reality in the market.

The second definition is used by appraisers. Depreciation is now a combination of (1) the natural result of age and (2) the inevitable result of change. Replacement cost is now used rather than the price for which the asset was originally purchased—the asset's historical cost. In other words, depreciation is now measured, not from the original or actual cost, but from replacement cost today, based on the current costs of new construction.

Depreciation now represents the decline in value due to all causes— physical deterioration, functional inadequacy, and economic obsolescence. Value-which-remains is the amount that the building contributes to the market value of the farm. Accrued depreciation is the difference between replacement cost new and the building's contributory value as of the same date.

Physical Deterioration: Physical deterioration is a loss in value resulting from use, wear and tear, structural defect, decay, and sooner or later, disintegration. A building's physical condition declines as the structure ages. Hence, deterioration is a loss in the physical ability of the building to perform that function for which it was originally designed and built. Physical deterioration is observable, recognizable, and fairly easy to estimate.

The various component parts of a building may differ as to their rate of physical deterioration. Hence, where a building is a major part of a property's total value, an appraiser may make a breakdown relative to each of the structure's components and then estimate separately first the costs and then the physical depreciation which has occurred. These values may later be combined into a single estimate or sum.

Functional Inadequacy: Functional inadequacy is a loss in value due to a change within the property or business, a change which has led to an increasing inability or failure on the part of the building to serve the purpose or perform the function for which it was originally built. However, this inability or failure is not a result of any physical change in the structure. It is a result of changes which have occurred in the farm or the business. New needs have been created. The number of crop acres or the number of livestock may have increased. The farmstead may have been rearranged. A new method of operation may have been adopted. Hence, the original building is no longer adequate, even though physically it is not worn out. In the eyes of typical informed farm buyers and farm sellers the building has experienced a loss in desirability, and to the extent that such has affected the salability or marketability of the farm.[9]

Economic Obsolescence: Economic Obsolescence is a loss in value due to changes in the economic environment surrounding the farm or business, a loss which, generally speaking, is outside of the control of the entrepreneur. New technologies have come along and made the existing farming system obsolete. The typical operator will undoubtedly replace the existing building or structure with something new or something that is more efficient. The use of the new technology will reduce his costs (per unit of output) even though the older building or improvement is still in good physical condition. The new technology will reduce the labor or the amounts of other resources being used to the extent that the costs associated with the new investment will be offset by these other reductions.

Many farm buildings are old and obsolete. They may still be lived in or used, yet they contribute very little to the market value of the farm.

Photos by Suter

Economic obsolescence is the result of external or off-farm changes. These changes usually affect a building as a whole rather than each of its parts; however, not always. The changes may be specific and immediate. They may also arise from the more subtle economic forces—a decline in the demand for a farm product, a technological change reducing production costs (hence, leading to an increase in supply), a government support program resulting in farm enlargement (hence a surplus of leftover farm buildings), or some restrictive legislation of recent origin. Obsolescence may also be the result of a general change in the character of the neighborhood. It may result from increased non-farm employment opportunities in the community.

Of all causes of depreciation, physical deterioration is the most easily observed or recognized. Yet functional inadequacy and economic

---

9. Personal property, for example machinery and equipment, may no longer adequately perform the function for which it was purchased. However, it may be traded in, sold, or transferred to another farm or business where such serves its original purpose in perfect fashion. Hence, there is a secondhand market for many assets which are functionally inadequate for some farms, yet are not fully worn out or fully depreciated physically.

obsolescence are also major components. In terms of modern agriculture, many older buildings have outlived their usefulness. They still have good structural value. However, they stand empty. They are not used, even though they are not worn out. When this occurs these buildings present real problems to farm appraisers.[10]

Curable Versus Incurable Aspects: The various kinds of depreciation may be subdivided into curable and incurable elements. The curable elements are those which can be repaired, remodeled, or remedied (at a cost, of course) and which, in the process, will bring that building's value back to where it is comparable to, or is just as adequate as, or as useful as, a new one. Hence, the cost to cure equals the amount of depreciation that has occurred, and the building when cured is comparable to a new one.

An incurable element is one for which repair or restoration is either (1) physically impossible or (2) economically unfeasible. In the latter case, the building or improvement is physically or technically curable, yet the expenditure cannot be justified from the economic standpoint. The cost to cure would equal the amount of depreciation, yet the expenditure would be greater than any value added to the value of the building. The remedy, or curing process in other words, must increase the value of a building by an amount at least equal to the cost to cure.

Physical deterioration is generally curable as long as there are no structural defects in the building. Examples are painting and small repairs which can be remedied without delay. Some repairs may not be curable immediately; however, they can become curable at some later date. For example, the roof on a barn may be only 10 years old. Its physical deterioration can be cured in another 10 years. However, it's incurable at the moment, primarily because it's only partially depreciated. The cost to cure will not add an equal amount to the value of the asset at the present time. When the building's roof deteriorates further, and when it becomes fully depreciated, it will then become curable, providing, of course, the rest of the structure still has value. Major defects in other parts of the building, due either to age or some

---

10. For some purposes, building valuations may ignore the depreciation caused by economic obsolescence. The rationale is that the factors which create obsolescence are, generally speaking, detached from the building or the improvement itself, that they are outside the influence or control of the owner. This is quite often the case in building valuation for reasons of obtaining property insurance. The owner wants to insure the building even though it is not being used. The underlying philosophy is to indemnify him in the event of an actual, fortuitous, and financial loss.

other phenomenon, could make the roof incurable.

Functional inadequacy is curable when major remodeling will restore the building's use to the extent that it can again serve its original function in an adequate fashion, as reflected in or by a current and hypothetical replacement. Functional inadequacy is curable to the extent that the building can be converted to a new use, or to the extent the building can perform another function comparable to that which could be accomplished with a new and hypothetical replacement. The interior of an old barn may be opened up. Companion equipment, such as the cow stanchions, may be replaced. A different layout, a new floor, a higher ceiling, additional wiring, and other building services may be added. Yet again, in order to be curable, such remodeling must be both physically possible and economically feasible.

Economic obsolescence is generally incurable. By definition it is outside the control of the owner or the entrepreneur.

Methods of Approximating Values That Remain: Most farm appraisers use a single overall percentage figure to estimate remaining value. This percentage figure is based on a building's approximate age and its probable remaining economic life. The dollar value is then based on the percent of remaining life. For example . . .

Cost	$16,000
Approximate Age	8 years
Remaining Life	12 years
Percent of Life Remaining	60% (12 ÷ 20)
Present-day Value	$ 9,600

The cost figure may be a reproduction or a replacement cost figure. Depending on the concept used, the estimates as to approximate age and remaining life may consider all three causes of depreciation (reproduction cost), or they may consider only physical deterioration (replacement cost). Using either method the estimates lead to a ratio between present-day value and cost.

This technique, often referred to as the age-life method, essentially assumes that depreciation to date bears the same relationship to cost that the asset's age bears to its economic life.[11]

---

11. The method also assumes that depreciation is linear. In other words, the asset depreciates or remaining values decline an equal amount each year. Actually, the market value of an asset usually declines more rapidly the first few years of its life; it then tends to level off and decline more slowly during the last two-thirds of its life. Farm appraisers recognize this; however, they have not been overjoyed with the mathematics involved in the double-declining-balance or the sum-of-digits methods of calculating depreciation—methods recommended and sometimes used by accountants and by the Internal Revenue Service.

$$\frac{\text{Depreciation}}{\text{Cost}} = \frac{\text{Age}}{\text{Life}} \quad \text{or} \quad \frac{\text{Remaining Value}}{\text{Cost}} = 1 - \frac{\text{Age}}{\text{Life}}$$

Many appraisers use effective rather than actual age figures in making their estimates. The appraiser may judge an asset's effective age to be longer or shorter than its actual or chronological age. The latter, in itself, is not necessarily significant. It is the appraiser's judgment that is important. The best example is the old but well-designed farm home or dwelling, which in some areas may be over a hundred years of age. This dwelling has been modernized and is well kept and cared for. As a result, its effective age is only 30 or 40 years. Further-

Other farm buildings are new and unique—sometimes highly specialized facilities. They are being built today because they add volume to the farm business, efficiency to the farming operations, and hopefully income for the farm family. They are being built even though their costs are greater than the values they contribute to the market value of the farm. On this and the next three pages, a machinery shed, a grain drying and storage facility, a milk house and parlor, and a slotted floor finishing barn for hogs.

Courtesy, Borkholder Buildings

more, this house is, upon occasion, in greater demand than a newer one. Buyers are sometimes willing to pay a premium for it over a new house. Where a new dwelling, however, has not been maintained in adequate fashion, its effective age may be equal to or greater than its actual or chronological age.

Farm appraisers typically observe the various parts of a building and then make a reasonably accurate overall estimate of depreciation. They can do so where the buildings make up only a small portion of the property's total value. However, in non-farm commercial and industrial work, the appraiser may observe and categorize a given building's component parts. He may compare each component—foundation, walls, roof, plumbing, wiring, etc.—to the same component new. He may also make a separate estimate of each of the various elements of depreciation.

The method used makes little or no difference. The appraiser and his client are interested in an accurate remaining value given (1) the

Courtesy, Behlen Company

importance of the value relative to the total appraisal assignment and
(2) the amount of time that is available. Whether or not a building is
broken down into various component parts, and whether or not
depreciation is allocated among the various kinds and causes may be
more work than it's worth; then again, such may be most helpful.
What matters is that each and all elements of depreciation are considered, that such are considered only once, and that the consideration
or effort is made apparent in the appraisal report.[12]

---

12. After observing a building and its component parts, some appraisers measure the adverse values arising from curable depreciation, that resulting from both
physical deterioration and functional inadequacy. They then observe and estimate
the amount of economic obsolescence. Other appraisers measure the inferiority
attributed to incurable physical depreciation and then add to that the inferiority
attributed to incurable functional inadequacy and economic obsolescence. Some
appraisers use dollar values (the curable part); some use percentages (the incurable portion). The method makes little or no difference as long as the values
that remain are accurate.

Courtesy, Babson Bros.

FIVE DIFFERENT VALUES

Many different values are placed on farm buildings and improvements. Generally speaking, this is a result of different philosophies and objectives as well as different techniques. The various values, and there are four or five different ones, have meaning only when they are defined.

1. Book value is the actual cost of a building or improvement minus any calculated depreciation allowed or allowable between the date of purchase and the date of value.

2. Structural value is the present-day reproduction cost of a building or improvement less any and all physical deterioration.

3. Contributory value is the dollar amount that the building or improvement adds to the market value of the property. It is based on replacement cost. Furthermore, depreciation now reflects not just

Courtesy, Borkholder Buildings

physical deterioration but functional inadequacy and economic obsolescence as well.

4. Value-in-use is the building or improvement's present-day value to the present operator and in the present farming operations.

5. Salvage value is the value of a building or improvement at the end of its economic life and in its next best alternative use or location. It is the value of a building when it is no longer usable in its present circumstances. It is its value sometimes as a whole, sometimes in pieces.[13]

Each of these values is based in theory. However, each of them can be applied to farm buildings, and at times, the use of each value is quite helpful in an appraisal. The challenge is to use each value only when and where it is applicable and to properly present each value in one's report. Unfortunately, many farm appraisers concern themselves only with contributory values. This is perhaps a mistake. Structural value, contributory value, and value-in-use are often desirable as a means of providing one's client with certain facts as well as figures. The use of all three figures avoids the later misuse of one's contributory values, which often occurs when they and they alone are presented in one's appraisal.

Book Value: Whatever the farmer pays for a building, that capital outlay is that building's cost. This cost is readily accepted by many persons as a given building's value and regardless of whether the figure is high or low relative to the cost of any other alternative resources (or substitutes) that could be purchased.

Practically all accountants use this actual cost figure, along with some arbitrary mathematical formula—any one of three or four—to calculate the annual amounts of depreciation and to determine a whole series of book or inventory values. The original capital outlay or cost is divided by the estimated life of the building to determine the annual amounts of depreciation. This depreciation figure is then subtracted from the first year's original cost, and from the beginning-of-the-year value each subsequent year, to determine end-of-year book values.

These figures find their way into many income and financial statements. A building's original cost is used to determine such items as investment credit, when legal; to set up depreciation schedules and

---

13. Salvage value also refers to an anticipated value at the end of a building's planned use or economic life. This salvage value is a pseudo- rather than an actual-salvage value and, along with cost, is used by accountants to determine book values.

claim whatever depreciation is allowed or allowable; and to calculate those values which remain at various later dates and which may some-day become the basis for calculating capital gains. However, these book values often bear little if any resemblance to a building's structural value, its contributory value in the farm real estate market, or the building's usefulness in the farming operations.

Estimating the life of the asset is, of course, the problem. There is considerable tendency to shorten the life of all capital assets today for income tax purposes. Most new buildings and improvements are depreciated as rapidly as possible, or as rapidly as is acceptable by the Internal Revenue Service. Thus the taxpayer claims as large a tax deduction as possible. This kind of depreciation merely represents the opportunity to recover the cost of a capital outlay.

According to many appraisers these book values are unrealistic. They bear little or no relation to the real world.[14] Economic trends, technological change, the farming pattern in the community, the balance between or among the farm's resources—all of these (and others)—have no effect on an asset's book value, once the building or improvement has been purchased and the depreciation schedule has been established.

Unfortunately, the accountant's concept of value is sometimes confused with appraisal. For example, the assessor often uses a single depreciation table on all buildings of a given type, even though the figures may have little or no validity as far as the individual property owner is concerned. Except when a building is relatively new, book values are of limited use as far as appraisers are concerned.

Structural Value: Structural value is based on present-day reproduction cost less the asset's physical depreciation to date, which is in turn based on its true economic life. Reproduction rather than actual cost is used. Depreciation now represents only physical wear and tear. Estimated life equals the asset's economic life and is based on its probable use. In the case of a new building, structural value equals present-day cost. In the case of an older building, it is again a value-that-remains.

Structural value perhaps approaches a value intrinsic. One might say it resembles a permanent type of value, however not really, because physical wear and tear is always operative, and that which is structurally sound today may not be structurally sound tomorrow.

---

14. The real world of the marketplace.

The farm appraiser, by placing a present-day structural value on each building and improvement, says to his client, "This building does or does not have value as it stands. It is or is not physically sound. It can be used as is, or the depreciation (physical) to date is curable. Thus, this building can be added onto, expanded, or remodeled without major difficulty."

At the same time, structural value may be of little or no use if in the meantime, changes in building designs, materials, and other technologies have occurred. The economic environment surrounding a building—economic trends, technological change, the changing patterns of farming, and the balance among the farm's resources—has no effect on a building's structural value.

Contributory Value: Many farm appraisers concern themselves only with contributory value. This value reflects value in the marketplace. By earlier definition, the purpose of a farm appraisal is to ascertain the present market value of the property. In arriving at this value the farm appraiser is interested only in the amount that a given building contributes to that market value.

Unfortunately, there exists a real dilemma between the concepts of cost and contributory or market value. The minute a building is built or erected its market value is usually considerably less than its cost. The market value declines immediately and oftentimes to the 75-, 60-, or 50-percent level. As a result, contributory values may be considerably below present-day replacement costs, even when a building is relatively new.

Contributory value is based on cost less depreciation. However, depreciation now reflects many factors. It encompasses not just physical deterioration, but functional inadequacy and economic obsolescence as well. Contributory values often reflect a lack of balance among a given farm's basic resources—particularly the balance between land, buildings, and improvements. Farm real estate values are both created and destroyed by the underinvestment and overinvestment in capital improvements. Contributory values may thus reflect the relationship between income and investment.

Contributory values may also reflect an honest error or two when the building is built. They may do so immediately. They may reflect improper design, poor quality materials, shoddy workmanship, or poor location. In an older building, contributory values may reflect the failure to repair, a decline in pride of ownership, and other factors.

The farm appraiser is well aware of the economic trends occurring in the agricultural community and the influence of various farm practices on farm real estate values. A building which is an innovation in the area often experiences a severe decline in value immediately after it is built. The traditional appraiser is very aware of this. He is cognizant of the new technologies, yet he also realizes that such must be accepted in the local area before they are fully recognized in the market.

Value in Use: Most farm buildings and improvements are built, not for speculative purposes, or for later sale or transfer, but instead for use in the farming operations. They are long-term capital investments purchased primarily (1) to expand the volume of the farm business and (2) to increase the efficiency of the farming operations. Farm buildings are purchased not with the idea that they will soon be sold, not with the idea that they will add equal value to the property, but because they will be used in the farming operations, because they will make the work more enjoyable, because they will increase the

One of the highly specialized feeding installations with a fan-shaped feedlot near Bryan, Texas.

Courtesy, A.O. Smith Harvestore Products, Inc.

efficiency of the farm family, and hopefully because they will add to the farm's income. To the extent that the latter occurs, the market value of the farm may increase. However, much of the additional income that is obtained goes to the farmer or the farm family. Only a fraction of this income is capitalized into the farm's value.

Thus a new building often contributes considerably more to the efficiency of a given farming operation under the present operator than it does to the market value of the farm under a typical operator. Utility values tend to remain high during the first few years of the life of a building, while contributory values decline both immediately and rapidly. This in part is because value-in-use reflects the desires and the capabilities of the present owner or operator, whereas contributory values are based on the typical operator concept.

The present operator often lets his managerial capabilities, along with his desires as to the use of a building in the future, influence his decision to build.[15] This is particularly the case where the building is a specialized facility. The present operator who builds the building himself often has considerable pride of ownership. He often builds a better building and makes better use of that building than does the typical operator. At the same time farm buildings are economically justified only if they effectively contribute to the farm's productivity.

The difference between contributory value and value-in-use is more clearly defined by asking two questions:

1. If this farm had (or did not have) this building on it and if it were (or were not) located here how much more (or less) would the typical buyer pay for this farm?

2. If this building were to burn or blow away, or be completely destroyed today, to what extent would it be replaced?

The first question requests the building or improvement's contributory value; the second question seeks its value-in-use.

Most appraisals seek merely to ascertain contributory values, yet utility values should be recognized. Unfortunately, value-in-use can approach cost. Furthermore, it can exceed contributory value.[16] This is difficult for some appraisers to comprehend. When a building's

---

15. At the time the building is purchased or constructed the present operator may or may not recognize that if, because of unforeseen circumstances, he should be forced to sell the farm he would not likely recover the cost of his investment. (This would be particularly so in the case of a specialized, unconventional, or odd building.)

16. This can be costly, unless the property owner or the insured also agrees to accept a deferred payment provision in his insurance contract. However, more of this in the next chapter.

value-in-use is above its contributory value, the appraiser is essentially saying, "If this 'valuable' building were to burn, blow away, or otherwise be destroyed, it would be rebuilt to this level, even though the cost of replacing it would not be fully reflected in the market value of the farm." Depending on the magnitude and difference in the figures this tells a client something about the building or improvement.

Value-in-use and insured value are typically the same. The purpose of property insurance, of course, is to indemnify a property owner for any and all actual, financial, and fortuitous losses that may occur. Value-in-use sets the stage for this indemnity philosophy which is presented in the next chapter.

Salvage Value: Lastly there is a salvage value, which enters into an occasional farm appraisal whenever a building's use is to be discontinued. This is often a forced discontinuation of use due to forces beyond the control of the property owner. A change in the use of the property may be desired, or a change in the location of the building may be required. Salvage value is the value of the building, or some or all of its parts or pieces, when that building or its component parts is relegated to its next best alternative use or location. The relegation may result from a change in the use of the property, or a change requiring the removal of the improvement; it may be the result of some unexpected action which has partially destroyed the building.

When a reservoir takes a farm or a new highway takes a set of farm buildings, the property owner is often given the opportunity to move his home or his buildings. Professional movers can usually do the job. Metal grain bins and Harvestores are often moved. A concrete stave silo is occasionally moved. Some buildings are moved in one piece. Some may be torn down or disassembled and moved in pieces. In other instances the materials only may be moved or sold.

Whenever a building is moved or torn down these costs are first estimated. They are then subtracted from either the cost of a new building or the utility value of the existing building in its new location. Some parts or pieces of course cannot be moved, for example, the footings and foundations. Some buildings cannot be moved or torn down, even piecemeal, without considerable labor and breakage being involved.[17] Yet in many areas, there is a market for secondhand buildings and building materials. In some areas, for example, old unpainted barns have considerable value due to the demand for rough hand-hewn

---

17. Traditionally, the cost of tearing an old barn or building down is about equal to the value of the salvageable materials.

beams, and weather-beaten boards as modern decor materials in restaurants, motels, and office buildings.[18]

In the physical description of the subject property, an appraiser should perhaps use several dollar figures in order to clarify the different farm building values. A building's replacement cost and its contributory value should always be specified. In addition, structural values and value-in-use figures are often helpful.

A detailed appraisal will often include facts with regard to the present use being made of the buildings and improvements. A figure or two, showing the extent to which value-in-use exceeds market value, indicates the extent to which a building is useful in the current farming operations. Thus, different building values often can be used to tell one's client something about the buildings and improvements on the subject property.

WHAT IF THE IMPROVEMENTS ARE MAJOR ASSETS?

On many farms, land makes up the major portion of the farm's value, and the buildings and improvements are minor. However, this is not so in all cases. There are farms where the improvements require a sizeable investment. Once the investment is made, these improvements tend to wear out or depreciate over time. They may be referred to as wasting assets. Here, the prudent investor may be interested not just in the return *on* his investment; he may also be interested in capital recovery or recapture, or in other words, the return *of* his investment as well.

In these instances, when the buildings or improvements are major, the farm appraiser often needs to adopt a more sophisticated valuation technique. In Chapter VI (see *A Major Footnote: How, When Not in Perpetuity*), a gravel pit and a 15-year lease were used to illustrate the technique of placing values on (1) an income stream of a given duration and (2) a reversionary interest available at some future date. These assets essentially existed alone, or by themselves. However, land and improvements may also be so attached to each other, both physically and conceptually, that each adds to the productivity of the other

---

18. In some areas there is a market for old barn beams and weathered barn siding. In fact, old barn boards have been priced at two or three times the cost of 4' × 8' walnut panelling at the retail level. However, this market is rapidly being replaced by the lighter weight plastic beams and siding.

and any income allocation between the two is extremely difficult to make.

Income capitalization must now encompass a residual technique. The appraiser may use either a land-residual or a building-residual approach, depending on whether the major portion of the investment is in the land or in the improvements, and also on whether the best currently available guides as to value are for land (sales data) or for improvements (construction costs). In applying the residual technique to a capital improvement, an appraiser goes through the following steps:

1. He estimates the total dollar returns and then the return, or income, to the land and improvements combined.

2. He then places a value on the land and subtracts its "cost" from the income.

3. He then capitalizes the difference, or residual, into the value of the improvements.

Land and improvements may be so attached to each other that any income allocation between the two is difficult to make. The return from land can be capitalized into perpetuity; however, the income stream from a wasting asset will someday "dry up," or cease to exist. The prudent investor in these instances may be interested not only in the return **on** his investment but also in the return **of** his investment.

Courtesy, U.S.D.A.

The rate of interest on the land and the capitalization rate used on the improvements should be based on the opportunity cost of money, or in other words, on the typical owner's next best investment alternative.

Let's illustrate: An apple orchard represents a sizeable investment in both land and improvements. The land will presumably persist indefinitely; however, an orchard has an economic life of approximately 40 years. The dollar return and the per-acre income from the orchard are considerably greater than that from the land unimproved. So the question is "What are the apple trees worth?"

The following data have been developed:

Per-Acre Returns		Remaining Life (Years)	25
Receipts	$715.00		
Expenses	640.00	Land Value (Unimproved)	$750
Income	$ 75.00		
Rates of Return on Comparable Investments			
Land	4.0%	Improvements	6.5%

The residual return to the improvements is $45.00. This is obtained by taking the total income per acre ($75.00) and subtracting the "cost" of the land ($750 × 4.0% = $30.00). This residual return can now be capitalized into value using either the straight-line or the compound-interest method. (Each of these methods was presented in Chapter VI.)

1. The straight-line method leads to a per-acre value of $428.57 for the trees (Table 40). This was obtained by dividing the residual return of $45.00 by a 10.5-percent capitalization rate. The capitalization rate consists of two parts in this case, a 6.5-percent rate of return on the investment plus a 4.0-percent rate of recapture or depreciation.

2. The compound-interest method leads to a per-acre value of $548.91 for the trees. This was obtained by using the present value tables and by multiplying the residual return of $45.00 by 12.1979. The latter factor is based on an income stream for 25 years and an interest rate of 6.5 percent.

The value of the improvements and the value of the land may now be added together to get the total value of the orchard.

	Straight-Line Method	Compound-Interest Method
Value of the Trees	$ 428.57	$ 548.91
Value of the Land	750.00	750.00
Value of the Orchard	$1,178.57	$1,298.91

Table 40. The Present Value of an Improvement Using the Residual Technique. An Apple Orchard.

The Asset(s)	The Method	The Figures
The Basics:		
Typically dollar income (receipts less expenses) averages	$75.00 per acre	
Remaining estimated tree life	25 years	
Comparable unimproved land value	$750 per acre	
Residual return to the improvements	$45.00 per acre	
(based on land cost of $75.00 × 4.0% = $30.00)		
Alternative No. 1. (Straight-Line Method)		
Value of the trees is based on the residual return divided by a capitalization rate reflecting both a return on the investment (6.5%) and a return of the investment over the next 25 years (4.0%)		
$45.00 ÷ 10.5% =		$ 428.57
Value of the land		750.00
Total per-acre value		$1,178.57
Alternative No. 2. (Compound-Interest Method)		
Value of the trees is based on the residual return multiplied by a factor representing the present value of an income stream for the next 25 years of a 6.5% rate of interest		
$45.00 × 12.1979 (Appendix Table A) =		$ 548.91
Value of the land		750.00
Total per-acre value		$1,298.91

An orchard raises another rather difficult question in that the trees, at the end of their productive, or economic, life may have negative value. They may have some salvage value as fireplace wood; however, the cost of cutting the trees down, burning the brush, removing the stumps, and recovering the land may be greater than the value of the wood. The value of the land, 25 years hence, should perhaps be reduced by the cost of removing the old apple trees.

Let's look at a second illustration: Sizeable investments in wells and irrigation equipment are now being made in areas which have been devoted only to dry land farming in the past. Corn can now be produced on about 132 out of each 160 acres (using a center-pivot irrigation system) in areas where only wheat could previously be raised on an every-other-year basis. The cost of the improvements may exceed the value of the land (on a per-acre basis). However, the per-acre returns and income are both increased. The following data are somewhat typical.

	Corn	Wheat
Acres per Quarter Section	132	80
Per-Acre Yield (bu.)	150	35
Price per Bushel	$ 1.15	$ 1.80
Per-Acre Returns		
Receipts	$172.50	$ 63.00
Expenses	123.30	52.50*
Income	$ 49.20	$ 10.50
Remaining Life (Years)		8
Land Value per Acre (Dry Land)		$175.00
Return on Comparable Investments		
Land		3.0%
Technology		8.0%
Income per Quarter Section		
Corn		$649.45
Wheat		$ 84.00

* $42.00 on wheat and $10.50 for summer fallow.

The value of the irrigation facilities may be based on the dollar returns from corn over and above the dollar returns from wheat. The additional income obtained is $38.70 ($49.20 − $10.50). This additional income, referred to as a residual return in the previous illustration, can now be capitalized into value.

1. The straight-line method leads to a per-acre value of $215.00 for the irrigation equipment (Table 41). This was obtained by dividing the additional income of $38.70 by an 18.0-percent capitalization rate. This rate consists of an 8.0-percent return on the investment and a 10.0-percent rate of recapture (10-year economic life).

2. The compound-interest method leads to a per-acre value of $259.68. This was obtained by using the percent value tables and by multiplying the additional income of $38.70 by 6.7101. The latter factor is based on an income stream for 10 years and an interest rate of 8.0 percent.

The value of the equipment plus the land may now be added together to get the total investment per quarter section of land.

	Straight-Line Method	Compound-Interest Method
Value of the Equipment		
132 Acres at $215.00 and	$28,380	$34,278
$259.68 per Acre		
Value of the Land	28,000	28,000
160 Acres at $175.00		
Total Value per Quarter	$56,380	$62,278

Table 41. The Present Value of an Improvement Using the Residual Technique. A Center-Pivot Irrigation System.

The Assets	The Method	The Figure
The Basics:		
Typical dollar incomes (receipts less expenses) averaging $49.20 on irrigated land (corn) and $10.50 on dry land (wheat—summer fallow)		
Estimated life, wells, and irrigation equipment, 10 years		
Dry land farm land value, $175 per acre		
Additional income to the improvements, $38.70 per acre ($49.20 − $10.50)		
Alternative No. 1. Straight-Line Method		
Value of the equipment is based on the additional income that can be generated, divided by a capitalization rate reflecting both a return on the investment (8.0%) and a return of the investment over the next 10 years (10.0%)		
$38.70 ÷ 18.0% =		$215.00
Value of the land		175.00
Total per-acre value		$390.00
Alternative No. 2. Compound-Interest Method		
Value of the equipment is based on the additional income multiplied by a factor representing the present value of an income stream for the next 10 years at an 8.0% rate of interest.		
$38.70 × 6.7101 (Appendix Table A) =		$259.68
Value of the land		175.00
Total per-acre value		$434.68

An irrigation system also raises another rather difficult question in that the well and the irrigation equipment should perhaps be depreciated using two different rates—for example, a 4.0- or 5.0-percent rate on the wells and a 10.0- to 12.5-percent rate on the equipment. This would be more realistic. Again, one would have to place a cost on one (for example, the well) and then capitalize the residual return to arrive at the value of the other (for example, the equipment).

In each case, the orchard and the irrigation installation, the compound-interest method again leads to the higher value. This is because in the straight-line method, the income stream includes the annual amount of recaptured capital only, whereas in the compound-interest method, that income includes interest on the portion of the capital not yet recaptured. As was pointed out in Chapter VI, there should be some penalty for waiting—namely, interest on one's investment. Hence, the compound interest method is the more accurate method.

LET'S ILLUSTRATE: THIRTEEN FARM BUILDINGS

All farm buildings go through a life cycle. First, they are new. Their cost and their use in terms of the present farming operations are both of major importance. However, as time goes by, several phenomena occur. One, the building ages and physical deterioration occurs. Two, the various farming operations may be updated. A building may be shifted to a new use, it may be delegated to a lesser use, sometimes storage only, or it may be replaced by a new technology. Three, a change in farm ownership may occur, with a new owner or operator taking over. Again, the building may be used in a different fashion, and it may be delegated to a more minor role.

Most farm buildings are built not for resale or speculative purposes; they are to be used and enjoyed. They expand the volume of the farm business. They increase the efficiency of the farming operations. They make farming a more enjoyable way of life. Economically speaking, they are justified only to the extent that they contribute to the productivity of the farm or to its market value. However, they serve as storage, as shelter, and in many other ways. They reduce labor requirements, ease the role of management, and make the farming operations more enjoyable. Farm buildings serve as productive resources; they play a consumptive role, and they're tax deductible.

When a building is first built or erected, the present operator often rationalizes his decision very well; he typically exhibits considerable pride of ownership. However, were he to build it again, he might just make a few changes. A year or two later he may wish he had built it somewhat differently. He may wish that it were larger or that he had built it over there. He may decide to make some modifications. At the same time the building's value, to him at least, is in terms of how he operates the farm business.

Sooner or later of course, and sometimes for an unforeseen reason, the present operator may step out of the above situation. The farm is then placed on the market; the typical operator now enters the scene. The most likely buyer, owner, or operator looks at the farm and at its buildings and improvements as a package. The typical operator often looks at the farm buildings quite differently than did the previous owner. He may question the design of a building. He may question its layout or arrangement, both inside and out. He may question its location. He may wish it weren't there. If or when he purchases the farm, he may remodel the building, he may move it, or he may burn or demolish it, and particularly if changes in the farming operations are contemplated.

In the process of acquiring ownership, the typical buyer conjures up all sorts of values, rationalized in part by the many rules and regulations of modern society. He may think about (1) a new book value, the depreciation and other tax offsets he can claim, (2) the amount of insurance coverage which should be carried, (3) the building's assessed valuation and the property taxes he will pay, and if he's thinking ahead, (4) the book value of the asset towards the end of its life, resale of the farm, and the income that can be someday claimed in the form of capital gains.

The cycle is now complete. The building may be 8 or 80 years old. It has deteriorated physically. It may be functionally inadequate. It may be economically obsolete. Whatever the case, its value has declined. This value will continue to decline until eventually it reaches a salvage value based on its use in some other alternative and either as a whole or in parts and pieces. Farm buildings typically vary all the way from those which are relatively new and useful to those which are relatively old and obsolete. Many farmsteads today are studies in contrast.

The Old Farm House Versus the New Ranch Dwelling: The old farm house exists on many a farm. For illustrative purposes, let's assume one built in 1890. It's a beautiful old structure with four large two-story pillars and considerable gingerbread across the front. It's an 11-room wood frame dwelling. The basement walls and several interior walls are built of rough sawn oak and solid brick. It has been remodeled several times, added onto several times, yet the downstairs rooms still have their 9½-foot ceilings and 7-foot windows. It has three fireplaces. However, central heating was added some 50 years after it was built. It has a modern kitchen and two baths. The house is in good condition. It is well kept even though the interior floors sag a little. It's been painted white at least five times during the last three decades; however, not recently. Today, the paint is peeling.

The present operator and his wife use only the first-floor rooms. The second floor primarily provides storage. However, it has also been used—for guests (one bedroom), for recreation (two bedrooms), as an early cold frame or green house, and to brood several batches of baby chicks. To reproduce this farm house today, as is, would cost at least $175,000. No farm owner or his wife would do so unless perhaps considerable sentiment continues to be attached and a surplus of dollars is available.

If this old farm house were to burn, blow away, or be replaced today, it would be replaced with a more modern one-story ranch house. These can be found on several farms of similar size in the same area. Most have three-bedrooms, full basements, modern heating systems, modern kitchen facilities, and other conveniences similar to many houses in town. Without making any specific assumptions as to the farm, its location, or the balance between the farm's resources (land versus buildings and improvements), a number of different values—structural value, contributory value, and value-in-use—have been presented below (Table 42).

The more modern house is relatively new (five years); hence, its reproduction and replacement costs are the same ($37,090). The old farm house is still a sound old structure ($37,910). However, the more modern farm house contributes more to the market ($20,400 as compared to $8,256). The values-in-use (or insured values) are very similar.

In studying these dollar values one must assume that the dwellings are located on farms with comparable land resources, that there is neither overinvestment nor underinvestment in the dwellings. One must also assume that there is no historical or sentimental dollar value incorporated in the old farm house. In other words, the structure is not located in an area where there is a demand for vintage homes. Not always are these assumptions realistic.

The Old Horse Barn Versus Today's Pole Barn: In many agricultural areas there is a surplus of old and obsolete farm buildings. The classic example is the old horse barn with six or eight horse stalls and 10 or 12 cow stanchions in the basement, a main floor, and a huge overhead hay mow. In some parts of the country these old horse barns have been converted to dairy barns; in fact a large number of cows are still milked in these barns in some areas. However, many of them are used for storage only, and oftentimes quite inefficiently for that.

An old horse barn, 40 × 64 which is used for storage only, and a converted barn of the same size plus a shed on one end, are presented below. The horse barn is empty except for some farm machinery and junk stored on the main barn floor. Its reproduction cost is $11,520, yet the old barn will never be reproduced as is, at least not for the current farming operations. If it were to burn down or blow away or be destroyed, it would be replaced with a modern pole barn or shed. Such a structure with the same square footage could be built for around $4,480. Hence, the old barn contributes little to the market value of the farm.

Similar barns in the same area have been converted to dairy barns and are being used quite intensively. The basement, depending on its size, may contain 20 to 80 or more stanchions. The main floor is often used for the storage of feed grains and some machinery. Even the hay mows may be partially used for baled hay and straw. There is considerable space available. If this converted barn were to burn down or blow away, it wouldn't be reproduced as is. It would instead be replaced by several one-story pole structures—one for machinery storage perhaps, and one with free stalls for the dairy herd.

Ever since the early 1950's, one-story pole buildings have become increasingly popular. They are easier to build, more convenient to work in, and more flexible in terms of any future changes that may take place in the farming operations. Old-barn replacement costs are thus based on the costs of these newer buildings utilizing pole construction techniques. Structural value, contributory value, and value-in-use are presented below.

Specialized Farm Buildings: Specialized farm buildings also exist on many farms. These are typically related to the type of farm. They are often built for a specific enterprise. Many are designed to save labor, to ease the role of management, and to make farming a more enjoyable way of life.

These buildings typically lack the universal use of a farm dwelling. They lack the flexibility of the modern pole barn. Functional inadequacy and economic obsolescence tend to occur long before the advanced stages of physical deterioration set in. If a change in ownership occurs, or if a change in the farming operations takes place, these buildings are quite subject to sizeable declines in their contributory values.

Many farm owners fail to recognize that when these specialized buildings are built, the value they contribute to the value of the property is but a fraction of their cost. Per dollar spent, these buildings add no more than $0.40 or $0.50 to the market value of the farm. This added value depends on the extent to which the investment is a strictly new and perhaps untried technology, the extent to which the enterprise or technology is typical in the area, and the extent to which the building is being built to suit the whims of the present operator.

Six illustrations, one quite old and the rest fairly new, are presented: an ear corn crib, a modern grain handling system, a 20 x 70 concrete silo, a 25 x 80 Harvestore, a double-5 herringbone milking parlor, and a slotted-floor farrow-through-finish hog house.

The old ear corn crib with its drive-through area, bucket elevator,

Table 42. Contrasts in Farm Buildings: Their Costs and Their Values.
Three Houses, Four Barns, and Six Specialized Facilities, 1970 Data.

	An Old Farm House	A Modern Farm House	A Second House
		Three Hypothetical Dwellings	
Present Use	Operator	Operator	Hired Man
Number of Rooms	6 Down, 5 Up	6 Down	6 Down
Approximate Year Built	1890	1965	1950
Dimensions			
Width, Length (Feet)	36 × 48, 12 × 28	28 × 64	24 × 40
Square Feet or Capacity[1]	1728 (2) + 336	1792	960
General Condition, Layout and Appearance	Above Average (First Floor)	Excellent	Average
Building Materials, Condition[2]			
Foundation	Brick, Stone 3	Cement Block, 1	Cement Block, 1
Siding	Wood 3	Brick Veneer, 1	Aluminum, 1
Roof	Wood Shingle, 6	Asphalt Shingle, 2	Asphalt Shingle, 10
Interior Features			
Basement Dimensions	36 × 40	28 × 64	None
Heating	LP Gas, Forced Air	LP Gas, Forced Air	LP Gas, Forced Air
Floors	Pine	Hardwood	Asphalt Tile
Interior Walls	Lath, Plaster, Papered	Drywall, Painted	Drywall, Painted
Kitchen	Modern, Excellent	Modern, Excellent	Average
Bathrooms	2½ Down, 0 Up 2	1	
Other	4 Fireplaces 1	Fireplace —	
		Air Conditioned	

	55 (Downstairs Only)	100	100
Use Factor or Percentage			
Reproduction Cost			
Per Sq. Ft. or Unit	$ 36.00 + 20.00	$ 20.00 +	$ 18.00 +
Total	$68,928	$37,090	$17,280
Replacement Cost[3]			
Per Sq. Ft. or Unit	$ 20.00	$ 20.00	$ 16.00
Total	$41,280[7]	$37,090	$15,360
Approximate Age (Years)	80	5	20
Effective Useful Life (Years Remaining)	40	45	30
Percent of Useful Life Remaining	50	90	60
Structural Value[4]	$37,910	$35,236	$12,960
Percent of Reproduction Cost	55	95	75
Contributory Value[5]	$ 8,256	$20,400	$ 5,376
Percent of Replacement Cost	20	55	35
Value-in-Use[6]	$30,960	$29,672	$11,520
Percent of Replacement Cost	75	80	75

Table 42 (Continued).

	Four Hypothetical Barns			
	Old Horse Barn	**Converted Horse Barn**	**New Pole Barn**	**Machine Shed, Shop**
Present Use	Storage Only	Storage Above Cow Stanchions Below	Free Stalls for 60 Cows Hay, Machinery Storage	Storage Repair
Approximate Year Built	1910-15	1910-15	1960	1960
Dimensions Width, Length (Feet)	40 × 64	40 × 64 + 16'	40 × 100 + 40 × 48	32 × 60, 16 × 32
Square Feet or Capacity[1]	2,560 (2-3)	2,560 (2-3) 640 (1)	4,000 + 1,920	1,920 + 512
General Condition, Layout, and Appearance	Poor	Below Average	Like New	Like New
Building Materials, Condition[2] Foundation	Stone, 4	Stone, 4	Pole, 2	Pole, 2
Siding	Wood Boards, 8	Board, Batten, 6	Galv. Metal, 3	Galv. Metal, 3
Roof	Wood Shingle, 7	Metal, 7	Galv. Metal, 3	Galv. Metal, 3
Interior Features	B-6 Horse Stalls 12 Cow Stanchions 1st F-Storage Farm Machinery Mow—Empty	B-40 Stanchions for Dairy Cows 1st F-Storage Farm Machinery Mow—Baled Hay, Straw	60 Free Stalls Plus Storage	Concrete Floor and Heat in Shop Only

	20	80	100	100
Use Factor or Percentage	20	80	100	100
Reproduction Cost				
Per Sq. Ft. or Unit	$ 4.50	$ 4.50 + 2.25	$ 1.75	$ 2.00 + 3.00
Total	$11,520	$11,520 + 1,440 or 12,960	$10,360[8]	$3,840 + 1,536
Replacement Cost[3]				
Per Sq. Ft. or Unit	$ 1.75	$ 1.75	$ 1.75	$ 2.00 + 3.00
Total	$ 4,480	$ 8,960 + 1,120 or 10,080	$10,360[8]	$3,840 + 1,536 or 5,376
Approximate Age (Years)	60	60	10	10
Effective Useful Life (Years Remaining)	5+	20	30	40
Percent of Useful Life Remaining	7½	25	75	80
Structural Value[4]	$ 3,500	$ 7,500	$ 9,250	$4,800
Percent of Reproduction Cost	30—	60—	90—	90—
Contributory Value[5]	$ 4,256[9]	$ 7,560	$ 7,750	$4,000
Percent of Replacement Cost	95	75	75—	75—
Value-in-Use[6]	$ 1,350	$ 7,560	$ 8,250	$4,300
Percent of Replacement Cost	30+	75	80—	80

Table 42 (Continued).

	Six Specialized Structures					
	Old Ear Corn Crib Remodeled	Grain Handling System	Concrete Silo	Harvestore	Milking Parlor	Farrow-to-Finish Hog Barn
Present Use	Shelled Corn Storage	Shelled Corn Storage	Corn Silage	Haylage Cornlage	Milking Parlor	Hogs
Approximate Year Built	1925+	1955	1960	1965	1965	1970
Dimensions Width, Length (Feet)	32 × 72	4 Bins	24 × 60	25 × 80	16 × 24 or 384 Sq. Ft.	32 × 168
Square Feet or Capacity[1]	7,500 Ear Corn +6,000 Sm. Gr.	40,000 Bu.	760 Ton Corn Silage	458 Ton Dry Matter		48 Crates 33 Pens
General Condition, Layout and Appearance	Old, Poor	Average	Average	Average	Like New	New
Building Materials, Condition[2]						
Foundation	Stone, 8	Concrete, 1	Concrete, 1	Concrete, 1	Concrete Block, 1	Concrete Block, 1
Siding	Wood, 7	Galv. Metal, 5	Conc. Stave, 4	Glass Lined, 1	Prefab, 3	Wood, 3
Roof	Metal, 4	Galv. Metal, 5	None		Built Up, 2	Metal, 2
Interior Features	3 Overhead Bins Old, Obsolete Leg Elevator	Dump Elevator Mix Mill 4 Bulk Bins	Top Unloader	Bottom Unloader	Double-5 Herringbone Auto. Grain Glass Pipe	

Use Factor or Percentage	75	100	100	150	100	100
Reproduction Cost[3]						
Per Sq. Ft. or Unit	$ 1.25 per Bu.	$ 0.55 per Bu.			3.60/Sq Ft	
Total	$16,875	$22,000	$14,312[10]	$27,543[10]	$ 1,350[9]	$44,000
Replacement Cost[3]						
Per Sq. Ft. or Unit	$ 0.45 per Bu.[8]	0.55 per Bu.				
Total	$ 6,075	$22,000	$14,312[10]	27,543[10]	$ 1,350[8]	$48,000
Approximate Age (Years)	45	15	10	5	5	0
Effective Useful Life (Years Remaining)	5	15	10	35	20	10
Percent of Useful Life Remaining	10	50	50	85+	80	100
Structural Value[4]	$13,500	$20,000	$10,700	$27,500	$ 1,300	$44,000
Percent of Reproduction Cost	80—	90—	75—	100—	100—	100
Contributory Value[5]	$ 3,000	$14,300	$ 7,200	$11,000	$ 540	$17,000
Percent of Replacement Cost	50—	65	50+	40	40	35+
Value-in-Use[6]	$ 3,000	$17,500	$11,500	$22,000	$ 1,000	$38,500
Percent of Replacement Cost	50—	80—	80+	80[11]	75—	80+

1. For dwellings, square feet of living area only; the square feet in a garage, breezeway, porch, or patio is not included.
2. The number following the materials indicates physical condition (1 is best, 10 is poorest).
3. Based on present-day construction costs of building either the present structure, if current, or a more modern version of the building or improvement, if somewhat obsolete or out of fashion.
4. Based on the soundness of the structure and physical deterioration only; with a realistic estimated life.
5. Value added to the present-market value of the farm.
6. Insured value for the present operator and in the present farming operations; with a deferred payment provision assumed when value-in-use is greater than contributory value.
7. Based on 2,064 sq. ft.
8. Does not include free stalls or companion equipment inside building.
9. Zero except for the demand for "that touch of antiquity"—for barn boards, shingles, and hand hewn beams (adz cut) half-century old—in this area. Prices being paid farmers in 1970 approximated $32.50 per square plus $62.50 per 1,000 board feet (beams only). Decor Materials, Inc., Appleton, Wisconsin.
10. Does not include unloader.
11. Insured value probably zero because of little or no risk.

and overhead storage bins is obsolete. It is like the old horse barn. It can be converted to shelled corn storage but it's more likely to be replaced by the newer, larger, and more efficient metal bins.

The new grain-handling system takes advantage of a pit, a higher-capacity elevator, a wet grain-holding bin, a continuous-flow dryer, large augers, and other items which make the movement and handling of grain much more efficient. These systems are usually designed for 50,000 to 100,000 bushels and up, (more in the agricultural Midwest), hence size of farm—the acres of corn and soybeans raised—must be in balance.

The concrete silo versus the Harvestore is a decision about which many farmers and farm managers are highly prejudiced. On many farms today two or three concrete silos or Harvestores have led to sizeable increases in volume and sizeable increases in income. Outstanding illustrations are not difficult to find. However, these investments have been made primarily to increase the efficiency of the farming operations rather than the market value of the farms. Their costs are only partially reflected in the value of the farm real estate. This is because their use is largely related to the farm families and their desires rather than to the value of the physical assets. Hence, the market value of the concrete silo declines rapidly. The market value of the Harvestore does likewise, although much less so, primarily because it can be moved. In most areas, the value of the Harvestore tends to eventually level out at (or decline to a figure no less than) one-third of its replacement cost new. Again, this is because the Harvestore can be moved. This value is typically equal to one-half to two-thirds of the structure's historical cost depending, of course, on when it was purchased and the inflation that has since occurred.

The double-5 herringbone milking parlor is a fixed resource with little if any flexibility. It has little or no alternative use in the future other than to perhaps store junk. However, the present operator may build a substantial building and include in it considerable companion equipment of a permanent nature. Most appraisers would do likewise if they were to spend six hours a day, 365 days a year there. However, this milking parlor adds little to the value of the farm unless perhaps the present farm operator remains on that farm, and/or unless that farm is a typical dairy farm—rough and rolling and with a major portion of the cropland in hay and pasture.

The confinement slotted-floor farrow-through-finish hog house (note: the word "house" being used rather than "barn") is an even more difficult building to value. In many areas, the majority of hogs are raised in small groups, on pasture, and in portable, open-front buildings. The costs of production are about the same whether the hogs are produced on pasture, in conventional facilities, or in these specialized confinement houses. The cost of labor is higher on pasture. The building and equipment costs are higher with the specialized facilities. The two tend to offset one another. The specialized buildings reduce the labor and increase the efficiency of the farming operations. However, for every dollar of cost, they add only $0.40 to $0.50 to the value of the farm real estate.

Most farm buildings are built to increase volume and farming efficiency. The decision to build a new farm building does not always recognize or include the fact that that building will not add an equal number of dollars to the market value of the real estate. The specialized farm buildings are good illustrations. Sizeable investments have been made in many of the new technologies by those farmers who have had the managerial expertise to make them work. In fact, these investments have sometimes exceeded the original investments in the farm. However, in many instances, they have paid off rather well in terms of increased income to the farm family.

The traditional farm manager-appraiser has not always recognized the role of farm buildings in modern present-day agriculture. The high prices placed on unimproved land, the surplus of leftover obsolete buildings in many areas, and the more recent and sometimes large investments in new technology have led to considerable confusion in the appraisal profession as to how to value farm buildings.

Many an appraiser merely estimates the subject property's present market value. However, the building values included in his report are often used at some later date for other purposes. It is for this reason that each of the various farm building values—present-day replacement cost, structural value, contributory value, and value-in-use should probably appear in any and all farm appraisal reports.

REFERENCES

Allison, N. F., "Fundamental Appraisal Thinking," *Appraisal Journal,* Vol. 32, No. 4, October 1964.

Bailey, R. R., "Valuation of Barns," *Journal of American Society of Farm Managers and Rural Appraisers,* Vol. 1, No. 2, October 1937.

Cherney, R. A., "The Problem of Depreciation," *Appraisal Journal,* Vol. 32, No. 1, January 1964.

Considine, C. R., and J. D. O'Bryan, "Income Tax Pitfalls in Appraising,

Part I," *Appraisal Journal,* Vol. 22, No. 2, April 1954.

Derbes, M. J., Jr., "Accrued Depreciation—Classical Method," *The Real Estate Appraiser,"* Vol. 31, No. 8, August 1965.

Farm Loss Adjustment Manual, National Association of Mutual Insurance Companies, 1958.

Forsberg, Winfield, "The Impact of Technological Changes on Farm Building Values," paper presented to Minnesota Farm Managers and Rural Appraisers, February 1969.

Free, V. J., "The Theory of Depreciation," *Appraisal Journal,* Vol. 26, No. 4, October 1958.

Hansen, E. L., "Farm Building Appraisal," V.A.S. 3017, University of Illinois (about 1964).

Justus, F. E., Jr., "Problems and Procedures in Farm Building Appraisals," *Mutual Insurance Bulletin,* October 1962.

Knowles, Jerome, Jr., "Estimating Accrued Depreciation," *Appraisal Journal,* Vol. 35, No. 1, January 1967.

Lundy, V. R., "The Why of Depreciation," *Appraisal Journal,* Vol. 33, No. 1, January 1965.

Pope, L. H., "Depreciation in the Cost Approach," *The Real Estate Appraiser,* Vol. 30, No. 6, June 1964.

Roche, J. K., "The Assessor's View of Depreciation," *Appraisal Journal,* Vol. 35, No. 2, April 1967.

Shenkel, W. M., "The Depreciation Estimate: A Reconsideration," *The Real Estate Appraiser,* Vol. 34, No. 5, July-August 1968.

Sommerfield, H. B., "Types, Rates, and Methods of Depreciation of Farm Buildings," *Journal of American Society of Farm Managers and Rural Appraisers,* Vol. 3, No. 1, April 1939.

Trowbridge, C. R., "Deterioration," *Appraisal Journal,* Vol. 32, No. 1, January 1964.

Trowbridge, C. R., "The Fallacies of Depreciation," *The Real Estate Appraiser,* Vol. 31, No. 12, December 1965.

CHAPTER X

Appraisals for Property Insurance

Property insurance is one of the nation's oldest and largest economic institutions. The first insurance company was founded in 1752, not quite a quarter of a century before the signing of the Declaration of Independence. It was the Philadelphia Contributorship for the Insurance of Houses from Loss by Fire. The City of Philadelphia had 2,075 dwellings at that time.[1] Today, much of the country's wealth is still subject to the uncertainty of a loss through fire, windstorm, or other peril.

THE PURPOSE AND NATURE OF INSURANCE

The basic purpose of all property insurance is to transfer the uncertainty of a large financial loss from the individual property owner to the large company or organization willing to assume such risks.[2] The property owner, or insured, agrees to pay a small-known loss—the fee, or the premium—in return for the opportunity of transferring the larger uncertainty to the insurance company. The insurance company, or insurer, agrees to indemnify the insured against any actual loss that may occur as a direct result of fire, windstorm, or other peril, as so stated in the contract, or insurance policy.

Insurance is a somewhat modern or more sophisticated refinement of the age-old custom of passing the hat to relieve distress. The funda-

---

1. Benjamin Franklin was one of the founders, pp. 21 and 41, *Biography of an Idea.*

2. Uncertainty and risk are not the same thing. Uncertainty is a highly subjective phenomenon consisting of chance elements so subject to sporadic change that any one single event seldom if ever repeats itself, at least not often enough to establish a pattern. However, risk is a phenomenon which has been reduced to a quantitative calculable probability. Due to the availability of a number of observations, the probability of a given outcome or loss can be established. The essence of any formal insurance scheme is that an uncertainty to one person or party may exist merely as a risk to some other person or party. The uncertainty of a possible loss by an individual property owner is thus assumed as a risk by an insurance company which insures a large number of properties on a probability basis.

mental principle is that many property owners contribute small amounts of money, thus setting up a common fund out of which any and all losses are paid. The insurance company's role is one of collecting premiums from the many whose property, generally speaking, is not destroyed and indemnifying the unfortunate few who do happen to have losses. To do so, the company depends on the law of large numbers. The cost is thus spread among the whole community, and no one property owner is heavily burdened.

The insurance concept is often misunderstood. Many persons think that the only way to win is to have a loss; and that if no loss occurs, then the insurer has won. In reality nobody wins. The property owner has merely traded the uncertainty of a large loss for the certainty of a small cost, the premium. The existence of the insurance policy merely guarantees that the property owner's financial position will not be substantially impaired should a property loss occur. It does not, and should not, improve the property owner's financial position.

The Policy or Contract: An insurance policy is a legal contract, unique perhaps, in that it deals with a single commodity—money. In order to be valid, an insurance contract is based on the same common law principles that apply to any other legal contract. The agreement has to comply with certain legal requirements and have for its purpose a legal object. In addition, an insurance contract must have an insurable interest as well as a valuable consideration. It must be made with a full and complete knowledge of the material facts, and such must be free from error, misunderstanding, and fraud.

The standard fire policy sets out in detail the obligations of both the property owner, or the insured, and the insurance company, or the insurer. The main provisions typically include the following items:

1. The parties involved, both insured and insurer.

2. The terms of the contract, including both renewal and cancellation provisions.

3. A physical description of the property, which today may include pictures of all buildings.

4. The general nature of the risks insured, and/or the extent of the liabilities assumed.

5. The amount of coverage, or insurance purchased, which is the face value of the policy, and, hopefully, the total exposure, or total value, of the property exposed (however, not always).

6. The consideration, or premium.

7. Numerous other promissory provisions and/or restrictions related to (a) the event(s) insured against, (b) the performance or

non-performance of certain acts, and (c) the presentation of proof of loss, etc.

These latter provisions, commonly referred to as "the fine print," are aimed at governing the conduct of the insured, who is responsible for safeguarding the property as well as protecting the company against the possibility of paying claims for unnecessary or dishonest losses.

The standard fire company may write many kinds of insurance: fire, fire and wind, fire and other peril, fire and allied lines, dwelling and contents, builder risk, farm, home, and extended coverage, personal property floater, and others. In the past, each peril has often been written as a separate policy; for example, fire and wind on buildings; fire on equipment, stored grain, and machinery; fire and casualty on livestock; liability; and fire and collision on truck and auto, etc.

However, today the insurance companies are packaging many various coverages into one policy. The intent of the package policy is to give one broad coverage. However, it is the responsibility of the property owner, or the insured, to determine the amount of coverage he needs or should have, and also to discern if his operation has some special needs not included in the standard package policy. Particular attention should be given to farm buildings; for a building which cost $8,000 to build several years ago may cost $15,000 to replace today. The farm property owner in particular needs to constantly review his coverage.

Farm building values based on the costs of new construction should be kept up-to-date. The major items of machinery and equipment should be inventoried as well as the numbers of each class of livestock. Special values should be noted. For example, many policies have a per-head limit on each class of livestock; this means that purebred livestock should be scheduled separately. Grain, hay, and feed coverage is difficult to keep updated. Many policies will cover losses only to the extent such items and amounts are declared ahead of time. All values are the responsibility of the property owner. While costs are involved, any additional premium expense is usually justified, particularly in the event of a loss.

A fire policy is essentially a personal contract. It does not insure the property per se. It insures the person or persons who either own or have an insurable interest therein.[3] The contract thus requests, in fact requires, good faith on the part of each party. Each is obligated to reveal to the other all known facts material to the contract. The insured especially is directed to answer fully any and all questions asked of him and without misrepresentation. He cannot intentionally conceal or withhold material facts from the insurer, either in negotiating the contract or in filing a claim. This is a major difference between an insurance contract, in which money is the sole commodity involved, and other contracts, in which both the buyer and seller have the opportunity to examine or inspect the item being transferred or conveyed.

THE INDEMNITY PRINCIPLE OR PHILOSOPHY

The purpose of insurance is to indemnify the property owner, but only for the destruction of any material values at the time of the loss and only for the actual loss or losses involved.[4] The objective is to restore the property owner to the same financial position which he enjoyed prior to the loss. This is the fundamental indemnity principle, and such is basic to all insurance underwriting.

The purpose is not to allow the insured to make a profit or even to provide him with the opportunity. The insured is not to be compensated to the extent that he improves his financial position. This is contrary to the indemnity principle or philosophy.

Insurance companies make every effort to insure on the basis of indemnifying policyholders only for any actual losses that occur. They attempt to avoid insuring property for more than it is worth. They tend to limit their liability to the property's actual cash value at the time the loss occurs. This latter provision is included in all standard policies, and is usually effective even though the face value of the policy is for a larger amount.[5]

The facts (1) that an insurance contract deals only with money and (2) that such is really a personal contract lead to some rather unique stipulations and valuation problems. Farm building inspectors, insurance adjustors, and farm appraisers are all involved.

1. The person insured must have an insurable interest in the property. It must be of a pecuniary nature in that occurrence of the event insured against would lead to or cause a financial loss to the

---

3. Policy assignment is not automatic. A policy does not typically follow the property, when or if a given property is sold, unless written consent is obtained from the insurance company. Otherwise a given property could be conveyed from a careful or honest owner to a careless and dishonest one with the insurance contract remaining effective. Policy assignment, or the lack of such, is based on the principle that all persons or parties have the right to choose with whom they will deal and that no one should be forced into a contract with any other person or party against his will.

4. To indemnify is to replace, repair, pay for, or to make good a loss only.

5. Unless, of course, the policy expressly provides to the contrary.

insured.[6] Insurable interest need not necessarily be ownership. In fact, more than one party often has an insurable interest. For example, a mortgagee, or lender, may be involved as well as the mortgagor, or property owner. A mortgagee has an insurable interest, by definition, in that destruction of the property would cause him a financial loss.[7]

In these instances, the insurance companies typically insert a mortgagee clause in their policies. This clause essentially joins the interests of the two parties—mortgagee and mortgagor—thus protecting the mortgagee whenever a property is encumbered, by designating that any loss is to be paid to both parties. The clause eliminates the need for having two policies. It eliminates the complications of double coverage and double premiums. It reduces supervision and, to some extent, the possibility of fraud.

2. Only accidental or fortuitous losses are insurable. Losses which are within or under the control of the insured are not insurable. The possibility of destruction or disaster occurring at the will of the insured is known as the moral hazard.

The standard fire policy contemplates indemnity, but only for losses arising from a hostile or malicious fire as contrasted to a friendly fire. No right of recovery arises so long as a fire is contained within its proper receptacle, for the fire is then said to have "remained friendly." But once that fire passes outside the limits assigned to it, in other words becomes uncontrollable, it becomes a hostile fire.

The concept of causation is very important. A loss, in order to be established, has to be sustained not only by the particular property or thing insured, it also has to be a direct and immediate, or proximate consequence of the peril, accident, or act insured against. The standard fire policy agrees to pay the insured for a financial loss, but only a loss due to the direct damage of physical property. The standard policy does not agree to pay for any indirect or consequential damage—for example, a loss arising out of the loss of the use of the property.[8]

The standard policy further promises to indemnify the insured only when there is compliance by him with regard to certain stipulated conditions both preceding and subsequent to the contract springing

---

6. If a person has no insurable interest in a property there can be no loss to him; hence there is no reason for indemnity. Insurance policies are contracts for indemnity and not for profit.

7. Destruction of the property does not cancel the mortgagor's financial obligation.

8. However, there may be an express provision in the policy stating otherwise—a provision that insures the property owner against such items as business interruption, living expenses, etc.

into life. Otherwise the contract cannot be consumated; or, it cannot remain in full force. In the event of a loss, the property owner must give immediate written notice to the company. It is now the insured's responsibility to furnish a complete inventory of the property, both damaged and undamaged, and show in detail all quantities, costs, and actual cash values as well as the total amount of any and all losses that are claimed. And, he is further obligated to protect the property from future damage.

3. The human element and its many idiosyncrasies cannot be overemphasized. There is perhaps no other legal contract in which one party (the insurer) is so absolutely at the mercy of the other (the insured) as in insurance. There is no other business which offers such an out-and-out temptation for gain to be achieved, in unethical fashion, as does insurance.

The great majority of policyholders are honest. The large majority of fires are accidental. However, a combination of financial difficulty and moral weakness occasionally leads to a situation in which the in-

Courtesy, U.S.D.A.

sured may deliberately bring about the event insured against. Fires have been set. The moral hazard is difficult to detect and distasteful to discuss. But it's there.

A related and even more difficult area is the lack of good house-keeping—the lack of any desire to look after or safeguard a given property. The insured, who finds himself operating an unsuccessful business, financially speaking, may not actually set fire to his property; but, he may, at the same time, either by design or carelessness, do little to prevent a fire from occurring. And, once a fire starts, he may do little to prevent it from spreading.

Very few policyholders are guilty of incendiarism. However, they are not averse to letting the size of a loss increase once a fire has started. Neither are they averse to occasionally presenting an exaggerated claim afterwards. Thus, many clauses in the standard fire policy relate to concealment, to misrepresentation, and to fraud.

ACTUAL CASH VALUE AND INSURED VALUE

Insurance appraisals present several unique problems.

1. Only buildings and improvements are insured. There is no total farm appraisal. Yet the values placed on the buildings should be in balance with the rest of the farm's resources.

2. Many farm buildings are leftover buildings, obsolete, and empty. Yet they are still insured. Others are specialized and include fixtures and equipment both new and costly. In either case costs and values are difficult to relate.

3. Many estimates as to value are made after a building burns down or after a loss has occurred. The physical condition of the building, as it was before the fire, has to be estimated by examining the remains. Blueprints, pictures, inventories, and prior appraisals taken or made by the company or by the insured are, or course, guides.

The property owner, or policyholder, is the person responsible for determining property values along with the amount of property coverage, or amount of insurance, in force. Many owners are not aware of this, nor the fact that in the event of a loss, it is also their responsibility to provide both building specifications and costs, an inventory of all fixtures, equipment, and personal property, and all dollar values. Many insurance agents assist the property owner, or policy-holder, in determining some of these property values; however, they do so merely as a service and not because of any legal obligation.

It is the insured's responsibility to decide how much insurance he should carry.[9] If he doesn't carry enough insurance, he runs the risk of being underinsured (in the case of a total loss).[10] During periods of rising farm building costs, insurance companies have to continue to point out to policyholders the need to frequently re-examine the face amounts of their policies in relation to current farm building values. If the insured is to be adequately reimbursed, the liability, or amount the insurance company is obligated to pay, should be sufficient to cover any reasonable loss that may be expected.

In most policies, the limit is the building's replacement cost, its actual cash value, or its insured value, the face amount of the policy. The latter figure may be below the total exposure or total property value.

What values are needed for insurance purposes? Most companies refer to reproduction cost, replacement cost, actual cash value, insured value, and the face amount of the policy. A utility value figure is also used with certain reservations. With the exception of actual cash value, these costs, or values, often bear little or no relation to the extent to which the buildings contribute to the market value of the farm. With the exception of utility value they bear little or no relation to the extent to which the buildings contribute to the efficiency of the farming operation.

Reproduction and Replacement Cost: In the appraisal of farm buildings today, the farm building valuator usually starts with the question of replacement. Will this building be replaced? This is the No. 1 question. At the same time, the insurance inspector and adjuster is interested in both reproduction and replacement costs. As was pointed out in the previous chapter . . .

1. Reproduction cost refers to the cost of rebuilding a building or improvement as it was built originally using the same identical design or pattern and the same materials and workmanship.

2. Replacement cost refers to the cost of replacing that building or improvement with its more modern version, hopefully, a building or improvement that is equally desirable, and one which has the same or a similar utility value.

The two cost concepts are not the same and should not be confused.

---

9. Only a small number of farm buildings are ever appraised for insurance purposes. However, the farmer-businessman may occasionally request an appraisal in order to be sure his coverage is sufficient to cover any losses that might occur. In doing so, he usually obtains a contractor's estimate of the cost of replacing each building.

10. Vice versa, if the property owner carries too much insurance he is paying more premium than necessary.

Yet insurance agents often do just that. This is because the insurance inspector or adjustor is primarily concerned with both cost concepts.

In the case of a partial loss, a company is generally obligated to pay for the repair and restoration of whatever was destroyed, or in other words, reproduce that part of the building or structure. The house may be old and the gingerbread no longer in style. If only part of the roof, part of the eave trough, and part of the gingerbread is destroyed, the problem is then to repair such so that it looks like the original. Reproduction cost is now the basis.

In the case of a complete loss, where a building or improvement is totally destroyed, that building or improvement can now be replaced with its more modern counterpart. Replacement cost now becomes the basis.

In any event, the reproduction and replacement concepts require considerable judgment on the part of a farm appraiser with regard to the questions "Will this building be repaired or replaced?" and "If so, with what, how and when?"

The standard fire policy typically covers the insured to the extent of the actual cash value of the property at the time of the loss. However, that amount is not to exceed the amount which it would cost to repair or replace the property with material of like kind and quality, and within a reasonable period of time.[11] Thus, reproduction and/or replacement cost have the tendency to establish the upper limit as far as insured values or the indemnification of a property owner is concerned.

Actual Cash Value: The standard fire policy usually refers to the actual cash value of the property. The normal procedure usually given for determining this value is to ascertain the "reproduction or replacement value," then deduct a fair amount for wear and tear, depreciation from age or from use, and for obsolescence resulting from technical progress or changes in style. These factors obviously reduce the value of any given building below its reproduction or replacement cost.

Most standard fire policies infer that actual cash value is that amount which the buildings contribute to the market value of the farm. However, seldom do the policies say that in so many words. Some policies say, that in order to determine the insured's loss, it is necessary to ascertain the value of the property at the time the loss occurred, along with the amount by which the value of the property has been lessened by the occurrence insured against. This infers that any loss should be

11. And also without allowance for the increased cost of repair or reconstruction by reason of any ordinance or law regulating such construction or repair and, usually, also without compensation for any loss resulting from business interruption.

based on the market value of the property immediately before minus the market value of the property immediately after the loss. Or, that the values to be ascertained are contributory values—dollars amounts representing the extent to which the buildings contribute to the present market value of the farm.

This contributory or exchange value concept is a difficult one. Seldom are buildings or improvements marketed or sold by themselves. Generally speaking, comparable sales are non-existent. And again, the problem is further complicated by the fact that the cost of a new building or improvement seldom adds an equal amount to the market value of the property.

Utility Value: Today there is more and more of a tendency to place the property owner back in the same financial position that he enjoyed before a loss. The desire to indemnify or to make good a financial loss leads one to the utility value concept. A building or improvement's utility value is based on the extent to which that building or improvement is useful to the present business or in the current farming operations. It is a building's or improvement's use value to the present owner or operator. It depends not on age but on use. Hence, it may or may not bear any particular relationship to the building's or improvement's contributory value.

Utility value is actually closer to the indemnity philosophy which says that if a loss occurs and if the building is built back, then the property owner should be reimbursed for that loss. Hence, farm buildings, for insurance purposes, have value in two respects: (1) their contribution to the market value of the farm and (2) their usefulness in the farming operations.

Insured Value: Insurance companies seldom insure farm buildings or improvements to their full value. First, there are certain exclusions or non-burnables. The typical ones include the concrete footings, the foundation, any piers or other supports, all pipes, drains, and wiring which are below the surface of the ground or inside the basement floor or foundation walls.

Most companies suggest that insured values approximate 80 percent of either full replacement cost or actual cash value (replacement value less depreciation). In the case of new buildings, insured values should equal 80 percent of replacement cost. In the case of older buildings, insured values should be 80 percent of actual cash values. The 80-percent figure supposedly encourages a property owner with a 20-percent equity to help put a fire out.

Insured values typically equal utility values. They may be limited

to 80 percent of a building's replacement value. However, there is a tendency to also make insured (and/or utility) value equal to replacement cost. Many policies contain provisions obligating the company to a replacement value level, actually a utility value, instead of an actual cash value. When this is the case, an additional provision, called the deferred payment provision, is usually used.

This provision is used whenever a building is insured to the level of its full replacement cost and/or whenever the building's insured value exceeds its actual cash or contributory value. The provision works as follows: The insurer agrees to pay only a portion, for example, 60 percent, of the insured value at the time of the loss. The remaining payment—40 percent in this case—is then paid if and when the building is actually rebuilt or replaced. Certain other restrictions may also be added: (1) the building must be rebuilt within one year and (2) within so many hundred feet of the original location of the structure.

Hence, utility and insured values may be above contributory or actual cash values. There is no problem. When this occurs, the appraiser is merely saying that this building is of considerable use in the present farming operations and to the present operator, and that in the event of loss, the building will undoubtedly be rebuilt. Hence, the insured should be indemnified for as much value as possible. The appraiser is also saying that the present property owner or operator is honest and that there is no particular moral hazard.

Whenever a building's insured value exceeds its contributory value by a sizeable amount, the deferred payment provision is a must. In the event of a loss, the provision reduces the insurance company's obligation unless or until the building is rebuilt. It reduces the extreme amount of judgment or responsibility placed on the insurance agent or the farm building appraiser.

The Face Amount of the Policy: While it is the property owner's responsibility to place a value on all buildings, the insurance companies often check these values and make their own recommendations. They do so in order to avoid overinsuring property. On the other hand, a property owner may also decide to keep the face amount of his policy below the company's suggested coverage. He may do so in order to reduce the cost of his insurance. This owner supposedly recognizes and is willing to accept some risk. He thus carries a fraction, for example, maybe only half, of the insurance he may need in the case of a total loss. He assumes or hopes that the face amount of his policy will be sufficient to cover any partial loss which may occur. He thus pays less premium, both in total and in proportion to all other property owners. This leads to one of the really tough problems in insuring farm buildings.

THE PROBLEM OF EQUITABILITY AND INSURANCE RATES

The overwhelming majority of fire, windstorm, and other losses are partial losses. Only a few are total losses. Many property owners experiencing a loss experience only a partial loss. Only a few experiencing a loss experience a total loss. In other words, there is a skewed distribution of property losses (Figure 21).

This may explain why some property owners willingly keep the face amount of their policies below their company's recommended coverage. They assume or hope that if a loss occurs, such will not wipe out all of their farm buildings, but will instead be a partial loss. However, when a property owner refuses to insure no more than to the level of some fraction of his company's recommended coverage, he is actually refusing to pay his fair share of the costs of insurance.[12]

The problem is that any loss to any part of the property obligates the insurance company to pay. It is not a part of, but the entire property which is exposed. The total exposure is the total value of all the buildings and whether the amount of coverage equals this total value or some fraction thereof.

The coverage could represent, of course, the particular part or fraction of the property exposed. Such coverage would have to be specifically assigned. If this were to be done, the company would then be liable for a loss only if the part or fraction that happened to be insured burned. This is not realistic.

The age-old problem is one of all policyholders sharing the operating expenses as well as the losses on an equitable basis. The burden of cost cannot be distributed accurately. Neither can insurance rates be fixed justly unless the relationship between coverage and the total property values is the same as the relationship between losses and total exposure. Algebraically . . .

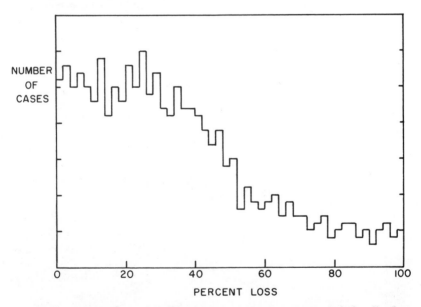

Figure 21. A Theoretical Skewed Distribution of Property Losses Relating Number of Losses to Percent of Loss.

12. Other property owners, being either naive or more willing to pay their share and perhaps also less willing to accept the risk of a total loss, insure their property to something near its full value. These property owners pay a larger share of the total costs than those willing to gamble.

$$\frac{\text{Coverage}}{\text{Total Property Values}} \text{ should equal } \frac{\text{Losses}}{\text{Total Exposure}}$$

Occasionally an insurance company will admit that it has no way of knowing the total value of all property it has insured. This is indeed unfortunate, for unless it knows the relationship between the amount of insurance written and the company's total exposure, it has no way of determining, on an equitable basis, its insurance rates.

Most insurance companies as well as their policyholders think that if they were obligated to determine the total value of all property in advance, such an obligation would greatly increase their insurance costs. Even though there are some practical difficulties involved, this is not necessarily true. If a knowledge of all total property values were ascertained, insurance rates could be more equitable, losses would be easy to estimate, and claims would probably be more accurate.

Thus, there is little or no substitute for a knowledge of the total value of all property, or the total exposure. Most insurance companies

Courtesy, J. C. Allen

are working towards such today, requiring more information—building specifications and costs—and upon occasion, detailed farm building appraisals.

Insurance Rates: The insurance rate is the premium, or price, paid per unit of insurance purchased. It is usually expressed as a given amount per $1,000 of coverage. Over a period of time the rate level must, of course, produce an income sufficient to (1) meet all of the company's operating expenses and (2) pay all losses.

One of the earliest and simplest systems of establishing insurance rates is still used occasionally by some of the small farm mutual insurance companies. These companies do not collect premiums in advance but instead operate on a post-assessment basis. They borrow from a local bank to pay their losses as they occur during the year. At the end of each fiscal year the company then adds up its operating expenses, along with all of its losses, and then prorates such among all policyholders.[13] All policyholders are then assessed an amount of money sufficient to repay the bank loan, the interest, and the company's operating expenses. Rate computation is a simple matter of arithmetic, and a very accurate rate can be established through this retroactive system. The technique is referred to as the post-assessment method of operation.

Down through the years property owners have become more adverse to risking the amount of loss—the cost or the premium—which they might have to contribute on a *postfacto* basis (after the losses have occurred). Hence, most insurance is now handled with the property owner paying his premiums in advance. The insurance company estimates as accurately as possible what its expenses and losses will probably be. The insurance premiums are then collected at the "beginning" of each year.

In the beginning years, and during those years with below-normal losses, a company can build cash reserves, which will hopefully handle any catastrophic loss which cannot be predicted as to occurrence or severity, and yet which may occur in the future. In subsequent years, a company may underestimate its losses; or it may collect insufficient premium monies. This company then makes up the deficit out of its surplus. In subsequent years, a company may also overestimate its losses; it may make a profit on the year's transactions. This, the company then adds to its reserves.

The development of an insurance rate structure is a complicated

13. The costs are typically prorated on the basis of the total amount of insurance carried. However, the allocation should be based on total property value.

task. In general, rates are varied according to (1) type of construction, (2) occupancy or use, (3) exposure to risk (nearby buildings or nuisances), (4) type of available fire protection, (5) geographic location, and (6) historical loss ratios. Most states have rating bureaus which specialize in this activity. Experienced engineers and underwriters classify and promulgate the various rates, usually on the basis of inspections of risks made and statistical data compiled by the bureau.

Some companies have adopted graduated rate structures in order to alleviate somewhat the equitability problem. Where a property owner prefers to remain underinsured, the companies essentially raise his premium rate based on the amount of insurance he wants to carry and then pay all losses in full. This gives the property owner the advantage of choosing any amount of insurance he desires. At the same time his costs are increased to the extent that he pays his fair share of the total burden. Most companies won't admit to such practice. They instead say their rates vary with the kind of coverage.

Lastly, the ratio between actual and recommended coverage may be applied. When this occurs, a company's rate structure is related to both coverage and loss experience.

CO-INSURANCE AND VALUED POLICIES

The insurance companies who know the total value of each insured property as well as its coverage have solved the equitability problem in a different fashion. They use a co-insurance clause.

Co-insurance: The insured is free to buy as much or as little insurance as he desires or thinks necessary, whatever the amount may be. However, in the event of a loss he then recovers from the company only an amount proportionate to that for which he willingly insured his property.

The purpose of co-insurance is to encourage property owners to increase their coverages and to insure their properties to uniform levels, by getting and keeping coverages in a constant relationship to total property values. In each case the insurance company designates or recommends the amount of insurance which it feels all property owners should carry. This is typically a percentage. The insured is still free to purchase any amount less than that. However, in the event of a loss, the claim paid is based on the amount of coverage accepted relative to the amount recommended.

Let's illustrate. The present-day value of a set of farm buildings is

$120,000. The insurer recommends 80-percent coverage; however, the insured decides that that's too much and that $72,000 is sufficient. (The insured perhaps realizes that in the event of a loss only one or two of the buildings at the most will burn or blow away, and that $72,000 will cover any loss he may have.)

Later the farrowing barn is struck by lightning and there is a $24,000 loss. How much is the insurance company obligated to pay?

Total Value All Property	$120,000
Suggested Coverage (80%)	96,000
Insurance Purchased (¾ of that recommended)	72,000
Loss	24,000
Amount the Company Pays (¾ of the loss)	$ 18,000

The company pays only $18,000. This figure is based on the ratio between the amount of insurance purchased and the amount recommended. In other words, the company considers itself liable for only that portion of any loss represented by the portion that the actual insurance coverage bears to the suggested or recommended coverage. In the above case this ratio was 75 percent.[14]

The use of a co-insurance clause leads to a more equitable relationship between property owners. It enables a company to collect premiums from all owners commensurate with the risks assumed—their total exposure. By indemnifying owners for losses, but only in proportion to the insurance purchased relative to that recommended, the co-insurance clause keeps insurance rates related to the company's total exposure and regardless of the amount of insurance purchased by the property owner. Such is a straightforward and honest method of achieving equitability among property owners.

However, persons who don't understand the concept of equitability often argue that when one buys any other commodity he is not told that he must purchase a certain amount. These persons contend that there is no reason why those persons who purchase insurance should not be free to purchase whatever amount they desire. Provided they are willing to pay the price, all their losses should then be paid in full up to the face amount of the policy.[15] Co-insurance, along with certain

14. In the event that the house and barn had both burned and the total loss would have exceeded the coverage purchased, the law in most states would then have generally required the company to pay the full amount (in this case $72,000).

compulsory features to purchase a given amount of insurance, has thus aroused considerable antagonism on the part of both property owners and state legislators.

The Valued Policy: A few states have passed what is known as valued policy laws. These laws specify that, in cases where the property insured is totally destroyed, the company is liable (in the absence of any increased risk without the consent of the insurer, and in the absence of any intentional fraud upon the party of the insured) for the total amount mentioned in the policy. In other words, the insurance company is obligated to pay the full amount of the policy regardless of the actual cash value of the property, and regardless of the total exposure or risk. If the face value of the policy is greater than the actual cash value of the property, the insured can thus recover more than the property is worth, and he profits by the loss.

These laws were passed by legislators who felt that insurance companies tend to sell insurance far in excess of total property values and then refuse to pay the full amount in case of a loss. In reality, there appears to be but little tendency for insurance companies to do this, particularly during the last 20 years or so during which building construction costs have risen rapidly. The real problem is instead to persuade property owners to buy an amount of insurance sufficient to cover the actual and total value of their properties.

Valued policies are undesirable. They ignore the indemnity principle or philosophy. They furnish a motive for fraud, can result in the payment of a dishonest claim, and are disadvantageous to the honest contributors, or property owners. They have proven to be expensive to the property owners in those states where valued policy laws have been enacted.

Much insurance is bought by habit. The typical comment of the insured is, "Oh, about the same as before." Most owners, when they pay their premiums, express the attitude that that building is not worth much. However, when it burns or blows away its value suddenly increases.

Agricultural technology, the increased costs of new construction, farm consolidation, and leftover and obsolete farm buildings have led to many problems for rural insurance companies. While construction costs have increased, insured values have lagged behind. Many a

---

15. These persons have never studied the equitability concept to the extent that they have acquired real understanding of such.

This old farm house is empty. If it were to burn, blow away, or be otherwise destroyed, would it be replaced? Probably not!

farmer, forced to replace a farm home, a barn, or other building, has found the amount of his insurance insufficient.

Many farm buildings are, at the same time, obsolete. They are no longer used, except perhaps to store junk. The insurance carried on these farm buildings should be reduced or cancelled. Yet insured values are used not only in determining losses but also in determining insurance rates. To reduce or cancel the insurance on very many farm buildings, old or obsolete or not, can quite conceivably lead to increased insurance rates, and particularly in those areas of declining agricultural activity.[16] Thus, the rural insurance company has been caught in a dilemma.

In property insurance, the determination of value is the obligation

---

16. Insurance companies have not only continued to insure old and obsolete farm buildings but, in some instances, have raised the insured values on these buildings. They have done this to avoid raising insurance rates.

of the property owner. It always has been and should remain his responsibility. However, the burden is also on the insurer to examine all properties and to determine his total exposure. There is no substitute for a knowledge of the total of all farm property values.

Compared to his colleagues in the farm appraisal field, the insurance man spends considerable time and effort on farm building valuation. He rationalizes his position by saying that there is a large number of buildings involved. Yet, with property values continuing to rise and with insurance rates continuing to increase, there will be a continued need to understand the theory of value and to use some of the more sophisticated appraisal techniques in the insuring of farm buildings and improvements in the future.

REFERENCES

Atkinson, J. H., and K. R. Krause, "Your Changing Farm Property Insurance Customer," Purdue University Cooperative Extension Service, EC-268, April 1963.

Bainbridge, John, *Biography of an Idea: The Story of Mutual Fire and Casualty Insurance*, Doubleday, 1952.

Botts, R. R., and R. C. Otte, "Insurance Against Losses on Farms," *The 1958 Yearbook of Agriculture*, U.S.D.A., 1958.

Hanson, H. W., *Hanson's Insurance Reference Guide and Manual of Examination*, Revised Edition, Illinois Insurance License Bureau, 1964.

Huebner, S. S., and Kenneth Black, Jr., *Property Insurance*, 4th Edition, Appleton-Century-Crofts, Inc., 1957.

Jones, L. A., "The Farmowner's Insurance Package," *Agricultural Finance Review*, Vol. 28, E.R.S., U.S.D.A., November 1967.

Keast, J. D., "Your Insurance Coverage," *Doane's*, October 1970.

Keefe, Richard, "Who Needs an Inspection Program?," *Mutual Insurance Bulletin*, June 1971.

Keeton, R. E., *Basic Text on Insurance Law*, West, 1971.

Krausz, N. G. P., "Property, Liability, and Medical Insurance for Farmers," Illinois Agr. Ext. Serv. Cir. 832, April 1961.

Magee, J. H., *Property Insurance*, 3rd Edition, Irwin, 1955.

Mehr, R. I., and Emerson Cammack, *Principles of Insurance*, 4th Edition, Irwin, 1966.

Perthou, A. V., *The Cost Approach to Appraisals for Property Insurance*, Prentice-Hall, 1963.

Purdon, John, "Appraisal for Insurance Purposes," *Encyclopedia of Real Estate Appraising*, Prentice-Hall, 1959.

Robbins, D. L., "Appraising Hurricane and Other Catastrophe Losses," *The Real Estate Appraiser*, Vol. 28, No. 7, July 1962.

Rodda, W. H., *Fire and Property Insurance*, Prentice-Hall, 1956.

Rodman, J. E., "Real Estate Appraisals Versus Insurance Appraisals," *The Real Estate Appraiser*, Vol. 35, No. 1, January-February 1969.

Smith, R. S., "Check Your Fire Insurance Policy," *Hoard's Dairyman*.

CHAPTER XI

Ad Valorem Tax Appraisals

The general property tax supplies the major portion of revenue to all local and county governments. It is the chief means of financing many government services—schools, roads, utilities, police and fire departments, public health centers, parks, recreational facilities, libraries, courts of law, and others. The property owner is the direct beneficiary. However, twice a year, whenever he receives his tax bills, he usually loudly complains. What's worse, every now and then he is mailed a notice of reassessment or reappraisal.

All property owners own or have certain property rights. Yet this ownership and these rights are subordinate to certain government rights, one of which is the power to tax. The tax on wealth is the oldest system of government finance in the history of mankind.[1] It is an ad valorem tax—a tax based on the value of each person's property.

The property tax is essentially a local tax.[2] Thus each local assessing agency has to *determine* (not the author's word) the value of all taxable property. Each local assessor has to establish an assessed valuation on each parcel of taxable property located within the district. This is the basis on which the property tax is levied. The tax is supposed to be distributed equitably, or according to the worth of the property owned by each property owner so that each taxpayer bears his fair share of the levy. By using market values, the inequalities in valuation

1. The Greeks and the Romans employed a form of property taxation for the raising of public funds as early as 600 B.C. One of the first assessment rolls was know as the census and was prepared by the Romans. The list included land, farming implements, carriages, garments, and money.

A biblical version of a property tax is also found in Luke 2:1 "And it came to pass in those days, that there went out a decree from Ceasar Augustus, that all the world should be taxed."

2. In most states a state commission is responsible for the supervision of the ad valorem tax system—for the legal framework, the definition of the tax base, the definition of value, and the adjustments in the level of tax rates.

Two extremely capable farm operators "help" the local assessor fill out a property record card indicating the acres of land and various buildings on their farm.

between different types of property and different property owners are eliminated.[3] At least that's the goal.

Down through history the general property tax has been damned as bad in principle and worse in practice. There are several features that deserve mention.

1. Property values are supposedly a measure of each individual taxpayer's ability to pay, regardless of whether or not the property is currently producing income. The property tax is not to be confused with the income tax. It is not necessarily related to the property owner's income. This was never the intent.

2. The taxes paid by various property owners are not necessarily related to benefits received. This also was never the intent. Right or wrong it is the older persons, many of whom have spent a lifetime in acquiring farm properties, who tend to pay the taxes. It is the younger, recently married couples, who produce the children that require the schools.

3. The general property tax may influence land use. There is a tendency for a land tax to speed land into a higher and better, or more profitable use, by squeezing the property owner's income. The farmer located in the transition area is pressured into either developing his land or selling it to someone who will.

4. Property values are thought to be capitalized; if so, the value of all property is less by the amount of the capitalized value of the property tax.[4] In this fashion, the property tax may affect property values, and perhaps adversely.

5. From the standpoint of most homeowners, the property tax is a tax on one of the necessities of life. Most homeowners feel the tax is most discriminatory. However, couples who rent, rather than own their home, pay the tax indirectly.

All of these features are inherent in the general property tax. However, a more valid criticism—and one more real than any of the above— is that the general property tax has, without question, been more poorly administered than any other major tax.[5]

In the days of the early American colonies the statutes assumed that the best informed, most fair minded, and most highly respected individual in the community would be elected as the assessor. At times

---

3. Agriculture, of course, is an industry which requires relatively large amounts of land per farm family. The continuous trend toward increased farm size along with rising land values for the last 35 to 40 years has made the farm family quite vulnerable to the general property tax.

4. Any repeal of the general property tax would undoubtedly lead to higher values and thus result in windfall profits to the owners.

this undoubtedly occurred. In more recent years, however, the assessor has often been a public-minded, yet relatively untrained and inexperienced individual, elected oftentimes on the basis of political appeal or popularity rather than on economic savvy. In many instances, his ability to remain in office has been dependent upon his ability to keep certain property assessments low. Camaraderies between certain influential property owners and the assessor have often led to assessed values on certain properties which are out of line.

The township trustee in the rural areas has sometimes conducted farm property assessments using a hodgepodge of arbitrary and haphazard methods. Values are guesstimated and kept conservative (low) so that even the most intelligent farmers will accept them as reasonable. Many critics to-day would label these local officials "amateurs." In fact, a practical rhymster once described the role of the assessor as follows:

> To find a value good and true,
> There are three things for you to do;
> Consider the replacement costs,
> Determine the values that are lost,
> Analyze your sales and maybe see
> What market values should really be.
> But if these suggestions are not clear
> Copy the figures you used last year.[6]

Despite these handicaps the property tax in America has worked, not as well as it could have or should have perhaps, but it nevertheless has worked. Unlike many other commodities, it is difficult to transfer realty "under the table." Unlike income, most property is difficult to hide.

Property taxation varies, of course, with the climate of public opinion as well as the level of economic sophistication. It tends to resist change. The assessor has recognized this. Even though some of the many details in an appraisal have perhaps remained unknown

---

5. Furthermore, the so-called heavy burden is due in part, not to the absolute dollar burden or even relative burden in terms of income, but to the failure to provide an easy or convenient means of making the payments. The sales tax requires a small payment every time a purchase is made. The income tax is largely deducted from one's earnings, placing the tax on a pay-as-you-go basis. If real estate taxes were prorated and each property owner were to have a portion of his tax withheld from each paycheck and forwarded to the property tax administrator, or revenue office in which the taxpayer lives, he would probably be much happier.

6. p. 15, Lynn.

to him, he has remained a practical man. Feeling the ire or the fire of
the taxpayers, the assessor has often engaged in the game of competitive underassessment. His sole purpose has been to keep the
levies in his district and for his constituents as reasonable as possible.

Furthermore, improvements in property assessment are being made.
Many states have adopted more definite, though somewhat elastic,
definitions and procedures. In many areas the qualifications as well as
the position of the assessor are being upgraded. Some states have
developed programs to train and employ full time property tax assessors. Some of the taxing districts, in order to update or reassess all
parcels, have employed outside professional appraisal firms.[7]

THE ASSESSOR'S JOB

Property assessing is governed by law and by the provisions set
forth in various state constitutions, statute laws, and court decisions.
The task is both legal and technical. The assessor must know the law.
He must understand land survey, building construction, and property
values.

The assessor should perhaps be schooled in economics, for value is
basically an economic concept. He should perhaps be conversant with
the principles of supply and demand and the trends that influence the
market value of every type of property in his area.

Lastly, the assessor has to like people and be able to work with them.
Unlike the school teacher, the minister, and many other public servants,
he has his fingers in Mr. Property Owner's pocketbook.

In its broadest context, the assessor's job involves the discovery, listing, and appraising of all property located within his jurisdiction. He
must have an appreciation for all types of properties—farm, residential,
commercial, and industrial.

The assessor's basic tools are the records kept in his office—maps,
ownership and title records, and property descriptions. Much of the
time spent there is devoted to the task of keeping these records up to
date.

The assessor's responsibility is to appraise each parcel of taxable real
estate at its current market value and to then place an assessed value
on it. This latter figure may be either the property's full market value

---

7. The term, *updating* does not necessarily mean an increase in value. The
term, *reassessment* does not mean that last year's appraisal was poorly done. The
goal is merely to make sure assessed values conform to the market and thus bring
about an equitable distribution of the property tax burden.

or some fraction thereof, depending on the state's statutes. Since the assessor depends largely on the market, it is important that he knows how to collect, tabulate, analyze, and use current sales data.

The assessor's job involves the following tasks:

1. He has to locate and identify all parcels of real estate located within his tax district or jurisdiction. This requires property ownership maps, a system for numbering the parcels, and some plan for keeping the property ownership records up-to-date.

2. He has to develop and keep a property record card on each parcel on which he inventories each of the various types of land and each of the different kinds of buildings and improvements that make up that property, along with some of their basic characteristics.

3. He has to develop a system for recording all information pertaining to property values in his jurisdiction, including real estate sales, for he has to ascertain, if not annually at least every few years, the value of each property in his district.

4. He has to determine (a) the extent to which each property is taxable, (b) the assessed valuation of each property, and (c) the tax base for all properties within his jurisdiction.

5. Upon the appeal of any property owner, he has to defend his assessments.

6. He has to establish a continuing program for evaluating uniformity between assessments.

A farm appraisal for property tax purposes is no different than one for any other purpose. The assessor's job is to estimate the present market value of that property and to use that value as the basis for assessment.

All property is assessed as of a particular date—in many states, March 1. Since it is physically impossible to inspect and appraise all properties on one day, the assessor often appraises various properties throughout the year; however, estimating his values as of that date. In other words, the date of the property inspection may precede or follow the date of the appraised value.

Most assessment laws require that land and buildings be valued separately. This is an archaic requirement that should perhaps be abolished. Farms, as well as other properties, are bought and sold as entire units. Bare land sales are obtainable; however, seldom are buildings or improvements sold separately from land.[8] The requirement that land and buildings be valued separately makes the cost approach to value the more applicable one. In fact, the cost approach is the one used most often by assessors, and sometimes, unfortunately, with little or no appreciation for the earnings or market approaches.

Most state tax laws include a uniformity clause. This means that the same methods must be followed in establishing the assessed values on all properties. The assessor has the job of appraising not just one or several but all properties and all types of properties. His job is to arrive at values on each that are fair and equitable to all property owners. Hence, the foundation of all tax appraisal work is uniformity among types of properties, among taxpayers, and among districts.

It is not the assessor's job to levy taxes or to produce revenue. The assessor's sole function is to obtain an equitable ad valorem distribution of the aggregate tax burden levied by the people, for the people, and through their elected representatives. When the assessor can maintain a reasonable degree of equitability, he is accomplishing a mammoth and thankless task. Few men will tackle it for the compensation or remuneration received today.

THE MASS APPRAISAL TECHNIQUE

The farm appraisal made for property tax purposes by the assessor and one made for some other purpose by a fee appraiser are much the same. Each is based on the same appraisal principles. Each is aimed at ascertaining the property's present market value as of a given date. Each requires some physical description of the property. Each should consider the productive capacity of the unit and the many factors that affect value. Each is based on the same typical buyer and seller. In other words, tax appraisals are based on the same value concepts as other appraisals. They require the same economic sense, or judgment.

The main difference is that in tax appraisal work the appraiser's job is to appraise not just 1, 4, 7, or 27 farms, but to appraise or assess all 47,391 or however many parcels of real estate there are in the taxing district. The job is to do so uniformly and within a relatively short period of time. As a result, the appraisal process has to be streamlined. Compared to other appraisers the assessor spends less time inspecting the properties; he spends (or should spend) more time studying maps, collecting data, developing thumb-rule guides or standards, and analyzing the major factors influencing property values in his area.[9]

---

8. Occasionally this occurs, but mainly where an improvement is a prefabricated unit and can be assembled in place and disassembled later, for example, metal grain bins or Harvestores. It may also occur when a property is condemned and an existing building is sold.

Appraisers who do some assessing and work with assessors have developed the mass appraisal technique. The term is used to describe the system or appraisal process used, or which should be used, and to distinguish between it and the more typical techniques of the fee appraiser.

The mass appraisal technique consists of the standardized collection of appraisal data for purposes of appraising as equitably or fairly as possible each and every parcel of property within a given tax district. The most efficient technique is hopefully used. Mass appraisal thus becomes a procedure whereby trained appraisers analyze these data and,

---

9. The tax appraiser may spend no more than 30 minutes inspecting a residence, no more than an hour or so inspecting a farm or ranch. This does not say he forms an opinion as to value during this period of time. It merely says that this is the time he takes to record the physical data which will later provide the foundation or basis for arriving at the property's value.

The appraiser's job in tax appraisal work is to appraise not just 1, 4, 7, or 27 farms, but to locate and assess all 47,391 or however many parcels of real estate there are in the taxing district.

Courtesy, Soil Conservation Service

subject to an inspection of each individual parcel, apply them to each and every property in the district, thus estimating their values. Although the term used is the mass appraisal technique, the final figures are both separately and individually appraised values. They are not mass appraisal values; nor are tax appraisals done by formula alone.

The mechanics are often highly organized. A large degree of specialization and a division of labor are key factors. Basic responsibilities are usually divided according to both technical ability and function. The work leading up to the placing of a value on each property is organized according to function. Different parties, or persons, with varying skills and expertise handle (1) the collection of sales data, rental data, and building construction costs, (2) the property inspection, including the recording of various acreages and the measurement of all buildings, (3) the classification of farm land and the grading of buildings, and (4) the clerical work and other special tasks.

A professional staff familiar with the entire appraisal or assessment process is responsible for the placing of the final values on all properties. To find persons interested in and able to value all types of property is difficult. Hence the staff often specializes as to type of property—farm, residential, commercial, and industrial. As long as the basis for assessment is present market value, uniformity is obtained.

The various activities are often organized to utilize and develop each person's skills—the farm boys inspect the farms, the college students measure the buildings, the clerks do the tabulating, and the professional appraisers determine the final values—as effectively as possible.

The mass appraisal technique has been developed largely by outside professional appraisal firms. These firms have learned to tackle and do the job on a systematic basis. The approach is often in direct contrast to many assessors' offices where the most frequently noted characteristic is political performance rather than economic efficiency.

A few assessors' offices, mainly those in the larger cities, employ a permanent staff of competent appraisers who estimate values throughout the year. In the rural areas, however, the assessor's staff is usually a small, non-professional one. The size of the tax unit does not supposedly justify a permanent or professional staff.[10]

As a result, most rural assessors reappraise or reassess the properties in their district only periodically, and usually only when a special apappropriation of money is made available. When reassessment is re-

---

10. In many rural offices everybody appears to do everything. The rural assessor often does work that should be delegated to the clerical staff and which could be done more efficiently by them.

quired, the local officials must decide whether to let the assessor and his staff, along with some temporary help, do the job or to hire an outside professional appraisal firm.

The outside firm does not generally know the area. However, it doesn't take long for the professional appraiser to get acquainted. He goes about it in an organized fashion. Local people are typically hired to do much of the work. However, the final values placed on each parcel are placed there by the professional. The outside firm does not usually know any of the people. This has the advantage of eliminating much of the preferential treatment. Furthermore, the responsibility— some or all—is taken off the shoulders of the assessor himself. In fact, many local assessors prefer to have an outside professional organization do their periodic reappraisal or reassessment for a number of reasons.

Data Collection: A first and essential step in the mass appraisal technique is to obtain a set of maps showing the location of each parcel of property and to develop a parcelling system designed specifically for mass appraisal purposes. A numbering system is generally more efficient than the township, range, and section numbers which have been used in the past. The system may be designed to expedite later coding and machine processing.

The next job is to collect any and all sales data which pertain to recent market transactions, any and all costs of constructing new buildings and improvements, and any and all rental data on income properties. Production-line collection of data is thus one of the real characteristics of the mass appraisal process.

The task is not completed, however, with mere collection. The data must be tabulated, analyzed, and related to the various areas. Maps of each area, along with tables and charts showing the economic trends, must be developed. Farm sales must be related to date of sale, location, farm size, productive capacity, and the extent to which the properties are improved. These should then be checked with the judgment of those persons having a knowledge of current farm real estate values.

Thus the task is that of collecting, organizing, and evaluating the essential data needed to estimate present market values on an efficient basis.

Standardization: The assembling of the data should be done in such fashion that such can be converted to a usable form and hence readily applied to a large number of properties. Both the methods of acquiring and the methods of utilizing the data should be standardized. At the same time, there must be flexibility in the system so that all final

figures can be modified in order to fit the peculiar or unique characteristics of each property. One might say the data should be developed
into both standards and standard modifications for each standard.

In the process, all data are first classified as to type of property—
farm, residential, commercial, or industrial—and as to location. The
latter is a major factor affecting value. In the farming areas, soil types
and soil productivities may be established, and land values may be
related to them. The basic per-acre values should be plotted on a
graph or chart, and a line or curve, whichever best fits the data,
fitted to them (Figure 22). This relationship can then be used to
establish land values over a fairly wide area. These land values, along
with whatever scattered sales data are available, can then be checked
by persons familiar with the area to see if the overall relationship
is realistic.

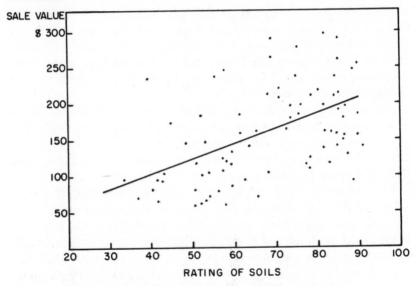

Figure 22. Farm Real Estate Values Related to Economic Soil Ratings.
76 Farms with Buildings, Saunders County, Nebraska, 1950-52.

Farm land is typically divided into several land use classifications—
tillable crop land, pasture land, woodland, and the home-site acreage.
The tillable acreage is then divided into several subcategories based on
its productivity—excellent, above-average, average, below-average, and
poor. Different per-acre values, based on the market, may then be
developed for each of these different land classes. Usually there is a
fairly wide range.

Variation: All values should be in line with the real estate market and in line with one another. At the same time, market data occasionally include individual sales which are badly off-target. There are always a few abnormal sales where the properties have sold considerably above or below their real or true market values. For this reason the selling price of an individual property is not always representative.

All sales should be screened for accuracy. Those that do not represent arm's length transactions should be eliminated. Family transfers, distress sales, transfers between corporations with interlocking directors, and others where the monetary consideration may have been secondary in importance should be discarded. These may add up to a number of sales which have to be discarded before satisfactory values can be used in any sales analysis.

Furthermore, some types of property do not enter the market as often as others do. This is particularly true of specialty properties—churches, school houses, and railroads. Occasionally it is true of the good farms in the good land areas.[11] A single per-acre value for one type of land throughout an entire county may be possible under some circumstances. However, that single value may also be difficult to defend. Some land has considerable uniformity; other land has not. Location and many other factors affect value. In other words, while comparable standards are needed for assessment purposes, a few variations are not particularly bad.

Property Inspection: The mass appraisal technique requires a uniform method of inspecting each individual property. A property record card is typically used to record property ownership as well as to inventory and tabulate each property's more important physical characteristics. The farm property data most often recorded include the various types of land and the quality and acreage of each, along with the various buildings, their dimensions, and the grade of each.

The property record card is a simple, yet reliable, approach to describe the various types of properties. In many respects the card represents a check-off system. The cards or forms are usually worked out in advance, and quite carefully, so that they can be used on all properties, and also, so that they can be used by relatively unskilled

11. Farms are often held in tight hands. Bona fide sales and arm's length transactions are then few and far between. Some critics say that this makes sale prices unsatisfactory as a base against which to levy taxes. These same critics seldom recognize that prices of several years back can be updated. Furthermore, they seldom suggest a more desirable alternative.

Courtesy, Assessor, Tippecanoe County, Indiana

The property record card is simply a means of describing each property, using a sort of a check-off system. The card is not necessarily a short-cut, but a technique which allows the inspection of each individual property to be accomplished as efficiently as possible.

persons. The card is not a shortcut, but a technique which allows the inspection of each individual property to be accomplished as efficiently as possible.

Unlike the appraisal reports made by most fee appraisers, the data pertaining to the general area are not repeated over and over on each card. These data, which are related to a number of properties or to various areas, are instead kept separate and by themselves. Typical land values and building costs are then placed on each property card at some later date.

An Assessor's Manual: Many states have put considerable effort into the development of a manual giving the specific requirements for property assessment. This is not an easy task. Some manuals leave much to be desired. However, they often provide excellent bases or guides for property assessment. In the majority of states they have led to a more uniform treatment of similar properties.

The primary purposes of an assessor's manual are (1) to delineate the state laws pertaining to the general property tax and to define the values underlying assessment, (2) to set up an organized system for collecting the economic data pertinent to each type of property, (3) to show how various empirical standards can be developed and then used to place values on each type of property, (4) to explain and illustrate an efficient property record card and record-keeping system, (5) to offer procedures for the processing of all data, including the formulation and maintenance of the tax role, and (6) to show general guides for dealing with the taxpayer for review and for achieving equalization.

Most assessors like a state manual. They learn to rely on them, sometimes too heavily. The better assessors also know how to use them as points of departure and when to depart from them. Knowing when not to use the manual is oftentimes as important as knowing when to use it.

A manual's real value is perhaps to minimize the extent to which an assessor must rely on his own personal judgment. It tends to eliminate much of the personal bias that cannot help but color even the best assessor's judgment. In fact, a manual often becomes a tremendous help. It can be used as a crutch when the assessor is subjected to outside influence or pressure.

The agricultural section of most manuals should provide considerable data on farm-land values. These data are typically based on the various soil productivities, for productive capacity is a major factor leading to differences in value. Most counties or rural tax districts have soils or land-use maps showing the various land areas. Crop-yield estimates can be made for each area and then related to recent sale prices. The assessor must recognize that location, as well as other factors, leads to considerable variation in per-acre values, even among a given soil type or within a given area.

Most assessors' manuals show or provide the method for developing standards for valuing farm buildings—building descriptions, current construction costs, grade classifications, and photographic illustrations. The latter are extremely helpful. Cost schedules are usually based on the typical buildings currently being constructed in the area. Replacement costs, both materials and labor, are presented, usually in terms of the costs per square foot or per unit, along with information on depreciation.

Most manuals also include standard modifications. Standard costs per square foot can be modified for differences in total area—one-story versus two-story dwellings, dwellings with and without basements, the quality of the building materials used, the quality of the construction, the type of heating system, the amount of plumbing, and other items similar in nature. By starting with a per-unit value and then modifying this value to fit the characteristics of the property, each property can be assessed both accurately and uniformly.

However, the final values are valid only to the extent that the data in the manual are applicable to the local area. Whenever an assessor's manual is developed, both the data and the mass appraisal technique should be tested against a representative sample of properties, each of which has recently sold. Key farms, representing arm's length transactions in the market, should be carefully selected and used to verify the accuracy of the manual's data. The farms selected should represent typical farms of all kinds. Type of farming, location, size, productive capacity, and the extent to which the farms are improved should be considered. The number of farms used depends on the number and variety of farms in the tax jurisdiction. Each farm property selected should be appraised in detail, using all three approaches to value as well as the standardized approach of the manual.

Electronic Data Processing: The main distinctions between the traditional farm appraisal technique and the mass appraisal approach is in the mass collection of economic data and in the large number of properties, each of which virtually requires the same arithmetic calculations in order to determine value. In the mass appraisal of property, considerable physical and economic data must be sorted, tabulated, and analyzed. A number of computations are required.

Electronic data processing equipment can be used most advantageously in performing this task. Regression analysis, sometimes called curve fitting, can be used to estimate the various weights given to each of the many factors affecting farm values. This statistical approach essentially says that value is a function of (1) date of sale, (2) location, (3) size of farm, (4) productive capacity, (5) the extent to which the farm is improved, (6) etc., (7) etc. Many factors ($\ldots x_n$) can be included. However, each factor must be definable and quantitatively measurable. Electronic data processing equipment can then calculate the influence (statistically speaking, the regression coefficients) that each factor has on value.

Prior to the availability of electronic equipment, such mathematical problems had to be solved by hand or with a mechanical desk calculator. Three or four factors was about all one wanted to handle. However, with electronic equipment, many factors can now be related to value. Many more computations can be made in a mere fraction of the time. Will these studies work? Not in all cases. Yet, statistical studies have provided considerable food for thought where such have been made.[12] Again various key farms in various locations should be appraised in detail and then used as a check on the regression coefficients or weights that have been developed.

Electronic data processing can be extremely helpful where the system of analysis is intelligently conceived and carefully developed. The equipment can handle complex equations and process a large number of computations with tremendous speed. Such can save large amounts of time. Yet computers are not a panacea for all problems. This is particularly true in appraisal where economic judgments have always been, and will undoubtedly continue to be, a large part of the job.

Unfortunately, the computer's ability to solve problems has been glamorized far beyond its present use. In some instances, it has become a status symbol. Too many computer technicians are overly impressed with the ability of complex mathematical formulas to solve problems. They have little or no knowledge of the real world or its problem-solving requirements. Also, these very capable persons sometimes have the idea that the more sophisticated the system the better the results. A reasonable level of sophistication is desirable. Yet those persons who merely add to the complexity of the system often divert the appraiser's attention to trivial details and away from the essential ele-

---

12. A sample listing of each is presented at the end of the chapter.

ments of valuation.

One cannot appraise a farm or any other property merely through the use of electronic data processing equipment. Anyone who attempts to do so indicates a lack of understanding of the appraisal process, and furthermore, a naiveté regarding the real usefulness of electronic data processing equipment.

Unfortunately, very few county governments have a sufficient volume of work to justify a computer. Their many operations are often performed by less glamorous means, such as a pencil and paper and desk calculator, and sometimes rather efficiently. At the same time, the mass appraisal technique requires a sizeable number of similar computations on each property record card. The number of repetitive tasks is tremendous. When these are done by hand, a great deal of drudgery is involved. Typically, there are a number of clerical errors. Thus electronic data processing is an opportunity to automate routine clerical work, to speed up the process, and to save time. All routine computational operations can and should be done on a computer today. The mathematics are not complex. The work is more efficient. The arithmetic is much more accurate.

Electronic data processing can save considerable time in collecting and tabulating economic data, in making all of the calculations required on the property record cards, in performing the more routine clerical and computational work, and in preparing the tax rolls and tax statements. When this is accomplished, the appraisers who work in assessor's offices will then be able to devote more time to the problems of appraising farms and less time to the chores.

PREFERENTIAL TREATMENT

Most state tax laws contain uniformity clauses which require all property to be assessed on a uniform basis. These same state laws, at the same time, usually call for special exemptions for special groups of people. There are many examples where certain members of the populace are excused from part or all of their property tax levy. A homestead exemption often excuses a homeowner from paying a property tax on a certain portion of his assessed valuation. There are similar exemptions for old people, for persons who are blind, for those with mortgage liens, for veterans, for educational institutions, for local governmental units, and for religious and philanthropic organizations. Thus, one of the assessor's first jobs is to determine the extent to which each and every property in his jurisdiction is taxable.

In the farming areas located near or around the larger centers of dense population, urban expansion has affected farm real estate values and property taxes. Farm-land values in these areas have risen to the extent that they are considerably above, if not double or triple, any value based on farm earnings. Thus, there exists a strong demand for preferential treatment for agriculture.

When the farm owner is taxed on the basis of what his farm will sell for in the marketplace, it may place him in a financial squeeze. His income may no longer support the taxes he has to pay. The price at which he can sell his farm may not yet fully pay whatever taxes may be involved, refinance a new farming operation, and reimburse him for his time, trouble, and moving costs. For these and other reasons,

Urban expansion has affected both farm real estate values and property taxes. In fact, farm land values around the larger centers of population have risen to the extent that they are often considerably above, if not double or triple any value based on farm earnings. Thus, there exists a strong demand for preferential treatment for agriculture.

Courtesy, U.S.D.A.

most farmers don't want to move. However, if the trends toward higher property taxes continue, they will sooner or later force farmers in these areas to liquidate, or sell their farm properties.

All this has led to the charge that the strict application of the ad valorem assessment principle has undesirable consequences for those farmers who are located in the urban areas, and that the general property tax is unfair to farm property owners.[13] The assessor is criticized for raising farm-land values, for increasing the farmer's taxes, and for forcing him off the land. However, the assessor, in performing his duties, may merely be following the market. Increased land values in those urban areas are a result of both the demand for and the need of that land for a higher or more profitable use. Much of the land that has been sold in these areas has been sold at prices which represent a change from agricultural to residential, commercial, or industrial use.

Maryland was the first state to adopt legislation providing for the differential assessment of land actively devoted to farming or to agriculture.[14] In 1956, the assessors in that state were admonished to no longer appraise agricultural land according to its market price. Instead, such was to be assessed on the basis of its agricultural value. This introduced a major change in both established property tax theory and practice. Furthermore, it gave rise to a multitude of problems.

The policy of preferential assessment has nonetheless drawn wide popular support, both from farm groups and from others. Advocates maintain that it confers not only the obvious benefit to farm owners but that it also benefits the public at large. It hopefully preserves farming. It guarantees that farm owners may retain the option of abandoning farming at their discretion rather than because of high real property taxes. It also maintains open space around our growing cities.

A total of 20 or so states have followed Maryland and have enacted similar legislation. The assessors in general have been directed to consider only those factors relevant to a property's present use and to ignore the influence that any potential use has on market value.

Three Alternatives: The various laws or proposals tend to fall into

---

13. The dramatic rise in the value of land located around many urban areas provides an almost classic illustration that the ad valorem tax burden bears little or no relationship to either the owner's ability to pay his taxes or the benefits or services he receives.

14. Walker, W. P., also House, P. W.

three categories—preferential assessment, tax deferral, and restrictive agreements.[15]

1. Preferential assessment is an assessment by which all farm land, so designated, is assessed not on the basis of its market value but according to its "prudent agricultural value." This provision essentially eliminates a property's potential for other use or the influence of this factor on value.

2. Tax deferral occurs when the owners of farm properties, so designated, are granted the option of postponing a portion of their real estate taxes until such time as the property is developed or changes ownership. The unpaid share of the tax is simply carried forward as a lien on the property. When the property is sold, the deferred portion becomes payable, sometimes with accrued interest. Thus, tax deferral may be combined with recapture.

3. Restrictive agreements limit the use of farm land for other purposes in the future either by contract or by zoning. The property owner may sign a voluntary—however binding—contract, which says he promises to keep his farm in agriculture. These contracts may be 5- or 10-year contracts. They may be subject to annual renewal; they may be combined with tax deferral and recapture. Local planning agencies may attempt to accomplish the same purpose through zoning regulations. These regulations are essentially restrictions on land use. They hold certain rights in abeyance or they expropriate certain of the owner's rights.

Some of the Problems: Preferential treatment of different properties leads to several administrative problems.

1. One of the more troublesome is that of definition. What is a farm? What constitutes farm land or agricultural use? What properties are eligible for preferential assessment and/or tax deferral? Should eligibility be contingent upon owner-occupancy? Should the farm home be included? All of it or part of it? What about the part-time farm? The owner and his wife both work in town. What about the country estate? The hobby farm? Should property which is being used to manufacture agricultural resources, for example, bulk fertilizer plants, and property which is being used to process agricultural products, for example, a grain warehouse or a hop drier, be included? What about greenhouses?

Farm land may be held for purposes of farming or it may be held on a speculative basis for eventual development. To distinguish be-

---

15. Hady, T. F.

WHERE FRINGE FARMLAND GETS A TAX BREAK

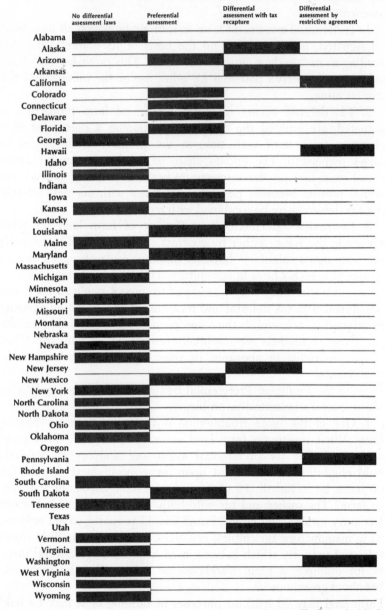

Courtesy, **The Furrow** by John Deere

The various laws with regard to preferential treatment for agriculture tend to fall into three categories—(1) preferential assessment, (2) differential assessment with tax deferral and recapture, and (3) restrictive agreements.

tween the two is very difficult. The property owner may be a bona fide farmer; he may be an investor or speculator. He may be a farmer today, yet think differently tomorrow. Unfortunately, the principal beneficiaries of preferential treatment have been speculators rather than farmers. Speculators often succeed in getting their land classified as farm land by conducting minimal farming operations. When this occurs, the law benefits the speculator more than it does the bona fide farmer. It merely subsidizes one more group of individuals.

Whatever the case, the assessor now has to classify land according to use and distinguish between agricultural and non-agricultural properties. Any decision here can be challenged and also overruled in court.

2. Another problem is to define *prudent agricultural value* or whatever other term is specified, and apply such. To distinguish between market value and agricultural use value presents a difficult challenge to the assessor. The laws essentially rule out the use of sales data. They instead require the use of only those factors which determine agricultural use value. In other words, market prices no longer provide reference points for farm-land assessments.

In the case of tax deferral, the assessor now has to estimate not one but two values—the first, one on which the full tax is based, the other, a lower value which represents only agricultural use. For most assessors, estimating market value is difficult enough; determining still another value, based on the property's use, presents even more of a problem. Thus tax deferral essentially doubles the assessor's job.

One can rationalize that, with tax deferral, the farmer or rancher can choose his own value, and that there is little reason to be concerned with the accuracy of the prudent agricultural value figure, when recapture is combined with tax deferral. This is perhaps correct.

3. Tax deferral and recapture, however, lead to an additional problem. Some if not all of the deferred taxes have to be paid at some later date, presumably when the property changes hands or is sold. To be perfectly fair to all taxpayers, interest should undoubtedly be charged on the unpaid portion of the taxes. Now then, should the interest be paid semiannually or annually? Should it too be deferred? Should it be simple or compounded? Tax deferral has a much firmer rationale than does tax abatement, both legally and economically. However, tax deferral again doubles the paper work.

4. Restrictive covenants are also used; however, seldom if ever are they fully recognized in the market. If zoning or other restrictions on land use are enforced (in other words, if they are real) they should be reflected into market values. If so, the ad valorem principle is

applicable and all property can be taxed according to value. However, in most communities exceptions to zoning classifications are easily obtainable. Zoning does not fully, nor in all instances, affect farm values.

5. A final problem is the erosion of the tax base. Most states have long had a propensity to fritter away the property tax base by concealing subsidies in the form of special exemptions to certain groups. A smaller and smaller tax base is an inevitable by-product of the wide variety of exemptions given by constitutional privilege or legislation over the years. These exemptions merely place an increased burden on the individual taxpayers who remain—those who do pay the taxes.

Many exemptions are granted without any real economic analysis as to their cost or to their effect on those taxpayers who do not receive such. These costs can be expressed in either of two ways: (1) cost to the district in terms of a smaller tax base, or (2) cost to the taxpayers not receiving such exemptions in terms of higher tax rates. The arithmetic is simple. Preferential treatment does not reduce taxes. It merely shifts the burden from those persons who receive such to those who do not.

The Principle of Uniformity: Local assessors have long sought to achieve uniformity among the various types of property and among individual property owners. Most state officials have worked to bring about this same uniformity among tax districts. Uniformity is achieved only when each property owner pays his fair share of the general property tax.

Assessors have always had a tendency to minimize those elements of value that reflect speculative considerations, including prospective changes in land use. When relatively few properties or property owners are involved, the problem can largely be ignored.

Preferential treatment for agriculture is a legitimate effort to align the tax burden more closely to the property owner's ability to pay and to smooth one of the rougher edges of the property tax. However, when farm property assessments are based on prudent agricultural values and other property assessments are based on market values, this establishes a double standard. Such is a glaring inconsistency. Equitability among types of property or property owners no longer exists.

TRUE CASH VALUE AND ASSESSED VALUE

The various state constitutions and statutory provisions employ many terms to describe the value to be used by assessors for property tax purposes. True cash value, fair cash value, full cash value, and value-in-exchange are common. The courts have consistently interpreted these terms to equal value-in-the-marketplace.[16] The courts have generally held that value to the owner, over and above that value to any other person, is not to be considered. For purposes of taxation, value cannot exceed that which the owner, after a reasonable effort, can obtain for his property in cash.

Several statutes have occasionally authorized property values to be based on either (1) market value or (2) value to the owner, whichever is the higher.[17] This is usually an incongruity, or inconsistency, for the same constitution or statutes usually have uniformity clauses which immediately negate value to the owner. Such might easily be proven to be unconstitutional.

Some statutes have made a distinction—calling for values at levels for which the properties would sell "ordinarily" as contrasted to "currently." In these cases, the courts have further interpreted such to be a true or sound value which (1) allows time to smooth out some of the gyrations in the market, (2) refers to a more nearly normal market value, thus eliminating both depressed or highly inflated values, and (3) may or may not coincide particularly with current selling prices. In actual practice it is impossible for anyone to define ordinary or normal, or to say how much of a price is sound and how much of it is due to either inflated or deflated prices. The results are interesting. The distinction may merely give those assessors, attempting to deal with values quite removed from the current market, a reason for their behavior.

Sooner or later all tax authorities recognize that the fundamental premise underlying property assessment must be market value, that the assessor's task is really to estimate present market value, that market values are determined not by assessors but by those persons who buy and sell properties, and that, in most instances, the various

---

16. Not since the Middle Ages have economists contended that a thing has a true, fair, just, or any other kind of value, other than that which various persons are prepared and willing to accept or pay in the marketplace.

17. Noble experiments have been suggested requiring property owners to set their own values. Provisions which allow the taxing unit (or others) to buy said property if the set value is low supposedly forces the property owner to be honest. This places an unfortunate burden on the taxpayer who normally owns a farm or home and desires to keep it, even though someone may be willing to pay more for it than the owner thinks it's worth. This approach is a pure and simple reflection of the inability, or perhaps unwillingness, of elected officials to accept their responsibilities and study appraisal technique.

properties are worth whatever they can be sold for in the market. Each party to a sale has an opinion based on his personal likes and dislikes, based on the selling prices of other properties, based on his ability to pay, etc. Each party backs up that opinion by either paying or receiving the agreed-to price. Whether that price is too high or too low, judged by some other standard, is immaterial. Recent sales are the best evidences of value.

Market values place all property on the same basis. Market values measure all property owners with the same yardstick. No one person can claim special privilege or suffer unfair abuse. Equitability between different types of property and between different property owners is established most easily in the market.

True cash value supposedly equals value in the market. However, unofficially (and sometimes officially) it does not. Unofficially, true cash value, fair cash value, full cash value, or whatever the term approximates 90 percent of market value, sometimes less. Most assessors have learned that they have more friends and fewer problems if they stay "a shade" under the market. In determining value, most assessors are extremely careful. They tend to stay or remain on the conservative or low side. Their values are often closer to prices bid than to either asking prices or market values. Underassessment has long been commonplace, and is one of the very significant faults in American property taxation.

Lastly, assessed values do not always equal true cash values. Many states specify that all property is to be assessed at some fraction or percent of its full value. Some states specify that property is to be assessed at 10 percent, some at 25 percent, some at 30 percent, and some at 50 percent of full value. This latter is frequently referred to as the level of assessment.

FULL VERSUS FRACTIONAL ASSESSMENT

In general, the courts have held that no injustice has occurred as long as all assessments are a given percentage of the market value. That percentage must merely be consistent and uniform for all types of property.

The Theory: In a purely technical sense, uniform assessment is all that matters. The general property tax yields the same amount of revenue, and the property owner pays the same amount of taxes, as long as all property is assessed on the same basis. It makes no difference whether property is assessed at full value or at some fraction thereof.

Whether one's real estate is assessed at 10 percent, 30 percent, or 90 percent is of little consequence to the individual property owner as long as the same percentage figure prevails throughout the entire tax district. An equitable ad valorem of the aggregate tax burden is obtained as long as all property owners are assessed at a uniform ratio.

Hence, the question of full versus fractional assessment is mathematically irrelevant. In fact, the arithmetic is so obvious that any choice between full and fractional value assessment appears to be purely academic.

The Problem: However, the problem is to avoid not just overassessment but underassessment as well, as either lead to inequities among taxpayers. Overassessment is the much greater sin. Property owners who happen to be overassessed promptly move to have their assessments reviewed; those who are underassessed rarely if ever complain. The property owner who thinks he is underassessed typically reasons that he is better off than his neighbors; yet this may be deceiving. Unknowingly, his neighbors may also be underassessed and even more so than he.

To many property owners fractional assessments bear little or no relation to anything in the real world. Generally speaking, the average property owner is unfamiliar with how his assessment was determined.[18] The figures are often a complete mystery. If, compared to the market, the values are low, the property owner typically accepts them and ignores the possibility of any inequity.

The solution is obvious, yet difficult. The solution is full-value assessment and full-public disclosure. The typical taxpayer reacts much more vigorously to full-value assessments and particularly when full disclosure is also the rule. Full-value assessments tend to remove not only overassessments but underassessments as well. Appeals to local boards of review are both more often and more effective. The foundation and goal of the general property tax is to encourage taxpayer participation in the assessing process. Full-value assessments and full-public disclosure make the typical property owner much more aware of his responsibilities. Public disclosure leads to a more uniform assessment and to increased equitability among taxpayers.

The Practice: The assessor looks at full-value assessment as an

---

18. The absentee-owner, the estate trustee, the widow, and the naive and uninitiated, in particular.

impractical if not an unattainable ideal. Fractional assessments are more palatable politically and much easier to defend, simply because the lower figures don't bear much relationship to the real world. Inequities are more difficult to determine and easier to overlook. Fractional assessments lessen the complaints and, generally speaking, lead to a less vocal, happier populace of taxpayers. One can readily agree that fractional assessments are politically more palatable.

In many states, fractional assessment is a matter of custom. Even where the legal level is 100 percent, the state tax commission or agency may go ahead and specify a lower level for purposes of administering the tax. In other words, fractional assessment is common even where it is contrary to the law. Furthermore, the various courts often uphold fractional assessment on the grounds that it is not unfair as long as all properties are assessed at the same percentage.

There are some valid arguments in favor of fractional assessment. One of those advanced is the continuous difficulty of maintaining assessments at current market-value levels. Economic growth, technological change, and price inflation continuously affect property values. This alone is not the problem. The problem is that various areas and various types of property are affected differently. Over time the rates of change among different types of properties tend to be both irregular and different. Assessors thus experience considerable difficulty in updating their assessments. When the assessor cannot or does not want to keep up-to-date, property values tend to be both fractionally assessed and underassessed.

The possibility of an abrupt drop in property values always exists. This hazard is not as serious as it might first appear. The changes that distort assessments are not the abrupt changes, which usually affect all properties, but instead are the longer and less perceptible changes which affect different types of property differently.

A second argument advanced is that property values based on fractional assessment are much simpler and easier to explain to the general public. This statement doesn't make sense. The problem is that when assessments are at full value, overassessments are much more apparent. The only real point is that when property values are less than full value, the assessor feels it is easier for him to defend his figures, that he has less difficulty with the taxpayers, and that his public relations are better. However, the inequities are still there; they are just not as readily apparent to the lay public.

A third argument is that in many jurisdictions there are rate limitations. By keeping assessments low, the tax rates remain high, all other things being held equal. When a rate limitation is reached, the assessor may then be pressured to keep his assessments, and thus property taxes, low. The assessor is then in the position of being the comptroller of the budget, even though that is not his job.[19] A similar argument follows. When assessed values are at full value, this leads, theoretically at least, to low tax rates, and low tax rates, to many persons, encourage higher expenditures.

A fourth argument is that various states allocate funds to various counties or tax districts on the basis of the total wealth in that county or tax district. Allocations are often set up so that the poor counties or districts receive more than the rich, percentagewise. Too-high values may thus place a county or district in a higher bracket and reduce it's share of state funds. In other words, the poor may need to remain poor in order to qualify for the distribution of such funds.[20] This latter quickly results in competitive underassessment, and it often appears easier to compete with the other tax districts when on a fractional basis.

The responsibility for equitable assessment rests heavily on the shoulders of conscientious public officials. Unfortunately, the magnitude of the job is seldom comprehended by those not intimately familiar with assessment problems. When all assessments are at full value, the taxpayer remains better informed. He has a better opportunity to protect himself from both overassessment and underassessment. The real problem is that the assessor should base his assessments on facts. He should have a thorough knowledge of current property sales and prices. He should know what he is doing. Whenever he takes the taxpayer into his confidence, he should know what he is talking about.

Full value assessment along with full public disclosure would be extremely useful in most communities and not just to assessors. The appraiser's, banker's, and loan man's work could all be materially shortened. Private builders, city planners, and development authorities would have data that would be immensely useful in developing com-

---

19. This also doesn't make sense to anyone who has not been an assessor. Whenever taxes increase the assessor often takes the brunt of the complaints. He is the one who can be reached and talked to, and he is blamed, whether or not such is his legal responsibility.

20. These grants are typically based on the total tax base or the total assessed valuation of all properties. When the poorer taxing districts receive a larger percentage share of state aid than do the richer units, those assessed at the smaller fraction of the market value tend to receive more than their legally authorized share of state aid (compared to those units assessed at the higher levels).

prehensive plans. Policy makers and others could more easily observe the real burden of taxation and apply exemptions with a more accurate understanding of the consequences.

THE PROBLEM OF EQUITABILITY AND EQUALIZATION

Local boards of review, state tax equalization commissions, and the tax courts have before them each year thousands of property owners who appeal their assessments, almost always on the grounds that "not only is the law bad, but I have been assessed unfairly." They argue long and eloquently, yet only occasionally with success, for the assessor is smart. His true cash values are often low or conservative; they seldom exceed those at which various properties could be sold.

The taxpayer who feels that he has been overassessed can ask to have his assessment adjusted by the local board of review on grievance day. Most property owners simply state that their taxes are too high or that their assessments are out of line. There is a good chance that these statements are true, however, seldom does the person making such a statement have any real evidence to substantiate his contention. In order to challenge his particular assessed valuation, he needs to demonstrate inequitable treatment. The best way to do this is to compare the value placed on his property with the values placed on other properties, which are similar in type and which are located in the same area. To do this, the property owner must select several examples and acquire several appraisals on the other farms.

Unfortunately, the property owner who does this finds himself responsible for increasing the property taxes in his neighborhood. For, after hearing a given case, most assessors are inclined to raise the assessed value on the farms used for comparative purposes rather than lower the value of the property owned by the complaining property owner. Hence, the property owner who appears before the board of review, rather than getting his assessment revised downward, runs the risk of having his neighbors' and friends' assessments revised upward. This strategy on the part of the assessor or review board transfers any stigma from them to the objecting taxpayer. It does not make friends in the neighborhood. For this reason, most taxpayers hesitate to make

---

The major goal in ad valorem tax appraising is to treat all property owners uniformly. Each property owner should contribute his fair share of the general property tax—no more and no less.

Courtesy, U.S.D.A.

comparisons themselves; more and more of them are requesting professional appraisers to do the next reassessment.

The major goal or objective in all ad valorem tax appraising is to treat all property owners uniformly. Each property owner should contribute his fair share of the general property tax, no more and no less. There are two levels of equitability: (1) among various types of property or property owners within each area or tax district and (2) among various areas or tax districts. The first is the job of the assessor; the second is the responsibility of the state tax equalization board.

Equitability Among Types of Property or Property Owners: The assessor's task is to prepare an assessment roll that is equitable to all property owners in his tax district. Under rapidly changing conditions this is a difficult task. Property values not only change over time, those on different types of property and those in different areas tend to change at different rates. What is equitable today may not be equitable tomorrow.

One of the problems in most rural areas is the infrequency of reassessment. Some properties become overassessed; others become underassessed over time. Any delay in reassessment leads to greater and greater inequities, especially if property values are changing rapidly. In fact, the longer reassessment is put off, the more various persons develop vested interests. They then work to further delay reassessment.[21]

The courts have held that all properties must be assessed either at market value or at some constant percentage of market value. They have held that uniformity means an equal ratio between the assessed values and market values. They have said that no injury occurs when property is assessed at less than its full value provided the same ratio is used on all properties.

Hence, assessment quality is measured by the ratios between assessed values and sale prices. During periods of rising prices, most ratio studies show both low ratios and wide variations both within and among assessing units. There are several major reasons for this.

1. The assessed values used in many ratio studies tend to reflect the assessed value before the property was sold rather than the assessed value afterwards. After a property is transferred or sold, the assessed value is typically raised, particularly if the property was purchased for a new and higher or better use.

---

21. The only way an assessor can avoid such a problem is to continually review current real estate sale prices and to continually update property values. A review of all new and current data should be made each year.

2. Many ratio studies are based on a limited number of transactions, or on transactions which have occurred over a relatively short period of time. Hence, those types of property that change hands rather infrequently—for example, the better farm land held in tight hands—may not be fully represented.

The wide variation in assessment level is related to a general lack of information with regard to the major factors affecting value, confusion among agricultural and non-agricultural land use, legal problems, political considerations, and many other personal factors. To generalize is usually most difficult. However, in the agricultural Midwest at least, several relationships have been observed.[22]

1. Land low in productivity—the lower-priced farm properties—tends to be overassessed and land high in productivity—the higher priced farm properties—tends to be underassessed.[23]

2. Newer farm buildings and improvements tend to be assessed at levels higher than older buildings and improvements.

Several generalizations concerning the assessment levels on farm properties versus those on other types of property have also been observed.

1. In areas where farm properties make up a small portion of the taxable wealth, there has been a tendency to assess farm properties at levels lower than the non-farm properties. In these areas a high portion of the farm sales quite conceivably involve a change of land use—from farming to some higher and better use. The higher sale prices may thus represent not farm real estate values but property values for other purposes.[24]

2. In areas where farm properties make up a large portion of the taxable wealth, there has been a tendency to assess farm properties at levels slightly higher than the non-farm properties. In the areas where this observation was made, many of the assessors were farmers. The farmer-assessor undoubtedly does his best where he is more familiar with a particular type of property; he is undoubtedly more hesitant where he is less familiar with a particular type of property.

---

22. pp. 13 and 14, Heneberry.

23. This is commonly referred to as regressive assessment, i.e., relative over-assessment of low-valued properties and relative underassessment of high-valued properties.

24. Farmers in the urban areas often feel that they are paying more than their fair share of the cost of new schools and other community improvements. There may be a reason for this feeling or belief. Often there is a delay of a year or two, and sometimes more, in getting the newly constructed homes, commercial buildings, and industrial facilities onto the tax roll.

Hence, rural assessors may place lower or more conservative values on those properties with which they are not well acquainted.[25]

The rural assessor makes the best estimate he can on the basis of whatever information is available to him. Unfortunately, the tax base in many a rural area is too small to maintain a professional staff. A lack of time and insufficient financial resources often exist. The effects of such often lead to an unequal sharing of the tax load among farm owners, and furthermore, an inequitable distribution of state monies to these rural districts.

Equalization Among Tax Districts: Most state constitutions and tax statutes require statewide equalization. The purpose is to provide among all tax districts (1) a fair and equitable distribution of any state levy and (2) a fair and equitable distribution of any state monies. Property values in each taxing district have to be made uniform either at current market values or at some percentage thereof. Thus most states now make periodic, if not annual, surveys of assessment practices and assessed values. These are carried on by a tax commission, a revenue department, or some state agency concerned with the administration of the tax laws.

There are various equalization tests, but again the most common tool is the ratio between assessed values and sale prices.[26] This ratio can be developed two different ways.

Method No. 1. An aggregate ratio may be based on the grand total of all of the assessed values of all properties recently sold or transferred divided by the grand total of all of their sale prices. This ratio weights each property transferred according to its value; hence, the larger properties with higher values have a greater effect. The ratio developed in this fashion proves very little. The average obtained may be the exact prescribed assessment percentage. Yet, half the properties may be badly overassessed; the other half may be badly underassessed.

Method No. 2. A more accurate and meaningful approach is to calculate and compare the ratios on individual properties. The assessed value of each property sold or transferred is divided by its sale price. One now has not a single aggregate ratio, but instead as many individual ratios as there are property sales. These individual ratios may

---

25. The period during which each of these relationships became apparent was one of rising land values.

26. The assessed value—sale price ratio has the weakness in that certain types of properties and properties in some areas sell more readily than others. Hence, a recent sampling of property sales does not always give an adequate cross-section of the level of assessment.

be averaged and analyzed. When the average of all ratios is calculated, each property receives the same weight; the smaller properties thus have the same or an equal effect on the average as do the larger properties. Using this method, the variation or dispersion in ratios can be studied. More sophisticated statistical measures, such as the standard deviation about the arithmetic mean or median, can be calculated.

Equalization among tax districts is accomplished through the use of a multiplier. This multiplier is merely another index—percentage or ratio—between the state's average ratio and the one for each tax district. The multiplier is used to change the value of all properties in a given, tax district, usually upwards, a given percent. While this brings about equalization among the various districts, it tends to accentuate the inequities among property owners within each district. When, for example, a multiplier is used to increase the value of all properties in a given district it increases the value of those properties which were overassessed more (in terms of total dollars) than it increases the value of those properties which were underassessed. The inequities among property owners have now been increased.

The assessor who is reluctant to adjust property values sometimes waits and says, "Let the state equalization board do it." However, equalization boards do not concern themselves with differences in the levels of assessment among the different types of property or individual property owners within the tax district. A state multiplier merely equalizes the tax burden, or the distribution of funds, among districts. It is, relatively speaking, quite ineffective in reducing the inequities among types of property or among property owners. Hence, the assessor who says, "Let the state do it," merely intensifies the inequities among his own property owners.[27]

GIFT AND ESTATE TAX APPRAISALS

The Federal Government, along with many states, also levies gift, estate, and inheritance taxes. They are kindred to one another in that each is a tax on the right, the power, or the privilege of an individual

---

27. Fractional assessments complicate the equalization process even more by requiring that the assessment level in each district be measured not against 100, but against the average assessed value—sale price ratio of all tax districts. Hence, recognition of an equalization rate in itself immediately implies that the property was not assessed at full value even though the assessor may say that this was what was done.

to transmit, or transfer, any or all of his property. Generally speaking, if a person gives property valued at $30,000 or more to some other person, a gift tax return is required. If one's estate amounts to $60,000 or more at the time of death, a Federal estate tax return must be filed.

It is the administrator's, the executor's, or the personal representative's job to prepare a complete inventory and appraisement of all assets and liabilities in the deceased person's estate. The inventory in particular is the administrator's job, not the appraiser's. The assets typically include a number of items with fixed values such as cash on hand, bank accounts, corporate bonds, mortgages, land contracts receivable, life insurance policies, some common stock, an automobile or two with known blue book values, plus several items with no established or readily ascertainable market value. The latter type of asset requires appraisement. An example is farm real estate.

The values are of major concern not only to the personal representative but to the probate judge, the federal and state tax authorities, creditors, attorneys, and, of course, distributees—expectant heirs, devisees and legatees, and relatives and friends of the deceased. These values are needed in order to calculate the personal representative's compensation, pay the federal estate and state inheritance taxes, make settlements with creditors, determine court costs, and distribute the residual estate. Where there are insufficient assets of a liquid nature, an early estimate of value may help the personal representative decide on which property to keep and which to liquidate or sell, in order to pay both the probate costs and the estate and inheritance taxes.

The value sought in most appraisals is market value. The courts frequently refer to such as fair market value. The United States Treasury Regulations define fair market value as "the price for which the property would change hands between a willing buyer and a willing seller, both having a reasonable knowledge of all relevant facts, and neither being under any compulsion to buy or to sell."[28] Needless to say, if the fair market value is too high, the estate is unnecessarily enlarged and capital is eroded through excessive costs and taxation. If the fair market value is too low, the estate runs the risk of becoming involved in a long, tedious, and costly dispute with the tax authorities. Thus, everyone is really desirous of a fair and honorable, and yet not too high, market value. Any opinion should be presented in an organized fashion and should be substantiated by whatever facts are relevant.

---

28. *Guide to Federal Estate and Gift Taxation.*

Most heirs, and oftentimes their attorney, do not want a professional appraisal. Instead, they want a low or conservative estimate. When they visit with an appraiser, they usually do not hesitate to influence or ask him to arrive at such a figure. Professional appraisers have sometimes withdrawn from, and in fact refused to take, an appraisal assignment when the heirs, or their attorney, have attempted to press for or dictate value. Ironically, a low value is often a mistake. Various heirs have often found themselves in both an embarrassing and a disadvantageous position when a low basis (or appraised value) established at the time of death later leads to increased capital gains and hence a higher income tax when they decide to sell the property at some later date.[29]

In the case of a gift, the appraisal date to which the value pertains is the date on which a gift was made. In the case of death there are two appraisal dates—the date of death and an alternative several months later. The appraiser may appraise a farm as of the date of death and then be asked to update his appraisal as of a particular date several months after the decedent's death. The personal representative may then elect to use either of the two market values, thus selecting the date on which to base his tax calculations. In each instance, only such facts as would be available to a prospective purchaser as of the date to which the value pertains should be considered, even though the farm inspection or appraisal may actually be made on some later date.

The appraisal report that is required varies with the jurisdiction. A mere letter or certificate report is often all that is prescribed. Yet the experienced appraiser should still go through the entire appraisal process—making a physical description of the property, preparing an estimate of its productive capacity, and where applicable, using all three approaches to value. He should develop and keep all supportive evidence substantiating his final value figure in his files.

Estate appraisals are subject to review by the Internal Revenue Service. If the appraisal is not satisfactory, it can become a part of litigation. The professional appraiser thus knows that he may have to defend his values at some later date. Hence, he does both a thorough and an honest job.

Unfortunately, many states have treated estate appraisals in an

---

29. As a general rule the federal estate tax value becomes a farm's "cost or other basis" for future calculations for income tax purposes. A low estate tax value may lead to a disadvantage in terms of higher income taxes which have to be paid in the future.

almost contemptuous fashion. The statutes in general call for a certain number of appraisers to be appointed by the probate judge, although in some instances they are appointed by the estate's personal representative. There are seldom any real requirements related to the appointee's education, professional ability, or his appraisal experience or reputation.[30]

The appointees are often political cronies, relatives on the wife's or spouse's side of the family, and courthouse employees. In some instances, they include a real estate broker willing to work for a small fee and sign the appraisement form as a matter of convenience. In some instances, they include a neighboring farmer or property owner who is a good friend of the family.[31] In some instances, the attorney for the estate makes the appraisal. Unqualified persons are often appointed; then when a professional appraiser is included, he ends up doing all the work and educating his colleagues. The others merely sign the same blank and collect an equal amount of money.

Walstein Smith put it very well when he said, "It would be unthinkable, as well as illegal, for a person not duly licensed to practice law, to provide legal advice and assistance to those interested parties involved in a certain estate. It would be unthinkable, as well as illegal, for a judge who was not either duly appointed or elected to serve as probate judge. Yet, many judges, lawyers, and legislators appear to have no objections to the use of unqualified appraisers in probate matters."[32]

Ad valorem tax appraisals are no less important than any other kind. However, there is no other area where professional appraisers and proper appraisal technique are more badly needed. If the general property tax and the federal estate and state inheritance taxes are to be administered properly, then appraisal objectives and political processes should be separated. The courthouse employees and their friends often keep true cash and fair market values as low as possible. However, they are doing a disservice to their friends and fellow tax-

---

30. The terms, *citizens in the county, property owners, disinterested parties,* and *impartial or without bias,* are often used. Most generally, the town drunk could meet the standards, even without ever having made a single appraisal.

31. If one takes the time to carefully examine a number of estate tax appraisals, it is not unusual to find where a neighboring farmer has made the appraisal, then several months later bought the property at a price considerably higher than his appraised value.

32. p. 10, Smith, *The Real Estate Appraiser.*

payers who are supposedly carrying their fair share of the tax burden, yet unfortunately remain uninformed.

The need for professional appraisers will undoubtedly become more and more apparent as farm land values and farm property taxes continue to increase. Hopefully, John Q. Public will some day be convinced that there is no substitute for full value assessment and full public disclosure, whether it is he or whether it is his heirs and assignees that pay his taxes.

REFERENCES

Bartlett, C. R., "What Every Appraiser Should Know About the Property Tax," *Appraisal Journal*, Vol. 31, No. 3, July 1963.

Bird, Ronald, *Taxes Levied on Farm Property in the United States and Methods of Estimating Them*, U.S.D.A., A.R.S., Statistical Bulletin No. 189, August 1956.

Broemmel, B. W., "Property Tax Assessment—Concepts and Problems," *The Real Estate Appraiser*, Vol. 30, No. 9, September 1964.

Groves, H. M., *Financing Government*, Holt, 1945.

Harris, C. L., *Property Tax Reform: More Progress, Less Poverty*, DePauw University, 1970.

Helmberger, J. D., "The Changing Role of the Property Tax," *Minnesota Agricultural Economist*, No. 539, February 1971.

Heneberry, W. H., and R. Barlowe, *Assessment of Farm Real Estate for Property Taxes in the North Central States*, Michigan State Agricultural Experiment Station Special Bulletin 439, 1962.

Keith, J. H., *Property Tax Assessment Practices*, Highland Publishing Co., 1966.

Lynn, A. D., Jr., Editor, *The Property Tax and Its Administration*, University of Wisconsin Press, 1969.

Meyer, H. F., "Market Value—Beacon Light of Appraisal for Taxation," *Appraisal Journal*, Vol. 33, No. 4, October 1965.

Netzer, Dick, *Economics of the Property Tax*, Brookings Institution, 1966.

(No Name), *Assessing and the Appraisal Process*, 2nd Edition, International Association of Assessing Officers, 1968.

Rackham, J. B., "Aspects of Property Taxation," *The Real Estate Appraiser*, Vol. 39, No. 1, January-February 1973.

Rountree, J. E., "Appraising the Assessment," *Appraisal Journal*, Vol. 25, No. 2, April 1957.

Stocker, F. D., "How Taxes Affect the Land and Farmers," *1958 Yearbook of Agriculture*, U.S.D.A., 1958.

The Assessor's Job

Mayhew, S. J., "How Assessed Valuations Are Established," Proceedings, winter meeting, *Illinois Society of Farm Managers and Rural Appraisers*, January 1965.

(No Name), *Assessing and the Appraisal Process,* 2nd Edition, International Association of Assessing Officers, 1968.

Stocker, F. D., "The Taxation of Farmland," *A Place to Live: The 1963 Yearbook of Agriculture,* U.S.D.A., 1963.

Zirkel, William, "Excessive Taxation and Its Effect on Real Estate Values," *The Real Estate Appraiser,* Vol. 36, No. 6, September-October 1970.

The Mass Appraisal Technique

Appelson, W. B., "Essential Contents for Assessment Manuals," *Appraisal Journal,* Vol. 27, No. 4, October 1959.

Ashton, P. M., "The Use of Multiple Regression Analysis in the Valuation of Real Estate," *The Real Estate Appraiser,* Vol. 38, No. 1, January-February 1972.

Bailey, R. R., "Appraisals for Tax Assessment," *Journal of American Society of Farm Managers and Rural Appraisers,* Vol. 13, No. 1, April 1949.

Carlson, D. M., and B. H. Story, Jr., "Computers in Real Estate Appraising," *The Real Estate Appraiser,* Vol. 32, No. 10, October 1966.

Carr, A. W., "Some Suggestions for 'Volume Appraisers,'" *The Real Estate Appraiser,* Vol. 33, No. 5, May 1967.

Case, F. E., "Electronic Data Processing and the Appraisal Function," *The Real Estate Appraiser,* Vol. 32, No. 9, September 1966.

Dasso, Jerome, and Paul Swadener, "Data Processing Implications for Property Taxation," *Appraisal Journal,* Vol. 38, No. 1, January 1970.

Freeman, R. J., "Real Estate Assessment and Electronic Computers," *Appraisal Journal,* Vol. 27, No. 2, April 1959.

General Appraisal Manual, California State Board of Equalization, 1968.

Hinton, W. L., "How to Propose and Staff for Reassessment Appraisal Projects," *The Residential Appraiser,* Vol. 26, No. 5, May 1960.

Indiana Real Property Appraisal Manual, Indiana State Board of Tax Commissioners, 1968.

James, M. H., Jr., "Some Notes and Thoughts on Multiple Regression Analysis," *The Real Estate Appraiser,* Vol. 38, No. 2, March-April 1972.

Keith, J. H., *Property Tax Assessment Practices,* Highland Publishing Co., 1966.

Nebraska Appraisal Manual, Nebraska State Board, 1965.

Rountree, J. E., "Appraisal for Tax Purposes," *Encyclopedia of Real Estate Appraising,* Prentice-Hall, 1959.

Preferential Treatment

Buchmiller, M. K., "Farmland Gets Tax Relief," *Doane's,* July 1967.

Ching, C. T. K., *Effects of Alternatives to Ad Valorem Taxation on Land Use,* New Hampshire Agricultural Experiment Station Report No. 4, September 1968.

Ching, C. T. K., and G. E. Frick, *Effect of Use Value Assessment on Assessed Valuations and Tax Rates,* New Hampshire Agricultural Experiment Station Report No. 13, June 1970.

Farmland Assessment Practices in the United States, International Association of Assessing Officers, 1966.

Friday, R. E., *Summaries of State Legislation Dealing with the Preservation of Farmland*, Cornell University, A. E. 547, October 1969.

Hady, T. F., "Differential Assessment of Farmland on the Rural-Urban Fringe," *American Journal of Agricultural Economics*, Vol. 52, No. 1, February 1970.

Hady, T. F., and T. F. Stinson, *Taxation of Farmland on the Rural-Urban Fringe: A Summary of State Preferential Assessment Activity*, Agricultural Economic Report No. 119, E.R.S., U.S.D.A., September 1967.

House, Peter, *Differential Assessment of Farmland Near Cities . . . Experience in Maryland Through 1965*, Report No. 358, E.R.S., U.S.D.A., October 1967.

House, Peter, "Farm Land Assessment in Rural-Urban Fringe," *Appraisal Journal*, Vol. 29, No. 1, January 1961.

House, Peter, "Partial Tax Exemption for Farmland Properties in the Rural-Urban Fringe," *Appraisal Journal*, Vol. 36, No. 3, July 1968.

Keith, J. H., "The Assessor and A. C. A. 4," *Appraisal Journal*, Vol. 30, No. 3, July 1962.

Poole, A. T., Jr., "Use-Value Assessment—What Is It?," Virginia Agricultural Economics 216, April-June 1970.

Stoevener, H. H., "Some Economic Aspects of Agricultural Zoning and Farmland Taxation," *Journal of American Society of Farm Managers and Rural Appraisers*, Vol. 30, No. 2, October 1966.

Walker, W. P., and W. D. Gardner, *Assessing Farm Land Under Maryland's Use Value Assessment Law*, Maryland Agricultural Experiment Station Misc. Pub. 522, June 1964.

Full Versus Fractional Assessment

Hogan, H. T., "Judicial Review of Real Estate Tax Assessments," *The Real Estate Appraiser*, Vol. 29, No. 1, January 1963.

Johnson, E. H., "The Merits of Full Value Assessments," *Appraisal Journal*, Vol. 26, No. 1, January 1958.

The Problem of Equitability and Equalization

Cherney, R. A., "Use of Sales Assessment Ratios in Assessing Real Property," *Appraisal Journal*, Vol. 23, No. 4, October 1955.

Heneberry, W. H., and Raleigh Barlowe, *Assessment of Farm Real Estate for Property Taxes in the North Central States*, Michigan State Agricultural Experiment Station, Special Bulletin 439, 1962.

Heneberry, W. H., and Raleigh Barlowe, *Property Tax Trends Affecting Michigan Farmers*, Michigan State Agricultural Experiment Station Special Bulletin 421, 1959.

Moss, Francis, "Improving Administration of Property Taxes," *Michigan Farm Economics*, No. 330, July 1970.

Sandstrom, Clayton, "Assessed Valuation, Equal or Unequal?," *The Residential Appraiser*, Vol. 27, No. 9, September 1961.

Gift and Estate Tax Appraisals

Beaton, W. R., and Phillip Pickens, "Estate Appraisals," *The Real Estate Appraiser*, Vol. 35, No. 4, May-June 1969.

Davis, W. D., "Valuations for Federal Taxation," *Journal of American Society of Farm Managers and Rural Appraisers*, Vol. 19, No. 1, April 1955.

Harl, N. E., "The Federal Estate Tax and Estate Planning," *Journal of American Society of Farm Managers and Rural Appraisers*, Vol. 35, No. 1, April 1971.

Higgins, J. W., "The Sale of Land: Capital Gain or Ordinary Income," *The Real Estate Appraiser*, Vol. 39, No. 1, January-February 1973.

Jackson, J. M., "Preparing Farm Appraisals for Federal Estate Tax Purposes," Proceedings, winter meeting, *Illinois Society of Farm Managers and Rural Appraisers*, February 1962.

Larch, J. A., "Appraisals and Sales in Trusts and Estates," *Appraisal Journal*, Vol. 39, No. 1, January 1971.

Lasser, J. K., *How to Save Estate and Gift Taxes*, Doubleday, 1969.

Smith, Walstein, Jr., "Appraising for Probate and Estates," *The Real Estate Appraiser*, Vol. 35, No. 5, July-August 1969.

Statistical Studies

Aandahl, A. R., W. G. Murray, and Wayne Scholtes, "Economic Rating of Soils for Tax Assessment," *Journal Farm Economics*, Vol. 36, No. 3, August 1954.

Ahmed, Mohammed M. A., and L. A. Parcher, *Assessing Farmland in a Metropolitan Area*, Oklahoma Agricultural Economics Series P-503, April 1965.

Ahmed, Mohammed M. A., and L. A. Parcher, "Equitability of Farm Real Estate Assessment for Tax Purposes," *Oklahoma Current Farm Economics*, Vol. 37, No. 4, December 1954.

Davis, I. F., Jr., *A Statistical Approach to Farm Land Values*, Bureau of Business Research, Fresno State College, Study No. 6, June 1963.

Haas, G. C., *Sale Prices as a Basis for Farm Land Appraisal*, Minnesota Agricultural Experiment Station, Technical Bulletin 9, November 1922.

Ottoson, H. W., A. R. Aandahl, and L. B. Kristjanson, "A Method of Farm Real Estate Valuation for Tax Assessment," *Journal Farm Economics*, Vol. 37, No. 3, August 1955.

CHAPTER XII

Appraisals for Farm Loans

A farm real estate loan is a temporary transfer of capital providing the means whereby the ownership of a farm can be transferred or a farming operation can be refinanced. A real estate loan may provide the money to purchase a given farm, to build a new set of improvements, to pay the estate taxes, to consolidate all previous debts, etc.

In the case of a farm transfer, any one of several legal instruments may change hands—sometimes a conventional deed and a mortgage (in some states, a deed-in-trust) and sometimes an installment land contract. The deed, which the grantor (seller) gives the grantee (buyer) is the instrument of ownership or transfer. The mortgage which the mortgagor (borrower) gives the mortgagee (lender) is the security, or the instrument of credit. An installment land contract may instead be used both as an instrument of transferring ownership (on a conditional basis) and as an instrument of credit. The previous owner or seller essentially finances the sale. The buyer obtains beneficial ownership, usually immediately; however, he does not obtain full ownership rights (or the deed) until he fulfills the obligations of the contract. The mortgage is held by the lender; however, the land contract is usually held by a third party called an escrow agent.

In either case, the new owner or borrower agrees to pay the seller or the lender certain predetermined amounts of money (interest) for the use of the capital; he also agrees to someday repay or return the capital itself. Most real estate loans are amortized, or in other words, paid back on a gradual or piecemeal basis over a period of time. Repayment plans typically specify a fixed number of monthly, quarterly, or semi-annual payments. There are two typical plans. One calls for level, or equal, principal and interest payments over the loan

---

The loan appraiser's job is to not only appraise the farm but to also interview the present operator and obtain a financial statement. The upper limit as to loan value may be established by (1) the value of the security, (2) the earnings capacity of the farm, or (3) the managerial ability of the present operator himself.

Courtesy, U.S.D.A.

period. Interest payments are high at first; however, they gradually decline and as they do so the principal payments increase. The two offset one another. The other calls for level, or equal, principal payments over the loan period and for interest on the unpaid balance of the loan. Hence, the interest and the total payments both decline over the period of the loan.

In the transfer of ownership, the seller and the buyer typically get together, bargain, and sooner or later decide on the consideration or the amount of money which is to change hands. However, when the lender is a third party, he typically wants an appraisal of his own. He also interviews the prospective borrower, obtaining from him a financial statement and some financial history. The farm loan appraiser is occasionally an independent fee appraiser. However, most generally, he's a full-time salaried employee of the lending institution or agency. He usually spends part of his time appraising and part of his time as a farm loan representative.

THE PARTICIPANTS: PAST AND PRESENT

Prior to the 1930's, there was no real objective method of farm-land valuation in this country. Agriculture was basic. It was worthy. Hence, money flowed into agriculture, particularly long-term loans. However, in the 1930's, farm income evaporated and land values tumbled. Farm mortgages became overdue and foreclosures took place.

Out of this chaos came the first really systematic approach to farm appraisal. Major developments included (1) basic farm value—based on earnings, (2) normal market value—supposedly a substantive long-run value, (3) yields representative of the area, (4) the use of average farm commodity prices, and (5) the typical operator concept. The primary contributors were the farm loan appraisers working for the insurance companies, the Farm Credit Administration, and several university farm economists.

Today there are five major participants in farm loan appraisal and farm mortgage lending—the insurance companies, the Federal land banks, the Farmers Home Administration, a large number of commercial banks, and a variety of individuals. The changing roles played by each has been an important part of agriculture's history (Figure 23).

The Life Insurance Companies: Farm appraisals by the life insurance companies go back to around 1910. Several insurance companies made loans prior to that date, but it was not until 1910 or 1920 that they began to experiment with various systems for reporting appraised values. In the last 50 years or so, some 30 different companies have been active in farm and ranch appraisal work and in the making of farm mortgage loans. Aetna, Connecticut General, Connecticut Mutual, Equitable, John Hancock, Metropolitan, Mutual Benefit, Mutual of New York, Northwestern Mutual, Phoenix Mutual, Prudential, and Travelers are a few of the names. These companies have had good farm mortgage loan departments and well-organized and capable field staffs. Their local representatives have worked with farm families over wide areas.

The insurance companies loan monies that "belong" to someone else (their policy holders). Many persons buy life insurance and many of them pay their premiums out of fairly modest incomes. They then depend on an insurance company to turn over to them, or to their designated beneficiaries at some date in the future, fairly substantial sums of money when they die or "cash in" their policies. Many corporations also rely on an insurance company to develop their pension program, and to invest various trust funds in common stock, in debentures, and/or in real estate mortgages.

These funds must be invested in relatively safe and productive assets. They must earn reasonable rates of return after deducting all

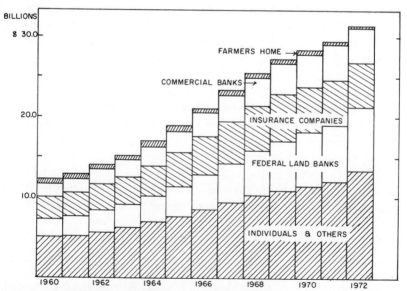

Figure 23. Farm Mortgage Debt Related to Principal Lenders.
United States, 1960-1972.

costs. A farm mortgage or loan department is thus faced with two questions: (1) Will the money be safe? (2) Will the investment be profitable? The latter must be evaluated both on an absolute basis and relative to other alternatives.

The monies left with an insurance company are usually left for a number of years. Hence, the insurance companies like to invest only on a long-term basis. Fortunately, this fits the farmer's needs quite well. Most farm mortgages are written for 20 to 40 years. The loans are usually amortized. They require either semiannual or annual payments of both principal and interest. The principal payments gradually reduce and then eventually retire the loans. In the event that the farmer has an extra good year, most contracts permit additional payments without penalty. Thus, if drought, low farm prices, or other difficulties occur after the first few years, the borrower has a cushion.

Beginning in the 1920's, the insurance companies expanded rather rapidly into the farm mortgage loan business. They invested in practically all farming areas. Many of their loans were made through the services of a local correspondent—a real estate broker, a banker, or an insurance agent—who was paid a finder's fee or commission. However, the inability of many farmers to meet their payments during the depression forced these same companies to become the unwilling owners of a large number of farms. They foreclosed loans, managed farms, and sold farms, often to the tenant-operator, and often at what now appears to be bargain prices. Lender experience during this period of time was neither enjoyable nor profitable.

As a result, the insurance companies began to curtail their farm loan operations. They got out of certain marginal agricultural areas. They loaned only on conventional farming operations. They loaned only to the better farm operators.[1] At the same time, they began to replace their local correspondents with college trained farm boys— young men who were more knowledgeable about agriculture.

Generally speaking, the insurance companies have remained competitive. Since the 1930's they have faced increased competition from the government agencies and more recently from seller-financed installment land contracts. The insurance companies are, of course, able to purchase a variety of both fixed payment obligations and equity

---

1. In the past, the insurance companies also avoided the specialty farms. The management factor is often the dominant one leading to financial success or failure. The factor varies greatly; however, it's more likely to be good to excellent today in many of the more specialized farming operations. Hence, today several of them have become involved, particularly when they have a man trained in that area.

investments. They are interested in those assets with the highest
dollar returns or earnings. As a result, the dollar returns on farm
mortgages have had to equal, over the long run at least, those yields
available on alternative investments.

The mortgage rates of interest charged farmers have varied somewhat among areas. They have varied somewhat among different types
of property. They have varied somewhat with the size of the loan and
the intensity of the competition. At the same time, the interest rate is
influenced mainly by the supply of and the demand for money in the
economy.

In the late 1960's, some of the insurance companies were again
forced to curtail their operations. Three things had occurred. The
money supply had been restricted, and with minor previous exceptions,
interest rates had increased sharply for the first time in almost 40
years. The usury laws in some states placed a ceiling on loan rates
and made the making of farm loans rather unattractive. At the same
time, the Federal government continued to sponsor, in fact subsidize,
loans to farmers at below-the-market rates of interest.

However, in spite of these events, the life insurance companies
have remained as major participants in the agricultural lending field.
They have become more selective perhaps; however, they continue to
make loans on the larger farms and ranches and to the commercial
farm operators with the higher levels of management.

The Federal Land Banks: In 1917, the Federal Farm Loan Act
established a farmers' cooperative credit system known as the Federal
Land Bank. The system consists of 12 banks, or districts, and numerous
local associations. The Congress of the United States created the land
bank system in order to provide a dependable source of farm mortgage
credit at reasonable rates and on terms adapted to the needs of farmers.
The program called for long-term, low-interest loans on an amortized
basis.

Most of the initial supply of capital was provided by the Federal
government. In fact, the Congress provided additional monies through
commissioner loans when farmers were in real need of mortgage credit
in 1933 in order to refinance their debts. However, down through the
years, each farmer-borrower has been required to buy stock in his
local land bank association in an amount equal to 5.0 percent of his
loan. The local association has in turn bought a similar amount of stock
in the district bank, and this, plus earnings, has gradually enabled the
land banks to retire the government's stock of capital. Thus, while the
Federal land banks were initially sponsored by the Congress, they

became totally owned by their member-borrowers in 1947.[2] Hence, the land banks are a unique alliance of government, the financial community, and the farmer.

Most of the current capital needs are today obtained through the sale of consolidated bonds to the investing public. The bonds are secured by the mortgages on farm real estate, by the assets of the banks and the local associations, and by the feeling that in case of dire emergency the Federal government will assist (even though there is no guarantee of this happening). Thus, many investors consider land bank bonds to be prime investments.

The Federal land banks have had several definite advantages over the institutional lenders. Their bonds have been valid securities, at one time constituting instrumentalities of the United States Government. Hence the risks, assumed by investors (and the interest rates paid), are low. Being farmer-owned cooperatives and hence tax exempt, the banks pay no federal or state income taxes. Their loans have, in general, been less subject to various state rules and regulations regarding loan ratios and terms. They have been exempt from the usury laws.

At the same time the Federal land banks are obligated by law to serve all commercial farmers, in all parts of the country, and at all times. The associations can't pick or choose or close down when business is bad. Thus, the land banks have played an increasingly larger role in the financing of farm real estate.

In the beginning, the land bank led the shift from five-year loans to long-term amortized farm loans. The term or period now ranges up to 40 years. In the beginning, the amount of the loan could not exceed 50 percent of the appraised value of the land plus 20 percent of the value of all permanent and insured improvements. A 1933 amendment to the Federal Farm Loan Act raised this loan limit to 65 percent of the normal value of the farm (which was then above market value). Later the loan could include the amount of stock the member-borrower was required to purchase.

In the early 1930's, the Federal land banks were restricted to a 1-percent spread between the interest rate on loans and the cost of their funds. The objective was to provide farmers with loans at the

---

2. The Farm Credit Administration, an independent agency within the executive branch of the government, still has regulatory and supervisory authority. These responsibilities provide uniformity in policy. They assure that the basic objectives are being achieved and that all lending operations are being conducted in the interest of the public.

lowest possible cost. While this restriction is no longer in vogue, the land banks have continued to make loans to farmers at interest rates below those typically charged by other commercial lenders.[3]

Traditionally, an appraisal of the farm by a qualified appraiser approved by the land bank has been required in order to obtain a Federal land bank loan. Up until 1972, the loans were supposedly based on each farm's normal agricultural value. The loans could not exceed 65 percent of that value. (These rules, however, were not always adhered to.) Furthermore, the loans are supposedly "tailored" to borrower needs—the durability of the security, the earnings capacity of the farm, and the borrower's debt-paying ability. This "tailoring" has been excellent theory; however, it's been (and is) very difficult to apply.

In 1969, the Farm Credit Board established a commission on agricultural credit to re-evaluate and recommend changes in the system. Among the recommendations were: (1) new programs to assist young farmers, (2) increased emphasis on borrowers' earning abilities, (3) broader eligibility for loans to farmer cooperatives, and (4) new programs for agricultural firms furnishing services directly to farmers. The commission further recommended (1) that management ability be given a greater weight in the making of loan judgments and (2) that the 65-percent-of-normal-value statutory limit on the amount of money that could be loaned be removed.

Many of these recommendations were incorporated into the Farm Credit Act of 1971. The land banks and the production credit associations became able to finance non-farm rural housing. For the first time they could finance non-farm businesses furnishing on-farm services. The law increased the loan ratio or limit to 85 percent of some "appraised value." Thus, the farm credit system continued to broaden its activities and serve the agricultural community.

The Farmers Home Administration: During the 1930's, the number of tenant-operated farms increased rapidly. These tenants, particularly in the agricultural Midwest and even more so in the South, faced considerable difficulty in becoming farm owners. Hence, in 1937, the Congress of the United States passed the Bankhead-Jones Farm Tenant Act, authorizing government loans to tenant farmers for purposes of purchasing farms. It was administered by the Farm Security Administration.

Farm loans were made available "in such amounts as may be neces-

---

3. And, as a result, some associations have experienced financial difficulty.

sary . . ." The period, or term, was 40 years, the interest rate was 3.0 percent, and the payment plans called for amortization. The borrowers could also elect a variable payment provision which essentially permitted them to increase their payments in the good years and reduce them in the poor years. The only limitation to the number of loans made was the size of the annual appropriations made by Congress.

These agricultural loan activities were then re-examined and reorganized by the Congress in 1946. In the process, the Farmers Home Administration was created. This act authorized loans for farm enlargement and farm improvement as well as purchase. It stressed the family farm; however, it limited the loan size to the average value of all family-type farms in each county. The Congress then liberalized the Farmers Home Administration loan policy in 1956, authorizing the

In farm mortgage lending the various "rules" vary with the participants. The insurance companies like to make loans in only the more productive farming areas. However, the Farmers Home Administration is limited, by law, to loan money only to those applicants who are unable to acquire long-term credit from some other source.

Photo by Suter and Courtesy, U.S.D.A.

refinancing of debt and raising loan limits to "the fair and reasonable value" of the farm.[4] In 1962, loan limits were broadened, and in 1969, they were broadened again. Today, money is generally available for farm ownership loans, farm operating loans, and rural housing.

The original purpose of the Farmers Home Administration loan program was to help farmers get started in farming and to help them adjust their farming operations so they could ride out temporary emergencies. The loans were not intended to provide permanent financing. The agency was instead established to fill the gap that supposedly existed in farm credit by making loans to farmers who lacked the collateral or other requisites needed to obtain conventional financing.

Theoretically, the Farmers Home Administration does not compete with the private lending institutions. An FHA loan is a non-competitive loan. The prospective borrower must be unable to obtain

---

4. The 1956 act also authorized a mortgage insurance program. Two types of farm ownership loans were made available—(1) direct loans made out of funds appropriated by Congress and (2) insured loans made by the agency and sold to private lenders.

financing from any other lender (at reasonable terms and rates). Furthermore, he must agree to refinance his loan as soon as certain adversities are overcome or as soon as he can obtain another source of credit. Sooner or later he is supposed to graduate.

Today, all FHA loans supposedly have the following characteristics:

1. They are restricted to farmers or applicants who are unable to acquire long-term farm mortgage credit on reasonable terms from some other source.

2. The borrowers often have little or no equity in their farms; hence, the amounts of money loaned are often from 90 to 100 percent of appraised values.

3. Farm values are determined by loan supervisors, and are based largely on the market. This is a recent change, for in the past, farm values were based on earning capacities, derived by capitalizing the net income that the average farm operator could earn on the farm.[5]

4. The loans granted are not based solely on the security or the amount of collateral available; they are also made on the basis of economic need.[6] Eligibility is determined by a three-man county advisory committee. Their recommendation may be based on the applicant's character, experience, and managerial ability as well as his financial resources. Final loan approval, or disapproval, is made by a loan officer at either the county or state level, depending on the size of the loan.

5. The 1973 farm ownership loans were limited to $100,000. They were being amortized over a 40-year period and the interest rate was 5.0 percent. Farm operating loans were limited to $50,000. They were amortized over a seven-year period, and the interest rate was 5.875 percent. All farm ownership and farm operating loans were amortized; however, the operating loans could contain a balloon payment at the end of the term.[7]

6. Repayment schedules are based on ability to pay and are

---

5. A county committee may also certify ". . . a fair and reasonable value" above that recommended by the appraiser if the long-term farm plan shows an income potential greater than that contemplated by the loan supervisor, or if the applicant has better-than-average managerial ability.

6. Social impact and political favoritism may also be factors.

7. This is the final lump-sum payment due at the end of the loan period. Oftentimes it is substantial in amount. A balloon payment has been referred to as a sort of nefarious scheme in the past. Hence, the use of such today is a reversal of the government's previous lending policies, if not philosophy, of the 1930's, which was to get all farm loans on an amortized basis.

geared to the expected cash flow.[8] In fact, the initial principal payments may be reduced; if need be, they may be postponed until the borrower effects a major reorganization or improvement.

7. The loans are supervised. Long-term farm and home plans are drawn up by the farm loan supervisor and the borrower to show the steps required to attain the long-run objectives. Annual plans are developed to show both expected cash receipts and anticipated disbursements. The latter include farm operating expenses, family living expenses, capital outlays, and debt retirement. The borrowers are then required to keep a financial record of both their farming operations and their family living expenses.

Supervision supposedly enables the making of these loans, up to 100 percent of value, to persons who lack adequate collateral or to persons who are unable to obtain financial backing elsewhere. At this loan level, supervision is much more necessary than with a conventional loan. Supervision supposedly protects the public's investment;[9] however, it undoubtedly makes the FHA loan program a costly one.

The Farmers Home Administration has helped transfer farm resources from the older, semiretired farmers to the younger ones who want to start farming and yet are unable to obtain credit. It has aided in farm consolidation and in the regrouping of small tracts into larger economic units. However, the program represents an extension of credit, the costs of which are in no way fully covered by the interest rate. It is essentially a source of subsidized credit which has meant increased competition for both the insurance companies and the Federal land banks.

During the period of its development (from the 1930's on), American agriculture has produced more farm products than the nation's markets have been able to absorb at what some persons refer to as "reasonable" prices. Farm income has had a tendency to decline, in real if not in dollar terms. The market for farm products has often indicated a need for some downward adjustment in agricultural production. Thus, the basic need has not been for a Farmers Home Administration, or for any other government agency, to bring more people into agriculture or more land into farming. Instead the need has been to move these resources in the opposite direction.

This thought imposes on the Farmers Home Administration the need to carefully select its farm borrowers. Otherwise it is working

---

8. These attributes are exceedingly difficult to measure. According to one ex-supervisor, little or no actual analysis is done.

9. The only actual protection is that thing called "moral integrity."

at cross-purposes with other government programs and farm policy objectives. If the program is to best serve the interests of both agriculture and the public-at-large, then only those persons who show real promise of becoming successful commercial farmers, and for whom there is real need—for example, replacements for retiring farmers—should be eligible for loans.

Commercial Banks: The commercial banks in most rural communities also make farm mortgage loans. In fact, a large increase has occurred in recent years in some areas. A commercial bank's funds consist of demand deposits, representing its patrons' day-to-day activities, and time deposits, representing these same patrons' savings.

The typical commercial bank has about 30 percent of its loan portfolio in real estate loans. However, the figure varies. Where the bank's funds are primarily demand deposits, which must be made available to the public upon demand, the bank is usually interested only in short-term investments. Where the funds are primarily time deposits or savings certificates, the bank is more interested in making long-term loans. Thus, some banks have sizeable real estate loan departments.

Long-term commercial bank loans are regulated by law. In Indiana, for example, real estate loans cannot exceed 40 percent of a bank's total deposits. They cannot exceed 75 percent of a bank's time deposits.[10] A commercial bank in Indiana may lend no more than 80 percent of the appraised value of the farm, for only a 25-year term, and with the proviso that the entire loan is amortized. If no amortization payments are to be made, the term is limited to five years, and the size of the loan is limited to 50 percent of the appraised value of the farm.

Most of the long-term commercial bank loans are temporary accommodations. They are arranged primarily for the good customers, pending on a more permanent financial arrangement being obtained with another lender. The banks have offered long-term farm mortgage loans through contact with various insurance companies and through the insured farm loan program of the Farmers Home Administration. Not always are the loans made for purposes of farm transfer. Occasionally, mortgages are assumed as collateral for purposes of consolidating various loans which were originally extended for other purposes.

In some areas, the commercial banks are much more active than any other lender. Yet, in other areas, farm mortgage loans by com-

---

10. Sec. 18-1307, *Indiana Banking and Related Laws.*

mercial banks are few in number. Bank loans are usually smaller, and they are usually for shorter terms. However, not always. There is a good bit of variation among areas.

Individuals: A large share of farm real estate credit has been and is being provided by individuals. In fact, more than half of all farmland sales are financed by sellers, and of these, a high proportion are conditional transfers using a land contract.

The installment land contract is a legal instrument which provides both a means of transferring ownership and a means of providing long-term credit at the same time. The previous property owner essentially finances the new one. These contracts often enable buyers to purchase farms with considerably less equity than that required using the more conventional farm mortgage. They provide sellers with the opportunity to spread the capital gains obtained, as a result of the sale, over a period of several years, thus reducing their income taxes.

The contract sale is actually a conditional sale. Title to the property does not pass from seller to buyer until certain obligations, as stated in the contract, are fulfilled, or until the buyer has paid a stipulated amount of money. The buyer's risk is considerably greater than with a deed and mortgage, for all instruments are usually placed in the hands of an escrow agent.[11] Should the buyer become unable to meet his payments, he may lose most of the amount he has paid the seller.

A land contract is a very flexible instrument. It can be adapted to the needs of each party and to each individual situation. Existing owners are often willing to grant credit on rather favorable terms with the interest rates typically one-half to one full percentage point below the rates charged by conventional lenders. This is because the sale of a farm, on contract and over a period of time, is much more favorable to most sellers, tax-wise, than is the sale of a farm for cash.

Most sellers are knowledgeable about agriculture. In the event of economic adversity, they are usually reasonable in their dealings. However, most of them are older persons. The death of the seller or lender may change a particular situation quite unexpectedly. Hence, a buyer should not only make sure the terms of an installment land contract fit his situation, he should also acquaint himself with the seller, his age, and his reputation before entering into a contract.

---

11. The seller places a warranty deed in escrow to be transferred to the buyer whenever he fulfills his obligations. The buyer is often asked to sign a quitclaim deed, which is also placed in escrow, and which is transferred to the seller in the event that he, the buyer, does not meet or fulfill his obligations.

The individual, as contrasted to a financial institution or agency, may be the most desirable source of credit. On the other hand, he may also be the most difficult person or party to deal with and the most undesirable source of credit.

THE FARM MORTGAGE LENDER'S PROBLEM

A farm mortgage loan is a loan for a long period of time. Principal and interest payments are typically made over 20 to 40 years—periods sufficiently long so that all kinds of economic change may take place. The role played by the lender is somewhat unique in that he does not generally stand to gain if or when property values rise. Yet he may be affected quite adversely if property values decline, and particularly if the decline is a severe one.

Hence, some very real questions are: "What will happen to farm land values over the loan period? Will farm prices go up? Will they someday level off? Or will they decline?" Whatever happens in terms of changing farm prices, farm costs, and farm property values affects the rate of loan turnover in the farm mortgage department. Whatever happens may also make the lender either (1) a shining success or (2) a dismal failure.

One can easily give credit to or lay blame on the appraiser who established the values on various farms in the first place. However, the appraiser's job is merely to ascertain the present market value of the property when the loan is made (as of a given date). Then or later, there is little or nothing he can do about the economic changes that take place.

Tremendous amounts of economic data relative to the international balance of trade, the monetary and fiscal policies of the Federal government, the economic shifts and adjustments within the economy, and the long-run prospects for agriculture are available. To analyze these data and make specialized projections as to the topography-of-farm-land-values-in-the-future is an intricate and sometimes hazardous job. It is not a part of the appraiser's job. It is instead the economist's domain.

This distinction between roles—that of an appraiser and that of an economic analyst—has not always been clearly designated in the past. This is unfortunate, for the best appraiser and the best appraisal system cannot avoid the occasional loan that backfires. No appraiser, for example, was responsible for the high interest rates which led to problems in California in 1970 and 1971. Nor could any appraiser really avoid the problems that occurred during the 1930's. However, the appraiser has had a tendency to blame himself when things have gone wrong, and oftentimes even after he has made a number of good appraisals. Furthermore, various lenders have had a tendency to place heavy responsibility on the loan appraiser and for problems that belong to lenders rather than appraisers.

Let's review a bit of history. In the 1920's, farm land values were rising. Institutional lenders were expanding their farm mortgage portfolios at profitable rates of interest. These institutions depended pretty much on faith—the belief that farm land prices would always go up, and on the so-called unearned increment of constantly increasing farm land prices. To many persons it was literally impossible to make a poor loan.

It was common for a real estate broker to take the loan man out into the country, drive by a farm, and ask, "How much will you loan on this one?" (What he meant was, "How much will you loan to the owner of this farm using the farm as security?") In those days, many a lender looked mainly, if not entirely, at the security. He did not take the time to estimate the earnings capacity of the farm or to inquire into the ability of the operator to repay the loan. When a formal appraisal report was submitted, the soils were often described as "mostly rich black loam soils." The farmers were described as "mostly industrious farmers." A simple statement from most anyone that "the value of this farm is at least double the amount of the loan" often sufficed as an appraisal.

A decade later, the lending institutions owned many of these farms. There was no question; loan policies had depended too much on security values, and not enough on farm earnings. Some of the really competent loan men were known to have made statements: "We drove past the farm a little too fast," and "That case failed because we didn't know enough about the farm."

As a result of the depression, loan policy turned away from tangible assets and towards a greater consideration of earning capacity. The income capitalization approach became the vogue. Normal value and typical operator concepts came into being. Loan committees wanted to know why, how, and who. However, the basic problem was not the lack of proper appraisal technique. It was that farm land values (from 1920 to 1933) had dropped 60 percent.

At the bottom of the depression the Congress of the United States developed considerable "emergency" machinery through the Farm Credit Administration and other agencies in order to provide the farmer credit.[12] Slowly the free play of competitive forces took over. Economic distress slowly began to evaporate. Beginning about 1935, the general price level began to rise. From then on farm prices began to rise and they rose faster than did farm costs. There were several ups and downs. However, farm incomes advanced. Thus farm real estate prices rose, at first slowly, then faster and faster.

The farm loan man was again successful. Compared to earlier periods he had few or no defaults. His loan policy became a good policy. In the 1950's and 1960's, the older appraisers, perhaps retired, could point with humility to quite a few of their loans that had gone sour. Yet, the younger men, with only 20 years' experience, could point with pride to the fact that no farm mortgage loan, made on the basis of their appraisal, had gone to foreclosure. Hence, one's reputation as a farm loan man depends, in part at least, on when he was born.

In 1950, a price-cost squeeze began to appear in the farm price-cost indices. The new technologies were advancing rapidly and farmers began to expand the size of their businesses. They spread their capital investments over a larger volume, maintaining, and oftentimes reducing, their costs per unit of output. They weathered a fairly tough price-cost squeeze. Surprisingly, farm incomes continued to rise and farmers continued to bid up the price of farm real estate.

The lender's problem soon became one of increased competition, particularly in the 1960's. The so-called emergency and temporary government programs were continuing to provide credit to farmers. In fact, these programs had been expanded. They were now making credit not just available but abundant. Simultaneously the Federal government's economic policies—both monetary and fiscal—had led to cheap money. More and more money appeared to be available to everybody and at low rates of interest. These policies contributed greatly to the continued increase in farm real estate prices.

In this era of increased competition many a lender became the victim of shrewd trading by loan applicants. Many an appraiser heard the statement, "Mr. _____ will loan $_____ and at _____ percent." (Such may or may not have been true.) At the same time many a farm loan man had been admonished by his company: "Get your values up so we can make more loans." Farmers and others knew this.

The farm loan appraiser does not determine farm values. These values are determined instead by the buyers and sellers of farms.

_____

12. This emergency credit had the effect of transferring farm assets into the hands of the less efficient farmers.

However, many farm loan appraisers were tempted to substitute the words "The Last Three Years" in place of the word "Normal" and the words "Highest and Best" for "Typical." Many were tempted to use "Probable Average for the Good Years" instead of "Probable Long-Term Average." One appraiser said he was tempted to title one of his column heads "Loan Value I Ought to Use" and another "Loan Value Required in Order to Get the Loan."[13]

The farm mortgage lenders did everything possible in the 1960's in order to make credit easier and to get the loans. They redefined "Normal Agricultural Value." They raised loan values or loan ratios. They reduced the interest rates on their larger loans, went to longer terms, and approved balloon payments at maturity. Some of them even eliminated principal payments the first few years. Thus, the money lenders themselves were in part responsible for the continued increases in farm real estate prices.

Today some persons have begun to cogitate permanent finance. (A few lenders refer to such as perpetual indebtedness.) Some persons have begun to think about equity participation with the lender assuming additional risks and obtaining additional though variable returns. Unamortized debt at a modest level perhaps has a place in agriculture. However, a high level of permanent debt is not sound. Any downward adjustment in farm values eliminates a borrower's equity quite rapidly.

Unfortunately, man's memory fades as time passes. The longer the period of continuing change, the more difficult it is to remember the dim, dark past. Farm land prices have now been on the rise for over 35 years. For many persons it is difficult to recall a time when they did anything else. Under such circumstances, most persons become permanently optimistic. They either forget, assuming they had first-hand experience, the years of economic distress, or they assume "it can't possibly happen again." Some lenders, assuming they were once knowledgeable, tend to forget what is sound lending policy. They say, "The present situation is different . . . our problems have changed." Oftentimes this merely represents a rationalization of current loan policies and practices.

Only an extremely lucky economist can predict the future. While the really smart economist is never wrong, he often has to wait, sometimes years, before his predictions turn out to be correct. Furthermore, while

---

13. The farm loan appraiser may recommend the amount of the loan; however, his appraisal is subject to review, and his loan recommendation is usually, if not always, subject to the approval of a loan committee.

predictions pertaining to upward price movements are always acceptable, he who points to a probable decline in prices is typically an unpopular fellow. Hence, the lender's problems with regard to loan policy is a much broader and more demanding one than the job of the appraiser.

What guideposts should the lender use? No one really knows. During periods of economic distress, farm real estate often sells at prices below its long-term average value. During periods of easy money and price inflation, farm real estate often sells at prices considerably above its long-term value. In each instance, expectations as well as economics are involved.

Only one conclusion is perhaps possible. The American farm family is best served by extremely courageous lending when farm real estate values are below normal or declining, and by extremely cautious lending when these values are above normal and continuing to rise.

THE FARM LOAN APPRAISER'S JOB

The farm mortgage lender makes loans on farms; he loans money to farmers. His success is closely related to the farm, yet equally and sometimes even more to the mortgagor. The farm provides the security or the collateral; the appraisal provides the basis for the loan. The farm owner or operator is the one who pays off the loan. The upper limit, in terms of loan value, may be established by either (1) the value of the security, (2) the earnings capacity of the farm, or (3) the mortgagor himself. No matter how valuable the farm, unless there are reasonable dollar returns, and unless that farm is in the hands of a capable operator, loan repayment may be in jeopardy. Thus any one of these three can limit the size of the loan, or for that matter, lead to refusal on the part of the lender.

In farm loan appraisal work, the role played by the appraiser and the role played by the loan man are often combined. This is due to the nature of the work. The job of the appraiser is to ascertain the farm's value—first, its present market value and second, its loan value. His job is to explain the origins of value. The job of the loan man is to interview the present owner or operator, obtain from him a financial statement and hopefully his financial history, and learn as much about his managerial ability and moral character as possible. These two jobs are often performed by the same person.

Hence, the farm loan appraiser may not only appraise the farm, he may also evaluate the ability of the operator. He typically has, or is bothered by, five questions.

1. What is the value of the farm or the security? The No. 1 value ascertained should be the present market value of the property. However, the loan institution or lending agency for whom he works may specify some other value as well. They may also specify the crop yields, the commodity prices, and the level of costs which should be used.

2. What is the earnings capacity of the farm and is there income from other sources? Estimates as to the productive capacity of the farm should be made in every appraisal. In a loan appraisal, these estimates are often made for the present operator as well as for a typical operator. Farm earnings tend to flow in several directions with loan repayment being quite low on the list of priorities. Family living expenses tend to have first priority, particularly when the chips are down. Farm operating expenses second, income taxes third, and capital outlays in the form of reinvestment and loan repayment last. All of this can be overshadowed by income from other sources.

3. What is the present operator's financial history and what is his future potential? The loan applicant typically fills out a financial statement which includes a fairly complete inventory of all assets and liabilities. Many lenders like to have a three-to-five-year financial history on the loan applicant. They can then analyze the applicant's financial progress, or lack of such, fairly easily. The farm loan appraiser may spend as much time obtaining this financial history as he does appraising the farm. And while there are fewer guides, he may spend as much time estimating the operator's future potential as he does studying his past.

4. Does the present operator have the required managerial ability? Is he equipped with the skills or expertise and does he have sufficient experience to operate successfully in agriculture today? How to recognize and measure managerial ability is a major task. Years ago the farmer who got high crop yields per acre and high rates of livestock production was a good manager. But today, his ability to manage money as well as other resources and to apply financial controls to the business he's operating is equally if not more important.[14]

5. What about the applicant's honesty, his integrity, and moral character? Who is the applicant? How old is he? What are his family

---

14. It is not difficult at all to find a farm operator, in most farming areas, who, in spite of being on a good farm, is being plagued with price-cost squeeze or some other problem or difficulty and is going broke. However, just across the fence is another farm operator, on the same kind of land, operating under the same conditions, who is making-a-go-of-it financially. This latter farmer is "just waiting" for the opportunity to buy out his less capable neighbor.

relationships? Is he ambitious? Does he have good judgment? What is his reputation with regard to money matters in the community? The loan appraiser must be reasonably assured that the man who borrows or uses his lender's dollars is not only capable but honest. He must be reasonably assured that his loan is more than a legal instrument or a sheet of paper, that he is helping someone who both needs and appreciates that help, that eventual repayment of the loan is not just a possibility, but that it is quite probable. The human factor is extremely important in the loaning of money, for it is exceedingly difficult to separate economic risk and moral hazard.

Traditionally, the lender accepts or rejects the borrower's loan application. If the proposal is reasonable, he makes him the loan. If it isn't, he turns him down. Not all loans are approved. There are many reasons. Maybe the value of the farm is fine, its productive capacity excellent, but the owner's attitude is poor. In other words, a loan is occasionally rejected regardless of the appraiser's appraisal or the loan man's recommendation.[15]

The farm appraiser and the farm loan man are typically one and the same person. Most farmers or loan applicants don't like to deal with two people. They want to know if and when they can obtain their money, and usually they're in a hurry.

However, each job is becoming more and more specialized today. The farm appraiser is trained to use the typical operator concept and to separate the farm from the farmer. His present market values should be based on the most likely or typical operator in the area. The farm loan man is trained to thoroughly investigate the present operator—the person to whom the loan will be made. Estimates as to the productive capacity of the farm are therefore made for both the present and the typical operator, and the appraisal summary may well contain a statement or two pertaining to the differences.

Traditionally, a farm property can be sold subject to a mortgage.[16] Real estate can thus pass from the present operator to some other person, or party, who may be more or less capable. To avoid this the lender may include in his mortgage contract various provisions or restric-

---

15. Furthermore, a farm property may have a good earnings value, yet have no loan value to a lender. This is, generally speaking, the lender's choice. A lender may or may not desire to make loans in some areas or on some of the more specialized farming operations. He may have alternative investments that yield either higher or more dependable returns or both.

16. Farm auctioneers occasionally advertise a farm sale with the statement, "This farm is already financed." What they are really saying is that the farm will be sold subject to the existing mortgage.

tions specifying that the mortgage cannot be assigned to another party without permission.[17] The contract may also require that if or when the property is sold that the balance of the loan is either due or that the amount of principal must be reduced to some given amount. These provisions eliminate some of the risk of an encumbered sale.

A farm mortgage lender may require life insurance on the borrower's life. (Actually very few of them do.) This protects the mortgagee. It supposedly reduces some of the risk. In the event of death, the mortgagor's estate can usually be settled both more readily and in a more orderly fashion. A mortgage lender may also recommend some long-term disability insurance. (Again, actually very few of them do.) This protects the mortgagor.

In other words, the loan man's job is not done when he has appraised the farm and made his loan recommendation. His real job is to assist farmers in acquiring capital resources, in making financial progress, and in avoiding financial difficulties. In many communities, the farm loan man provides considerable advice relative to real estate purchase (or sale), legal problems (not officially), repayment plans, insurance clauses, partial mortgage releases, etc. Lastly, when the loan is made, loan collection and servicing begin, and it continues until the loan is paid off.

Traditionally, the institutional lender has never taken a loan applicant on with the idea that he would change him, his farming practices, or his business techniques. This has not been the business of the farm mortgage lender. The farm mortgage lender has typically assumed that the farmer himself knows enough to operate his own business. However, with the advent of low-equity financing all this has changed, and in one instance at least, the lending agency has entered the arena called "supervision."

The farm loan supervisor employed by the Farmers Home Administration supposedly does just that. He supervises the business. He helps the farm family budget its farming operations, not just loan repayment but farm operating expenses and family living expenses as well. He helps the family develop both five-year and annual plans. Thus he assumes the role of a financial counselor as he advises the borrower and his family on financial matters. This loan man must be a skilled individual.

---

17. Technically the borrower does not free himself of his personal liability merely by selling his farm subject to the mortgage. In general, he remains liable until the mortgage is paid in full or until he is given a release by the mortgagee. (This varies among states.)

THE BENCH-MARK APPROACH TO APPRAISAL

At various times in their history, several insurance companies as well as the Federal land banks have developed and used a bench-mark approach to farm loan appraisal. The bench-mark approach is one in which several typical farms are appraised in detail. Their values are used to establish the level of all appraised values for each type of farm in each agricultural area. Bench-mark values are supposedly based on an exhaustive study of all sales data in the area. Their values are worked out with considerable analysis and thought. The amount of time spent is perhaps 8 to 10 times the amount spent on each subsequent loan appraisal.

1. The loan appraiser first classifies the various farming areas and then the various types of farms within each area. An area is essentially a group of farms with a reputation as to soils, land use, earnings capacity, type-of-farming, and income. That reputation may be excellent, good, average, fair, or poor.

2. All farm sales within each area are obtained and sorted into groups similar in type. Each farm is visited, and the sale price is verified by visiting with the new owner. The farms are listed in order of their descending desirability (not necessarily sale price), and the modal values are studied.[18]

3. The appraiser selects from his recent loan appraisals a typical farm or unit for each type of farm within each area. These typical units become the bench-mark farms.

4. He reworks his recent appraisal on this typical unit in accordance with the typical cropping patterns in the area, the typical operator who might buy or own the farm, and whatever level of commodity prices and farm costs may have been specified by the lending institution. This more detailed appraisal includes a careful estimate of the farm's earnings capacity and a more detailed listing of all income and expense items based on either normal or expected prices.

5. All bench-mark appraisals are carefully reviewed by loan supervisors who not only confer with their local appraisers but also make sure there is consistency between areas.

6. The values assigned to each bench-mark farm are also reviewed, either annually or whenever land values in the area change significantly. The bench-mark values are adjusted up or down, de-

---

18. These values, obtained over a period of time, can be very useful in developing an index showing the change in farm real estate values in a particular area. The information is extremely useful.

pending on whatever change has occurred.

The main feature of the bench-mark approach is the time saved relative to digging up and verifying comparable sales each time a new appraisal has to be made. Once a year the loan appraiser essentially looks at all farm sales. He essentially does a market data study and brings the present market value on each of his bench-mark farms up-to-date. When a loan appraisal in the area is called for, the appraiser then raises the question, "How does this subject farm I'm appraising compare to the bench-mark farm in this area?"

In his report, the loan appraiser uses an abbreviated form of classification. He may report, for example, "This is a B farm in a II area." Hence, the subject property is given a value based on, or relative to, the value of the bench-mark farm. The local committee who approves all loans supposedly knows exactly what the appraiser means.

With an annual study of all farm sales in his area, the farm loan appraiser keeps himself well informed of the changes that are occurring with regard to farm real estate prices. With a detailed appraisal on two or three typical units in each area, he can appraise individual farm properties rather efficiently. For this reason, the farm loan appraiser does not always spend as much time on each farm or in making each appraisal as many fee appraisers think he should.

The bench-mark approach works best in those areas where there is considerable uniformity among farms. It is most useful where the lender is making a large number of loans and desires or requires each appraisal to have the same format. Furthermore, individual farm appraisals or loans can be compared more easily with one another. The review appraiser has a somewhat easier job.

NORMAL AGRICULTURAL VALUES

In the 1930's, farm lending and foreclosure problems led the insurance companies, the Farm Credit Administration, and the Farm Security Administration to each adopt a normal agricultural value concept. Normal agricultural value is essentially a combination of basic farm value and normal market value, each of which was presented in Chapter II.

Normal agricultural values were developed primarily to avoid overlending during periods of high, or inflated, prices and underlending during periods of low, or depressed, prices. The concept, or idea, was essentially a safety factor built into the extension of credit in order to allow lenders to loan more than the subject property's present market value when farm prices are low, and to prohibit lenders from loaning more than they should when farm prices are high.

However, following the 1930's, farm prices and farm values both increased. There gradually developed two problems. Basic farm value, with its major emphasis on earnings, was no longer equal to, or even very well related to, present market value, even when adjustments for location, home use, and other economic features were made. Farmers and others who were buying farms had become more and more willing to pay for things other than the opportunity to obtain a given dollar income. Farm real estate prices were rising; so also were the expectations that they would continue to do so.

The normal value concept largely assumed that cyclical swings in farm land values would occur. This has not happened. Instead, agriculture has undergone structural and technological change; and the economy has experienced a continued decline in the value of the dollar. These factors have led to an almost continuous increase in farm property values.

A normal agricultural value concept has meaning only when the lending institution, or agency, specifies those conditions—yields, prices, and costs—which it considers to be normal. Normal values have to have some basis. Hence, most of the lending institutions and government agencies have all used various price periods and various methods to calculate average prices. They have then required their loan appraisers to assume or use these prices and costs.

The five-year average for 1910 through 1914 was the first one recommended. This base was changed to the 1935-1939 price level. It was then changed again to the 1947-1949 price level, and again to the 1959-1963 price level. Some persons recommended 10- and 12-year moving average prices for the period immediately preceding the date of the appraisal. As the data for each year became available, the oldest year's prices were discarded and the latest year's prices were added. The 10-year moving average appeared to have considerable merit, however, 12- and 15-year averages were advocated. Later, the placing of greater weights on the more recent years was also recommended. Many calculations were required as the moving averages became more and more involved. In the end, many a company decided to use only recent and actual price data. These data were simpler to obtain and easier to understand.

In each case, a particular price period and a given price-cost relationship was specified. The influence of short-term price fluctuations was supposedly minimized. The single stabilizing factor was a set of normal prices, based on a specific price period. However, farm prices and farm price-cost relationships have continued to change, and farm real estate prices have continued to rise.

Sooner or later first one and then another loan man found himself in an untenable position where he didn't get a particular loan. Sooner or later each lending institution or government agency began to "scratch its head" and change the basis for its normal agricultural value.

The following sections are largely history. However, they illustrate (1) the unwieldy definitions that were developed, presumably by committees; and (2) the unfortunate, in fact very difficult, situation in which many farm loan men found themselves in making farm mortgage loans.

The Equitable Life Assurance Society: In 1948, the Equitable Life Assurance Society defined normal agricultural value as ". . . the price for which a property will sell for agricultural purposes including farm home advantages under forecasted normal farm commodity price considerations, with a substantial down payment and with a reasonable amount of effort by a willing but not forced seller to sell to a typical, desirous, but not anxious purchaser experienced in the area."[19] Normal market value was the same, except the words ". . . for agricultural purposes including farm home advantages" and the words ". . . experienced in the area" were omitted. Normal market value, unlike normal agricultural value, could be based on a typical purchaser buying for purposes other than agricultural use. Thus normal market value could quite conceivably be above normal agricultural value.

Both normal agricultural and normal market values were supposed to represent ". . . prices during periods free from extremes of climate, of the price level, and of conditions in the farm real estate market. They were not (supposed to represent) values of a past period but (instead) the best estimate of values that would result from reasonably stable future economic conditions. (These) levels (were) to be adjusted from time to time to reflect changes in the long-term outlook for the farm commodity price level and cost relationships. . . ."[20]

In 1948, Equitable selected the five-year period 1935-1939, with certain adjustments, as a base for estimating normal prices and expected costs. This period was relatively free from violent market fluctuations. Later the company recommended a set of interim normal prices which were very close to the 1951-1954 level. The task was to

19. "Appraising Farms for Loans," The Equitable Life Assurance Society of the United States, 1948.
20. *Ibid.*

select a period of years when the price level was at neither extreme—
a period free from violent fluctuations and one with prices and costs in
a reasonable relationship. If the price of a single commodity happened
to be out of balance, such could be adjusted individually. However,
their real problem was to base their loans on the price and cost levels
that would most likely exist in the future.

Equitable was one of several institutional lenders who readily admitted early in the game, that ". . . various levels of normal land value
need to be adjusted . . . to reflect changes in the long-term outlook
for the farm commodity price level and costs relationships . . . "[21]

The Federal Land Banks: When the Farm Credit Administration
was established it was directed by law as well as by policy to use income as the principal factor in the making of its farm appraisals, and
to base its loans on normal agricultural value. Like many of the insurance companies, the Farm Credit Administration established or
specified the prices and the costs to be used. It started out with a
1910-1914 price level, then switched to a 1935-1939 level, then to a
1957-1959 level, and more recently to "the last few years."

The Farm Credit Administration defined normal agricultural value
as ". . . the amount a purchaser who is representative of the area and
type of farm would be willing to pay or be justified in paying for the
property for agricultural purposes, including farm home advantages,
under usual conditions, based on average production and normal
prices for farm products."[22] Its justification was based on two ideas.
One, that during relatively prosperous times people are inclined to
pay more for a farm than it is worth and that during an economic
depression the exact opposite occurs. Two, that among the buyers and
sellers of farms there may be either too much or not enough competition. Using a normal rather than present market value thus gave the
land banks legal sanction to refinance much farm mortgage debt in
the 1930's.

Normal agricultural value was later defined as "the amount a typical
purchaser would, under usual conditions, be willing to pay and be
justified in paying for the property for customary agricultural uses, including farm home advantages with the expectation of receiving normal net earnings from the farm and other dependable sources."[23] And

---

21. Supplement No. 1, "Appraising Farms for Loans," The Equitable Life
Assurance Society of the United States, 1951.

22. Nowlan, R. E., "Prices Versus Value," *Journal of the American Society of
Farm Managers and Rural Appraisers,* Vol. 3, No. 1, April 1939.

23. p. 16, *Federal Land Bank System: How It Operates,* Circular 35, 1965.

in 1968, the land banks changed the definition again. The adjective, *agricultural*, was dropped and the market was recognized. Normal value, newly defined is " . . . that value which duly reflects dependable farm income from the property, home advantages, other dependable income available to the typical owner, and prices paid informed sellers by informed and able buyers for comparable properties."[24] Four major parts—farm income, home advantages, other dependable income, and prices paid informed sellers—became coordinate considerations, any one of which could establish the upper limit of value.

Elimination of the word "agricultural" did not particularly change the normal concept. However, in 1970, one Federal land bank fieldman said, " . . . a farm's normal value can vary from 50 to 90 percent of its present market value, depending on the area and the class of farms in the area." He said, " . . . a good many farms can sometimes be assigned a normal value the same as its present value, for these kinds of loans are highly desirable."[25] The desire to get the loans thus became justification for not one but several changes in the definition of value.

Farmers Home Administration: The Bankhead Jones Act, passed in 1937, also required an earnings capacity appraisal with all appraisals based on normal values. At the time, the law established the guidelines for all appraisals made by the Farm Security Administration. More recently the law has guided the Farmers Home Administration.

Without going into detail, the Farm Security and Farmers Home Administration experienced the same problem of keeping their bases or price levels up-to-date. The most recent definitive period, or base, was 1959-1963. Yet by 1968, farm real estate prices had risen to the extent that they were above even the "normals" of 1959-1963. In 1968, the level of normal was revised to represent average sale prices of comparable farm properties sold during the most recent three-year period. In 1970, one executive said, " . . . we are now using an average of the last three years as . . . normal. (We made) this change because of the rapid advance in the price of land. (It) results in a level somewhat less than the present market price of land, however affords a sound basis for making loans."[26]

---

24. Correspondence from J. W. McWilliams, Appraisal Division, Federal Land Bank of Louisville, May 6, 1968.

25. This fieldman presented his approach to appraisal to a Purdue University class of farm appraisal students for several years. The words were his personally and perhaps not Federal land bank policy. However, they are an indication of the broadened interpretation of the word "normal" as practiced in the field. Needless to say, this young man was one of the more aggressive land bank appraisers.

Normal was first defined as " . . . the amount a typical informed purchaser would be willing to pay under normal conditions. . . ."[27] However, today the appraiser is to consider three values: (1) normal agricultural value, (2) normal market value, and (3) present market value. The first is based on agricultural assets only. The second recognizes the non-agricultural assets. However, the third value, authorized by the Rural Development Act of 1972, has become the basis for most appraisals. Present market value is defined as " . . . the amount a typical purchaser would be willing to pay and be justified in paying for the property considering (both) agricultural and non-agricultural assets. It is assumed that the property would sell for this amount with a reasonable sales effort and that the purchaser will be a willing but not an anxious buyer, and the seller would be a willing but not a forced seller."[28]

Today no one really wants to recall that period of time when normal values were specified by law. The normal concept is obsolete. It no longer has meaning. It's been replaced by present market value, even by the farm mortgage lenders who, through no fault of their own, were in trouble in the 1930's, and who, while they have tried to remain conservative ever since, have not been very successful in doing so.

LOAN RATIOS AND LIQUIDATION PRICES

Once a farm loan appraiser ascertains a farm's present market value, the lender must decide how much to loan. This amount is typically stated in terms of a loan value or loan ratio which expresses the current relationship between the amount of the loan and the appraised value of the farm. For example, if the price of the farm is $180,000 and the loan is 80 percent, the lender will loan $144,000.

$$\$180,000 \times 80\% = \$144,000$$

For years, from 1930 up to 1970, the lending institutions used a normal or an appraised value rather than a present market value as the bases for their loans. Most of their loans were then based on 65 percent (approximately two-thirds) of the farm's value.[29]

---

26. Private correspondence, dated May 8, 1970.
27. F.H.A., Instructions 422.1.
28. *Ibid.*
29. Exceptions are those loans made by or insured by the Farmers Home Administration. They have equalled 90 and 100 percent of the farm's value; however, one could raise the question as to whether they are conventional loans or government grants to be repaid someday.

This two-thirds thumb rule was the traditional green light for farm purchase. When a prospective owner, through thrift and earnings, had saved enough capital to make a one-third down payment on whatever farm he wanted, the loan was assumed to be safe. History showed, that with the exception of those who purchased their farms just prior to the depression, very few farmers became chronic delinquents or lost their farms with a one-third equity. History also showed that those farmers who had the one-third down payment, yet who had acquired such through marriage, inheritance, or speculation, were much more of a problem for lenders. At the same time, the 65-percent figure has always been a sort of semi-mystical thumb rule. No one really knows from where it came.[30] It's been referred to as good judgment when correct, however, misfortune when "things went wrong."

Many lenders have said that the two-thirds should be raised to 75 percent when one is reasonably sure that farm real estate values are low in relation to earnings and when those values are likely to rise in the future. They have said that the figure should be reduced to 50 percent when real estate values are high relative to earnings and when they are likely to decline in the future.[31] Again, these are thumb rules— useful, however recommended only occasionally, possibly due to the lack of better alternatives. In actual practice, the figures are seldom referred to today.

Today, many of the lending institutions and agencies use an "appraised value." It's a very loose term, almost impossible to define; however, it typically ranges from 90 to 100 percent of present market value. Appraised values are said to be conservative market values. Loan ratios range from 75 (conservative farm mortgage lender) to 85 (seller hoping to keep the buyer honest) to 90 and 100 (government agency) percent of appraised value. Thus, it is now possible in many of the good land areas to shop around and obtain a farm loan equal to 80 to 100 percent of a given farm's present market value. There is a tendency to finance improvements up to 80 percent or more of their cost. And in many instances, where one lacks the downpayment, he can go and borrow that too on a personal note basis.

---

30. The Federal Farm Loan Act at first made it mandatory that all Federal land bank loans be based upon the normal value of the farm and that the loans not exceed 65 percent of such value plus the amount of stock which the member-borrower is required to purchase. This was perhaps one of the first green lights to appear and the basis for many since.
31. This suggestion was perhaps first made by Professor Stanley Warren at Cornell University.

The farm, or the security, is still important. However, increased emphasis is placed on the farm's earnings capacity, the mortgagor's managerial ability, and in some instances, on the farm family's needs. This is perhaps a mistake, for some lenders will now loan such amounts that the principal and interest payments, which are higher than ever before, can become extremely difficult to meet. Some lenders will loan today, to the extent that, in the event of financial difficulty on the part of the mortgagor, or what's worse—a small down-turn in farm real estate prices, these lenders cannot possibly recover the amount of their loan, along with the costs of foreclosure.

No one likes to talk about foreclosure. It's an unpopular topic. However, loan values, foreclosure costs, and liquidation prices can also be related. When a mortgage is foreclosed and the loan is liquidated, the farm has to be sold. The characteristics of both the seller and the buyer are now changed.

The seller is not unwilling to sell, he is instead most willing. He

Courtesy, U.S.D.A.

wants to get rid of the problem. By choice, no lending institution or agency wants to own or manage a farm, or for that matter any other kind of real estate. Through loan default and foreclosure it sometimes has to. However, with exception, ownership is not always profitable, and management is not usually the lender's area of expertise. Thus, most lenders get rid of their problems by selling the property. They take their losses and run, hopefully minimizing their costs in the process.

The buyer is not an unwilling buyer. He is instead a most willing buyer, but usually only at his price. He recognizes, usually quite well, the seller's problem. The willing buyer will thus lower his offering price because he knows the seller is no longer desirous of exerting much control over the sale. The seller is in a disadvantageous situation and the buyer is usually aware of this fact. The buyer is ready and willing to help him solve his problem, even though he may later be accused of taking advantage of him. In general, it's a buyer's market. Farm real estate prices are weak.

Liquidation price is that price at which a farm property will sell if sold immediately and under adverse conditions. Immediately is a much shorter period of time than is desirable from the standpoint of the most advantageous sale. When a lender is forced to foreclose and put a farm on the market, it will sell, but usually at a price considerably below other farm sales prices in the area. How much below? Oftentimes, as much as 20 to 25 percent.

Liquidation price usually recognizes and takes into consideration such factors as the farm's appearance—there may no longer be any pride of ownership, its earnings (which may be negative), the current conditions of the market (which are adverse to the seller), and the relative resalability of the property in the near future.

The first problem in a loan foreclosure is that the lender has difficulty in recognizing when the loan, or installment land contract, has gone sour. The borrower typically experiences financial difficulties and personal problems simultaneously. He can usually rationalize an overdue payment or two fairly easily. He usually has some fairly good excuses. The lender seldom realizes he's in trouble until the mortgagor begins to really let some things slip. The mortgagor may go light on fertilizer (unbeknownst to the lender), and crop yields, come fall, are down (due to the lack of rain of course). The mortgagor fails to cut or spray the weeds or mow the lawn. Building repairs are no longer made. A certain amount of garbage and junk collects in the dooryard. That thing called "pride of ownership" is gone.

REAL ESTATE

AUCTION

Due to the death of my husband and my advancing age, I will offer my farm at the location of the farm located as follows: 1 mile south of Coleta on the blacktop, then 1½ miles west, then ¾ mile south, then 1½ miles northwesterly, (watch for arrows); or, east of Morrison on Route No. 30 to Round Grove Corners, then 4 miles north to the blacktop, then 1 mile east, then 2½ miles north and ¾ mile west, (watch for arrows) on

WED., DECEMBER 22, 1965
1:30 P. M.

172 ACRE FARM
(more or less)

LEGALLY DESCRIBED AS FOLLOWS:

The Southeast Quarter of the Southwest Quarter of Section 18 and the South 15 acres of the Northwest Quarter of the Southwest Quarter of said Section 18. The East Half of the Northwest Quarter; Lots 11 and 12 of the Northwest Quarter of the Northeast Quarter; Lots 4 and 8 of the Northeast Quarter of the Southwest Quarter and Lot 1 of the Southwest Quarter of the Northwest Quarter of Section 19, all in Township 22 North, Range 6 East of the 4th P. M., Whiteside County, Illinois.

The farm, consisting of 172 acres, more or less, has 110 acres of good producing tillable ground, the balance in blue grass pasture with a flowing stream providing a constant supply of clean fresh water for livestock or possibility for a sizeable lake. The property is improved with a 7-room home with new kitchen, water and partial basement; barn with 20 stanchions; double crib; machine shed. The fences are in fair condition.
An adjoining tract of pasture with about 20 acres of tillable ground and the flowing stream, is available should you wish a larger tract than the above described 172 acres.

TERMS OF SALE: 20% down on day of sale, balance upon delivery of deed and abstract showing merchantable title. Or, anyone wishing to purchase the farm on a land contract, contact auctioneer for details on down payment, interest and annual payments.

POSSESSION will be given on or before March 1, 1966. Farm may be seen at any time, but for an appointment to see the house, contact the auctioneer of sale.

Mrs. MAUDE ROE, owner

Liquidation price is that price at which a farm property will sell if sold immediately and under adverse conditions. It usually recognizes and takes into consideration such factors as the farm's appearance (no pride of ownership), its earnings (may be negative), current market conditions (usually adverse to the seller), and the relative resalability of the farm.

Photo by Suter

Realizing he is in trouble, the mortgagor often reneges on one, sometimes two, and occasionally three or four principal and interest payments. The lender, recognizing that he has a problem, may then discover the borrower has skipped one or two of the property tax installments. The insurance premiums may also be unpaid. At this point, anywhere from 6 to 18 months of time have elapsed.

The mortgagor is eventually ejected. The farm mortgage lender has to pay the taxes.[32] He often has to meet with the other creditors before any part of the crop, machinery, livestock, real estate, or anything can be sold. The day the mortgagor moves, he sometimes turns around and throws a rock through the glass in the front door or causes other damage to the property. And once a given property is vacated, it's typically subject to widespread vandalism. In the meantime, the entire community waits and watches. Will the lender rent the property? Will it be put up for sale?

To all lending institutions and government agencies, who may or may not listen, one can only say ". . . it is not practical to loan more than 75 percent of the market value of the farm." When a lender does so, he accepts considerable risk. To foreclose a loan costs money. Liquidation price minus the foreclosure costs tends to lead to an amount of money which is less than the remaining balance or unpaid portion of a loan whenever that loan is above 75 percent of value.

Let's illustrate. A friendly farm buyer has purchased a 240-acre farm for $150,000 ($625 per acre). He has put up a 25-percent equity and acquired a 20-year loan ($112,500) at 7.0 percent. His semiannual principal and interest payments are $5,474. His property taxes are $1,140 per year. After three years of mediocre success, the borrower is faced with a price-cost squeeze and two years of drought. He becomes completely discouraged. He fails to pay his taxes and defaults on his loan, beginning with the tenth payment. Twenty-four months later the loan is foreclosed and six months later the farm is sold.

In the seven-year interim farm real estate prices may have increased, remained steady, or declined. This situation, a situation a lender could easily find himself in, is illustrated in Table 43. Real estate taxes, overdue interest payments (both prior to acquisition and during ownership), foreclosure costs, management fees, attorney fees, and brokerage all add up rather rapidly.

The data are hypothetical.[33] They illustrate one, that liquidation price may easily be less than the remaining balance of a loan plus the

---

32. A tax lien has priority over a mortgage.

Table 43. Changing Farm Land Values Related to Mortgagee Profit or Loss in the Event of Foreclosure.
A Hypothetical Illustration.

	Farm Land Values		
	Declining	Remaining Steady	Increasing
1. Value of the Farm When Purchased (240 Acres × $625)	$ 150,000	$ 150,000	$ 150,000
2. Annual Change in Value (Percent)	−2.5	0	+2.5
3. Value of the Farm 7 Years Later	123,750	150,000	176,250
4. Liquidation Price When Sold 85% of Value	105,188	127,500	149,812
5. Original Loan or Mortgage (75%)	112,500	112,500	112,500
6. Balance Due on Mortgage After 9 Semiannual Payments[1]	99,349	99,349	99,349
7. Foreclosure Costs 8% of Balance Due on Mortgage	7,948	7,948	7,948
8. Interest Accruals During Period up to Acquisition Payments 10, 11, 12, 13	14,499	14,499	14,499
9. Interest Accruals During Period[2] of Ownership Payment 14	3,448	3,448	3,448
10. Real Estate Taxes[3] 4 Semiannual Installments	2,280	2,280	2,280
11. Management Costs and Income During Period of Ownership	—	—	—
12. Attorney and Brokerage Fees $35.00 for Title Inspection Plus 5.0% Commission on Sale	5,294	6,410	7,526
13. Total Costs to Date (7 Through 12)	33,469	34,585	35,701
14. Remaining Profit or Loss to Mortgagee (4 − 6 Through 11)	$ −27,630	$ −6,434	$ +14,762

1. Based on a $112,500 loan (75%), a 20-year term, a 7.5-percent rate of interest, and semiannual payments of $5,474.19.
2. Tenth semiannual interest payment is $3,726.
3. Based on $4.75 per acre.

costs of foreclosure, acquisition, management, and brokerage; and two, that a lender's success or failure often depends, not just on a loan or two or three that may go sour, but on the changes that occur in farm real estate prices. As contrasted to the government agency, the institutional lender has often been ultra-conservative. He has been reluctant

33. However, the guides used to develop the table were based on actual loan experiences obtained from three different lending agencies through private correspondence.

to loan over 75 percent on farm real estate and for good reason. He has also learned to pray for rising farm land values over the repayment period.

PRIVATE LOANS VERSUS GOVERNMENT GRANTS

During the early history of agriculture, credit was highly selective. Private initiative was encouraged, and only those farm families who could demonstrate their ability to use agricultural resources in an efficient fashion were able to obtain money. The mortgagee-mortgagor relationship was strictly contractual. Money was loaned on certain terms, and the borrower was, in general, obligated to meet those terms. There was no creditor involvement, either directly or indirectly, in the borrower's business—his farming operations, his pattern of living, or his methods of discharging financial obligations.

Then came the Great Depression. Farm incomes dropped severely. Farm real estate prices declined. Owners' equities evaporated. Through no particular fault of either the mortgagee or the mortgagor, many farmers defaulted on their loans. There were at least four categories.

1. Farm owners who were unable to pay their loans, primarily because they had acquired their farms just prior to the drop in farm prices and in farm real estate values. This group included many young farmers. Their equities were almost immediately wiped out. Many of these farm loans were foreclosed and the farms were sold.

2. Farm owners who were unable to pay their loans, but who, because of their asset structure, and if given sufficient time, could probably work off their debt by a further extension of credit—either by deferring several principal payments or by reamortizing their loans.

3. Farm owners who were undercapitalized and who could not have carried a reasonable burden of debt even under normal conditions. They lacked farm size, farm organization, or they themselves were lacking in managerial ability. The lender should never have made these loans in the first place.

4. Farm owners who, because the-chips-were-down, became discouraged to the extent that they lost faith. Many of these persons were found lacking in moral integrity. These folks just up and left their farms. They went to town and looked for other alternatives. They found largely unemployment and welfare.[34]

---

34. Huston, J. M.

Experience with each of the above raised many questions about agricultural credit in the bottom of the depression. These problems led to a decision on the part of the Congress of the United States to extend credit to agriculture. A number of so-called emergency government programs and farm loan practices were developed. These programs changed, not at first perhaps but over time, many of the rules of the game. Loan ratios have been increased to the extent that today the government agencies will loan 100 percent of the value of most farm properties. Interest rates have now been pegged, at least by one agency, at rates which remain below the competitive market. Credit has been extended to persons, who by previous standards, have not heretofore had such available to them.

When credit is so extended, (1) using security values which may not be adequate, (2) based on farm properties where the earnings capacities are marginal, and (3) to farm operators whose managerial abilities are below average—the financial risks cannot help but be high. The Congress of the United States recognized this and recommended a policy of supervision. Guidance was to be furnished each worthy client not only in connection with his farming operations but also in connection with the budgeting of his family's living expenses. Thus the government, under the guise of an emergency program, began to assume a managerial role helping farm families make major financial decisions.[35]

However, the man in the government job—county agricultural agent, soil conservationist, farm loan supervisor, or other—has seldom had or shown any real inclination towards management. There are a lot of good county agents and loan men in the business today. Yet many of them realize, that given the risks, they can make more money advising the farmer or rancher than they probably can farming. If they really have that thing called "managerial ability," they could undoubtedly make more money by becoming farm owners, particularly with the capital availability being what it is today.

The loan man's personality is invariably one that seeks to avoid rather than accept risk. If the college graduate doesn't have some of this philosophy when he joins one of the government lending agencies, he soon acquires it. Sooner or later, his desire for safe and secure

---

35. There is, of course, a difference between (1) accepting a temporary management function because some loans, made on business-like basis, may have broken down and (2) accepting a permanent management function in the making of farm loans, knowing in advance that the mortgagor is marginal and supervision will be required.

The college graduate without experience in either finance or management sometimes makes a poor teammate for a farmer who has been selected for a loan on the basis of his proven inability to obtain credit elsewhere.

repayments lead him to counsel farm families into minimizing maximum losses rather than maximizing financial gain. The college graduate without experience in either finance or management sometimes makes a poor teammate for a farmer who has been selected for a loan on the basis of his proven inability to obtain credit elsewhere. He soon learns to duck managerial responsibility, and, consciously or unconsciously, he may soon veto enough of the business risks that he keeps a subsidized client at the semi-poverty level of farming. Some lenders will, of course, disagree.[36]

Most lending institutions tend to measure success by the number and amount of loans outstanding and their loss ratios. Several other variables, such as the costs of servicing or the costs of collection, are

---

36. One of our reviewers strongly disagreed. He said, "This chapter is full of innuendos, half truths, biased opinion, and slanted interpretations of facts. People of limited knowledge will no doubt be taken in by such; however, those who are knowledgeable will doubt the veracity of the remainder of the book."

seldom mentioned. However, most fieldmen indicate a skewed distribution of loan collection costs (in normal times). Collection problems are concentrated, with perhaps 85 percent of the problems being related to 15 percent of the loans. The lender's time, trouble, and frustration—overhead costs that should perhaps be allocated to loan foreclosures—were not included in Table 43. Here is a major question —"What are the costs of supervision, the costs of servicing, and the costs of collection?"

Each lender—private or government—should separate his loans into (1) those for which the interest rate is sufficient to cover pure interest, risk, collection, and other overhead; and (2) those in which the interest rate is not sufficient to do the job. Credit, in the first case, is a loan; in the second case, it's a grant or subsidy. If the dollar earnings on various loans are not sufficient to cover pure interest, along with all legitimate administrative expense, then the lender ceases to be a lender in the traditional sense.

Government loan policy in particular needs to be evaluated in terms of both the normal costs of making and servicing farm loans, and the costs of supervision and collection. A large percentage of delinquent loans may ultimately be repaid. However, to what extent do the costs of collection approach the amount of the loan? A number of persons would like to see some research on this. The findings might even astonish those persons close to the problem.

The easy availability of government credit has provided tough competition to private lenders—both the financial institutions who have made farm mortgage loans to farmers and the individual farm owners who have wanted to sell their own farms, yet who have wanted to finance the sale as well. The government puts a squeeze play on free enterprise whenever it pegs the interest rate on its own loans at one level, and at the same time tightens the supply of money to the extent that interest rates in the private sector rise rapidly. In the late 1960's, the usury laws in several of the midwestern states compounded this problem. Several of the insurance companies met this competition by curtailing their activities in agriculture and placing their monies elsewhere. Those individuals interested in selling their farms met the competition by raising the farm real estate prices.

There are today two issues. One is how far should credit be extended —whether it should be extended on a self-sufficient, self-liquidating basis, or whether it should be further subsidized? Credit to those persons who cannot succeed without supervision presents not an economic but perhaps a social problem in agriculture. The Congress of the United States and the administrators are undoubtedly aware of this. For at various times, government credit has had many different objectives. It has been an instrument for solving tenure problems, for aiding settlement and rehabilitation, for the regulation of land use, for the redistributing of wealth, and for the forwarding of social justice. It has implied, in all cases, a degree of control over agricultural resources not previously contemplated.

A final issue perhaps is whether the American economy can successfully continue with a 5.0-percent, more or less, rate of inflation without either falling upstairs or downstairs completely. This rate of inflation now appears to be built into the political economy. It may decline somewhat in the future; it may increase at an increasing rate.

Using a 5.0-percent assumption, what does such do to the value of a farm? A 240-acre farm worth $625 per acre or $150,000 today is equal to $245,793 in 10 years, $402,759 in 20 years, and $1,081,436 in 40 years. This assumes not a simple 5.0-percent rate but one which has been compounded semiannually. In the meantime, the value of the dollar, say it's worth $1 today, is worth $0.61 in 10 years, $0.37 in 20 years, and $0.14 in 40 years. There is one advantage. All of this guarantees that there will be more work for farm appraisers in the future.

REFERENCES

Agricultural Finance Review, E.R.S., U.S.D.A., Recent Issues.
Agricultural Statistics, U.S.D.A., Recent Issues.
Crouse, E. F., and C. H. Everett, *Rural Appraisals*, Prentice-Hall, 1956.
Farm Real Estate Market Developments, E.R.S., U.S.D.A., Recent Issues.
Nelson, A. G., and W. G. Murray, *Agricultural Finance*, 5th Edition, Iowa State University Press, 1967.
Norton, L. J., *Financing Agriculture*, The Interstate, 1948.

The Participants: Past and Present

Brake, J. R., "Capitalizing Agriculture in the Coming Years," Agricultural Law Center, Monograph No. 11, University of Iowa, June 1970.
Down the Road Together: The Federal Land Bank System, The Federal Land Bank of Louisville, 1967.
Federal Land Bank System—How It Operates, Farm Credit Administration Circular 35, Revised 1965.
Helmberger, Peter, and Reynold Dahl, *Financing Farms with 100 Percent Loans*, Minnesota Agricultural Experiment Station Bulletin 447, May 1958.

Herr, W. McD., "Characteristics of New Borrowers Obtaining Farm Ownership Loans from the Farmers Home Administration," A. E. Report 184, E.R.S., U.S.D.A., May 1970.

Kristjamson, B. H., and J. A. Brown, "The Farmers Home Administration Approach to Farm Credit Problems," North Dakota Agricultural College Bulletin 388, January 1954.

Munger, J. A., "Borrowing Money to Purchase Land," *Land: The 1958 Yearbook of Agriculture*, U.S.D.A., 1958.

Rose, Sanford, "The Future Largest Landlords in America," *Appraisal Journal*. Vol. 38, No. 4, October 1970.

The Farm Mortgage Lender's Problem

Brandt, Karl, "A Public Farm Land Appraisal Service: Its Desirability and Practicability," *Journal of Farm Economics*, Vol. 27, No. 3, August 1945.

Buzzard, G. W., "Trends in Appraising Farms for Loans," *Journal of American Society of Farm Managers and Rural Appraisers*, Vol. 27, No. 1, April 1963.

Hershman, Mendes, "The New Look in Real Estate Financing Techniques," *Appraisal Journal*. Vol. 39, No. 2, April 1971.

Norton, L. J., *Financing Agriculture*, The Interstate, 1948.

"Résumé of Farm Loan Experience: 1928-1937," by members of the Farm Mortgage Conference of Life Insurance Companies, December 1939.

Stanford, M. J., "Forecasting Future Land Values with Present-Value Techniques," *Appraisal Journal*, Vol. 41, No. 1, January 1973.

Westbrook, S. F., "Farm Mortgage Investments of Insurance Companies," *Journal of American Society of Farm Managers and Rural Appraisers*, Vol. 1, No. 2, October 1937.

The Farm Loan Appraiser's Job

Buzzard, G. W., "Trends in Appraising Farms for Loans," *Journal of American Society of Farm Managers and Rural Appraisers*, Vol. 27, No. 1, April 1963.

Ellwood, L. W., "Appraisal for Mortgage Loan Purposes," *Encyclopedia of Real Estate Appraising*, Prentice-Hall, 1959.

Farm Manual, Mortgage Loan and Real Estate Investment Department, Prudential Insurance Company of America, Various dates through 1968.

Financing Farming Activities, Farm Credit Banks of Louisville, May 1963.

Gaddis, P. L., "Some Fundamentals of Farm Appraisal," *Appraisal Journal*, Vol. 14, No. 2, April 1946.

Hall, H. C., "Adapting American System of Appraisal to Life Insurance Loan Committee Requirements," *Journal of American Society of Farm Managers and Rural Appraisers*, Vol. 4, No. 1, April 1940.

"Instructions Regarding Mortgage Loans on Real Estate," Revised, The Prudential Insurance Company of America, October 1930.

Murray, W. G., *Farm Appraisal and Valuation*, 5th Edition, Iowa State University Press, 1969.

Richart, F. D., "Importance of the Appraiser to the Lender," *Appraisal Journal*, Vol. 16, No. 3, July 1948.
Stenard, E. W., "Factual and Easier Capitalization Approach and Financing," *The Real Estate Appraiser*, Vol. 33, No. 5, May 1967.

The Bench-Mark Approach to Appraisal

Browne, G. C., and G. R. Burns, *Appraisal Manual for Federal Land Banks*, Farm Credit Administration, Various dates up to 1967.
Mounsey, C. J., "Report on Appraisal Standards of Tippecanoe County, Indiana," Tippecanoe-Warren Federal Land Bank Association, December 1954.

Normal Agricultural Values

"Appraisal of Farms and Leasehold Interests," FHA Instruction 422.1, U.S.D.A., F.H.A., January and March 1968.
Brooker, M. A., "Problems of Normal Value with Rising Prices," *Journal of Farm Economics*, Vol. 34, No. 5, December 1952.
Browne, G. C., and G. R. Burns, *Appraisal Manual for Federal Land Banks*, Farm Credit Administration, Various dates up to 1967.
Colvin, Carl, "Factors in Establishing Prices and Costs for Normal Value Appraisals," Paper presented Farm Appraisal Conference, University of Illinois, June 1948.
Engberg, R. C., "Federal Credit Agencies as an Influence upon Land Values," *Journal of Farm Economics*, Vol. 29, No. 1, February 1947.
Mayer, L. B., "Farm Appraisal in a Period of Declining Prices," *Journal of American Society of Farm Managers and Rural Appraisers*, Vol. 13, No. 1, April 1949.
McLean, E. E., and P. L. Gaddis, *Appraising Farms for Loans*, The Equitable Life Assurance Society of the United States, February 1948.
McLean, E. E., and P. L. Gaddis, *Appraising Farms for Loans*, Supplement No. 1, The Equitable Life Assurance Society of the United States, September 1951.
Morse, T. D., "The Gyroscope of Rural Appraisals," *Journal of American Society of Farm Managers and Rural Appraisers*, Vol. 1, No. 1, April 1937.
Murray, W. G., "A Review of the Farm Appraisal Panel Meeting, Appraisal Section," *Journal of American Society of Farm Managers and Rural Appraisers*, Vol. 16, No. 1, April 1952.
No Author, "Farm Appraisals," Reprint from *Agricultural Engineering*, *Journal of American Society of Farm Managers and Rural Appraisers*, Vol. 5, No. 2, October 1941.
Norton, L. J., "Some Fallacies of Normal Values in Farm Land Appraisals," Paper presented at Farm Appraisal Conference, University of Illinois, June 1948.
Nowland, R. E., "Price Versus Value from the Viewpoint of Pure Economic Theory," *Journal of American Society of Farm Managers and Rural Appraisers*, Vol. 3, No. 1, April 1939.

Stewart, C. F., "The Concept of Normal Value in Farm Land Appraisal,"
Journal of American Society of Farm Managers and Rural Appraisers,
Vol. 11, No. 2, October 1947.

Loan Ratios and Liquidation Prices

Church, Byron, "Mortgage Value—Wrong Then and Wrong Now," *The
Real Estate Appraiser,* Vol. 29, No. 3, March 1963.
Davis, W. D., et al., "The Relationship of Mortgage Interest Rates and
Percentage Loaned to Farm Values," *Journal of American Society of
Farm Managers and Rural Appraisers,* Vol. 31, No. 1, April 1967.
Hanford, L. D., Jr., "Mortgage Loan Appraisal or Rubber Stamp?,"
Appraisal Journal, Vol. 40, No. 3, July 1972.
Huston, J. M., "How Can Delinquent Loans and Foreclosed Properties Best
Be Serviced and Handled?" *Journal of Farm Economics,* Vol. 22, No. 1,
February 1940.
Norton, L. J., "When and Under What Conditions Should a Mortgage on
a Farm Be Foreclosed?," *Journal of Farm Economics,* Vol. 22, No. 1,
February 1940.
"Résumé of Farm Loan Experience: 1928-1937," by members of the Farm
Mortgage Conference of Life Insurance Companies, December 1939.
Tootell, R. B., "The Role of Credit in Modern Agriculture," *Journal of
American Society of Farm Managers and Rural Appraisers,* Vol. 26, No.
2, October 1962.

Private Loans Versus Government Grants

Kristjamson, B. H., and J. A. Brown, "The Farmers Home Administration
Approach to Farm Credit Problems," North Dakota Agricultural College
Bulletin 388, January 1954.
Norton, L. J., "When and Under What Conditions Should a Mortgage on a
Farm Be Foreclosed?," *Journal of Farm Economics,* Vol. 22, No. 1,
February 1940.
Sackett, J. H., "The Place of Competition in the Ranch Loan Market,"
Journal of American Society of Farm Managers and Rural Appraisers,
Vol. 31, No. 2, October 1967.
Young, E. C., "The Function of Credit in Modern Agriculture," *Journal of
American Society of Farm Managers and Rural Appraisers,* Vol. 5, No. 1,
April 1941.

CHAPTER XIII

Condemnation Appraisals[1]

In the very early European days, the sovereign had the right to confiscate a subject's property. He took whatever property he desired on the theory that the sovereign could do no wrong and with the assumption that any confiscation was for the benefit of all his subjects. This right was first limited by the Magna Charta, the acceptance of which was forced upon King John by the English barons at Runnymede in 1215. The nobles had become tired of being overridden by the crown, and hence demanded a limiting of the King's rights. Even though the takings had supposedly been for the benefit of all, there had, at the same time, been grievous injury to the few.

In 1625, the famous Dutch jurist, Hugo Grotius, referred to a law of eminent domain. He called it the law of expropriation. His theory was that the state had both original and absolute ownership of all land, and that the individual held possession and enjoyment always subject to the implied reservation that ultimate ownership might at any time be resumed by the state. Needless to say, his conclusions did not meet with the happy approval of the liberty-loving forefathers who later came to this country.

Anglo-American law developed the theory of sovereignty: (1) a theory that in the absence of the sovereign state no man could acquire land in this country and (2) that the sovereign power must reserve the right to take back certain easements, and in certain circumstances

---

1. Actually eminent domain or condemnation appraisals. An eminent domain appraisal is one typically made for an authority with the power of eminent domain and prior to the time a declaration of intent has been filed. A condemnation appraisal is one which follows this court action, indicating that a particular property or part thereof is to be taken, and may be made for either the taking agency or the property owner.

Eminent domain or condemnation appraisals are an ultimate test of an appraiser's skills. Oftentimes only a part of the property is taken. When this occurs, the property owner, or condemnee, is to be paid for the value of the part taken plus the value of any severance damage and minus the value of any special benefits to the part(s) that remain. The basis for the compensation is the difference between the fair market value of the farm **before** the taking and the fair market value of the farm **after** the taking.

Courtesy, Indiana State Highway Commission

virtual ownership, whenever the sovereign could prove beyond a doubt that such expropriation would be needed for the public good.

THE LAW OF EMINENT DOMAIN

Eminent domain is the right of the state to take private property for public use, provided, (1) there is shown a public need and (2) the property owner is paid just compensation. All real property is held subject to the paramount power of the United States of America and to the sovereign state in which it is located. The sovereign can expropriate private property for the benefit of the public whenever the necessity exists and whenever the public interest cannot be served any other way.[2]

The power of eminent domain was in existence before the Constitution of the United States was written. The power was not created by a constitutional provision; instead, a constitutional provision limits or restricts its exercise. The framers of the Constitution recognized not only the need for the right of eminent domain but also the need for adequate restrictions.

The Fifth Amendment (1798) states, ". . . No person shall be . . . deprived of life, liberty, or property, without due process of law; nor shall private property be taken for public use without just compensation."

This Fifth Amendment has generally been held to apply primarily to the Federal Government. Thus, the Fourteenth Amendment added later (1868) reads, ". . . nor shall any state deprive any person of life, liberty or property without due process of law. . . ." Thus, all citizens of the United States have the protection that their property cannot be taken unless (1) such is for public use and (2) they receive just compensation.

The Public Necessity or Purpose: Any property taking must result in substantial benefits to the public or to a relatively large group of persons. Some private purpose may be served incidentally. However, the principal use or benefit must be to the public.

There are three broad categories.

1. To enable various government agencies to obtain housing, in other words, buildings for offices.

---

2. The sovereign also has police power, the right to tax, and that of escheat (reversion of property to the state through failure of persons legally entitled to hold the same).

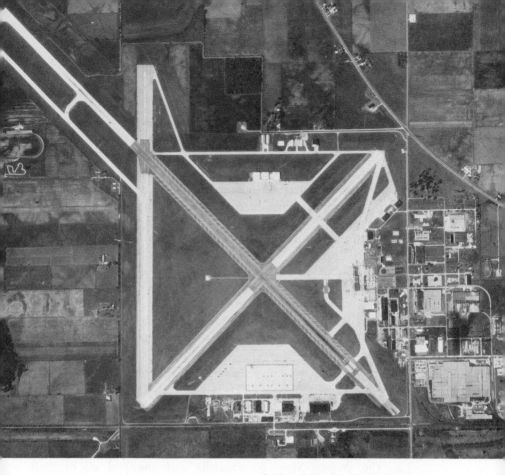

2. To enable various government units to perform their various functions—construct highways, airports, navigational facilities, military or defense installations, reservoirs, dams, schools, parks, conservation and public welfare projects, slum clearance, and urban development.

3. To enable the various public utilities to provide their various services—railroads, electric power and telephone lines, and pipelines.

Few persons would argue that the law of eminent domain is not basic to the general welfare of the public. A country could not operate without this prerogative. Even in rural areas land has to be taken in order to build roads and to provide access to various farms and farm properties. Easements have to be taken in order to provide electricity, telephone, and other services. Without the law of eminent domain, new highways could very easily be circuitous, highly inefficient, and costly. Without the law of eminent domain many persons could not share in the so-called low-cost public utilities and other services.

In the early days an abutting farm owner donated his land for the road or right-of-way. He often helped construct the road, or the pole line, and, as a result, had a proprietary interest. Today, an abutting land owner has little to say about a new highway or powerline; it may even go diagonally across his farm. Oftentimes he does not even acquire direct access to it. As a result, he no longer freely contributes land, right-of-way, or labor. And furthermore, even though he is supposedly compensated for any land taken, any property rights acquired, and any damage to that which remains, he doesn't like the idea.

Exercise of the law of eminent domain often proves to be irritating and seemingly ruthless. When the condemnee (or property owner) finds that a lifetime of ownership is about to be forcibly taken, he is not only unhappy but often resentful. Yet, willingness to surrender his rights is unnecessary. Due process merely requires that adequate notice, along with the opportunity to be heard, be given. The owner needs only to be paid for the value of the property taken and the amount he is damaged.

The Taking Agencies: The power of eminent domain is an inherent power of the government. The taking agencies are those by which a nation is both governed and served. They include:

1. The Federal Government and any and all of its agencies—the Federal Highway Administration, the United States Army Corps of Engineers, and others.

2. The various State governments and any and all of their agencies—State Highway Commissions, Flood Control and Water Resources Commissions, and others.

3. Local governments, such as counties, civil townships, and municipalities.

4. Public corporations such as school districts, fire protection districts, drainage, and irrigation districts.

5. Public utilities and service corporations such as the power, light, gas, telephone, telegraph, and water companies.

Private property owners—individuals or corporations—do not have the power of eminent domain. However, property owners may grant certain rights to others or restrict certain rights (which may otherwise belong to others) through the purchase and sale of such rights.

Acquisition policies and procedures vary with the various taking agencies. In general, a taking agency must announce the taking publicly before private property can be taken. The agency must state the nature of its intent and the magnitude of the project. A public hearing is then held. The purpose of the hearing is to present the general features of the project, the reasons for choosing or selecting the proposed location, the construction and engineering specifications, the property and property rights to be taken (or severed), the probable barrier effects, both temporary and permanent, the disruption of existing services, and the eventual benefits.

The hearings are usually held before a project is finalized. Hopefully, the taking agency presents several alternatives with the idea of increasing the amount of useful planning information. All property owners who may be affected by the project should attend. These hearings are open to the public. In fact, any person or party may attend. All property owners—in the area and elsewhere—have the right to express their views—both at the hearing and afterwards. They may do so individually, or they may join together, hire legal counsel, and make sure their opinions are heard. The best time to make suggestions is in the early planning stages.[3]

If, after a public hearing, the proposed project still appears feasible, the taking agency is then issued a Certificate of Public Necessity. This certificate authorizes the persons responsible to proceed with the acquisition of the required property, or property rights, and with the project itself.

THE PROPERTY OWNER'S PROBLEM

The property owner's problem is often one of frustration. The farmer typically sees a surveyor or engineer walking across his land driving several stakes without permission. His (or his wife's) first reaction is, "Who is that? Doesn't he know he's on private property?" The project leader, negotiator, or the surveyor himself should have stopped beforehand to visit with the farmer. Maybe the project leader did. Maybe he didn't. The farmer may not have been at home.

The property owner or farmer now has two problems: one, to learn of his rights, and more important, to study and think about the exact land or property rights which will be taken and two, to decide whether to accept the offer of the taking agency when it is made, or to let the taking agency sue him and defend himself in court.

In the early stages, the property owner often has little or no knowledge as to the project, how it will affect him, whether or not

---

3. Once a project is started it is usually too late for a group of property owners to successfully prevent the government from taking their properties. The property owners must then show that the officials involved acted in an arbitrary or capricious manner in taking the property, or that they are guilty of fraud, collusion, or gross abuse of discretion. This is quite difficult to prove.

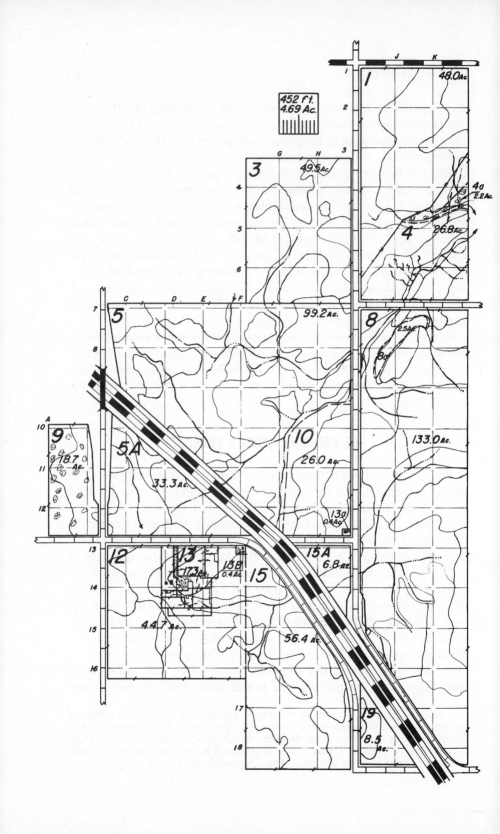

his property will be taken, when such taking will occur, what is involved, etc. Furthermore, he often has little knowledge of his legal rights or of eminent domain proceedings.

The Take: The laws of each state, along with the project's purpose, its needs and its requirements, determine the property or property rights taken. A take may consist of both real estate and all of the property owner's rights to it (in other words, the entire farm), or, a take may consist of only one of a property owner's rights (for example, a right to cross his property and bury a pipeline). When a project requires a permanent change in the use of the property (for example, a highway or a reservoir), the subject property, or land, is usually purchased outright with the title taken in fee simple. However, when a project allows the land to continue to be farmed (for example, a power line or pipeline), the take typically purchased consists only of an easement or right-of-way to cross the land, to erect a tower, or bury a pipe, etc. Compensation in each case has to be made even though in the latter instance little or no land is taken and little or no damage occurs.

The take may be a total taking or a partial taking. In the first case, the take consists of the entire farm or property. Title to the property is transferred from the condemnee, or property owner, to the condemnor, or taking agency. In the second case, the take consists of only a part of the farm or property. Here only part of the property is transferred. A highway project may take a strip of land, for example, 240 to 300 feet or more wide.

When the entire farm or property is taken, there are far fewer appraisal problems than when only a part of it is taken. When the entire farm is taken, the property owner is compensated for its fair market value. There is no remainder or residual property left. There is no damage to what's left or to the part not taken. Neither do any special benefits accrue to the property owner.

When only part of the property is taken, the basis for the compensation is the difference between the fair market value of the farm before the taking and the fair market value of the farm after the taking. This essentially requires two farm appraisals, with the after-appraisal including an estimate of any and all damage to

---

The appraiser's first job is to sit down with the project leader, the negotiator, or the engineer in charge of the project, and find out exactly what property or property rights will be taken.

the remainder, as a result of the taking, and an estimate of any special benefits to the property owner.

Lastly, the take may be a permanent one (a highway), or it may be merely temporary (a right-of-way to be used only during the period the project is under construction).

. In some states, the taking agency may not legally take more than the exact acreage required by the project. In other states, the taking agency may take the entire tract then resell whatever acreage is not required by the project at some later date (providing that the interests of the public are best served by doing so). In other words, a taking agency may, in some instances, both buy and sell land. The portion not required, of course, is the portion that is resold. In this fashion, partial takings are avoided; usually the cost to the taxpayers is less; and there are fewer appraisal problems.

Where the property in its entirety is taken and where the remainders or residuals are later sold, the original property owner is often given first opportunity to buy back the leftover residuals or tracts which belonged to him originally (and usually at the same price). The original property owner may also be given priority on any parcels or tracts that abut or lie adjacent to his original property. In this fashion, farms can be put back together, at least to some extent.

Property owners may also be given permission to retain title to and to later remove certain buildings and improvements.

Thus a taking agency may:

1. Purchase the entire farm or property (a total take).

2. Limit its acquisition to the exact acreage required, (typically, a partial take).

3. Purchase the exact acreage required, along with any parcel separated from the farm's headquarters, and/or any landlocked parcel (only an abutting property owner has access).

4. Purchase only certain property owner rights, thus acquiring an easement or a right-of-way, and thus allowing a property owner to continue possession and enjoyment of the property.

5. Purchase the entire farm or property, make the improvements desired, and then resell the remaining parcels or leftover residuals. In this latter instance, the original property owner may or may not have priority in repurchasing his own land or any that lies adjacent.

Many citizens are critical of the way in which the entire acquisition process—administration, appraisal, negotiation, condemnation, and management—has been performed or conducted by various government agencies. Thus, in 1970, the Federal Government moved to eliminate much of the variation in practice(s) among various agencies with regard to the acquisition of private property. Some of the fundamentals were defined as follows:

1. All reasonable effort should be made to acquire property expeditiously and through negotiation. All transactions are to be conducted so that the property owner shall not be worse off economically after his property is taken.

2. An appraisal of the property must be made before any negotiations can be started. The property owner is to be given the opportunity to accompany the appraiser when he inspects the farm, and the property owner is to be furnished a copy of the appraisal report. Where appropriate, just compensation for the property taken and damages to the remainder are to be stated separately.

3. A taking agency must establish whatever amount it believes to be just compensation before initiating any negotiations, and the full amount of just compensation must be offered to the property owner. The full amount may not be less than approved government appraisal of fair market value.[4] Such an offer should be made or presented in writing and should be made promptly.

4. The taking agency may in no way advance the date of condemnation, defer negotiations, deposit funds with the court, or perform any other act coercive in nature in order to compel agreement with the property owner.

5. No owner shall be required to surrender possession before the taking agency pays the agreed purchase price to the property owner or deposits such with the proper court.

6. Development or construction, which requires the farming operations to be discontinued or which requires the farmer to move his business (or to move from his dwelling), is not to be started without giving the farm family at least a 90-day written notice. Where such is practical the property owner is to be permitted to move a fixture, a building, or other permanent improvement not required by the taking agency.

7. If the acquisition of only part of the property leaves an uneconomic residual, or remainder, the taking agency is supposed to offer to acquire that remaining parcel, or parcels, from the property owner.

8. No agency can intentionally make it necessary for the property

---

4. No increase (or decrease) in the fair market value of the property prior to the date of take, and caused by the taking, is to be included in compensation to the property owner.

owner to start legal proceedings in order to prove the fact that his property is being taken. The taking agency is to institute condemnation proceedings.[5]

The 1970 law hopefully eliminates some of the inconsistencies which exist among federal and federally sponsored programs with respect to land acquisition. It recognizes that the taking agencies have major responsibilities: to delineate whatever property is to be taken, to arrive at a fair value, to offer said value to the property owner, and to perform both expeditiously and courteously.

The Offer: The property owner's first job is to sit down with the project leader, the negotiator, or the engineer and find out exactly what property or property rights will be taken, along with the amount of money they are willing or prepared to pay. The owner is typically provided a map or blueprint showing where the new road or power lines will cross his farm and the exact amount of land which will be taken. Under the new law, he should be provided with a copy of the taking agency's appraisal.[6]

---

5. Public Law 91-646.

6. This is correct for all Federal agencies and all agencies which are a part of a federally sponsored program. Federal and state agencies usually have trained personnel. However, many local government units lack experience in appraising and in acquiring land. They may lean over backwards to be fair or lenient to the parties involved; however, they may or may not use those techniques or arrive at realistic values.

Courtesy, Indiana State Highway Commission

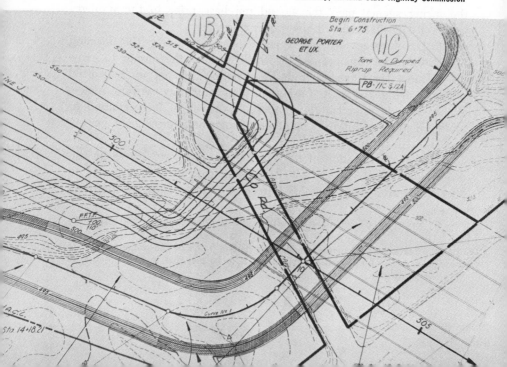

When only a partial taking is involved, one needs to study quite carefully the acreage to be taken; the acreage(s) in the parcel(s) that remain; the extent to which these remaining parcel(s) are disconnected or isolated from one another (or from the farmstead or main headquarters); the effect that the taking will have on irrigation, drainage, both surface drainage and water runoff, and tile drains and outlets; the building and maintenance of fences, both during and after construction; the continued growing and perhaps harvesting of certain crops; and, of course, access to various parts of the farm both during construction and after the project is completed. The location and design of all buildings, improvements, and other fixtures should be noted, particularly the location and preservation of any existing irrigation or tile drain system, any existing terraces or waterways required to control erosion, and the design and height of any culvert, irrigation facility, or drainage outlet underneath the take.

The property owner should discuss these items not only with the engineers and with the representatives of the taking agency but also with a professional appraiser who has done condemnation work. A farmer can usually make reasonable requests to the engineer in charge of the project. (Sometimes these requests have to be through a negotiator.) This transfer of information between a farm owner and the engineer can result in lowering the costs of the construction and in reducing the damage done to the property that remains. In the event that a particular problem cannot be eliminated, then it is the taking agency's responsibility to pay for whatever damage results.

And the Decision: The property owner's second job is to decide whether or not he should accept the taking agency's offer. He wants a fair price for the value of the land taken as well as any damage. Before making his decision a property owner should have an attorney explain to him the specific laws that apply in his case. He should hire a farm appraiser to estimate the fair market value of the farm or, in the case of a partial taking, the value of the farm before and the value of the farm after the taking. The three of them working together should then decide whether or not the offer should be accepted.

Taking agencies acquiring private property typically attempt to acquire the property through negotiation and agreement with the property owner. If the property owner feels the offer is reasonable and accepts it, then nothing more needs to be done other than to complete the formalities of the transfer of ownership. If the owner feels he is not going to be compensated adequately, he may then refuse to convey his property or his property rights, and he can then wait until condemnation proceedings are filed against him by the taking agency and legal action is begun.

Most farm property—80 percent or thereabouts—is acquired by negotiation. The methods differ somewhat among taking agencies. The usual procedure is for the negotiator, or buyer, to visit the property owner, explain the project to him, and show him exactly what property or property rights will be taken. One or more appraisals are usually made by the taking agency—either by members of its staff (staff appraisers) or by outsiders (independent fee appraisers). Then, the negotiator, or buyer, makes an offer.[7]

The property owner does not have to accept this offer. He has every right to a reasonable period of time to think about how the taking will affect the value of his property. He can ask for outside advice. He can talk with his neighbors. He should not, however, rely on the dollar amount paid his neighbors, for each situation is usually different.

If the property owner feels the offer is insufficient he may refuse to sell. The taking agency must then file condemnation proceedings. The court issues a notice of taking. It appoints two or more appraisers, giving them authority to review the property, appraise it, and make their recommendations as to the amount of compensation due the property owner. The taking agency then pays the court the amount recommended and the court issues a writ of authority or right to proceed. The property owner is given "due notice," and the taking agency may proceed.

The property owner may accept the amount recommended by the court appointed appraisers, or, he has the right to appear before the court and present his own evidence. The property owner cannot be fined, jailed, penalized, or intimidated. If he desires, he can ask for a jury of property owners (6 or 12) to hear his case and decide what is "fair" value.

Before a farmer, or property owner, decides to go to court, he

---

7. In the past, various negotiators have had a certain amount of flexibility in in the amount they could offer. A flexible policy is somewhat desirable, for the buyer can then settle for an amount slightly above the appraised value and thus save everybody time, trouble, and money. However, this same policy is also thought to be undesirable, for if the buyer can do this on some properties, he should then perhaps make his first offer to other property owners at a figure below the appraised values on their properties. No one likes the latter and the 1970 law disapproved of such.

should have at least one, and preferably more than one, professional farm appraiser appraise his property. He should consult with an attorney and have that attorney discuss his fees and provide him with an estimate as to the costs of litigation. The taking agency pays the costs of the condemnation proceedings. However, the property owner pays his own appraisers and his own attorney. In terms of costs, a property owner needs to consider the following items:

1. His own time, effort, and frustration.

2. The cost of acquiring the services of expert witnesses—appraisers, engineers, and perhaps others.

3. His attorney's fees and his court costs, if any. Attorney fees are often a percentage. They typically range from one-fourth to one-third of the amount the jury awards the property owner, over and above the original offer made by the taking agency.

4. Miscellaneous costs, such as additional taxes.

Given these costs, a property owner can then speculate on the "breakeven" amount he must receive in order to make the final award (the jury's decision as to value) comparable to the taking agency's initial offer plus his costs. The ultimate question in the property owner's mind when he is trying to decide whether or not to go to court is what will he (the property owner) get out of it? Is going to court worth the effort? Will the costs eat up the difference between the condemnor's original offer and the final award that can reasonably be expected?

The property owner has no assurance that the judge or the jury will grant him more money when he goes to court. The judge or jury may decide on a figure above the offer. They could quite conceivably decide on one below the offer, although the latter is not very likely. In fact, 80 percent of the time, the property owner obtains more money by going to court.[8] The rest of the time he seldom if ever loses in monetary terms, but there is a lot of time, trouble, and frustration.

THE DEFINITION OF "JUST COMPENSATION"

The Fifth Amendment to the Constitution of the United States specifies that private property shall not be taken for public use without payment of just compensation. It provides no further definition or formula, and neither has any subsequent legislation. Hence, the

8. *Iowa Law Review*, Vol. 54, No. 5, April 1969.

determination of just compensation has been largely left to the courts. The determination does not rest with the public or with the taking agency; it is instead a judicial function.[9] Over a period of time, various court decisions have developed the rules of the game.

In general, the courts have said that just compensation must guarantee payment of the dollar equivalent for whatever property is taken, and that, if market value can be ascertained, it is to be the measure of that equivalent. There are many legal restrictions as to what may be considered or included and what is and what isn't compensable. Down through history, and particularly during the last decade, there has been steady progress in favor of the property owner.

Unfortunately, there is considerable confusion and sometimes a wide divergency of opinion as to what constitutes just compensation. This is particularly the case in a partial taking where damage occurs to the remainder(s). The interpretations vary between taking agencies and between states. Judges and juries sometimes tend to set their own rules; they sometimes differ from those given an appraiser. De-

---

9. The United States Supreme Court once made the decision which indicated that determination of just compensation is a judicial inquiry. This had the effect of casting some doubt on the validity of any statute which might later attempt to provide standards for property valuation. As a result, the laws of most states carefully avoid any real definition, and furthermore, any opinion as to value by an appraiser is subject to review by the courts.

Courtesy, Indiana State Highway Commission

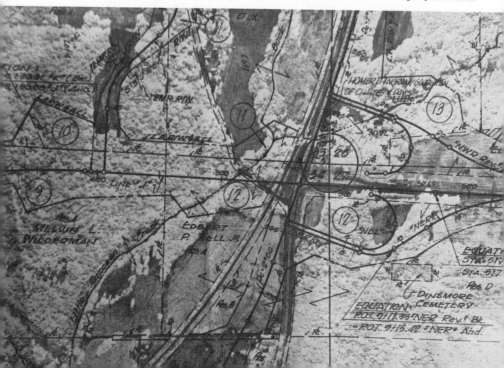

pending on the laws of the various jurisdictions, conflicting courtroom decisions have occasionally been handed down. All of this has sometimes led to widely varying appraisals and frequently unreasonable verdicts and awards.

The farm appraiser occasionally finds himself in a dilemma caused by conflicting legal opinions or interpretations of the law, and by requests for values (including damages) based on unrealistic assumptions. In some cases, the courts have defined the value they desire. The appraiser's job is then to follow that particular court's instructions, accepting whatever definition it prefers, even though that definition may at times be at variance with the definition and the interpretations given here.

The following guidelines as to "just compensation" are perhaps helpful.

1. When property is condemned and taken, the property owner, in order to be entitled to compensation, must have some possessory interest in the property or the property rights being transferred to the condemning authority. The term, *private property*, as typically used, includes both real and personal property and also all rights to that property including the right to use and to enjoy such. On the other hand, the owner is not entitled to compensation simply because his use or enjoyment is curtailed by the law or by certain rules and regulations. Zoning restrictions are an example.

2. All persons who own the property, or some or all of the property rights taken, are entitled to just compensation. These persons include owners with fee simple title, all joint or co-owners (whether they be tenants-in-common or joint-tenants), trustees and the beneficiaries of trusts, life tenants, remaindermen, reversioners (persons who own the fee during the time of possession by a life tenant), the grantees of property conveyed during condemnation proceedings, mortgagees (the mortgagee has an equitable lien against the award), guardians and those they represent, receivers and those holding redemption rights, the holders of tax titles, and tenants.[10] Any and all persons with an interest, whether partial or absolute, temporary or permanent, are entitled to compensation; however, only in relation

---

10. A tenant operator who leases land from another party has the right to intervene and present evidence of damage. Furthermore, he is entitled to the value of his estate in that land as long as he has it leased. He is not entitled to more than the portion of his interest in that which is taken, nor is he entitled to any compensation if his lease terminates before his possession is disturbed. Furthermore, a tenant and his landowner must agree on how compensation is to be shared; separate payments are not made by the condemning authority.

to or in proportion to the damage to his particular interest. Furthermore, the total amount of compensation cannot exceed that due, say, a single owner with a fee simple title.

3. In general, a property owner must be compensated for the loss of any or all of the following interests.

a. All land, buildings, and permanent improvements—fences, irrigation and drainage systems, orchards, groves, trees, shrubbery, wells, and growing crops.

b. All natural resources that are a part of or which accompany land—mineral, coal, and gravel deposits, underground waters, springs, woods, and both drainage and riparian rights. (If the natural drainage or if a stream channel is altered, damages may be assessed.)

c. The right of access to an existing point of ingress or egress and all easements, including any additional use of any previously taken right. (A public utility, for example, may erect a powerline over a right-of-way previously acquired for a pipeline.) However, covenants and contractual rights by themselves are not compensable, for there must be an interest in the land itself.

d. All land, buildings, and improvements made useless by a public project that may cast large amounts of water, sand, dirt, or other materials on it (for example, permanent flooding as in the case of a reservoir). In general, compensation is limited to (or required only when) injury to property is involved as distinguished from injury to a property owner. Typically, some property or property right has to be taken before the owner can be compensated. There are occasional instances of property damage without any actual property or property rights having been taken. In these instances, no compensation is generally allowed. Sometimes an exception occurs when one and only one property owner is involved.

4. Just compensation is the value of the property taken on the date of take. The date of take is when the condemnation petition is filed or when eminent domain proceedings are begun.

5. Just compensation is the full and perfect equivalent of the property taken in terms of money. The intent of the courts is that the property owner must be made "whole," in other words, compensated for what he has lost, and that he must be left in as good a position financially as he would have been had his property not been taken. At the same time, the courts just as carefully assert that the property owner must not be made "more than whole," in other

words, compensated for more than he has lost. The property owner shall be neither damaged nor benefited.

6. Just compensation is based on three items.

a. The value of the take (the land and any and all buildings and improvements actually taken). This is generally the minimum amount of compensation that can be awarded to a property owner.

b. Damages to any and all of the land, buildings and improvements not taken but which remain and are adversely affected by the taking.

c. Special benefits which accrue to the property owner as a result of the project.

In some states, the law requires the payment to the property owner to be reduced by the amount of any special benefits which accrue to him. However, the amount of benefits subtracted is usually limited to (they cannot exceed) the amount of the damages to the property not taken. Not always is this the case.

7. The three items: (1) value of the take, (2) damages, and (3) special benefits are reconciled in a before-and-after-value approach. The amount which the condemning authority pays and the amount that the property owner receives must equal the difference between the fair market value of the *whole* property immediately before the taking and the fair market value of the *whole* property which remains immediately after the taking.

Recapitulation of Values

1. Value of the Property **Before** the Take $_____
   (_____ Acres at $_____ per Acre)

2. Value of the Property **After** the Take $−_____
   (_____ Acres at $_____ per Acre)

3. The Difference (No. 1 − No. 2) $_____

4. Value of the Property Taken $_____
   (_____ Acres at $_____ per Acre)

5. Severance Damages to the $+_____
   Remaining Parcel(s)

6. Special Benefits Accruing to $−_____
   Remaining Parcel(s)

7. Total Compensation Due the Property Owner $_____
   (No. 4 + No. 5 − No. 6)

8. The term, *just compensation*, does not require or include payment for all of the injuries imposed on the property or the property owner by the various acts or actions of the taking authority. Sentimental values, speculative values, and the property owner's own time, trouble, and frustration are not compensable. At the same time, neither may the property owner's mode of ownership (or his mode of occupation) limit his right of recovery. Just compensation merely requires that the property owner should be paid for that which has been taken from him.

9. Just compensation is measured not by what the property is worth to the condemning authority; it is instead measured in terms of the dollar loss to the property owner. The question is not what the property taker has gained, but what the property owner has lost. The property owner is the one who is to be "made whole."

10. Neither is just compensation to be based on the value of the property to the property owner; it is to be measured only by that value which can be supported in the market. An uninformed authority occasionally maintains that just compensation is equal to whichever is the higher, (1) the market value of the property or (2) the value of the property to the property owner. This is not correct. This tends to recognize certain unique features of value to a particular property owner. These features are not always fully recognized or appreciated by the market. The basic legal concept is thus centered on market value or value-in-exchange as contrasted to cost, value-in-use, or value to the property owner.

11. Just compensation is not measured by or necessarily equal to cost. Many a jury, and sometimes a naive or inexperienced appraiser, maintains that just compensation is synonymous with indemnity and that the property owner should be indemnified or reimbursed for his costs. This also is not correct. The amount of compensation can only equal the amount of loss which a property owner can reasonably and justifiably claim as a result of two values—before and after—both of which are to be ascertained in the market.

12. Just compensation means "just" not only to the party whose property is taken, but also to the public or to the taxpayers which have to pay for such property.

The burden of establishing just compensation is the responsibility of the taking agency or condemning authority. However, the property owner also has the right to offer any and all of his own evidence as to value.

FAIR MARKET VALUE

Down through history two slightly different definitions of fair market value have been used. They have slightly different wordings yet each has had general acceptance in the courts.

1. Fair market value is " . . . the highest price, estimated in terms of money, which a property will bring if exposed for sale in the open market allowing a reasonable time to find a purchaser who has a knowledge of all uses to which it is best adapted and for which it is capable of being used."[11] The words, " . . . with neither the buyer or seller acting under duress, either to buy or to sell" are sometimes added.

2. Fair market value is the amount that would, in all probability, have been arrived at between an owner willing to sell and a purchaser desiring to buy, and in ascertaining that figure, taking into ac-

---

11. p. 131, *Appraisal Terminology and Handbook.*

count all considerations that fairly might be brought forward and reasonably be given weight in such bargaining.[12]

The two definitions have substantially the same meaning. The appraiser is in effect told to estimate what the subject property would sell for assuming that both the buyer and seller are willing, that neither is compelled to act, that both are fully informed, that there exists a reasonable period of time for the transaction, and that the times (supposedly demand and supply) are normal.

However, several notations are in order.

1. " . . . the value of the property to the parties seeking to condemn it, or to the owner is immaterial."[13]

2. " . . . while evidence that (the property) is valuable for this or that or some other purpose may always be given, and should be freely received, the value . . . which one or another witness may think the property would bring for this or that or some other specific or special purpose is not admissible as an element in determining market value."[14]

3. " . . . when it might be said that a property has no market value, value must be arrived at from the opinions of well-informed persons based upon the purposes for which the property is suitable, and . . .

4. " . . . that value-in-use, as contradistinguished from market value, is not acceptable."[15]

The first definition of fair market value goes back to 1909. The Heilbron definition was set forth by the Supreme Court of the State of California and has been widely accepted as authoritative ever since.[16] In fact, seldom has an attorney, a judge, or a jury been willing to go beyond citing the exact 1909 definition, word for word. None of them have given any further interpretation to the definition; nor have they attempted to give any real meaning of the word "fair."

---

12. Circuit Court of Appeals, Karlson vs. U.S. in 82 Fed. (2nd) 330.

13. Santa Ana vs. Harlin, 99 Cal. 538. Also U.S. vs. Honolulu Plantation Co., 122 F 581 (C.C.A. 9, 1923).

14. p. 132, Schmutz', *Condemnation Appraisers Handbook*. Also U.S. vs. Pamelson 319 U.S. 266, 282.

15. *Instructions to Appraisers,* Department of Justice Circular 3534, Bulletin 14.

16. Sacramento Southern Railroad Co. vs. Louise R. Heilbron, 156 Cal. 408. (The case involved the acquisition by the railroad of a strip of right-of-way 100' wide and containing 5.47 acres; the acquisition represented a partial taking from an approximate 53-acre parcel. The property was located in the southerly part of the City of Sacramento, California. The complaint was filed February 14, 1906. The defendant asked for total damages in the sum of $14,360.00. Judgment decree was filed September 13, 1906, in the amount of $3,494.75.)

Use of the adjective "fair" may appear to be desirable; there is little doubt but that it adds ethical content, which was perhaps the original intent. Yet, for all practical purposes the word is meaningless. It sometimes causes more harm than good. The term has been imposed upon society, not by the scholarly economists, not by persons experienced in the business world, but instead by the legal profession.

The ingenuity exercised by some persons desirous of twisting its meaning before a jury of 6 to 12 men or women is often astounding. In fact, its continued use has served to confuse the courts, many jurors, and sometimes appraisers as well.

The typical attorney does not worry about a little confusion. He does not always worry himself about an objective value. The attorney is an advocate. It is his job to look after his client and he often is remunerated for his services on a contingency basis.[17]

Depending on whether he represents the taking agency (the condemnor), or the property owner (the condemnee), he wants either a low fair value, or a high fair value. When he represents the property owner, he wants a fair value which is as high as possible, because he presumes (unofficially . . . don't quote us) (1) that the attorney representing the taking agency will come to court with a fair value which is as low as possible and (2) that the jury, upon hearing the evidence from both sides, will add the two figures together, divide by two, and thereby arrive at a "fair and reasonable" compromise. This is referred to as a quotient verdict. In many cases, unfortunately, the quotient verdict is neither equal to, nor even similar to, fair market value. (The legal profession may disagree.)

The condemnation appraiser tries to base his values on the market. However, when he knows that he may go to court, he often, consciously or unconsciously, lets his values creep upward. He knows that the property owner is not a willing but an unwilling seller. He knows that the property owner cannot prevent the taking of his property. He knows that if the property owner goes to court his case is typically a one-time-only case, or in other words, not subject to appeal in the event some item left out is later discovered. The condemnation appraiser is also guided by several additional legal requirements, one of which (in the author's opinion) leads him quite logically to place a fair value on the property which is higher than its market value.

---

17. The attorney usually receives a percentage of whatever award the jury makes over and above the initial offer made by the taking agency. This is usually in addition to any out-of-pocket costs.

Highest and Best Use: The fair market value definition requests "the highest price" and requires "a purchaser with a knowledge of all uses." Over a period of time, the two inferences have led to the concept of highest and best use. In fact, "highest-and-best-use" rather than "most-likely," "most-probable," or "typical use," is now recommended by most all courts where fair market values are established. The concept is commonly accepted and is used in most condemnation appraisals.[18]

Highest and best use is defined as " . . . that use which will most likely produce the highest income both in terms of money and amenities over a given period of time, or, in the case of an improvement, for its remaining life."[19] It is that use to which a property would be devoted were it owned by a man of excellent wisdom, and a man possessing adequate resources or means, or whatever else it takes to develop the property.[20]

Highest and best use is that use to which a property may logically be put, that use to which it is clearly adapted, and that use to which it may be clearly adapted in the future by reason of its intrinsic nature, its location, and its surroundings. Supposedly, highest and best use is to be considered to the fullest extent, but only to the extent that the current or prospective demand for such use affects market value. The property must be properly held.[21] Its use must be . . .

1. Legal, and not prevented by deed restrictions or zoning regulations.

2. Available, applicable, and adaptable to the property at the time of the appraisal, and not impossible due to any of the property's physical characteristics.

3. In demand while the property is still privately held, or needed, or likely to be needed in the immediate or reasonably near future.

4. Commensurate with the present value of all future benefits.

5. Logical and reasonable, not just possible, in other words, within the realm of probability.

6. Neither conjectural, speculative, nor dependent upon the uncertain acts of another person.

---

18. Mississippi and Rum River Boom Co. vs. Patterson, 98 US 403; 25 L Ed. 206. Kerr vs. South Park Comm. 117 US 379; 29 L Ed. 924; 6 SCT 801 Montana R. Co. vs. Warren 137 US 348: 34 L Ed. 681 11 S Ct. 98 Shoemaker vs. U.S. 147 U. S. 282; 37 L Ed. 170; 13 S Ct. 361 U.S. vs. Chandler-Sunbar Water Power Co. 229 U.S. 53; 57 L Ed. 1063; 33 S Ct. 667.

19. American Society Farm Managers and Rural Appraisers Manual.

20. Nichols, *Eminent Domain,* Section 12.314.

21. Court of Appeals, Olson vs. U.S. 292 U.S. 246.

Correct application of the concept permits a present enhancement in value but only by reasonable likelihood of adaptation of the property to a higher and better use in the near future.[22] Highest and best use accounts for all reasonable anticipations. It minimizes all hazards as much as possible, and in general, assumes the best possible operator—not necessarily a typical farm operator, but an all-seeing property owner. No allowance is to be made for remote, imaginary, or purely conjectural use. No particular consideration should be given an owner's vague plans or dreams. However, neither is the property's value to be limited to its present use or to that use for which it is currently being devoted by the present owner. Highest and best use is to be arrived at only after considering all uses for which the property is suited or suitable; fair market value is then based on the most advantageous use of all.

The highest and best use concept is most applicable, and is both used and misused, mostly in the transition area where land use is mixed and changing, where two or more uses are currently being made of various properties (each of which is fairly typical; however, one may be expanding, the other declining), and thus where interim use is apparent.[23] For example, in an urban area located around a large center of population a number of farms may be in the process of slowly, and yet gradually, being purchased for development purposes. Agricultural opportunities are declining and are being overshadowed by residential, commercial, and/or industrial developments. Property values are rising and farms are selling at prices considerably above their values based on earnings due to location. In the same area, there may be farms which are farmed intensively, yet others which are partially abandoned. The latter may lay right along side of a developed property (with all utilities and services for such readily available). It may someday be purchased for development purposes. However the time may not be quite "ripe."

What most attorneys and some appraisers forget is that, if all the farms in the area were to be sold or developed immediately into whatever eventual use appears likely, an oversupply of that kind of property would be created, and this, in turn, would destroy much of the value. Hence, the reasons for interim use, for holding and speculat-

---

22. *Instructions to Appraisers,* Department of Justice Circular 3534, Bulletin 14.
   23. Interim use is that to which a property may be put between now and the time when it will be used most advantageously.

ing, yet also the reason for reasonable values even in this kind of an area. In other words, highest and best use may be considerably above that of the current or typical use of many of the farms.

Value Before and Value After: The condemnation appraiser's job is a relatively easy one when the taking involves the entire farm property. Just compensation is the fair market value of the property. However, when a partial take is involved, two additional concepts underlie fair market value. The first is fairly obvious, the second is not. The appraiser needs a thorough understanding of each.

When only part of a property is taken, just compensation now becomes the difference between the fair market value of the property immediately before the taking minus the fair market value of the property immediately afterwards. The appraiser's job is now to ascertain the values of that property *as a whole* both before and after. In a partial taking, a property owner may end up with a single yet smaller tract or he may be severed (cut in half) and end up with two (or more) separate tracts or properties. In the latter case the naive

Courtesy, U.S.D.A.

and inexperienced appraiser is inclined to appraise each of the two remaining residuals as separate properties and add them together. This procedure is incorrect. His job is to arrive at the value of the property *as a whole* both before and after the taking.

If or when the two (or more) remaining residuals are sold the parcels will, in all probability, be sold separately. The total of the two (or more) prices received for the residuals or remaining properties will, in all probability, be greater than any single price that would be received for the two properties were they to be sold together. *However, the appraiser's job is still to value the property as a whole both before and after the taking.*[24]

The Unit Rule: A number of questions—What is a whole property? What is a complete farm unit? What is the larger parcel?—are often raised. These questions have led to the unit rule. It states that a property, in order to be considered a complete unit (i.e., a whole property), must meet three requirements. Furthermore, that any property, in order to be considered a part of the remaining property, must have . . .

1. Unity of ownership or title, which implies that the remaining tract or parcel must be held under the same ownership as that from which the taking occurs. The property can be acquired at different times, but at the time of the taking it must be under the control of the same owner or owners.

2. Unity of use or operation, which implies that the remaining tract or parcel must be devoted to the same use as the parcel from which it is taken. Furthermore, the parcels must be used in connection with each other; mere devotion to the same use does not serve to fuse the two.

3. Reasonably close physical location, which implies that the remaining tracts or parcels must be so located or arranged geographically that the farm has clearly functioned as a unit before, and thus is materially affected when severed.

Separate parcels under the same ownership do not necessarily have to be contiguous in order to be treated as a single unit. There is still unity of use if the two (or more) parcels are used in such a way, and, as a result of the taking of any part of the property, the value of the part that remains is less than its proportionate value of the larger parcel before the taking.

---

24. This approach, widely accepted and used, makes any study of the values of residuals rather absurd.

Some Exceptions: There are, of course, exceptions to almost any concept, and this is true of both values before and after and the unit rule as well. One exception occurs where the part taken is extremely small relative to the size of the property owned originally. For example, a 5-acre tract for a new school house may be taken off the corner of a 6,840-acre ranch. County and local officials often compensate the property owner by paying him for the value of the part taken as a separate unit. All they have essentially done is to buy a small tract of land. One might argue that this is not a valid measure of just compensation for it does not comply with the before and after requirement. However, no appraiser, in his right mind, really wants to appraise that ranch first as a 6,840-acre spread and then as a 6,835-acre tract, and estimate the difference in value. In some of the best range areas, the part taken would represent the hay and pasture requirements for only about one-third of a beef cow.

Another exception occurs where the part taken can be considered to be a separate economic unit in itself. For example, a large dairy farm consisting of 450 acres has a small milk processing plant and a retail outlet on 1.5 acres across the road from its headquarters. The milk plant is taken. It is owned by the same owners. It is a part of the farm and the farm business. It is located conveniently to the dairy barns and the rest of the farm. Other farmers 5 and 10 miles away also deliver milk to the same plant. The real question is whether the part taken should be considered as a part of the whole or whether it is really a separate economic entity. It is the author's opinion that it is a separate economic entity.

Another exception or question pertains to the widening of a highway where there is potential commercial frontage or use. If the owner is not losing access, then for all practical purposes he is not losing frontage; he is instead losing depth, or land to the rear. The property should be valued as a whole. If, however, the owner is losing access, he is then losing frontage. This property may be valued separately.

In spite of these, and perhaps other exceptions, the fair market value immediately before the take and the fair market value immediately after a take is the most widely used and most widely accepted method of establishing just compensation in a partial taking.

THE PROBLEM OF DAMAGE

The law of eminent domain requires that the property owner be compensated not only for the value of any property taken but also for any damage to the property which remains and which is made less valuable by reason of the taking. The requirement—payment for damages to the remainder—applies only to partial takings; it does not or cannot apply when an entire farm or property is taken.

Many property owners appear to have the attitude that they are entitled to compensation for practically every conceivable damage or inconvenience there is, both real and imaginary. However, the courts have never construed just compensation to include payment for all possible injuries. Such a decision would virtually render many government actions impossible. Many a legislative enactment (for example, the property tax, the police power, or a zoning regulation) imposes a burden on the property owner. These may lead to a diminution in the value of one's property. However, none of these particular ones are compensable. Neither are all of the acts which result from the exercise of eminent domain.

The appraiser's job is thus to obtain a working knowledge as to what constitutes severance damage (as contrasted to consequential damage) and as to what kinds of damage are compensable and what are not. His job is to then place a value on all of the compensable damages that can reasonably be attributed to the taking. These values are most difficult to estimate. They require considerable thought and judgment.

There are two types of damage—severance and consequential. They are similar in that each involves damage to the part or parts of the property not taken, in other words, to the propery that remains. However, they differ in origin and in compensability. Severance damage is caused by and can be directly related to a taking of part of the property; whereas with consequential damage, no physical property need necessarily be taken. Under federal law and under most state laws severance damage is compensable; consequential damage, generally speaking, is not.

Severance Damage: Severance damage is damage to the remainder due to the taking of part of the property. It is a diminution or loss in the market value of that which remains. It essentially recognizes that if a farm owner were to sell part of his farm, he would expect the selling price to include not only the value of the tract sold, but also any decrease in the value of the part he kept. The condemnation appraiser may first assume the part taken is paid for, then raise the question, "How much less (proportionately) is the remaining property as a whole worth (after rather than before the taking) by virtue of the fact that such is no longer a part of the original property?"

Severance damage may result from a fee taking or an easement taking. It can be based on any and all property or property rights owned now or in the future.[25] Severance damage must be estimated in light of a full knowledge of all the uses to which the property might be put both before and after the taking. It must be fully supported by all presently known facts; it cannot be based on remote, uncertain, conjectural, or speculative elements. Unfortunately, every farm and every taking presents a different problem. There is oftentimes a wide divergence of opinion among appraisers.

Consequential Damage: Consequential damage is that which arises as a consequence of a taking of (or as a result of construction on) some other nearby property. This may occur without any part of a property owner's property being physically expropriated and without any of his rights being taken. In other words, consequential damage is not particularly unique as far as a single property is concerned; it is instead general in nature. To the individual property owner the loss is incidental. It is often an inconvenience—one to be endured by all persons involved, as one of the prices we pay for progress in our society.

Consequential damage may be personal in nature. An adjacent owner, none of whose property is taken, may have some diminution in his ability to use or enjoy his property. He thus feels that he personally has been damaged. However, such damage, even when it occurs, is generally suffered by all properties or property owners in the area. It is of a general nature and consequential.

Just compensation is considered to be payment for a thing expropriated, in other words, payment for property loss as contrasted to personal loss. A property owner is entitled to be compensated only for that which is taken from him. While the taking of private property often produces additional hardships (hardships which are the proximate result of a taking, and hardships which have to be classed as unintended or incidental), compensation for these hardships, even though they are sometimes substantial, is not recoverable. Personal inconvenience and annoyance are too uncertain, too conjectural, too remote, and too speculative to be proven, or for their worth to be estimated. Thus, consequential damages are most generally non-compensable.

The appraiser's job is (1) to insure that all elements of damage,

_____
25. There must exist merely a unity of ownership, a unity of use, and a reasonable geographic location with respect to both the part taken and the part or parts that remain.

which have occurred as a result of the taking and which are considered to be compensable, are included in his report and (2) to eliminate any damages, which, although real, are not considered to be compensable under the laws of the state in which the property is located. In arriving at these decisions, the condemnation appraiser should ask for and receive instructions from his client's legal counsel.

Compensable Damage: As a general rule, severance damage is compensable, and consequential damage, except in specific and unusual circumstances, is not. Broadly classified, damages are compensable when an actual taking of a property or a property right is involved. They are non-compensable when they are general in nature, suffered by all property owners in the area, unintentional, incidental, and in the nature of a personal inconvenience. Because of the variations found, the following list of compensable damages should be used as a guide only. However, in general, the following damages are compensable.

1. Separation of a property into two separate tracts with the loss of some land. A partial taking often severs or divides a farm into two (or more) separate tracts. The main headquarters may be located in one tract and some of the land located some distance away. Travel from one parcel to the other may now be indirect and over a circuitous route. This may require a change in the farm organization, particularly if the disconnected portion is not readily accessible to livestock. It may affect the farming operations by increasing the amount of travel and thus the costs of operation, particularly on the disconnected portion of the farm. To the extent that this occurs, it tends to reduce the salability or marketability (and hence value) of the parts which remain. To this extent, damages are compensable.

2. Separation of the farm property into two separate tracts, along with a loss of some or all of the buildings and improvements. A partial taking may not only divide a farm, it may also lead to a partial and sometimes complete loss of all buildings and improvements. This may be a result of the take itself, or by virtue of the fact that the improvements are severed. The diminution in the value of any and all buildings and improvements, which are no longer useful in the farming operations, and which have little or no other alternative use or value, constitutes damage. The cost of moving any building or improvement not taken constitutes damage. The cost of replacing or reconstructing any and all severed improvements, along with the construction of any additional improvements required to operate the

remaining parcel or parcels, constitutes damage. The replacement of permanent irrigation installations, the construction of new tile drains, and the building of new fences to enclose the property are illustrations.

3. Irregularity in the shape and size of the parcels or tracts that remain. A new highway, power line, or pipeline often crosses a farm diagonally, leaving odd-shaped fields and smaller fields. This is sometimes referred to as triangulation. Any change from large, rectangular fields to smaller, irregularly shaped fields increases the time required to plow, plant, cultivate, and harvest various crops. This leads to an increase in the number of point rows and to a reduction in the efficiency of the farming operations. The degree to which the above occurs depends on the size of the fields in the beginning.

4. A reduction in farm size. A partial taking often leads to a reduction in the number of acres farmed and sometimes in the number or amounts of available buildings and improvements. This reduction may be small or large and it may take place in the better or poorer parts of the farm. When the reduction in acreage is large (percentage-wise) this tends to greatly affect farm profits, for certain fixed or overhead costs remain, even though the size of the farm is reduced. A reduction in acreage may also affect the balance between land and buildings. If the remainder ends up with more buildings and improvements than the land will support, this reduces their value.[26]

5. Disruption of service resulting from construction. Farmland is often cut off from a water supply—a spring, a well, a windmill, or an underground pipe and hydrant. Irrigation systems, tile drains, and sewage facilities are frequently severed.[27] In the construction of highways the natural flow of surface water is often disturbed. Water from adjacent land may flow over the property owner's land in a sheet. However, the building of a highway may concentrate this surface drainage into or through a single culvert, which then releases all the water in one spot. Such interference is a proper element of damage to the remaining property.

---

26. At one time, a percentage formula was recommended for purposes of determining damage to buildings and improvements when a take upsets the balance between land and buildings. The appraised value of all buildings and improvements (not including the dwelling) was multiplied by the percentage of land taken. This approach is mathematically precise. However, it does not differentiate in the quality of land (that taken relative to that not taken); it does not recognize differences in age or condition of the buildings; nor does it recognize the extent to which various improvements are really related to a given land base.

27. A farm owner should have an authentic map showing the location of any and all underground installations.

6. Loss of access, either partial or total, and inaccessibility. Interference with an easement of ingress and egress to and from an existing public highway both material and substantial is compensable. The closing of a road justifies compensation when it causes additional travel from one part of the farm to another, or from the farm to the nearest shopping center, and when it causes increased risks (fire protection is denied) or increased costs (fire insurance rates are increased). Where access rights to an existing highway have previously existed, but are now being denied, this loss of access is compensable.

At the same time, the property owner is not entitled to unlimited access to an abutting property at all points along a highway. Where a highway is constructed on a new right-of-way, the courts have held that the abutter is not entitled to compensation for a particular right he never owned or never used. If no access rights previously existed, then nothing has really been taken. Furthermore, the fact that access is made more circuitous or inconvenient by the manner in which the highway was constructed (such as by placing divider strips in the center) does not, in and of itself, constitute damage. Such constitutes damage only to the extent it results in a diminution of the value of that which remains.

A partial taking sometimes leaves a parcel or tract of land completely inaccessible or isolated. When a small, irregular tract is left without any access whatsoever, it is said to be landlocked. Severance damage may now approach the total market value of the parcel (as a part of the whole). However, the number of adjacent property owners who may be desirous of acquiring said landlocked parcel influences one's final judgment as to value.

7. A reduction in the use of the property. This may be the result of a number of factors—a reduction in size, loss of some or all of the improvements, elimination or disruption of certain services, loss of certain services, loss of access, etc. An objectionable use of the land taken may also cause damage to that which remains (and conversely, of course, a project may enhance the value of the remainder).

8. Proximity damage. Proximity damage may occur when a project comes sufficiently close to an existing building or improvement to either limit the access to such or restrict its use. A loss of utility and/or a loss in attractiveness often results. A highway cut or an elevation may lead to an unusual change in grade and thus create an undesirable circumstance. The property may be left above or below the level of the highway; lateral support may be removed; view may be impaired. To the extent that they result in a diminution of the

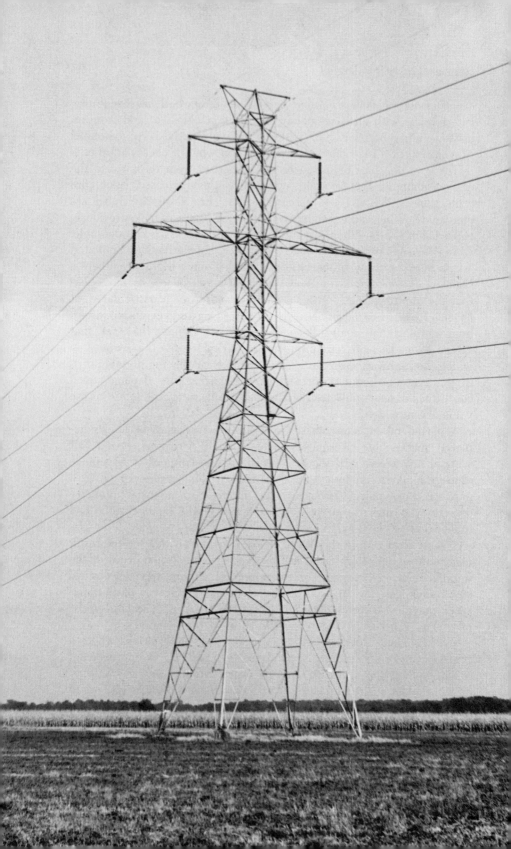

value of that which remains, all are compensable.

9. A temporary right-of-way taken during the period of construction. Its value (or damage) depends on the rights acquired, the period of time over which the right-of-way is to be held, the provisional rights to re-enter, and the characteristics or condition of the property or reversion after the right has been terminated.

10. Damage to growing crops and to livestock being raised or fattened is not usually appraised. However, the date of taking may be most inopportune to some of the farming operations. A crop may have been fertilized, planted, and cultivated, only to be destroyed before it could be harvested. This constitutes damage to the extent that it affects the before and after value(s) of the property.

Non-Compensable Items: There are numerous elements that arise in almost any condemnation case that are non-compensable, even though the farm's market value may be adversely affected. To receive compensation a property owner must, in general, show that the damage or inconvenience that he has suffered is peculiar to his property and to him, and that this damage or inconvenience differs from that suffered by the public in general. Under the laws of eminent domain, the following damages have not been and are not today generally compensable.

1. Damages considered to be uncertain, speculative, remote, or a matter of conjecture—fancied, assumed, or imagined, and hence difficult to ascertain or establish. Compensable damage must be real. It must be measurable, and it must be recognizable in the market.

2. Inconvenience, annoyance, and nuisances, which are common to all properties in the area and are to be suffered by the public in general. Increased amounts of, or the taking away of, traffic during construction, or a permanent rerouting of traffic (sometimes the vacation of a road by the public) due to a relocation of a highway, temporary roadblocks or obstructions, annoyance, such as noise, fumes, or dust due to additional traffic, fear of danger from the project itself or from the results of the project, for example, the increased risk in crossing a highway—none of these are compensable.

3. Private rights taken solely under action or power of police protection. Private rights relative to highway use may be regulated many different ways under the police power, and if so, such is without compensation. For example, if ingress and egress is changed 500 feet

from the present location, this change is not compensable if it is done solely under police action.

4. Damage to the business. Farm receipts may decline, operating expenses may increase, and the farm income may be reduced. However, all this is irrelevant (unless it affects, or except to the extent it reduces, the value of the remaining property). This, generally speaking, has been considered *damnum absque injuria* or damage without injury. The farming operations may become less profitable. However, a property owner is to be paid for the property taken and the loss in value of that which remains and not for any of the business.

Business interruption during the course of construction, the costs of moving, and the costs of starting up again in a new location have not been and are not now a part of just compensation.[28] Business losses (including the loss of good will) are dependent upon the business acumen of the operator, his personality, and his managerial skills. These losses are generally regarded as speculative and conjectural; too nebulous and too intangible to measure. They are not compensable under the traditional definition of just compensation.

5. The cost of finding and acquiring a new, or additional, or adjoining property to replace that which has been taken, relocation costs, and moving expenses have not been a part of just compensation.[29] In general, a property owner has had no recourse for the time spent, the miles driven, the legal counsel and the fees incurred, or the mental stress to which he and his family are sometimes subjected in locating a new farm, or in effecting a settlement with the taking agency. The condemnation and taking of an entire farm or property often upsets the family pattern of living, often moving them to entirely different surroundings—schools, shopping centers, religious, and social activities. Considerable time and effort are required in order to locate an acceptable substitute. Such are not compensable.

In the case of a partial take and a relatively small acreage, the farm owner can seldom find a similar acreage, adjoining or not. For example, he may have lost 14 or 21 or 34 acres. However, he can typically purchase only 80 or 160 acres. Usually he is one among several farmers desirous of obtaining more land in the area. An heir or a group of heirs may be dependent on the income received from the farm and they may experience some loss when they shift that investment to some alternative. There may be a sizeable increase in the cost or value

---

28. See section on "Advisory Assistance and Relocation Payments."
29. Ibid.

of the surrounding farm properties. However, none of this is compensable.

6. Damages caused by the taking of an adjoining property belonging to another. For example, the use and enjoyment of property owned by an abutting property owner may be damaged. However, if no property was taken from this particular owner, such is usually consequential. It is not generally compensable.

Yardsticks as to Measurement: The appraiser's real problem is to sort out what is and what is not compensable damage, and to measure the extent of this damage. There are two yardsticks: one, the salability or marketability of the property which remains and two, the cost to cure.

The first question, "Does this take really affect the salability of the remaining property?," must be applied to the remainder *as a whole;* it is not to be applied to the remainders, parcel by parcel. Unfortunately, a severed farm is seldom sold *as a whole.* Instead, the remaining parcels are typically sold separately. Hence, considerable judgment is required in order to value the farm *as a whole* both before and after the taking.

The condemnation appraiser often arrives at an amount of damage far less than that generally computed by the property owner. This is because many remaining parcels or tracts, even the small and irregularly shaped ones, have often been sold at some later date to a neighboring farmer with little or no loss in value. This is even true of isolated (not necessarily landlocked) parcels, which are often considered to be severely damaged in terms of their remaining value (as a part of the whole). The property owner is frequently able to sell a parcel (by itself and at some later date) at a price considerably above its estimated value (as a part of the whole) immediately after the taking.

This occurs because, where the demand for farm land exceeds its supply, most farm owners are not very selective—even when small size, irregular shape, or limited access is involved. These so-called objectionable or undesirable features are often discounted very little in the market place; and this is particularly true when there is more than one abutting owner who may be desirous of owning such. Furthermore, the typical farmer will often purchase or rent additional land not always located right next door. He prefers an adjacent tract; however, he will often travel 5 or 10 miles, and in some areas even further, in order to obtain additional land and thus expand his farming operations.

The cost-to-cure approach to damage applies mainly to buildings and improvements. It has all of the inherent characteristics of the cost approach to value (Chapter VIII) and many of the same problems; for example, the problem of estimating depreciation and then value that which remains (Chapter IX). Damage with regard to buildings and improvements is to be based on contributory values or the dollar amounts that the building and improvements contribute to the market value of the farm. The cost to cure cannot exceed the market value of the item being cured.

The property owner often disagrees. He typically feels that he should be reimbursed for the cost of whatever is taken from him—in other words that he should be indemnified. Many juries sometimes agree. If this indemnity philosophy were to be fully accepted, then such monies should perhaps be paid out, as they are by some insurance companies, with deferred payment provisions. The property owner could be partially compensated immediately; he would receive the remainder only if and when he rebuilt the building or the fence or did carry out the improvement.[30] This would be an interesting twist.

There usually are but few disagreements as to the value of the land taken; however, landowners often take issue with the taking agencies, and even their own appraisers, with regard to their estimates of damage. This is good, because it requires an appraiser to make a very thorough study of the various elements of damage inflicted upon the remaining property in order to assign a value to such.

Some condemnation appraisers prefer to itemize, and some states allow them to itemize, each of the various damages. This is advantageous because the condemnation appraiser can thus demonstrate that he didn't merely pull the figures out of his hat. (This is what the inexperienced and unethical appraiser often does.) However, when all of the various items are totaled, they often exceed any amount that is realistic.

The honest appraiser faces a very real question here as to the contributory values. Again he (and others) need to be admonished: (1) cost and value are not necessarily equal and (2) the cost of a new improvement does not add an equal number of dollars to the value of the farm.

---

30. In the agricultural Midwest at least (largely a cash grain area), the farmer is often paid (sometimes quite well) for several new corner sets and fences. However, only a fraction of these are ever rebuilt by the farmer.

THE QUESTION OF BENEFITS

Whenever a public authority takes private property, it may show that, as a result of the project, the remaining property will be benefited. In other words, a taking of private property for public use may lead to an enhancement of the property that remains. Remainders are just as likely to be enhanced sometimes as damaged. The extent to which this occurs—a given property is enhanced in value—a taking agency may mitigate or offset part or all of the compensation due a property owner. The benefits must be a result of the project itself—either the taking or the construction—and they must be special to the property involved.

Benefits do not apply, of course, when an entire property is taken. They are similar to damages in that they apply only where there is a partial taking. Benefits must be caused by, flow from, or be the result of the taking or an improvement for which the taking was made. The value of the remainder must be more than the worth of its proportionate part of the property as a whole before the taking. Benefits must also be real and imminent. They cannot be uncertain, remote, speculative, or conjectural. They apply only to the property that remains. They cannot (as some persons argue) be used to increase the cost of the land taking by the condemning authority.

A property owner may be the recipient of two types of enhancement—benefits that are special to the property involved and benefits in general.

Special Benefits: Special benefits are those conferred upon a particular property. They are the result of an increase in the value of the property not taken. They may accrue to each remaining tract or residual. Special benefits must be peculiar to the particular tract or parcel retained by the property owner. They must be in physical contact, in other words, they must touch the property taken. They need not necessarily enhance the value of the other tracts in the same area.

Special benefits must be based on the increase in the value of the remaining property *as a whole;* they must equal the increase in the value of the property *as a whole* immediately after, as contrasted to immediately before, the taking. At the same time, special benefits must be more than peculiar to the property in question. These must differ in kind, rather than degree, from those benefits which are shared by the public-at-large.

General Benefits: General benefits are those which arise from the fulfillment of the public project. They supposedly justify the taking in the first place. They benefit all persons or parties who use said project, and are common to and shared by the public-at-large. They thus enhance the entire area. They accrue to all properties involved and to all property owners. For this reason, benefits are sometimes classed according to the area they affect. They are classed as individual or special when they affect only one or two properties. They are classed as general when they benefit a large number of properties.

Deductible Benefits: The laws vary, not only in terms of what is and what is not a deductible benefit but also to the extent to which benefits can be used to offset the amount of compensation due the property owner. In general, the value of a special benefit is deductible from part (sometimes all) of the compensation due the property owner.

The following benefits are, in general, both special and deductible.

1. An increased use for the remainder(s). The largest benefits that accrue to remaining properties are usually the result of changes in land use. Remainder studies in a number of states show that a

Photo by Suter

major public improvement often enhances the values of other properties in the area, and that considerable enhancement usually occurs
in the value of the residuals. This takes place when a new highway
goes through a rural area (unless access is limited) and particularly
when a highway interchange is located on or near the property. A
sizeable increase in value often accrues to parcels of farm land which
may have been previously suited only to agriculture, but which can
now be adapted for residential, commercial, or industrial use. An
interstate highway interchange with access to and from a local community often creates immediate site or location value (particularly the
right-hand quadrant between the highway and downtown). Likewise, a reservoir often creates a number of summer home sites—again
shifting land use and increasing property values.

2. Improved access to a property. A public improvement often
provides an additional access to a property—an access not formerly
enjoyed. The creation of new ingress and egress to a site may enhance
its value considerably by increasing the salability, or marketability, of
the land. Highways may be widened. A railroad switching or shipping
facility may be created.

3. Farm drainage and other improvements may become available.
A public project sometimes provides better drainage to the owner's
remaining land. A drainage system, previously thought to be impractical or too costly, may result. Swampy areas are often drained.
Land fill is sometimes made available, additional sewage facilities
are sometimes provided; and overflow dams sometimes provide special
privilege.

4. Detrimental buildings and improvements and other hazards
adjacent to a particular property may be removed.

5. Remaining tracts are sometimes improved in terms of shape,
use, enjoyment, and view.

Deductible benefits must be caused by, or be the result of, the public
project for which the taking or expropriation was instituted. They
must affect or be peculiar to the individual property; and, they must
affect the market value of the property that remains. They may thus
be used to reduce the amount of compensation due the property
owner.

General benefits, on the other hand, accrue to all property owners
in the area—those whose property is not taken as well as those whose
property is taken. To subtract the value of general benefits from the
compensation due those property owners whose property is taken
would be unfair. To do so would force these property owners to bear

more than their fair share of the costs. Vice versa, if the property owner whose property is taken is not fully compensated, then the neighbors who receive the same general benefits should help pay for such.

The Offsets: The laws of various states differ as to whether special benefits are allowed as offsets against the total compensation due a property owner, or whether they are deductible only up to the extent to which the property owner was damaged. Most states do not allow benefits to be offset against the value of the part taken. They allow such offset only to the extent that the remaining tracts or parcels are damaged. The latter (special benefits offset against severance damages) is more logical, for both the benefits and damages are the result of a partial taking; both affect only the part(s) of the property not taken.

Most states recognize enhancement. Most of them permit offset against severance damage only (not against the value of the part taken). If the special benefits are equal to or greater than the severance damage, the owner receives only the value of the part taken. The states which do not allow offsets against the value of the land taken base their ruling on the Constitutional provision that property should not be taken without compensation in the form of pecuniary means (not benefits).

Unfortunately, there are no clear-cut formulas which show where a special benefit ends and a general benefit begins. It is the condemnor who bears the burden of proof regarding special benefits; just as it is the condemnee who bears the burden of proof regarding damages. The taking agencies are obligated to recognize the rights of the property owner; however, they also are responsible to the public in general. More emphasis will undoubtedly be placed on special benefits in the future, as taxpayers continue to bear the burden of various public projects. While the public has designed certain safeguards to protect the owners of private property, they should also be assured that the just compensations are only just and not overly generous. The awards should approximate what the property owner could have sold or exchanged his property for in the market and in a realistic bargaining situation.

SUPPLEMENTAL APPRAISAL TECHNIQUE

Condemnation appraisals require more painstaking detail than any other type of an appraisal, and also some additional appraisal technique. First, the condemnation appraiser must recognize that the legal counsel for the person, or party, involved, either the condemnor or the condemnee, will want to coordinate his appraisal assignment with the other various parts of the project. Legal procedures usually advance one step at a time. Second, the condemnation appraiser must realize, that in the case of a partial taking, two appraisals are required—one immediately before and one immediately after the taking. Third, in a partial taking the condemnation appraiser must ascertain very carefully exactly what property—the precise acreage, its exact location, and all attached fixtures—and what property rights are to be taken. Fourth, he must be prepared to estimate both severance damages and special benefits. And finally, he must prepare his appraisals so they can withstand extremely careful scrutiny and perhaps oral examination.

In a condemnation case the legal counsel plays the role of the quarterback. The appraiser consults with the attorneys and acquires from them a general understanding as to the nature of the proceedings, the bases on which the court will determine just compensation, and the types of evidence which will be permissible. More specifically, the condemnation appraiser obtains the following information.

1. The date of take, which usually establishes the date of the appraisal.

2. A copy of the petition for the taking, along with the answer filed, if such is available.

3. A brief on the title to the property, including any existing restrictions, easements, or right-of-ways.

4. A copy of the taking agency's plans, showing what is to be taken, its exact location, and what and how the improvements are to be constructed. In the case of a road, such things as grade, profile, cut, fill, slope, concrete strips, median strips, berms, local access roads, the location of overpasses and underpasses, culverts, drainage, access rights, easements, and utilities. Boundary lines for the entire property should be obtained, if not from the plat showing the taking, then from other sources.

5. Any special facts concerning the project, the take, or the property. For example, one needs to be sure the plans for construction are not preliminary plans which may be changed prior to the actual taking.

There should be a mutual understanding with the client's attorney as to the laws of eminent domain—what constitutes just compensation, the definition of fair market value, the before and after values, what constitutes compensable damage, what constitutes deductible benefits, the extent to which the final value figure is to be itemized—usually into the value of the part taken, damages to the remainder, benefits— the laws of discovery, and any and all rules pertaining to the admissibility of any testimony given to support an appraisal.

There should also be a mutual agreement with the client or his attorney as to when the appraisal is to be completed, how complete it is to be, the probable number of days involved, and the fee both for the appraisal(s) and for courtroom testimony.

An appraiser should feel free to ask for legal advice from his client's attorney prior to initiating his appraisal assignment. Otherwise, he can easily find himself in an embarrassing situation. He cannot afford to commit himself to a value related to a legal premise that is unreasonable, to a damage that is not compensable, or to a benefit that is not deductible.

The appraiser may need to spend some time with other persons. For example, when a flowage easement is under consideration, he should visit with the engineers who planned the project or reservoir. These engineers will generally give him copies of their hydrological charts and records which include a history of past floods, their frequency, and their duration, along with their estimates as to any anticipated flooding in the future. These then become the basis for estimating the loss in market value resulting from the flowage easement.

A condemnation appraiser will also spend some time with the property owner determining some of the probable changes that may have to be made in his farming operations. There may be reductions in use, buildings that have to be moved, fences that need to be changed (causing irregularly shaped fields), irrigation problems, drainage difficulties, and changes in access. In the case of a flowage easement, there may be deposits of debris or silt. There may also be benefits.

In making a condemnation appraisal, the appraiser first appraises the property in its entirety (before the taking) just as he would any other property. There is no difference in the method or the procedure between the before-value appraisal for condemnation purposes and any other appraisal for any other reason. The value to be estimated here, as elsewhere, is the present market value of the property. If the taking involves the entire property, the appraiser is perhaps lucky. His job is done, with the exception perhaps of appearing in court.

However, in cases involving a partial taking, the appraiser must now appraise the property that remains, in its entirety and as a whole, and less the part taken, thus arriving at the property's value *as a whole* immediately after the taking. The difference between the two values, before and after, is the amount due the property owner.

The after-value appraisal requires that the appraiser know exactly:

1. The land area, along with any buildings and improvements, which are to be acquired.

2. The exact location of the take, its relationship to the property which remains.

3. Any property rights that are to be acquired.

(When an easement is involved, it is particularly essential that the appraiser know exactly what rights are to be conveyed and what rights are to remain with the property owner.)

The appraiser should carefully ascertain the effect that the acquisition or take will have on the property which remains, particularly those factors which affect the property's value. The after-value appraisal is often done quickly, and without as much thought as is desired. However, it requires just as many, and sometimes more, details than the before-value appraisal.

Lastly, the condemnation appraiser should point out the differences between his two appraisals. He should present all supportive evidence, along with the reasons for the difference between his before and after values. This should include:

1. A physical description of how the project or taking will damage the farm—acres, buildings and improvements, and property owner rights actually taken, along with the size, shape, and access to each of the parcels or tracts remaining. The part taken is always a part and never a percentage.

2. A map, drawn to scale, showing the proposed severance, giving the acreages and locations of the part taken as well as the parcels which remain, and all other important land features, such as irrigation, drainage, access, etc.

3. How the land being taken will affect the farm's value *as a whole*, how the buildings and improvements being taken will affect the farm's value *as a whole*, and how each will affect the use of the property.

4. A list of all damages that are compensable and a list of all benefits that are deductible.

5. A summary showing before and after values, along with the lump sum estimates of (a) the value of the take, (b) damages, and (c) benefits. A recapitulation of the five values is often presented.

In addition, many appraisers keep a detailed diary of various dates or days they work on a condemnation appraisal assignment. This should be brief. Among other items, the diary usually shows the dates of the initial visit, those on which the property was inspected, those on which the work was done, and the date on which the final report was delivered. This diary is often of value to the appraiser when he is appearing on the witness stand.

COURTROOM TESTIMONY

Most takings of private property resulting from eminent domain are settled by negotiation. At the same time, no professional appraiser ever accepts a condemnation appraisal assignment without being willing to later appear in court.

The time to begin preparing for courtroom testimony is when the appraisal assignment is accepted, for every hour of work done and every bit of information collected should be done with the knowledge that the case may go to court. If any of the work is sloppy, if any of the details (minor though they may be) are missing, or if any of the facts are erroneous, some attorney, upon cross-examination, is bound to reveal one's incompetence. The condemnation appraiser's appraisal —good, bad, or otherwise—is literally held up for all the world to see.

The professional appraiser is permitted to appear and testify in court as an expert witness, or under what is known as the Opinion Rule. Many early English cases ruled that mere opinion was not evidence. In fact, many a lay witness has been admonished to state only the facts as he knows them. The court makes its decisions based on these facts. But once the expert witness is qualified, he is entitled to express an opinion; thus the professional appraiser can present his entire appraisal in his own words, and in a straightforward fashion. He is never (at least practically never) forced into an absolute yes or no answer, when it is his opinion that such an answer is not sufficient, or when that answer will not disclose all the facts. He further has the right to take all the time he needs to carefully consider each question and answer it to the best of his ability.

Unfortunately, many so-called expert witnesses appear to be extremely naive, oftentimes unconsciously partisan, and sometimes even openly willing to develop their testimony to fit the requirements of their client. Even widely accepted appraisal technique is sometimes readily manipulated to achieve certain desired results. Herein lies not only a real danger to opinion testimony but considerable discredit to many good appraisers. The practice of advocacy is a major sin within the appraisal profession. Evidence that it exists is manifested by the wide variation in values often presented by appraisers on opposite sides of some condemnation cases.

Fortunately, most attorneys are capable persons. They often catalog appraisers as to whether they are competent or incompetent, sincere or insincere, stuffed or genuine, and clever or stupid. Most attorneys, who have had condemnation trial experience, are able to quickly identify the dishonest appraiser through cross-examination. For unless the appraiser is objective, certain inconsistencies soon appear to be self-evident. Furthermore, the really competent appraiser soon realizes that it isn't his opinion or his value that makes a good appraisal; such is instead a result of the thoroughness of his investigation, his analysis of the facts, and the way he presents his analysis in the courtroom.

The expert witness is typically subjected to four or five types of questions. The attorneys may ask any number, but in general, they can be categorized as follows.

First, the expert witness will be asked to briefly state his qualifications to the judge or jury. A *vita* or résumé of education, employment, previous activities, and past experience, particularly that related to one's current appraisal practice, should be provided the client's legal counsel.

Second, the expert witness will be asked questions relative to appraisal methodology. He should be able to outline, in general, his appraisal technique—how he went about developing the physical description of the property, estimating the farm's productive capacity, and arriving at its present market value. He should be able to present, in summary fashion, the three approaches used to establish value, along with the characteristics of each.

Third, the expert witness should be prepared to define fair market value using whatever definition is preferred by the court. He should be prepared to quote this definition verbatim, state the assumptions underlying such, and then add his own interpretation, in terms of what the definition and the assumptions mean to him. He may be asked his understanding as to what constitutes such items as just compensation, damage, and benefits. The appraiser should not only know, but use precise and correct terminology. He does not need to impress the jury with his legal expertise, but should instead try to convey to them the idea that he is a knowledgeable and competent appraiser.

Fourth, the expert witness will be asked to state when he made his appraisal, when he inspected the farm, what he did, and how he arrived at his conclusions. He will be asked what values he arrived at, using each method of establishing value, and in a case involving a partial taking, what his before and after values are. He will then be asked to summarize his appraisal and give the jury a breakdown as to the final compensation due the property owner.

Fifth, the expert witness can expect to be questioned as to his fees and how much he has profited by making this appraisal for his client, or, how much his appraisal has cost the taxpayers.

Appearance in court requires careful beforehand preparation and skillful courtroom presence. Most farm appraisers take an additional quick look at the property the day before going on the witness stand. This not only helps to refresh their memory about the property and their appraisal; it also brings to their attention any improvements or changes that have been made since their inspection of the property.

Many appraisers wonder what they should take with them when they go on the witness stand. Here, there is considerable difference of opinion. The author likes to take everything to the witness stand so that any and all questions about the property can be answered. All notes and materials should, of course, be organized so that, if need be, they can be quickly referred to. The author further likes to have his final report prepared to the extent that should legal counsel desire to introduce such into evidence he may do so.

The author likes to make full use of visuals—much of his data are put into large tables, charts, and diagrams. Such evidence is more effective than mere oral testimony. It is sometimes extremely difficult for a jury of 6 or 12 lay persons to follow a complicated appraisal without visual assistance. The data can be more understandable, the judge or jury can follow one's line of reasoning more closely, and one's presentation can be more easily remembered when it has been presented visually. The members of a jury may also request, and usually are allowed, to take such exhibits into the jury room, thus later refreshing their memories if they want to do so.

In presenting one's appraisal, or one's testimony, it is wise to face either the judge or the jury and to speak to them directly. They are the ones for whom the appraisal was prepared. They are the ones who will make the final decision. Personality, skill, and adroitness give force to a witness's testimony. The expert witness should attempt to inject himself into whatever he has to say. He should speak to the jury, not just in words, but with a sincere warmth and with personality. Otherwise the jury will not be impressed.

Lastly, the expert witness can expect to be cross-examined on everything he did and some of the things he didn't do. One needs to remember that the purpose of a trial is to find all the facts and to lay them before the court for its consideration. The court is interested in the appraiser's opinion, but it is far more interested in the facts on which he has based that opinion. The appraiser who prepares himself and is capable of discussing all the facts, both favorable and unfavorable, is the one most respected by the court and the one most likely to be remembered and believed by the jury.

The lawyer's role on cross-examination is to separate truth from falsehood, sound observation from faulty analysis, and unbiased opinion from prejudice. If all parties in a litigated case were honest, used good judgment, and were not prejudiced, there would be no need for cross-examination. Thus, lawyers attempt to discover any and all weaknesses in one's testimony. They then attempt to exploit those weaknesses to their advantage and sometimes to the embarrassment of the witness who is testifying.

Courtesy, U.S.D.A.

Many persons have a natural fear of cross-examination. However, the expert should never permit himself, under any condition, to be harried, or flustered, or excited, or disturbed. Once a witness loses his temper, he ceases to think. He then becomes befuddled and is a pathetic figure.

Each question should be answered briefly whenever that is possible. If a brief answer is not sufficient, the expert witness may qualify his answer.

The witness should answer all questions asked to the full limit of his ability in a sincere and honorable manner, and sufficiently loud for the judge or jury to hear his answers. He should approach or accept cross-examination somewhat as a challenge, realizing that it may be possible to bring out some facts that were overlooked in the direct-examination and that, in doing so, such may even strengthen one's appraisal.

The most important factor to keep in mind is intellectual honesty. The expert witness makes a friend of the court by the content of his testimony and his manner and his appearance. The expert witness should at all times show the utmost courtesy to employing counsel, to cross-examining counsel, to the court reporter, to the judge, and to the jury.

ADVISORY ASSISTANCE AND RELOCATION PAYMENTS

The population growth and the accelerated demand for public services of all kinds, particularly in the more urban states, has caused increased distress to those persons displaced by property acquisitions. Farmers, small businessmen, low income families, and elderly persons have been particularly affected. They are sometimes forced to leave a farm or a home in an area where they have spent their entire lives, and at times some of them have had no alternative whatsoever in terms of a new property or place to go and live.

The acquisition process has been dominated by the Heilbron definition of fair market value. This definition has been property-oriented rather than people-oriented. It has paid almost exclusive attention to the "thing" taken (the value of property), and to damage to the "things" (residual parcels) that remain. Up until recently personal values and personal damages have been ignored.

A 1970 law made advisory assistance and relocation payments available to all affected property owners.[31] In addition to payment for property, certain payments are to now be made for person-related problems—such things as inconvenience, trouble, and dislocation or relocation costs which result from property acquisitions.

Relocation Assistance: The relocation assistance and advisory program is available to all property owners. It has four basic functions: (1) to determine the need for and provide relocation assistance, (2) to provide information on the availability, prices, and rentals of comparable farm properties, (3) to assist a displaced farmer and his family in obtaining and becoming established on a suitable relocation property, and (4) to minimize the hardships of adjustment to a new location. These advisory services are available to any property owner where substantial economic injury has been caused by property acquisition. Such a property owner does not need to have all, or for that matter any, of his property taken; he may merely own or occupy property immediately adjacent to that which is being acquired.

Reimbursement for Personal Expenses: The property owner may now receive just compensation for the value of his property taken. In addition, he may be reimbursed for certain relocation, moving, and related expenses. The following items are, in general, reimbursable.

1. The costs of discontinuing, relocating, and moving the farm business and the contents of the home. These costs include (a) all actual and reasonable expense in searching for a new farm—the cost of time, travel, meals, and lodging, (b) all actual and reasonable moving expenses—the costs of removing, packing, insuring, transporting, and installing certain fixtures or equipment, (c) the costs of moving one's personal property, and (d) any actual and direct losses of tangible personal property as a result of discontinuing or moving the farming operations.

Relocation costs are limited to $10 per day and a $500 maximum. The costs related to moving oneself, one's family, one's business (or farming operations) and one's personal property may be actual; or, the farmer may elect to receive a single fixed payment. This latter is to equal his average annual net earnings (before all federal, state and local taxes) during the two previous tax years (providing those average annual net earnings are less than $10,000). Payments for moving the farming operations cannot be less than $2,500 nor more than $5,000. Payments for moving to a new dwelling are not to exceed $5,000.

2. All closing costs—including title search, contract preparation, survey expense and legal fees, all transfer taxes and recording fees,

---

31. Public Law 91-646.

and all appraisal, inspection, and loan application fees incident to (a) the conveying of the taken property and (b) the obtaining of the replacement property. In order to be reimbursable, these expenses must be incurred within 12 months after (a) the date the property owner receives final payment for all costs or (b) the date on which the property owner moves, whichever is the later date.

3. The pro rata portion of any prepaid real property taxes, which are allocable to a period prior to the date of take.

4. Any penalty cost for the prepayment of any pre-existing recorded farm mortgage and any additional expense, including increased interest costs incurred, as a result of financing a new property.

Additional interest costs are based on either the unpaid balance of the existing mortgage or the new mortgage. Principal and interest payments at the two different rates of interest are calculated for each, and the differences are then reduced to their discounted present values. The discount rate to be used is that paid on savings accounts by commercial banks in the general area. The lesser of the two discounted values is then the present value of the increased interest payments, and the amount to be paid the owner (Table 44).

Some persons infer that if the property owner does go to court and if he does receive an award above the taking agency's offer, then his (property owner's) attorney fees and other costs should be paid by the taking agency. This is not generally so. The property owner's costs of litigation—appraisal, engineering, attorney fees, and other costs—are not reimbursable unless (1) the property owner can prove that the taking agency cannot lawfully acquire his property through eminent domain proceedings or (2) the taking agency abandons or discontinues its efforts to acquire the property after condemnation procedures have commenced. Furthermore, neither are any of the following personal items reimbursable.

1. Any additional expense—business or living—incurred solely because of the new location.

2. The cost of any improvements made on the new property (except when required by law).

3. The cost of modifying any personal property in order to adapt it to the new site or property (again except when required by law).

4. The cost of moving any fixture, building, or permanent improvement (real property) in which the displaced person reserved ownership.

5. Any personal injury.

6. Any loss of business, or profits, or goodwill.

Table 44. The Present Value(s) of Two Different Farm Mortgage Obligations.

Basic Data	Existing Mortgage		Mortgage on New Property
Interest Rate	5.75%		7.50%
Remaining Term (Years)	12		20
Remaining Balance (Principal)	$33,468		$50,000
Semiannual Principal and Interest Payments	$ 1,949.68		$ 2,432.97
Existing Mortgage Computation			
Semiannual Principal and Interest			
$33,468 for 12 Years at 7.50%		$ 2,139.24	
$33,468 for 12 Years at 5.75%		−1,949.68	
Semiannual Interest Difference		189.56	
Present Worth of $189.56 Semiannually			
for 12 Years Discounted at 5.5%		$ 3,298.50[1]	
Local Savings Bank Rate			
($189.56 × 17.4008)			
New Mortgage Computation			
Semiannual Principal and Interest			
$50,000 for 20 Years at 7.50%		$ 2,432.97	
$50,000 for 20 Years at 5.75%		−2,119.63	
Semiannual Interest Difference		313.34	
Present Worth of $313.34 Semiannually			
for 12 Years Discounted at 5.5%		$ 5,452.37[1]	
Local Savings Bank Rate			
($313.34 × 17.4008)			
Amount to Be Paid Property Owner[2]		$ 3,298.50	

1. The factor 17.4008 is obtained from a present worth of one per period (see Appendix Table A).
2. The lesser of the two present values of the differing principal and interest payments.

7. Interest on a loan to finance relocation or moving expense.

8. Losses due to negligence on the part of the displaced property owner (or anyone under his employ).

9. The cost of preparing the application for payment of relocation, moving, and related expenses.

None of the above payments are to, in any way, affect or be affected by the just compensation paid to the property owner.[32] In fact, a displaced property owner must make separate application for reimbursement of these expenses.[33] They are not to be included or confused with the appraisal of a farm property for reasons of condemna-

32. Furthermore, no payment for these items shall be considered as income for purposes of the Internal Revenue Code of 1954 or for purposes of determining eligibility under the Social Security Act.
33. With proper application, payment in advance can be authorized.

tion. They are not a part of the law of eminent domain. The 1970 law merely specified that there should be fair and equitable treatment of persons displaced so that they do not suffer disproportionate injuries as a result of programs designed for the benefit of the public as a whole.

REFERENCES

Appraiser's Handbook, U. S. Army Corps of Engineers, 1957.

Everett, C. H., "Proper Application of American Rural Appraisal System to Condemnation Appraising," *Journal of American Society of Farm Managers and Rural Appraisers,* Vol. 22, No. 1, April 1958.

Miller, J. D., "Recent Developments in the Eminent Domain Field," *Appraisal Journal,* Vol. 40, No. 2, April 1972.

Ratcliff, R. U., "Real Estate Valuation and Highway Condemnation Awards," *Wisconsin Commerce Reports,* Vol. 7, No. 6, 1966.

Ratcliff, R. U. (Editor), Wisconsin Colloquium on Appraisal Research, Papers and Proceedings, University of Wisconsin, March 1963.

Sando, Laurence, (Chr.), *Condemnation Appraisal Practice,* American Institute of Real Estate Appraisers, 1961.

Sando, Laurence, "Highway Land Acquisition in the United States," *Appraisal Journal,* Vol. 37, No. 2, April 1969.

Schmutz, G. L., and E. M. Adams, *Condemnation Appraisal Handbook,* Prentice-Hall, 1963.

Vlasin, R. D., W. C. Pendleton, and J. L. Hedrick, *The Effects on Farm Operating Units of Land Acquisition for Controlled-Access Highways,* U.S.D.A., ERS-69, June 1962.

The Law of Eminent Domain

Davis, W. D., "Principles and Practices of Condemnation Appraisal," *Journal of American Society of Farm Managers and Rural Appraisers,* Vol. 14, No. 1, April 1950.

Diamond, Josef, "Condemnation Law," *Appraisal Journal,* Vol. 23, No. 4, October 1955.

Dunn, Dominick, "Appraisal in Condemnation Proceedings," *Encyclopedia of Real Estate Appraising,* Prentice-Hall, 1959.

Enfield, C. W., "Highway Appraisal Problems," *The Residential Appraiser,* Vol. 26, No. 7, July 1960.

Fisher, G. L., "Eminent Domain and the Appraiser," *The Real Estate Appraiser,* Vol. 35, No. 4, May-June 1969.

Goddard, M. K., "Land Acquisition by Public Agencies," *A Place to Live: 1963 Yearbook of Agriculture,* U.S.D.A., 1963.

Hannah, H. W., and N. G. P. Krausz, *Condemnation: The Public Taking of Illinois Farm Land,* University of Illinois, Cooperative Extension Service Circular 974, December 1967.

Lostetter, E. K., "The Four-Way Test," *Appraisal Journal*, Vol. 31, No. 4, October 1963.

MacBride, D. D., "Decisions that Influence Value Concepts," *The Real Estate Appraiser*, Vol. 33, No. 1, January 1967.

Roby, R. H., "Police Power in Aid of Condemnation," *Appraisal Journal*, Vol. 35, No. 4, October 1967.

Sargent, C. A., and L. T. Wallace, *Your Land and Public Reservoir Development*, Purdue University Agricultural Economics EC-271, about 1965.

Snitzer, E. L., "The Law and Condemnation Appraising: The Increase or Decrease in Fair Market Value Because of a Future Condemnation," *The Real Estate Appraiser*, Vol. 34, No. 5, July-August 1968.

Stewart, C. L., et al., *Condemnation, Land Value, and Severance Damage on Farmland*, University of Illinois, Agr. Exp. Sta. Bul. 707, March 1965.

Thies, C. K., "The Law of Eminent Domain, Its Origin and Development," *Appraisal Journal*, Vol. 25, No. 1, January 1957.

Wallace, L. T., C. A. Sargent, and J. H. Atkinson, *Your Land and Indiana Highways*, Purdue University Agricultural Economics, EC-273, about 1965.

The Property Owner's Problem

"Eminent Domain," *Iowa Law Review*, Vol. 54, No. 5, April 1969.

Gifford, C. W., "What to Do When the Highway Comes Through," *Farm Journal*, August 1955.

Hodges, M. B., Jr., "Public Relations in Eminent Domain Appraising," *The Residential Appraiser*, Vol. 28, No. 3, March 1962.

Mathias, P. E., "Legal Concepts of Highway Takings," *Journal of American Society of Farm Managers and Rural Appraisers*, Vol. 22, No. 1, April 1958.

The Definition of "Just Compensation"

Allard, J. L., "Is Market Value Just Compensation?," *Appraisal Journal*, Vol. 35, No. 3, July 1967.

Davis, W. D., "Using Remainder Studies in an Appraisal," *The Real Estate Appraiser*, Vol. 29, No. 2, February 1963.

Dolan, H. T., "Federal Condemnation with Special Reference to Severance Damage," *The Appraiser's Job in Eminent Domain Proceedings*, Bureau of Business Research, University of Pittsburgh, 1957.

Edmunds, J. T., "What Constitutes Just Compensation," *The Residential Appraiser*, Vol. 27, No. 4, April 1961.

Hollebaugh, C. W., "On Definition Accuracy," *Appraisal Journal*, Vol. 30, No. 4, October 1962.

Lum, Y. T., "Problems in Achieving Just Compensation," *The Real Estate Appraiser*, Vol. 36, No. 7, November-December 1970.

McGough, B. C., "The Concepts and Practices for Compensation in Eminent Domain," *The Real Estate Appraiser*, Vol. 35, No. 2, March 1969.

Mortimer, J. R., "Highway Right-of-Way Valuation," *Journal of American*

Society of Farm Managers and Rural Appraisers, Vol. 23, No. 1, April 1959.
Streukens, H. H., "Appraising and Acquisition for Right of Way Purposes," The Residential Appraiser, Vol. 27, No. 5, May 1961.

Fair Market Value

Appraisal Terminology and Handbook, 5th Edition, American Institute of Real Estate Appraisers, 1967.
Ashton, M. D., "Highest-Best Use," Appraisal Journal, Vol. 7, No. 1, January 1939.
Cherney, R. A., "The Principle of Highest and Best Use," The Real Estate Appraiser, Vol. 30, No. 2, February 1964.
Clickner, E. K., "Highest Land Use as a Planning Tool," Appraisal Journal, Vol. 37, No. 2, April 1969.
Crouch, W. H., "A Perspective Look at Highest and Best Use," Appraisal Journal, Vol. 34, No. 2, April 1966.
Davis, W. D., "What Is Market Value?," Appraisal Journal, Vol. 28, No. 1, January 1960.
Dolman, J. P., "Some Reflections on Terminology," Appraisal Journal, Vol. 31, No. 3, July 1963.
Everett, C. H., et al., "Rural Appraisal Requirements in Federal Condemnation," Journal of American Society of Farm Managers and Rural Appraisers, Vol. 25, No. 2, October 1961.
Hollebaugh, C. W., "On Definition Accuracy," Appraisal Journal, Vol. 30, No. 4, October 1962.
Huck, Robert, "The Use of Real Estate," Appraisal Journal, Vol. 33, No. 2, April 1965.
Hyde, J. V., "Condemnation Appraisals," The Real Estate Appraiser, Vol. 36, No. 4, May-June, 1970.
Lum, Y. T., "The Highest and Best Use," The Real Estate Appraiser, Vol. 32, No. 6, June 1966.
Mulcahy, J. V., "Before and After: Fact or Fiction?," The Real Estate Appraiser, Vol. 36, No. 6, September-October 1970.
Randall, W. J., "Clearly State the Appraisal Premise," Appraisal Journal, Vol. 26, No. 2, April 1958.
Ratcliff, R. U., "Condemnation Awards and Appraisal Theory," Journal of American Society of Farm Managers and Rural Appraisers, Vol. 28, No. 2, October 1964.
Rowlson, J. F., "Highest and Best Use," The Real Estate Appraiser, Vol. 32, No. 4, April 1966.
Seymour, C. F., "Market Value vs. Court Restrictions Against 'Speculative Assumption,'" Appraisal Journal, Vol. 34, No. 2, April 1966.

The Problem of Damage

Baumgartner, J. H. Jr., "Adequacy of Compensation in Federal Condemnation," Appraisal Journal, Vol. 31, No. 1, January 1963.
Carpenter, P. E., "Experience in Partial Eminent Domain Takings," The

Real Estate Appraiser, Vol. 33, No. 6, June 1967.

Crouch, W. H., "What Does Just Compensation Mean to the Appraiser?," *Appraisal Journal*, Vol. 28, No. 2, April 1960.

Davis, W. D., et al., "Rural Appraisal Requirements in Federal Condemnation," *Journal of American Society of Farm Managers and Rural Appraisers*, Vol. 26, No. 2, October 1962.

Davis, W. D., et al., "Rural Appraisal Requirements in Federal Condemnation," *Journal of American Society of Farm Managers and Rural Appraisers*, Vol. 29, No. 1, April 1965.

Dolan, H. T., "Federal Condemnation with Special Reference to Severance Damage," *The Appraiser's Job in Eminent Domain Proceedings*, Bureau of Business Research, University of Pittsburgh, 1957.

Goetsch, F. L., "Evaluating Fields Cut up by Highways," *Journal of American Society of Farm Managers and Rural Appraisers*, Vol. 13, No. 2, October 1949.

Grace, A. B., Jr., "Severance Damage Studies," *Appraisal Journal*, Vol. 34, No. 3, July 1966.

Maxwell, G. I., "Severance Damages in Highway Appraisals," *Journal of American Society of Farm Managers and Rural Appraisers*, Vol. 22, No. 2, October 1958.

Martz, C. O., "The Federal View of Damages and Benefits," *Appraisal Journal*, Vol. 37, No. 2, April 1969.

Pearl, M. A., "Review of Efforts to Minimize Losses in Condemnation," *Appraisal Journal*, Vol. 26, No. 1, January 1958.

Pilmer, C. L., "Is 'Just Compensation' Just?," *Journal of American Society of Farm Managers and Rural Appraisers*, Vol. 31, No. 2, October 1967.

Rogers, R. R., "Partial Taking," *Appraisal Journal*, Vol. 25, No. 3, July 1957.

Smith, L. H., "After Value Support for Highway Taking Remainders," *Appraisal Journal*, Vol. 33, No. 1, January 1965.

Streukens, H. H., "The Economics of Partial Takings," *Journal of American Society of Farm Managers and Rural Appraisers*, Vol. 25, No. 2, October 1961.

Walther, H. O., et al., "Divergencies in Right-of-Way Valuations," *Appraisal Journal*, Vol. 39, No. 4, October 1971.

Wilson, William, (Editor), "Damages Occasioned by Change of Water Flow," *Appraisal Journal*, Vol. 26, No. 2, April 1958.

The Question of Benefits

Darsey, G. S., "General and Special Benefits," *Appraisal Journal*, Vol. 34, No. 1, January 1966.

Enfield, C. W., and W. A. Mansfield, "Special Benefits and Right of Way Acquisition," *Appraisal Journal*, Vol. 25, No. 4, October 1957.

Hagman, D. G., "The Special Benefit: What Is It? How Is It Measured?," *The Real Estate Appraiser*, Vol. 33, No. 11, November 1967.

Luttrell, R. J., "Eminent Domain—the Realtor, the Appraiser, and the Lawyer," *Appraisal Journal*, Vol. 31, No. 4, October 1963.

Supplemental Appraisal Technique

Beaton, W. R., et al., "Appraisal and Acquisition of Borrow Pits," *The Real Estate Appraiser*, Vol. 35, No. 6, September-October 1969.

Bowes, W. A., "The Function of the Appraiser in Condemnation," *Appraisal Journal*, Vol. 26, No. 3, July 1958.

Free, R. L., "Preparing a Condemnation Appraisal," *The Appraiser's Job in Eminent Domain Proceedings*, Bureau of Business Research, University of Pittsburgh, 1957.

Garrett, H. J., "Reservoirs, Partial Takings, and Easements," *Journal of American Society of Farm Managers and Rural Appraisers*, Vol. 27, No. 1, April 1962.

Maxwell, G. I., "Condemnation Appraising and Related Problems," *Journal of American Society of Farm Managers and Rural Appraisers*, Vol. 27, No. 1, April 1962.

Pittle, Herbert, "The Appraiser's Role in Federal Eminent Domain," *The Real Estate Appraiser*, Vol. 32, No. 5, May 1966.

Wright, Carroll, "Appraisal of Rural Lands for Highway Improvement," *Appraisal Journal*, Vol. 27, No. 1, January 1959.

Courtroom Testimony

Cochran, J. D., "What Is Expected of the Expert Witness?," *Appraisal Journal*, Vol. 27, No. 4, October 1959.

Crouch, W. H., "Pretrial Conference Checklist of Factors Affecting Valuation," *Appraisal Journal*, Vol. 32, No. 4, October 1964.

Davis, B. E., and R. E. Wiley, "49 Thoughts on Direct Examination," *The Young Lawyer*, American Bar Association, 1965.

Diamond, T. M., Jr., "The Appraiser in Court," *The Residential Appraiser*, Vol. 27, No. 4, April 1961.

Hall, R. W., "Speak for Yourself," *Appraisal Journal*, Vol. 28, No. 4, October 1960.

Hanley, D. J., "Expert Testimony in Condemnation Trials," *The Residential Appraiser*, Vol. 26, No. 9, September 1960.

Horgan, J. P., "Ten Courtroom Commandments for Appraisers," *Appraisal Journal*, Vol. 28, No. 1, January 1960.

Johndroe, S. G., Jr., "The Attorney-Appraiser Team," *The Residential Appraiser*, Vol. 27, No. 1, January 1961.

Jones, W. B., "A Judge Looks at the Expert Appraiser-Witness," *Appraisal Journal*, Vol. 24, No. 2, April 1956.

Kraehe, Enno, "Taking the Stand," *Appraisal Journal*, Vol. 22, No. 2, April 1954.

Krasniewski, W. J., "Credibility of Witnesses and Opinion Evidence," *Journal of American Society of Farm Managers and Rural Appraisers*, Vol. 25, No. 2, October 1961.

Labrecque, T. J., "The Court and the Expert Witness," *Appraisal Journal*, Vol. 29, No. 1, January 1961.

Lee, A. W., "The Appraiser's Deportment in the Courtroom," *Journal of* the *American Society of Farm Managers and Rural Appraisers*, Vol. 28, No. 2, October 1964.

Lesher, R. A., "The Role of the Appraiser as an Expert Witness," *The Real Estate Appraiser*, Vol. 38, No. 2, March-April 1972.

Licht, Frank, "What Courts Expect of Appraisers," *Appraisal Journal*, Vol. 37, No. 3, July 1969.

Lindas, Leonard, "The Valuation Witness," *The Residential Appraiser*, Vol. 26, No. 6, June 1960.

Maxwell, G. I., "The Appraiser in Court," *Journal of American Society of Farm Managers and Rural Appraisers*, Vol. 29, No. 1, April 1965.

Roberts, J. A., "Eye Opener—The Appraiser in the Jury Room," *Appraisal Journal*, Vol. 31, No. 4, October 1963.

Rogers, R. R., "The Expert Witness," *Appraisal Journal*, Vol. 24, No. 4, October 1956.

Rupert, J. F., "The Appraiser Prepares for Testimony," *The Real Estate Appraiser*, Vol. 29, No. 11, November 1963.

Smith, Walstein, Jr., *Is the Appraisal Witness Qualified?*, Society of Real Estate Appraisers, 1968.

Snitzer, E. L., "The Law and Condemnation Appraising: Discovery of Appraisal Reports in Condemnation Cases," *The Real Estate Appraiser*, Vol. 34, No. 6, September-October 1968.

Wenger, R. W., Jr., "The Courtroom Loometh," *Journal of American Society of Farm Managers and Rural Appraisers*, Vol. 31, No. 2, October 1967.

Wilson, William (Editor), and F. C. Ash (Asst. Editor), "Power to Subpoena the Appraisal Reports of Experts—The Appraisal Docket," *Appraisal Journal*, Vol. 24, No. 1, January 1956.

Wilson, William (Editor), and F. C. Ash (Asst. Editor), "Power to Subpoena the Appraisal Reports of Experts—The Appraisal Docket," *Appraisal Journal*, Vol. 24, No. 2, April 1956.

Winner, F. M., "The Expert Witness—From a Lawyer's Viewpoint," *Appraisal Journal*, Vol. 23, No. 2, April 1955.

Yates, D. H., "Testimony of the Expert Appraiser on Condemnation Proceedings," *Appraisal Journal*, Vol. 26, No. 3, July 1958.

Advisory Assistance and Relocation Payments

"Land Condemnation Under the Relocation Act," *Doane's Agricultural Report*, December 1971.

MacBride, D. D., "S-1: Every Man's Home Is (More Nearly) His Castle," *Valuation*, Vol. 18, No. 1, April 1971.

Muskie, E. S., (Chairman), Uniform Relocation Assistance and Land Acquisition Policies Act of 1969, United States Senate Report 91-488, October 1969.

Public Law 91-646, An act entitled, "Uniform Relocation Assistance and Real Property Acquisition Policies," The Congress of the United States, 1970.

Reynolds, W. C., "The Relocation Assistance Act: An Appraiser's Experience," *The Real Estate Appraiser*, Vol. 39, No. 1, January-February 1973.

Smith, W. F., "The Relocation Dilemma," *Appraisal Journal,* Vol. 37, No. 3, July 1969.

Snitzer, E. L., "The Uniform Relocation Assistance and Real Property Acquisition Policies Act of 1970: A New Era," *The Real Estate Appraiser,* Vol. 37, No. 3, May-June 1971.

Turner, F. C., "Relocation Assistance and Payments—Interim Operating Procedures," Federal Highway Administration, April 1971.

APPENDIX

Methods of Land Measurement
An Appraisal Report
The Organization of an Appraiser's Handbook
Present Value Tables

Methods of Land Measurement

Linear

Mile	Furlongs	Chains	Rods	Yards	Feet	Links	Inches
—	—	—	—	—	—	1	7.92
—	—	—	—	—	1	—	12
—	—	—	—	1	3	—	36
—	—	—	—	2	6	—	72
—	—	—	1	5½	16½	25	198
—	—	1	4	22	66	100	792
—	1	10	40	220	660	1,000	7,920
1	8	80	320	1,760	5,280	—	—

Square

Town-ship	Square Miles (Sections)	Acres	Square Chains	Square Rods	Square Yards	Square Feet	Square Inches
—	—	—	—	—	—	1	144
—	—	—	—	—	1	9	1,296
—	—	—	—	1	30¼	272¼	—
—	—	—	2½	40	1,210	10,890	—
—	—	1	10	160	4,840	43,560	—
—	¼	160	1,600	25,600	77,440	—	—
—	1	640	6,400	102,400	—	—	—
1	36	23,040	—	—	—	—	—

One Mile - 80 Chains - 320 Rods - 5,280 Feet

NW 1/4 160 Acres	W 1/2 NE 1/4 80 Acres	E 1/2 NE 1/4 80 Acres

40 Chains - 160 Rods - 2,640 Feet | 20 Chains - 80 Rods | 440 Yards - 1,320 Feet

| W 1/2
NW1/4 SW1/4
and
W 1/2
SW1/4 SW1/4
40 Acres | E 1/2
NW1/4 SW1/4
and
E 1/2
SW1/4 SW1/4
40 Acres | NE 1/4 SW 1/4
40 Acres

20 Chains - 80 Rods

SE 1/4 SW 1/4
40 Acres | 2-1/2 A. / 2-1/2 A.
5 Acres / 5 Acres
40 Rods / 10 Chains

W 1/2
SW1/4 SE1/4
20 Acres
10 Chains
40 Rods | 5 A. / 5 A.
20 R. 5 Ch. / 110 Yd 330 Ft.
10 Acres

E 1/2
SW1/4 SE1/4
20 Acres
220 Yards
660 Feet | W 1/2
NE1/4 SE1/4
20 Acres / E 1/2
NE1/4 SE1/4
20 Acres
220 Yards / 660 Feet

N 1/2
SE 1/4 SE 1/4
20 Acres
20 Chains - 80 Rods
S 1/2
SE 1/4 SE 1/4
20 Acres
440 Yards - 1,320 Feet |

10 Chains / 220 Yards | 440 Yards - 1,320 Feet | 10 Chains / 220 Yards
40 Rods / 660 Feet | | 40 Rods / 660 Feet

Miles	1/4	1/2	3/4	1,0
Chains	20	40	60	80
Rods	80	160	240	320
Feet	1,320	2,640	3,960	5,280

1 Link is 7.92 inches
1 Yard is 3 feet or 36 inches
1 Rod is 16-1/2 feet, 5-1/2 yards or 25 Links
1 Chain is 66 feet, 4 rods, or 100 links

1 Mile is 8 furlongs, 320 rods, 80 chains, or 5,280 feet
1 Acre contains 160 square rods or 43,560 square feet

An Appraisal Report

RETUS, INC.

120 Suter Place
West Lafayette, Indiana 47906
Tel. 317-583-4994

Retus, Inc.   **OUR APPRAISAL OF YOUR FARM**   Page 1

Appraisal of _____ Farm as of _____ _____, 19____
                                         (Month)   (Day)   (Year)
Address _____

Purpose: To ascertain the present market value of this property as of the
above date.

Reason: _____

____Acres, Sec.____ Twn.____ Rge.____ _____, _____
____   ____   ____   ____   (County)   (State)

____Total Acres Located in _____ Township _____

Appraisal Certificate

I, the undersigned, hereby certify, that to the best of my knowledge the
statements contained in this appraisal are correct, that the opinions stated
are based on a full and fair consideration of all pertinent facts; however,
recognizing the following limitations:

1.

2.

3.

Furthermore, I have no present or contemplated interest in the property
or in any surrounding circumstances, which would affect the statements
I have made or the values I have ascertained.

Final Value

The value of this property after weighing all data reported herein as of
_____ 19____ was as follows:

Present Market Value, $_____ Total Farm, or $_____ per Acre

_____ Value, $_____ Total Farm, or $_____ per Acre

Retus, Inc.   **A SUMMARY OF OUR APPRAISAL**   Page 2

Brief History of Farm:

Appraisal of the Physical Resources:

Difference Between Typical and Present Operator:

Origins of Value:

Methods Used to Establish Value and Values Ascertained:

	Total Farm Value	Value per Acre
Income Capitalization or Earnings Approach	$_____	$_____
Sales Comparison or Market Approach	$_____	$_____
Inventory or Cost Approach	$_____	$_____

In ascertaining the final value figure (previous page) major emphasis has been placed on the _____ approach, and for the following reason(s).

                              Respectfully submitted,

Date of Property Inspection: Robert C. Suter
_____ _____, 19____   Economic Consultant
(Month) (Day)   (Year)   Farm Management and Appraisal

Retus, Inc.   **A FARM APPRAISAL**   Page 3

Some Introductory Remarks

A farm appraisal is a definite, detailed, and in this case, formal, or written, opinion as to the value of a given property, as of a given date.

The purpose of an appraisal is always to ascertain the market value of the property in a thorough and objective fashion. This value may then be used as the basis for determining various other values—an earnings value (for investment purposes), farm building values (or insured values), as assessed value, a loan value, or before and after values (for reasons of condemnation), etc.

Market value is hereby defined as the most likely price at which the subject property can be sold or transferred from a willing and knowledgeable seller to a desirous and informed buyer with a satisfactory down payment changing hands and with the change in ownership occurring within a reasonable period of time.

The reason for, or use to be made of, an appraisal may substantially affect the time required to inspect the property; it may influence the data included in the appraisal report; however, in no way does the reason for the appraisal affect the market value ascertained.

An appraiser essentially has three jobs: (1) to make a physical description of the property, (2) to estimate the farm's productive capacity, and (3) to give his opinion as to its value, along with the supportive evidence and the line of reasoning used to arrive at that value. In most appraisals three methods of establishing value are used: (1) the farm's income is capitalized, (2) recent and nearby farm sales are tabulated, and (3) an inventory of all resources—land, buildings, and improvements—is made.

These three approaches to value may be weighted equally; or any one of them may be given greater or lesser consideration in arriving at the subject property's value. The final figure is not just an arithmetical average; it typically involves a great amount of judgment.

Please read this entire report. Our accuracy lies not so much in our final market value figure perhaps, as in the facts we have obtained and the logic we have hopefully followed to ascertain the subject property's value.

TABLE OF CONTENTS

	Page
Legal Description and History	4
A Physical Description of the Farm	5
Maps and Photos	7
The Farm's Productive Capacity	19
The Earnings Approach to Value	20
The Sales Comparison Approach to Value	25
The Inventory Approach to Value	32

Retus, Inc.   **LEGAL DESCRIPTION AND HISTORY**   Page 4

Legal Description and Acreage:

Right-of-Ways, Easements, Exceptions:

A Brief History of the Farm:

The Present Operator:

Retus, Inc.   **A PHYSICAL DESCRIPTION OF THE FARM**   Page 5
                        Location, Community Characteristics

Location: The subject farm or property is located _____ miles
_____ of _____ in
              (Direction)   (Nearest Town)
_____Township, _____County, State of_____

Kind of roads   _____   _____
General condition   _____   _____
Accessibility   _____   _____
Amount of travel   _____   _____

Name of school   _____
Quality of school   _____
Electricity   _____
Telephone   _____
Other   _____

Community Characteristics (types of farming, quality of farms, neighbors,
tenure pattern, residential opportunities):

Local Markets (grain elevators, milk plants, livestock markets, farm service
and supply centers):

Retus, Inc.   **Physical Features**   Page 6

Climate:
Nearest Weather Station _____; Elevation _____ Feet;
Annual Rainfall _____ Inches; Growing Season Rainfall _____ Inches;
Last Killing Frost _____; First Killing Frost _____; No. of
Days in Typical Growing Season _____; Frequency of Drought, Hail,
Floods, etc. _____

Farmstead Elevation: _____ Feet

Topography: (effect on cultivation; travel to and from buildings, air drainage, etc.)

Irrigation Facilities: (permanent installations)

Tile Drains and Ditches: (location, adequacy, present condition)

Woods, Timber: (species, condition, etc.)

Minerals, Gravel, Oil, Gas, etc.:

The Following Pages . . .

Land Ownership Map   7
    showing location of the farm
Farm Layout Map   8
    showing all important land features
Aerial Photo   9
    obtained from _____
U.S.G.S. Map   10
    showing the farm's topography

Summary of Soils Information

The soils on the subject property along with the approximate number of acres of each is as follows:

1. Upland and Terrace Soils   2. Bottom Land Soils

_____ _____   _____ _____

_____ _____   _____ _____

_____ _____   Total Acres _____

_____ _____

_____ _____   3. Organic Soils

_____ _____   _____ _____

_____ _____   _____ _____

        Total Acres _____   Total Acres _____

579

Retus, Inc.   **Soils Information**   Page 12
                        1. Upland and Terrace Soils_____ Acres

Brief Description of Each Soil Catena: (Darkness of surface, physiographic
position, origin or parent material, native vegetation, texture, clay content
(%), lime content, other features).

1.

2.

3.

Soil Types

Catena   ....Soil Names......................

_____ _____ _____ _____ _____ _____ _____ _____

_____ _____ _____ _____ _____ _____ _____ _____

_____ _____ _____ _____ _____ _____ _____ _____

Hydromorphic Classification:
   V   IV   III   II   VII   VIII   IX

Surface Form and Predominant Slope: ......Depressional......

Flat to	Moderate	Slight	Very	Very		
Sloping	Slopes	Slopes	Slight	Slight	Slight	Deep
0-25%	4-15%	2-4%	1-2%	0-1%	0-1%	0-1%

External or Surface Drainage:

| Slow to | | Moderately | | | | |
| Rapid | Rapid | Slow | Slow | ....Intermittent.... | | Ponded |

Internal Soil Drainage:

| Well to | Well | Moderately | Imperfectly | | | |
| Excessive | Drained | Well Drained | Drained | ...Very Poorly Drained... | | |

Color (Surface):

| ....Grayish Brown.... | | | Brownish | Gray | Dark | Very |
| | | | Gray | | Gray | Dark |

Color (Subsoil):

| Reddish | Yellowish | | ...Mottled Gray Yellow... | | | |
| Brown | Brown | Yellow | and Brown | | | Gray |

Degree of Erosion:

_____ _____ _____ _____ ....None..........

Acres in Each Group:

_____ _____ _____ _____ _____ _____ _____ _____

Productivity:

_____ _____ _____ _____ _____ _____ _____ _____

Retus, Inc.   **Soils Information**   Page 13
                          2. Bottom Land Soils _____ Acres

Brief Description of Each Soil Catena: (Darkness of surface, source of
sediments, native vegetation, pH level, other features).

   1.

Soil Types

Catena .... Soil Names.......................

_____ _____ _____ _____ _____ _____ _____ _____

_____ _____ _____ _____ _____ _____ _____ _____

_____ _____ _____ _____ _____ _____ _____ _____

Hydromorphic Classification:

  V   IV   III   II   VII   VIII   IX

Surface Slope:

  0-5%   0-3%   0-1%   0-1%   0-1%   0-1%   0-1%

Probability of Overflow:

Infre-   Quite
quent   ...Occasionally...   Frequent Frequent ....Ponding......

Color (Surface):

Gray and   Grayish   Brownish   Dark   Very
Brown   Brown   Brown   Gray   Gray   Gray   Dark

Color (Subsoil):

Gray and Light
Brown   Brown   .... Mottled.............. Gray

Acres in Each Group:

_____ _____ _____ _____ _____ _____ _____ _____

Productivity:

_____ _____ _____ _____ _____ _____ _____ _____

Retus, Inc.   **Soils Information**   Page 14
                          3. Organic Soils _____ Acres

Brief Description of Each Soil Catena: (Origin, degree decomposition, pH level, other features).

   1.

Soil Types

Catena   .... Soil Names.......................

_____ _____ _____ _____ _____ _____ _____ _____

_____ _____ _____ _____ _____ _____ _____ _____

Depth of Organic Matter:
   0-12"   Over 42"
   Shallow   .... 12-42" or Various.............. Deep

Subsoil:
   Mucky
   Mineral   Over   Over   Over   ....Over Marl....   Same as
   Soil   Sand   Mixture   Clay   0-12"   12-42"   Surface

Color (Surface):
                                                                 Dark
   Mixed   .... Black.................... Brown

Color (Subsoil):
   Various   .... Gray..........   ...Light Gray...   —

Acres of Each:

_____ _____ _____ _____ _____ _____ _____ _____

Productivity:

_____ _____ _____ _____ _____ _____ _____ _____

Retus, Inc. **Farm Layout and Farmstead Arrangement** Page 15

Farm Layout (field sizes, shapes, travel routes, obstructions):

Farmstead (location, arrangement, ease of travel, feed and livestock efficiency, general appearance):

Rough Sketch of Farmstead Arrangement:

Water Supply (wells, location):

Retus, Inc.   **The Farm's Buildings and Improvements**   Page 16

Summary of Values: (Ranked in order of their contributions to the market value of the farm)

Building No.	Name	Replacement Cost[1]	Structural Value[2]	Contributory Value[3]	Value-in-use[4]
		$	$	$	$
All Other					
Total		$	$	$	$

Building Valuation

Unlike a farm appraisal, the reason for a farm building valuation often affects the value concept used and also the final value figure. Hence, an understanding of the following definitions is perhaps necessary.

1. Replacement cost is based on present-day costs of constructing whatever structure might be built if this structure were to burn, blow away, or be the subject of other peril. If relatively new—the same building, but if relatively old or obsolete—a more modern version.

2. Structural value is based on replacement cost less depreciation using a realistic estimated life. Depreciation, in this case, represents physical deterioration or wear and tear only; hence, structural value reflects the present-day construction costs and physical soundness.

3. Contributory value is the dollar amount that a building contributes to the market value of the farm. Contributory value may be a function of cost less depreciation, however, depreciation in this case, encompasses physical deterioration, functional inadequacy, and economic obsolescence. Contributory value may also reflect an honest error or mistake or two when the building was originally built.

4. Value-in-use is the building's present-day value to the present operator and in the present farming operations. It largely reflects the real reason for building farm buildings—to increase the volume of business and the efficiency of the farming operations. Value-in-use often equals insured value, at least where and when the indemnity philosophy is fully applied. When value-in-use is considerably above contributory value, however, the insured may have to accept an insurance contract with a deferred payments provision included.

Retus, Inc.   **The Farm's Buildings and Improvements**   Page 17

Farm Buildings: (Dwellings, Barns, Specialized Structures)

	(1)	(2)	(3)	(4)	(5)
Present Use					
Approximate Year Built	19___	19___	19___	19___	19___
Dimensions, Width, Length	___x___	___x___	___x___	___x___	___x___
Square Feet or Capacity					
General Condition and Appearance					
Bldg. Materials (Condition)[1]					
Foundation	( )	( )	( )	( )	( )
Walls	( )	( )	( )	( )	( )
Roof	( )	( )	( )	( )	( )
Interior Features					
Use Factor or Percentage					
Reproduction Cost Per Sq. Ft. or per Bu. or Ton	$___	$___	$___	$___	$___
Total	$___	$___	$___	$___	$___
Replacement Cost Per Sq. Ft. or per Bu. or Ton	$___	$___	$___	$___	$___
Total	$___	$___	$___	$___	$___
Approximate Age (Years)					
Remaining Useful Life (Years)					
Percent of Life Remaining	___%	___%	___%	___%	___%
Structural Value (Reprod. Cost Less Deprec.)	$___				
Contributory Value Ratio to Replacement Cost	$___	$___	$___	$___	$___
	___%	___%	___%	___%	___%
Value-in-use Ratio to Replacement Cost	$___	$___	$___	$___	$___
	___%	___%	___%	___%	___%

1. 1—excellent, 10—very poor.

Retus, Inc.   **The Farm's Buildings and Improvements**   Page 18

Farm Buildings: (Dwellings, Barns, Specialized Structures)

	(6)	(7)	(8)	(9)	(10)
Present Use					
Approximate Year Built	19___	19___	19___	19___	19___
Dimensions, Width, Length	___x___	___x___	___x___	___x___	___x___
Square Feet or Capacity					
General Condition and Appearance					
Bldg. Materials (Condition)[2]					
Foundation	( )	( )	( )	( )	( )
Walls	( )	( )	( )	( )	( )
Roof	( )	( )	( )	( )	( )
Interior Features					
Use Factor or Percentage					
Reproduction Cost Per Sq. Ft. or per Bu. or Ton	$___	$___	$___	$___	$___
Total	$___	$___	$___	$___	$___
Replacement Cost Per Sq. Ft. or per Bu. or Ton	$___	$___	$___	$___	$___
Total	$___	$___	$___	$___	$___
Approximate Age (Years)					
Remaining Useful Life (Years)					
Percent of Life Remaining	___%	___%	___%	___%	___%
Structural Value (Reprod. Cost Less Deprec.)	$___				
Contributory Value	$___	$___	$___	$___	$___
Ratio to Replacement Cost	___%	___%	___%	___%	___%
Value-in-Use	$___	$___	$___	$___	$___
Ratio to Replacement Cost	___%	___%	___%	___%	___%

2. 1—excellent, 10—very poor.

Retus, Inc.   **THE FARM'S PRODUCTIVE CAPACITY**   Page 19

	Present Operator			Typical Operator			Landlord's Share	
Crops Raised	Acres	Yield	Total	Acres	Yield	Total	Per-cent	Total

Total crop ____   ____

	Present Operator			Typical Operator			Landlord's Share	
Livestock Raised	No.	Rate	Total	No.	Rate	Total	Per-cent	Total

Feed Requirements per Head and Total Farm

Type of Livestock	Number of Head	Feed Required per Head			Total Feed Required		
		Corn Equiv. (Bu.)	Protein (Lbs.)	Hay Equiv. (Ton)	Corn Equiv. (Bu.)	Protein (Lbs.)	Hay Equiv. (Ton)

Total Feed Required (Farm)   ____   ____   ____
Total Feed Produced   ____   XXX   ____
To Be Purchased (Corn Equiv.[3]) Deficit (Hay)   ____   ____   ____
To Be Sold (Corn Equiv.[3]) Surplus (Hay)   ____ (Ton)   ____

---

3. Include oats at 2 to 1 ratio.

Retus, Inc.   **THE EARNINGS APPROACH TO VALUE**   Page 20

Summary of Earnings Values
and Plus (or Minus) Adjustments

The value of the subject property, based on its probable future earnings plus or minus certain comparative adjustments, the value of the home, other economic use, and location, is . . .

	Total Farm	Per Acre
Earnings Value		
Based on Landlord's Return	$_____	$_____
(Capitalization Rate ____%)		
Based on Owner-Operator Income	$_____	$_____
(Capitalization Rate ____%)		
Adjustments for		
Home Value	$_____	$_____
Location	$_____	$_____
Other Economic Use	$_____	$_____
Total Value Based on Income Capitalization	$_____	$_____

Income Estimate Based on a Landlord's Return (Crop-Share)

Dollar Receipts (Landlord Only)

Amount	Unit	Crop	Price	Total
_____	_____	_____	_____	$_____
_____	_____	_____	_____	_____
_____	_____	_____	_____	_____
_____	_____	_____	_____	_____
_____	_____	_____	_____	_____

Privilege Rent, Pasture, Use of Buildings   _____
    Total Dollar Receipts $_____

Retus, Inc.   **Income Estimate Based on Landlord's Return**   Page 21

Landlord's Total Dollar Receipts (from previous page) $_____

Landlord's Total Dollar Expenses (below)

		Per	Total	Landlord's	Landlord's
Seed	Acres	Acre	Cost	Share	Cost
Corn	_____ × $_____		= $_____	× _____%	= $_____
Soybeans	_____				
Small					
grain	_____				
Meadow	_____				
Total					$_____

Lime

_____ Tillable Acres × $_____ per Acre $_____

	Nitrogen		Phosphate		Potash	
	Lb.		Lb.		Lb.	
Fertilizer	per A.	Total	per A.	Total	per A.	Total
Corn	_____	_____	_____	_____	_____	_____
Soy- beans	_____	_____	_____	_____	_____	_____
Small grain	_____	_____	_____	_____	_____	_____
Meadow	_____	_____	_____	_____	_____	_____
Total Lbs.	_____		_____		_____	
Price	$_____		$_____		$_____	
Total Cost	$_____		$_____		$_____	
Landlord's Share	_____%		_____%		_____%	
Landlord's Cost	$_____		_____		$_____	

Total Cost, Nitrogen, Phosphate, and Potash $_____

		Cost	Total	Landlord's	Landlord's
Combining-Baling	Acres	per A.	Cost	Share	Cost
Corn	_____ × $_____		= $_____	× _____%	= $_____
Soybeans	_____				
Small grain	_____				
Meadow	_____				
Total					$_____

Shelling-Hauling $_____

Building Maintenance

$_____ Replacement Cost × _____ Percent $_____

Retus, Inc.   **Income Estimate Based on Landlord's Return**   Page 22

Insurance on Buildings
    $_____$ Insured Value $\times$ $\$\_\_\_\_\_$ Insurance Rate $\$\_\_\_\_\_$

Line Fences
    $_____$ Rods $\times$ $\$\_\_\_\_\_$ per Rod $\$\_\_\_\_\_$

Tile Maintenance
    $_____$ Rods $\times$ $\$\_\_\_\_\_$ per Rod $\$\_\_\_\_\_$

Water Supply
    $_____$ $\times$ $_____$ $\$\_\_\_\_\_$

Real Estate Taxes
    Assessed Value, $\$_____$ $\times$ $\$\_\_\_\_\_$ Tax Rate 19__ $\$\_\_\_\_\_$

Special Taxes
    _____ $\$\_\_\_\_\_$

Management Charge
    $_____$ $\times$ $_____$ $\$\_\_\_\_\_$

Interest on Above Expenses
    $_____$ $\times$ $_____$ $\$\_\_\_\_\_$

Total Dollar Expenses (Landlord Only) $\$\_\_\_\_\_$

Summary of Income Estimate (Landlord's Return)

Total Dollar Receipts $\$_____$
Total Dollar Expenses $\$_____$
Receipts Less Expenses $\$_____$

Income Estimate Based on Owner-Operator's Income

Dollar Receipts:

Source(s):	Farm Records Comparison[4]	Amount	Typical Operator Product	Price	Total
_____	$_____	_____	_____	_____	_____
_____	_____	_____	_____	_____	_____
_____	_____	_____	_____	_____	_____
_____	_____	_____	_____	_____	_____
_____	_____	_____	_____	_____	_____
Total	$_____				$_____

Retus, Inc.   **Income Estimate Based on Owner-Operator Return**   Page 23

Owner-Operator's Total Dollar Receipts (from previous page) $_____

Dollar Expenses	Farm Record Comparisons[4]	Method of Budgeting[5]	Total
Hired Labor	$_____	_____	$_____
Improvements	_____	_____	_____
Seed	_____	_____	_____
Fertilizer	_____	_____	_____
Machine Hire	_____	_____	_____
Livestock Purchased	_____	_____	_____
Feed and Supplement	_____	_____	_____
Livestock Expenses	_____	_____	_____
Taxes, Insurance	_____	_____	_____
Miscellaneous	_____	_____	_____
Total	$_____	_____	$_____

Summary of Income Estimate (Owner-Operator)

	Farm Record Comparisons[4]	Method of Budgeting[5]	Total
Cash Balance	$_____		$_____
(Receipts Less Expenses)			
Inventory Change ($\pm$_____)			$\pm$(_____)
Unpaid Family Labor	(−_____)	_____ Months $\times$ $_____ = − (_____)	
Farm Income	$_____		$(_____)
Operator's Time	(−_____)	_____ Months $\times$ $_____ = − (_____)	
Interest, Non-Real Estate Capital	(−_____)	$_____ $\times$ _____%	−(_____)
Return to Land	$_____		$(_____)

---

4. These data are for _____ farms located in _____ and for the year _____. The farms averaged _____ farm acres, _____ acres in cropland, _____ acres of corn, _____ acres of soybeans, _____ head of _____ and _____ head of _____.

5. Feed and supplement costs are based on productive capacity. For seed, fertilizer, lime, and machine hire see previous page.

Retus, Inc.   **Comparative Adjustments**   Page 24
                                Other Origins of Value

	Comments	Total Farm Plus or Minus		Per Acre Plus or Minus	
Value of the Home:					
Attractiveness of Home		$____	$____	$____	$____
Churches and Schools		____	____	____	____
Neighbors and/or Nuisances		____	____	____	____
Recreational Facilities		____	____	____	____
Scenic Advantages		____	____	____	____
Total		$____	$____	$____	$____

Economic Use:					
Natural Resources		____	____	____	____
Physical Features		____	____	____	____
Farm Improvements		____	____	____	____
General Efficiency		____	____	____	____

Location:					
Off-Farm Employment		____	____	____	____
Community Features		____	____	____	____
Neighborhood		____	____	____	____
Roads		____	____	____	____

Other Adjustments:					
Bonded Indebtedness		____	____	____	____
Leases		____	____	____	____

Total (Plus or Minus)   +____ −____ +____ −____

Net Effect of All Adjustments $_____ $_____
                                   (Total Farm)   (Per Acre)

Retus, Inc.   **THE SALES COMPARISON APPROACH TO VALUE**   Page 25

Summary

The value of the subject property based on the recent sale of nearby farms comparable in the following factors—sale date, farm size, productive capacity, improvements, and location, or, with proper adjustments where they are not, is . . .

$_____$ Total Farm or $\$\_\_\_\_\_$ per Acre

Nearby and Recent Farm Sales

Comparable Sales	1	2	3	4	5	6
Seller						
Buyer						
Date of Sale						
Total Acres						
Tillable Acres						
Sales Price						
Total	$___	$___	$___	$___	$___	$___
Per Acre	$___	$___	$___	$___	$___	$___

Adjustments (Per-Acre Value)

Date of Sale	±					
Farm Size	±					
Productive Capacity	±					
Extent of Improvements	±					
Location	±					
Other	±					

Adjusted Sale Value

Per Acre	$___	$___	$___	$___	$___	$___

The Following Page . . .

. . . shows the location of each of these farms
in relation to the subject property.

Retus, Inc.   **Comparable Sale No.** _____   Pages 27-32

County _____ No. Acres _____   Seller _____
Township _____   Buyer _____
                                       Sec. _____ Twn. _____ Rge. _____

                                       Legal Description: _____

                                       Deed or
                                       Contract Date _____
                                       Book No. _____ Page No. _____
                                       Consideration Shown $_____
                                           Downpayment $_____
                                           Contract $_____
                                           Mortgage $_____
                                           Balloon $_____
                                           Interest Rate   _____%
                                           Term (Years)   _____

Section _____ or   *Transfer Verified by:* _____
      _____ ¼ of Section _____   Date _____ Place _____
                                       Consideration Paid $_____
Location in Relation to   Per-Acre Value $_____
Subject Farm:

      _____ Miles (North) (South)   *Farm Inspected by:* _____

      _____ Miles (East) (West)   Date _____

General Description:
  1. Land _____

_____

_____

  2. Buildings and Improvements _____

_____

_____

  3. Other Remarks _____

_____

_____

Retus, Inc.   **THE INVENTORY APPROACH TO VALUE**   Page 33

Summary

The value of the subject property based on an inventory of the various types of land and an inventory of all of the buildings and improvements is . . .

$_____ Total Farm, or $_____ per Acre

Inventory of Land

Cropland	Acres	Per-Acre Value	Total Value	
Class	_____	$_____	$_____	
Class	_____	_____	_____	
Class	_____	_____	_____	
Class	_____	_____	_____	
Total	_____			$_____
Pastureland Untillable	_____	_____		$_____
Woodland				
Commercial	_____	_____	$_____	
Other	_____	_____	_____	
Total				$_____
Farmstead	_____	_____	_____	$_____
Roads, Waste	_____	_____		$_____
Total Farm Acres	(_____)	Total Value of Land		($_____)

Inventory of Buildings and Improvements

Buildings and Improvements	Replacement Cost	Remaining Life	Contributory Value
_____	$_____	_____%	$_____
_____	_____	_____	_____
_____	_____	_____	_____
_____	_____	_____	_____
_____	_____	_____	_____
_____	_____	_____	_____
_____	_____	_____	_____
_____	_____	_____	_____

Total Value of Buildings and Improvements ($_____)

The Organization of an
Appraiser's Handbook

THE APPRAISER'S HANDBOOK

Maps and Sources

		Sources
10	County Highway Maps	F, I
20	Plat Books	F, I
30	Aerial Photos	A, B, G, J
40	Geological Survey	C, D
50	Soil Survey	E, H
60	Land Use Capability	H
70	Area Planning	J

A. Eastern Laboratory
   Aerial Photography
   A.S.C.S.–U.S.D.A.
   45 S. French Broad Avenue
   Asheville, North Carolina
   28801

B. Western Laboratory
   Aerial Photography Division
   A.S.C.S.–U.S.D.A.
   2505 Parley's Way
   Salt Lake City, Utah 84109

C. Washington Distribution
   Section
   Geological Survey, 18th & F
   St, NW
   Washington, D.C. 20242
   or
   Denver Distribution Section
   Geological Survey (Federal
   Center)
   Denver, Colorado 80225

D. State Department of
   Conservation

E. Department of Agronomy
   State University

County Offices

F. Agricultural or Cooperative
   Extension Service

G. Agricultural Stabilization
   and Conservation

H. Soil Conservation Service

I. County Surveyor

J. Area Planning

THE APPRAISER'S HANDBOOK

1. Basic Organization

File		Sources[1]
0	Organization	—
10	Basic Outline	—
20	Sources of Information	2, 3, 4, 5
30	Addresses, Telephone Numbers	
100	Physical Features	
110	Soils and Topography	I, N, Q
120	Climate	D, I
130	Market Facilities	W
140	Types of Farming	70 D
200	Agricultural Trends	
210	Farm Land, Farm Numbers, and Farm Size	6, 7, 32, 50
220	Kinds of Farm Organization and Ownership	6
230	Farm Population and Production	14
240	Acres of Harvested Crops and Crop Yields	7, 33, 41-43
250	Livestock Numbers and Rates of Production	7, 34, 44-48
260	Farm Practices and Leasing Arrangements	40, 61, 81
300	Economic Statistics	
310	Farm Real Estate Values and Market Activity	7, 11, 51
320	Prices Received by Farmers	7, 31, 62
330	Farm Costs (Buildings, Wages, Taxes)	7, 12, 16, 22, 31, 39
340	Farm Receipts, Expenses, and Income	5, 15, 50
350	Farm Record Summaries, Various Areas	17, 63
360	The Asset and Debt Structure	18
370	Farm Mortgages, Loans, Interest Rates	19-21
400	Community Characteristics and Customs	
410	Population and Other Trends	13, 14
420	Community Services, Activities	K, R, W
430	Government Planning Agencies	K, R
440	Social Traditions, Attitudes	W
500	Miscellanea Compacta	
510	Land Measurement	—
520	Weights and Measures	7
530	Graphic Illustration Technique	
540	Photographic Technique	

1. See next page.

THE APPRAISER'S HANDBOOK

2. References

		Write
01	Publications About Available Publications	
02	Guide to U.S.D.A. Statistics	A
03	Periodic Reports of Agricultural Economics	A
04	Bulletins Regarding Things Agricultural	E
05	Agricultural Outlook, Economic Facts	G
06	U.S. Census of Agriculture	C,D
	(County and State Data Obtained Every 5 Years)	
07	Agricultural Statistics	C
	(Annual Publication, Both Current and Historical Data)	
10	Economic Research Service Periodicals	A
11	Farm Real Estate Market Developments	
12	Agricultural Finance Review	
13	Farm Population Estimates	
14	Changes in Farm Production and Efficiency	
15	Farm Income Situation	
16	Farm Cost Situation	
17	Farm Costs and Returns	
18	Balance Sheet of Agriculture	
19	Characteristics of Farm Mortgages	
20	Farm-Mortgage Lending Experience	
21	Farm-Mortgage Debt	
22	Farm Real Estate Taxes	
30	Statistical Reporting Service Reports	B
31	Agricultural Prices	
32	Farms	
33	Crop Production	
34	Livestock and Poultry Inventory, January 1	
35	Milk Production	
36	Hogs and Pigs	
37	Livestock Slaughter and Meat Production	
38	Sheep and Lambs	
39	Farm Labor	
40	State Crop and Livestock Publications	F
41	Crop Acreage, Yield, Production	
42	Crop Production Practices	
43	Annual Crop Summary	

(Continued)

THE APPRAISER'S HANDBOOK

2. References (Continued)

Write

44   Livestock on Farms
45   Cows Milked and Milk Production
46   Pig Crops
47   Cattle on Feed
48   Annual Livestock Summary
49   Assessor's Enumeration of Crops, Livestock Numbers
50   Gross Cash Income
51   Farm Land Values

60 Agricultural Publications   E, G
61   Agricultural Technologies, Farm Practices   E
62   State Farm Prices Received by Farmers   G
63   Farm Record Summaries   G

70 State Climatological Data Summaries   C, D, H

80 Other
81   Doane Agricultural Reports   L
82   Rural Appraisal Manual   S
83   Assessor   J

90 Appraiser's Handbooks

THE APPRAISER'S HANDBOOK

3. Places to Write or Visit

A. Economic Research Service
    U.S. Department of
    Agriculture
    Washington, D.C. 20250

B. Statistical Reporting Service
    U.S. Department of
    Agriculture
    Washington, D.C. 20250

C. Superintendent of Documents
    Government Printing Office
    Washington, D.C. 20250

D. U.S. Department of
    Commerce
    Bureau of the Census (or)
    Environmental Data Service
    Washington, D.C. 20250

E. Mailing Room
    Agricultural Administration
    Bldg.
    State University

F. Department of Agricultural
    Statistics
    Agricultural Administration
    Building
    State University, or
    State Office Building
    State Capital

G. Department of Agricultural
    Economics
    State University

H. Main Library
    State University

I. Department of Agronomy
    State University

J. State Highway Commission
    Division of Land Acquisition
    State Office Building
    State Capital

K. State Chamber of Commerce

L. American Society of Farm Managers and Rural Appraisers
    470 S. Colorado Blvd.
    Denver, Colorado 80222

County Offices

M. Agricultural Stabilization and
    Conservation Office

N. Cooperative Extension Service

O. Federal Land Bank

P. Production Credit Association

Q. Soil Conservation Service

R. Area Planning

S. Assessor

T. Auditor

U. Recorder

V. County Surveyor

W. Other Local Offices
    Banks
    Chambers of Commerce
    Elevators
    Farm Loan Agencies

Present Value Tables

Appendix Table A. The Present Value or Worth of One per Year for the Next N Years. Various Terms and Interest Rates and Assuming the Investment Is Compounded Annually.

Year	Rates of Interest									
	4.0	4.5	5.0	5.5	6.0	6.5	7.0	7.5	8.0	9.0
1	0.9615	0.9569	0.9524	0.9479	0.9434	0.9390	0.9346	0.9302	0.9259	0.9174
2	1.8861	1.8727	1.8594	1.8463	1.8334	1.8206	1.8080	1.7956	1.7833	1.7591
3	2.7751	2.7490	2.7232	2.6979	2.6730	2.6485	2.6243	2.6005	2.5771	2.5313
4	3.6299	3.5875	3.5460	3.5052	3.4651	3.4258	3.3872	3.3493	3.3121	3.2397
5	4.4518	4.3900	4.3295	4.2703	4.2124	4.1557	4.1002	4.0459	3.9927	3.8897
6	5.2421	5.1579	5.0757	4.9955	4.9173	4.8410	4.7665	4.6938	4.6229	4.4859
7	6.0021	5.8927	5.7864	5.6830	5.5824	5.4845	5.3893	5.2966	5.2064	5.0330
8	6.7327	6.5959	6.4632	6.3346	6.2098	6.0888	5.9713	5.8573	5.7466	5.5348
9	7.4353	7.2688	7.1078	6.9522	6.8017	6.6561	6.5152	6.3789	6.2469	5.9952
10	8.1109	7.9127	7.7217	7.5376	7.3601	7.1888	7.0236	6.8641	6.7101	6.4177
11	8.7605	8.5289	8.3064	8.0925	7.8869	7.6890	7.4987	7.3154	7.1390	6.8052
12	9.3851	9.1186	8.8633	8.6185	8.3838	8.1587	7.9427	7.7353	7.5361	7.1607
13	9.9856	9.6829	9.3936	9.1171	8.8527	8.5997	8.3577	8.1258	7.9038	7.4869
14	10.5631	10.2228	9.8986	9.5876	9.2950	9.0138	8.7455	8.4892	8.2442	7.7862
15	11.1184	10.7395	10.3797	10.0376	9.7122	9.4027	9.1079	8.8271	8.5595	8.0607
16	11.6523	11.2340	10.8378	10.4622	10.1059	9.7678	9.4466	9.1415	8.8514	8.3126
17	12.1657	11.7072	11.2741	10.8646	10.4773	10.1106	9.7632	9.4340	9.1216	8.5436
18	12.6593	12.1600	11.6896	11.2461	10.8276	10.4325	10.0591	9.7060	9.3719	8.7556
19	13.1339	12.5933	12.0853	11.6077	11.1581	10.7347	10.3356	9.9591	9.6036	8.9501
20	13.5903	13.0079	12.4622	11.9504	11.4699	11.0185	10.5940	10.1945	9.8181	9.1285
25	15.6221	14.8282	14.0939	13.4139	12.7834	12.1979	11.6536	11.1469	10.6748	9.8226
30	17.2920	16.2889	15.3725	14.5337	13.7648	13.0587	12.4090	11.8104	11.2578	10.2737
40	19.7928	18.4016	17.1591	16.0461	15.0463	14.1455	13.3317	12.5944	11.9246	10.7574

(Continued)

Appendix Table A (Continued).

Rates of Interest

Year	10.0	11.0	12.0	13.0	14.0	15.0	16.0	18.0	20.0	24.0
1	0.9091	0.9009	0.8929	0.8850	0.8772	0.8696	0.8621	0.8475	0.8333	0.8065
2	1.7355	1.7125	1.6901	1.6681	1.6467	1.6257	1.6052	1.5656	1.5278	1.4568
3	2.4869	2.4437	2.4018	2.3612	2.3216	2.2832	2.2459	2.1743	2.1065	1.9813
4	3.1699	3.1024	3.0373	2.9745	2.9137	2.8550	2.7982	2.6901	2.5887	2.4043
5	3.7908	3.6959	3.6048	3.5172	3.4331	3.3522	3.2743	3.1272	2.9906	2.7454
6	4.3553	4.2305	4.1114	3.9975	3.8887	3.7845	3.6847	3.4976	3.3255	3.0205
7	4.8684	4.7122	4.5638	4.4226	4.2883	4.1604	4.0386	3.8115	3.6046	3.2423
8	5.3349	5.1461	4.9676	4.7988	4.6389	4.4873	4.3436	4.0776	3.8372	3.4212
9	5.7590	5.5370	5.3282	5.1317	4.9464	4.7716	4.6065	4.3030	4.0310	3.5655
10	6.1446	5.8892	5.6502	5.4262	5.2161	5.0188	4.8332	4.4941	4.1925	3.6819
11	6.4951	6.2065	5.9377	5.6869	5.4527	5.2337	5.0286	4.6560	4.3271	3.7757
12	6.8137	6.4924	6.1944	5.9176	5.6603	5.4206	5.1971	4.7932	4.4392	3.8514
13	7.1034	6.7499	6.4235	6.1218	5.8424	5.5831	5.3423	4.9095	4.5327	3.9124
14	7.3667	6.9819	6.6282	6.3025	6.0021	5.7245	5.4675	5.0081	4.6106	3.9616
15	7.6061	7.1909	6.8109	6.4624	6.1422	5.8474	5.5755	5.0916	4.6755	4.0013
16	7.8237	7.3792	6.9740	6.6039	6.2651	5.9542	5.6685	5.1624	4.7296	4.0333
17	8.0216	7.5488	7.1196	6.7291	6.3729	6.0472	5.7487	5.2223	4.7746	4.0591
18	8.2014	7.7016	7.2497	6.8399	6.4674	6.1280	5.8178	5.2732	4.8122	4.0799
19	8.3649	7.8393	7.3658	6.9380	6.5504	6.1982	5.8775	5.3162	4.8435	4.0967
20	8.5136	7.9633	7.4694	7.0248	6.6231	6.2593	5.9288	5.3527	4.8696	4.1103
25	9.0770	8.4217	7.8431	7.3300	6.8729	6.4641	6.0971	5.4669	4.9476	4.1474
30	9.4269	8.6938	8.0552	7.4957	7.0027	6.5660	6.1772	5.5168	4.9789	4.1601
40	9.7791	8.9511	8.2438	7.6344	7.1050	6.6418	6.2335	5.5482	4.9966	4.1659

Source: Financial Compound Interest and Annuity Tables, 2nd Edition, Boston Financial Publishing Co., 1960.

Appendix Table B. The Present Worth of One N Years from Now. Various Terms and Interest Rates and Assuming the Investment Is Compounded Annually.

Year	Rates of Interest									
	4.0	4.5	5.0	5.5	6.0	6.5	7.0	7.5	8.0	9.0
1	.96154	.95694	.95238	.94787	.94340	.93897	.93458	.93023	.92593	.91743
2	.92456	.91573	.90703	.89845	.89000	.88166	.87344	.86533	.85734	.84168
3	.88900	.87630	.86384	.85161	.83962	.82785	.81630	.80496	.79383	.77218
4	.85480	.83856	.82270	.80722	.79209	.77732	.76290	.74880	.73503	.70843
5	.82193	.80245	.78353	.76513	.74726	.72988	.71299	.69656	.68058	.64993
6	.79031	.76790	.74622	.72525	.70496	.68533	.66634	.64796	.63017	.59627
7	.75992	.73483	.71068	.68744	.66506	.64351	.62275	.60275	.58349	.54703
8	.73069	.70319	.67684	.65160	.62741	.60423	.58201	.56070	.54027	.50187
9	.70259	.67290	.64461	.61763	.59190	.56735	.54393	.52158	.50025	.46043
10	.67556	.64393	.61391	.58543	.55839	.53273	.50835	.48519	.46319	.42241
11	.64958	.61620	.58468	.55491	.52679	.50021	.47509	.45134	.42888	.38753
12	.62460	.58966	.55684	.52598	.49697	.46968	.44401	.41985	.39711	.35553
13	.60057	.56427	.53032	.49856	.46884	.44102	.41496	.39056	.36770	.32618
14	.57748	.53997	.50507	.47257	.44230	.41410	.38782	.36331	.34046	.29925
15	.55526	.51672	.48102	.44793	.41727	.38883	.36245	.33797	.31524	.27454
16	.53391	.49447	.45811	.42458	.39365	.36510	.33873	.31439	.29189	.25187
17	.51337	.47318	.43630	.40245	.37136	.34281	.31657	.29245	.27027	.23107
18	.49363	.45280	.41552	.38147	.35034	.32189	.29586	.27205	.25025	.21199
19	.47464	.43330	.39573	.36158	.33051	.30224	.27651	.25307	.23171	.19449
20	.45639	.41464	.37689	.34273	.31180	.28380	.25842	.23541	.21455	.17843
25	.37512	.33273	.29530	.26223	.23300	.20714	.18425	.16398	.14602	.11597
30	.30832	.26700	.23138	.20064	.17411	.15119	.13137	.11422	.09938	.07537
40	.20829	.17193	.14205	.11746	.09722	.08054	.06678	.05542	.04603	.03184

(Continued)

Appendix Table B (Continued).

Rates of Interest

Year	10.0	11.0	12.0	13.0	14.0	15.0	16.0	18.0	20.0	24.0
1	.90909	.90090	.89286	.88496	.87719	.86957	.86207	.84746	.83333	.80645
2	.82645	.81162	.79719	.78315	.76947	.75614	.74316	.71818	.69444	.65036
3	.75131	.73119	.71178	.69305	.67497	.65752	.64066	.60863	.57870	.52449
4	.68301	.65873	.63552	.61332	.59208	.57175	.55229	.51579	.48225	.42297
5	.62092	.59345	.56743	.54276	.51937	.49718	.47611	.43711	.40188	.34111
6	.56447	.53464	.50663	.48032	.45559	.43233	.41044	.37043	.33490	.27509
7	.51316	.48166	.45235	.42506	.39964	.37594	.35383	.31393	.27908	.22184
8	.46651	.43393	.40388	.37616	.35056	.32690	.30503	.26604	.23257	.17891
9	.42410	.39092	.36061	.33288	.30751	.28426	.26295	.22546	.19381	.14428
10	.38554	.35218	.32197	.29459	.26974	.24718	.22668	.19106	.16151	.11635
11	.35049	.31728	.28748	.26070	.23662	.21494	.19542	.16192	.13459	.09383
12	.31863	.28584	.25668	.23071	.20756	.18691	.16846	.13722	.11216	.07567
13	.28966	.25751	.22917	.20416	.18207	.16253	.14523	.11629	.09346	.06103
14	.26333	.23199	.20462	.18068	.15971	.14133	.12520	.09855	.07789	.04921
15	.23939	.20900	.18270	.15989	.14010	.12289	.10793	.08352	.06491	.03969
16	.21763	.18829	.16312	.14150	.12289	.10686	.09304	.07078	.05409	.03201
17	.19784	.16963	.14564	.12522	.10780	.09293	.08021	.05998	.04507	.02581
18	.17986	.15282	.13004	.11081	.09456	.08081	.06914	.05083	.03756	.02082
19	.16351	.13768	.11611	.09806	.08295	.07027	.05961	.04308	.03130	.01679
20	.14864	.12403	.10367	.08678	.07276	.06110	.05139	.03651	.02608	.01354
25	.09230	.07361	.05882	.04710	.03779	.03038	.02447	.01596	.01048	.00462
30	.05731	.04368	.03338	.02557	.01963	.01510	.01165	.00697	.00421	.00158
40	.02209	.01538	.01075	.00753	.00529	.00373	.00264	.00133	.00068	.00018

Source: Financial Compound Interest and Annuity Tables, 2nd Edition, Boston Financial Publishing Co., 1960.

INDEX

Index

A

Abandonment, 91
Absentee-owner, 123, 249, 273, 333
Actual cash value, 69, 76, 405-407
Aerial photos, 133-134, 166-171
Affidavit, 151
Agricultural-use value,
(*See* Prudent agricultural value)
Alienation, 92
American Rural Appraisal System, 62-63, 248
Appraisal certificate, 151, 572
Appraisal report, 147-152, 455, 571-594
Appurtenance, 97
Arm's length transaction, 76, 295, 304-305
Assessed value, 76, 442-444
Assessor's manual, 433-434

B

Balance, 357
Base lines, 105-107
Basic farm value, 62, 71, 76, 464, 486
(*See also* Earnings value)
Before and after values, 74, 532, 550-551
Bench-mark approach, 484-485
Benefits, 525, 545-547, 551
deductible, 546-547; general, 545-547; special, 545
Bona fide market transaction
(*See* Arm's length transaction)
Book of Deeds, 99, 297
Book of Mortgages, 300

B

Book value, 67, 354, 371-372
Buildings and improvements, 22, 30-31, 68, 84, 121, 126-127, 144, 222-223, 275-278, 331-335, 338-339, 353-354, 375, 384-388, 390-392, 395, 417, 519, 547, 583-585
Bundle of rights
(*See* Property rights)

C

Capitalization rates, 247, 252, 260-261, 265-277, 342, 587
Cash balance, 250, 590
Climate, 120, 172, 189, 198-199, 577
Co-insurance, 414-415
Comparable farm sales, 266, 295, 320, 345, 429
Condemnee, 75
Condemnor, 75
Contract sale, 35, 269, 304, 320-324, 463, 475
Contributory value, 67-69, 122, 354, 358, 371, 374-376, 389-393, 408-410, 583-585
Corporeal, 92
Correction lines, 105
Cost approach to value
(*See* Inventory approach to value)
Cost-less-depreciation, 341, 362
Cost to cure, 366, 543-544
County plat books, 131
County Recorder's Office
(*See* Office of the Registrar of Deeds)
Curable vs. incurable depreciation, 366

D

Damage, 525, 534-537, 541, 551
   compensable, 537; consequential,
   536; non-compensable, 541; severance, 535
Deed, 92, 95, 98, 463
Deferred payment provision, 69, 409-
   410
Depreciation, 259, 265, 278-280, 340-
   341, 362-363, 370
Dollar returns to land, 251, 260
Drainage, 174, 182-186, 519, 547

E

Earnings approach to value, 245-248,
   277, 285-286, 342
Earnings value, 247, 250-251, 267,
   277, 587-591
   (*See also* Basic farm value)
Easement, 92, 511
Economic obsolescence, 331, 341,
   364-367
Electronic data processing, 434-436
Encroachment, 93
Encumbrance, 85
Equalization, 449, 452-453
Equitability, 410, 449-450
Equity returns, 262-263, 279
Equity values, 72, 498
Erosion, 188-191
Escrow, 93, 321
Exceptions, 97
Exchange value, 355
Expert witness, 552-556

F

Fair market value, 73, 76, 454, 527-
   529
Farm definition, 9-14, 439
Farm earnings, 19-21, 63, 228
Farm expenses, 228, 249-252, 255,
   588-590
Farm layout, 121, 140-141, 582
Farm production, 131, 204-205
Farm real estate market, 55-58, 266,
   336

Farm receipts, 228-230, 249-250, 252,
   587, 589
Farm size, 13, 31, 131, 200-201, 295,
   317, 353
Fee simple title, 84
Fixtures, 85-86, 93
Forced sale, 304
Foreclosure, 492-493, 496-497
Fractional quarter, 107
Freehold estate, 93
Full cash value, 69
Full vs. fractional assessment, 70-71,
   444-447
Functional inadequacy, 331, 341, 363,
   367

G

General property tax, 70, 421-423
Government payments, 253
Grantee, 96, 297
Grantor, 96, 297

H

Highest and best use, 74-75, 530-531
History of the farm, 120, 575
Home, 17-19, 32, 62, 121, 276, 587,
   591

I

Important land features, 140-142
Improvements
   (*See* Buildings and improve-
   ments)
Income capitalization, 21, 245-248,
   260
   (*See also* Earnings approach to
   value)
Income stream, 275-283, 378-382
Indemnity principle, 69, 402, 408, 416
Informed buyer, informed seller, 293
Installment land contract
   (*See* Contract sale)
Insurable interest, 402-403

Insured value, 68, 76, 377, 405, 408-410

Interest rates, 222, 227, 261-262, 268, 274-275

Inventory approach to value, 22, 245, 329-330, 342-343, 346, 594

Inventory value, 67

Irrigation, 256, 380-383, 519

J

Judgment, 94

Just compensation, 344, 521-526, 536

K

Key sort card, 309-310

Kinds of farm organization, 9, 202, 295, 309

L

Land acquisition, 556

Land classification, 191, 196

Landlord-tenant arrangements, 62, 94, 211, 250, 319, 587-589
cash rents, 222, 226, 252; crop-share lease, 62, 212, 252, 333; livestock-share lease, 212, 252

Land measurement, 103, 238, 568-569

Land use capabilities, 196, 422

Law of eminent domain, 73, 92, 509-512, 534

Lay-of-the-land,
(*See* Topography)

Lease
(*See* Landlord-tenant arrangements)

Leasehold estate, 94, 284

Legal description, 97, 101, 110, 120, 152, 575

Lessee, 283-284

Lessor, 283-284

Liquidation price, 72, 76, 492-496

Loan value, 71, 76, 490-491, 499

Location, 17, 120, 129 297, 311-313, 358, 576, 587, 591

M

Maps, 128, 131-135, 139-141, 191, 196-197, 294, 551, 577, 596
county highway, 131; geological survey, 133, 136; land ownership, 132, 294; land use, 196; soils, 133, 143, 191, 196-197, 578

Market data approach to value
(*See* Sales comparison approach to value)

Market price, 53-54

Market value, 53, 59-60

Mass appraisal technique, 426-428

Meridians, 105

Metes and bounds, 101, 112

Mortgage, 35, 94, 463, 482-483

Mortgagee, 94, 403, 463

Mortgagor, 94, 463, 496

N

Normal agricultural value, 64, 71, 485-489

Normal market value, 63-65, 71, 76, 464, 486

O

Office of the Registrar of Deeds, 99, 128, 297

Offsets, 548

Opinion rule, 552

Opportunity cost of money, 261, 267-268

Origins of farm value, 16, 19, 268, 277, 346

Owner-operator, 59, 61, 70, 123, 249, 273-274, 589-590

P

Partial taking, 515-519, 537-539, 542, 545

Pasture, 144, 334-335

Physical description, 69, 120, 122, 152, 329, 345, 355, 378, 388, 390-392, 551, 576-585

Physical deterioration, 331, 341, 363, 366

Preferential assessment of farm land, 436-440
Present market value, 23, 59-62, 73, 76, 559
Present operator, 145-146, 376, 384, 481, 575, 586
Present value of an income stream, 277-283, 378-382, 602-603
  compound interest method, 280-282, 380-382; straight-line method, 280-281, 380-382
Present value of a reversionary interest, 281-282, 378, 604-605
Prices, 51-53, 59, 219, 253
  cyclical change, 32, 33, 65; paid by farmers, 218-222; received by farmers, 35, 218-221, 253, 464
Principal and interest payments
  (See Repayment schedule)
Principal meridians, 102, 106-107
Productive capacity, 123-124, 152, 251, 266, 295, 311, 315, 586
Property inspection, 139-142, 144-145, 431
  (See also Physical description)
Property insurance, 399
Property owner, 76, 85, 87-91, 512-513, 520-521, 544
Property record card, 425, 431-432
Property rights, 59, 83, 87-91, 421
Prudent agricultural value, 438-441
Public disclosure, 445-447, 457

Q

Quantity survey technique, 339
Quit claim deed, 96

R

Rate of return, 247-251, 260, 263, 279
Ratio, assessed value to sale price, 451-452
Real property, 83-84
Reasons for appraisal, 22, 25, 61, 147, 346, 354
Recapture rate, 263, 441
Rectangular survey, 105-106, 113
Relief
  (See Topography)

Repayment schedule, 261-262, 464
Replacement cost, 67, 337, 359-361, 389-393, 406-407, 583-585
Reproduction cost, 67, 360, 389-393, 406-407, 584-585
Reservations, 97
Residual technique, 379
Restrictive agreements, 97, 439-441
Revenue stamps, 99, 297-299
Right-of-way, 94, 541, 575
Riparian rights, 94-95

S

Sales comparison approach to value, 21, 245, 293, 325, 342, 592-593
Sales data, 296, 308, 316
Salvage value, 372, 377
Slope
  (See Topography)
Soils, 162-163, 175, 198, 578-581
  acidity, 175, 188; alkalinity, 188; classification, 193, 195, 330, 578-581; formation, 165; permeability, 175, 182-184, 189; productivity, 28-29, 195-197; profile, 175-177, 188; surveys, 133, 191; texture, 178-180, 189; types, 121, 193-195
Standard fire policy, 400-403, 407
Structural value, 66-67, 122, 354-355, 371-373, 389-393, 583-585
Substitution cost principle, 337
Summation process, 330-331, 573

T

Taking agency, 75, 512, 516, 520, 549
Tax base, 425, 442
Tax deferral, 439-441
Tax rates, 222, 226-227
Technological innovation, 9-10, 35, 200, 236, 334, 417
Temporary right-of-way, 541
Tenancy-in-common, 95
Tenant-operator, 95, 249
Thumb-rule costs (buildings), 338
Thumb-rule approach to value, 340
Topography, 121, 173, 182, 189, 196-198

Township, 105-106
Township lines, 106-107
Township trustee, 423
Transfer of ownership, 23, 51, 95, 213, 307, 311, 463
(*See also* Contract sale)
Transmittal letter, 154
True cash value, 69, 76, 442-444
Type of farming, 13, 120, 129, 295, 309
Typical operator concept, 60, 75, 123-125, 249, 384, 464, 543, 586, 589

U

Uniformity, 442-450
Unit rule, 523
Utility value
(*See* Value-in-use)

V

Value, 50, 53, 59-60
Valued insurance policies, 416
Value-in-exchange, 69
Value-in-use, 50, 58, 68, 354-355, 372, 375-377, 389-393, 408, 583-585
Values that remain, 340-341, 367

W

Warranty deed, 96
Water rights
(*See* Riparian rights)
Willing buyer, willing seller, 73, 493

Z

Zoning, 235, 523